M000005409

*TO THE STUDENT:* A Study Guide for the textbook is available thro[...]
title STUDY GUIDE TO ACCOMPANY REFRIGERATION [...]
ENERGY APPROACH by Edward G. Pita. The Study Guide can help you with course material by acting as
a tutorial, review and study aid. If the Study Guide is not in stock, ask the bookstore manager to order a
copy for you.

# REFRIGERATION PRINCIPLES AND SYSTEMS
## An Energy Approach

# REFRIGERATION PRINCIPLES AND SYSTEMS
## An Energy Approach

### Edward G. Pita

New York City Technical College
of the City University of New York

## John Wiley & Sons

**New York  Chichester  Brisbane  Toronto  Singapore**

*Library of Congress Cataloging in Publication Data:*

Pita, Edward G.
  Refrigeration principles and systems.

  Includes indexes.
  1. Refrigeration and refrigerating machinery.
I. Title.
TP492.P48   1984        621.56        83-21780
ISBN 0-471-87611-9

Printed in the United States of America

10  9  8  7  6  5  4  3  2  1

# About the Author

**Edward G. Pita** is an Associate Professor in the Environmental Control Technology Department at New York City Technical College of the City University of New York. He received his B.S. from Purdue University, M.S. from Columbia University, and Ph.D. from the University of Maryland, all in mechanical engineering.

He has had extensive experience in the refrigeration and air conditioning industry. He has worked in applications and development for the Carrier Corporation and the Worthington Corporation, and was Chief Engineer for a major consulting engineering firm.

Dr. Pita is also the author of *Air Conditioning Principles and Systems: An Energy Approach* (Wiley, 1981), and numerous articles and manuals. He is a member of the American Society of Heating, Refrigerating and Air-Conditioning Engineers.

# Preface

This book is a fundamental text covering refrigeration principles, equipment, and systems. It is intended for students in refrigeration courses in colleges or technical institutes. It should also be useful for self-study by sales and application engineers, contractors, service technicians, and operating engineers.

Throughout the book, energy utilization and conservation are stressed and highlighted, in both principles and applications. This is based on the belief that energy consideration is an essential part of refrigeration technology education, and that it should be an integral part of the learning process.

There is a review of the basic applied physics needed before the discussion of refrigeration fundamentals. Both the vapor compression and absorption systems are explained in detail. Emphasis is placed on the use of the $p–h$ diagram in understanding and analyzing performance, and in evaluating energy effects. The equilibrium diagram and its use are introduced.

The major features and construction of modern equipment are described. Considerable manufacturers' rating data are provided, along with worked-out cases of selection. Examples of component balancing and its use are also given.

There are extensive tables, charts, and worked-out examples of refrigeration load calculations and pipe sizing. Proper piping installation practice is discussed and reinforced with simple illustrations. Emphasis is given to oil and refrigerant flow problems. An individual focus is given to lower temperature system practices, defrost, and heat pump refrigeration problems.

The book concludes with chapters on electric service systems, motors, and controls. The material included is a sufficient introduction for those studying refrigeration, but who do not have access to separate courses or texts at the same time.

The book contains many worked-out examples, problems, and review questions. There is also an end-of-book glossary, and property tables and $p–h$ diagrams are provided for a number of refrigerants. A Solutions Manual and Study Guide are available from the publisher.

The book is designed for a two-semester, two- or three-hour course if full use of it is made. However, certain major topics can be selected for a shorter course. For example, most of Chapters 1 through 9, with parts of Chapters 11 and 12, comprise a basic course.

My thanks to my colleagues in education and industry who have offered helpful comments. Many manufacturers have kindly furnished material. I also thank my students, who by their curiosity, questioning, and goals become the final arbiters of the degree of success of teaching and textbooks.

Edward G. Pita

# Contents

# REFRIGERATION
# PRINCIPLES AND SYSTEMS
## An Energy Approach

# Chapter 1

# INTRODUCTION: PHYSICAL PRINCIPLES 1

Refrigeration was used by ancient civilizations when it was naturally available. The Roman rulers had slaves transport ice and snow from the high mountains to be used to preserve foods and to provide cool beverages in hot weather. Such natural sources of refrigeration were, of course, extremely limited in terms of location, temperatures, and scope. Means of producing refrigeration with machinery, called *mechanical refrigeration,* began to be developed in the 1850s. Today the refrigeration industry is a vast and essential part of any technological society, with yearly sales of equipment amounting to billions of dollars in the United States alone.

## OBJECTIVES

A study of this chapter will enable you to:
1. Define refrigeration and the methods of achieving it.
2. Identify applications and uses of refrigeration and distinguish between refrigeration and air conditioning.
3. Convert from one set of units to another, and properly round off numbers.
4. Calculate density, specific volume, and specific gravity.
5. Express the relationship between pressure and head, and between absolute, gage, and vacuum pressure.
6. Distinguish between energy and power, and between stored energy and flow energy, and describe the forms of energy.
7. Explain the difference between temperature and heat, and show the relationship between temperature scales.

## 1.1 Uses of Refrigeration

It is convenient to classify the applications of refrigeration into the following categories: *domestic, commercial, industrial,* and *air conditioning* (Figure 1.1). Sometimes transportation is listed as a separate category. Domestic refrigeration is used for food preparation and preservation, ice making, and cooling beverages in the household. Commercial refrigeration is used in retail stores, restaurants, and institutions, for purposes the same as those in the household. Industrial refrigeration in the food industry is needed in processing, preparation, and large-scale preservation. This includes use in food chilling and freezing plants, cold storage warehouses, breweries, and dairies, to name a few. Hundreds of other industries use refrigeration; among them are ice making plants, oil refineries, pharmaceuticals. Of course ice skating rinks need refrigeration.

Refrigeration is also widely used in both comfort air conditioning for people and in industrial air conditioning. Industrial air conditioning is used to create the air temperatures, humidity, and cleanliness required for manufacturing processes. Computers require a controlled environment.

## 1.2 Methods of Refrigeration

Refrigeration, commonly spoken of as a cooling process, is more correctly defined as *the*

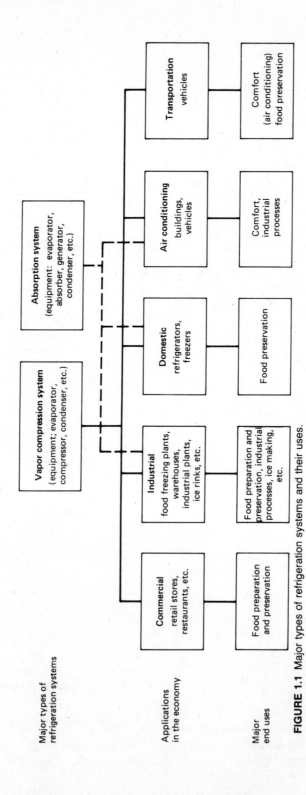

**FIGURE 1.1** Major types of refrigeration systems and their uses.

*removal of heat from a substance to bring it to or keep it at a desirable low temperature,* below the temperature of the surroundings. The most widespread method of producing mechanical refrigeration is called the *vapor compression system.* In this system a volatile liquid refrigerant is evaporated in an *evaporator;* this process results in a removal of heat (cooling) from the substance to be cooled. A *compressor* and *condenser* are required to maintain the evaporation process and to recover the refrigerant for reuse.

Another widely used method is called the *absorption* refrigeration system. In this process a refrigerant is evaporated (as with the vapor compression system), but the evaporation is maintained by absorbing the refrigerant in another fluid. Later we will explain how the vapor compression and absorption refrigeration systems function.

Other refrigeration methods are *thermoelectric, steam jet,* and *air cycle* refrigeration. These systems are used only in special applications and their functioning will not be explained here. Thermoelectric refrigeration is still quite expensive; some small tabletop domestic refrigerators are cooled by this method. Steam jet refrigeration is inefficient. Often used on ships in the past, it has been largely replaced by the vapor compression system. The air cycle is sometimes used in air conditioning of aircraft cabins. Refrigeration at extremely low temperatures, below about $-200°F$ ($-130°C$), is called *cryogenics.* Special systems are used to achieve these conditions. One use of refrigeration at ultralow temperatures is to separate oxygen and nitrogen from air and to liquefy them.

## 1.3 Refrigeration Equipment

The main equipment components of the vapor compression refrigeration system are the familiar evaporator, compressor, and condenser. The equipment may be separate or of the *unitary* (also called *self-contained*) type. Unitary equipment is assembled in the factory.

The household refrigerator is a common example of unitary equipment. Obvious advantages of unitary equipment are that it is more compact and less expensive to manufacture if made in large quantities.

There is a variety of commercial refrigeration equipment; each has a specific function. *Reach-in cabinets, walk-in coolers,* and *display cases* are widely used in the food service business. Automatic ice makers, drinking water coolers, and refrigerated vending machines are also commonly encountered equipment.

We will not treat details of specialized equipment, except as they affect general practices. An excellent discussion of features of commercial refrigeration equipment can be found in the 1983 Applications and 1982 Equipment volumes of the ASHRAE Handbook.

Refrigeration versus air conditioning. The subject matter in this book covers refrigeration, not air conditioning. Since similar refrigeration equipment is used to cool air for comfort purposes as well as for other uses, no distinction is made in the beginning of our study of refrigeration fundamentals. Differences in practices and in equipment involving different temperatures and uses will be pointed out as the exposition develops.

Air conditioning includes the heating, cooling, humidifying, dehumidifying, and cleaning (filtering) of air in internal environments. Occasionally it will be necessary to mention some aspects of air conditioning when we deal with the interface between the two subjects, but we will make no attempt to go further. A study of the fundamentals and equipment involved in air conditioning is nevertheless of great value even for those primarily interested in refrigeration.

## PHYSICAL PRINCIPLES

An understanding of refrigeration requires a basic knowledge of applied physics. In this and in the following chapter we will explain some principles of physics and give examples of their application to refrigeration. The material covered is not intended to substitute for a course in physics, but it will be adequate for our needs. For people with a reasonable knowledge of physics, this chapter may serve as a review, or even be omitted.

## 1.4 Units and Conversions

Standard quantities called *units* have been established to measure the amount of any physical characteristic. For instance the foot (abbreviated ft) is one of the standard units used to measure the characteristic of length.

There are many different units for measuring the same physical characteristic. These units have a fixed relationship to each other, called *equivalents* or *conversion factors.* Some common examples of equivalent units are:

| Charac-<br>teristic | Unit Equivalents<br>(Conversion Factors) | |
|---|---|---|
| Length | 1 ft | = 12 inches (in.) |
| | | = 0.30 meters (m) |
| Volume | 1 ft³ | = 7.48 gallons (gal) |
| Time | 1 minute (min) | = 60 seconds (sec) |
| Mass | 2.2 pounds (lb) | = 1 kilogram (kg) |

Appendix 2 lists some useful unit equivalents. Appendix 1 lists abbreviations and symbols used in this book.

*Conversion of Units.* The equivalence between any two units can also be written as a ratio, by dividing both sides of the equality by either term. For instance, from Appendix 2, the relation between area expressed in $ft^2$ or $in.^2$ is 1 $ft^2$ = 144 $in.^2$ Dividing both sides by 144 $in.^2$ gives

$$\frac{1\ ft^2}{144\ in.^2} = \frac{144\ in.^2}{144\ in.^2} = 1$$

Or, dividing by 1 $ft^2$ gives

$$\frac{1\ ft^2}{1\ ft^2} = \frac{144\ in.^2}{1\ ft^2} = 1$$

This arrangement is used when it is desired to change a unit a quantity is expressed in to a different unit. The procedure is carried out in the following manner:

1. Arrange the equivalency (conversion factor) between the units as a ratio, choosing that ratio that will give the results in the desired units, by canceling units that are the same in the numerator and denominator (units can be multiplied and divided in the same way as numbers).

2. Multiply the original quantity by the ratio. The result will be the correct value in the new unit.

The following example illustrates the procedure for converting units.

*Example 1.1* Some frozen food case panels measuring 28 in. by 33 in. require insulation. The insulation is to be ordered in square feet. How much insulation would you order for each panel?

*Solution* The area of the insulation for each panel is

$$area = 28\ in. \times 33\ in. = 924\ in.^2$$

The area is not in the units needed, however. The equivalent between the known and required units is 1 $ft^2$ = 144 $in.^2$ (Appendix 2). Arranging this as a ratio, multiplying, and canceling units as shown:

$$area = 924\ \cancel{in.^2} \times \frac{1\ ft^2}{144\ \cancel{in.^2}} = 6.42\ ft^2$$

This is the amount of insulation required for each panel.

An important point to note in this example is that there are always two possible ratios that can be used in converting units. In that situation it was either

$$\frac{1\ ft^2}{144\ in.^2} \quad or \quad \frac{144\ in.^2}{1\ ft^2}$$

Only one can be correct. Suppose we had used the other ratio. The results would be

$$\text{area} = 924 \text{ in.}^2 \times \frac{144 \text{ in.}^2}{1 \text{ ft}^2} = 133{,}000 \frac{\text{in.}^4}{\text{ft}^2}$$

We know that this is incorrect, because the units resulting are not ft$^2$. The student should adopt the habit of always writing out the unit names when doing computations.

The procedure for changing units is the same when more than one unit is to be changed, as seen in the following example.

**Example 1.2**   A U.S. manufacturer ships an air cooled condenser to Venezuela, with the note "design air velocity 600 ft/min." The contractor installing the condenser wishes to inform the operating engineer what the design velocity is in meters per second (m/sec). What information should be given?

*Solution*   We must use both the conversion factor between feet and meters and that between minutes and seconds. Arranging the ratios in the form that will give the correct units in the result, and multiplying,

$$\text{velocity} = 600 \; \frac{\cancel{ft}}{\cancel{min}} \times \frac{1 \; \cancel{min}}{60 \text{ sec}} \times \frac{0.30 \text{ m}}{1 \; \cancel{ft}}$$
$$= 3.0 \; \frac{\text{m}}{\text{sec}}$$

**Combined Conversion Factors.**   Example 1.2 involved converting velocity from units of feet per minute to meters per second. That is, two separate units were converted, for length and time. It is convenient to combine two or more conversions into one for commonly encountered cases. Here the conversion for velocity from units of feet per minute to meters per second is

$$1 \; \frac{\text{ft}}{\text{min}} = 1 \; \frac{\cancel{ft}}{\cancel{min}} \times \frac{1 \; \cancel{min}}{60 \text{ sec}} \times \frac{0.30 \text{ m}}{1 \; \cancel{ft}}$$
$$= 0.005 \; \frac{\text{m}}{\text{sec}}$$

That is, 1 ft/min = 0.005 m/sec. The student can easily develop combined conversion factors in the same way. Appendix 2 lists some of these.

**U.S. and SI Units.**   There are two general systems of units used throughout the world. One is called *U.S.*, *customary*, or *English* units, and the other *SI* (international system) units. The U.S. units are still generally used in the United States in refrigeration work, whereas most other countries use SI units. The United States has committed itself to changing to SI units, but this may be a long process. In this book I will use both types of units, with U.S. units emphasized. However, SI units will be introduced in two ways. In some examples and tables, units will be converted from U.S. to SI units, or vice versa. In a few cases I will also show examples and problems in SI units. In this way there will be no interruption of the learning process, yet those students who wish to begin working in SI units may do so.

The SI system of units uses only one unit of measurement for each physical characteristic. For instance, the meter is the standard unit chosen for length. Conversion from one kind of unit to another is therefore not generally required. Multiples of 10, 100, and so forth of the standard unit are used to handle large and small quantities. For example, 1 kilometer (km) = 1000 m, and 1000 millimeters (mm) = 1 m. (The prefix *kilo* means one thousand and the prefix *milli* means one-thousandth.) Compare this to the many units used in the U.S. system for length (inch, foot, yard, mile, etc.), as well as the irregular numerical equivalencies between each unit (e.g., 36 in. = 1 yd).

Appendix 2 includes conversion factors for both the U.S. and SI units. The SI system is part of a broader system of units called the metric system. Only certain units of the metric system are standard in the SI system. For instance the SI unit of length is the meter, not the centimeter or kilometer. We may occasionally use metric units that are not standard SI units, because this is common practice in the refrigeration industry in countries using the SI system.

## 1.5 Mass, Force, Weight, Density, and Specific Volume

*The **mass** (m) of an object or body is the quantity of matter it contains. The U.S. unit of mass is the pound mass. The SI unit is the kilogram.*

*A **force** is the push or pull that one body may exert on another. The U.S. unit of force is the pound force. The SI unit is the Newton (N).*

*The **weight** (w) of a body is the force exerted on it by the gravitational pull of the earth. That is, weight is a force, not a mass.*

Unfortunately the word *weight* is often used for mass of a body. The confusion also occurs because the word *pound* is used for both mass and force in U.S. units. However, the numerical value in pounds for the mass and weight of an object in U.S. units is the same, therefore no error should occur in calculations. In any case the nature of a problem generally indicates whether mass or weight is being considered.

### Density and Specific Volume.

***Density** (d) is the mass per unit of volume of a substance. **Specific volume** (v) is the reciprocal of density.*

That is

$$d = \frac{m}{\text{volume}} \qquad (1.1)$$

$$v = \frac{\text{volume}}{m} \qquad (1.2)$$

The density and specific volume of a substance may vary with temperature and pressure, especially for liquids and gases. Densities for a few substances are shown in Table 1.1.

Mass, density, and specific volume are examples of properties of a substance. A *property* of matter is any physical characteristic or condition that it has. Some other properties of substances that are important in refrigeration are pressure, temperature, enthalpy, and specific heat. These properties will be defined shortly.

**Example 1.3** Before installing a cooling tower on a roof, a contractor informs the structural engineer how much to allow for the mass of water in the tower basin when designing the roof. The tower basin is 15 ft by 10 ft in plan, to be filled with water to a depth of 1.5 ft (Figure 1.2).

*Solution* The mass of water in the tank is found from Equation 1.1, after finding the volume of water. The approximate density of water is shown in Table 1.1.

volume = 15 ft × 10 ft × 1.5 ft = 225 ft³

**TABLE 1.1** Physical Properties of Some Substances

| Substance | Density | | Specific Heat | | Notes |
|---|---|---|---|---|---|
| | lb/ft³ | kg/m³ | Btu/lb-F | kJ/kg-C | |
| Water | 62.4 | 1000 | 1.0 | 4.19 | At 39°F (4°C) |
| | 60.1 | 962.8 | 1.0 | 4.19 | At 200°F (93.3°C) |
| Ice | 57.2 | 916.3 | 0.50 | 2.09 | |
| Steam | (see | | 0.45 | 1.88 | For water vapor in air |
| | Appendix 3) | | | | |
| Air | 0.075 | 1.20 | 0.24 | 1.01 | At 68°F (20°C) and 14.7 psia (I atm) |
| Mercury | 849.0 | 13,600 | | | At 32°F (0°C) |

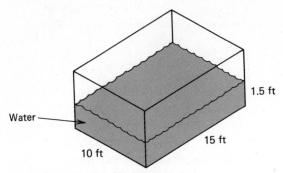

Water

1.5 ft

15 ft

10 ft

**FIGURE 1.2** Sketch for Example 1.3.

Solving Equation 2.1 for $m$

$$m = d \times \text{volume} = 62.4 \ \frac{\text{lb}}{\text{ft}^3} \times 225 \ \text{ft}^3$$
$$= 14,040 \ \text{lb}$$

### Specific Gravity

*The **specific gravity** (s.g.) of a liquid is defined as the ratio of its density to the density of an equal volume of water, at 39° F.*

The density of water at 39° F is 62.4 lb/ft³, so the specific gravity is

$$s.g. = \frac{d}{d_w} = \frac{d}{62.4} \qquad (1.3)$$

where

$$d = \text{density of substance,} \\ \text{lb/ft}^3$$
$$d_w = \text{density of water at} \\ 39° \ \text{F, } 62.4 \ \text{lb/ft}^3$$

The value of specific gravity may change slightly with temperature, but for most calculations the values determined from the Equation 1.3 are satisfactory.

**Example 1.4** A refrigeration brine (salt water) has a density of 69.5 lb/ft³. What is its specific gravity?

*Solution* Using Equation 1.3,

$$s.g. = \frac{d}{62.4} = \frac{69.5}{62.4} = 1.11$$

## 1.6 Accuracy of Data

In reporting results of measurements or calculations of data, decisions must be made as to the number of *significant figures* to use in numerical values. The procedure by which this is done is "rounding off." For example, suppose the results of some calculations produced a value of 207.4 kilowatts (kW) for the required power to drive a refrigeration compressor. This number is said to have four significant figures or four places of accuracy because the value of the fourth digit from the left is known. The number might be used to select a motor, and then to measure its actual power consumption. However, neither the motor rating nor most measuring instruments can produce that accurate a value. Equipment and instrument ratings are often only accurate within 1 to 5 percent of listed values, therefore there is no point in calculating or measuring data to an excess number of significant figures. Data in refrigeration work are usually rounded off (that is, the number of significant figures are reduced) to three or four places, and sometimes even two places. If 207.4 is rounded off to three places, it would be recorded as 207 kW, and if rounded to two places, 210 kW. Until you become familiar with good practise in rounding off values, you should use the numerical examples in this book as a guide.

## 1.7 Pressure

**Pressure** (p) *is defined as force* (F) *exerted per unit area* (A).

Expressed as an equation, this is

$$p = \frac{\text{force}}{\text{area}} = \frac{F}{A} \qquad (1.4)$$

If force is measured in pounds and area in square feet the units of pressure will be

$$p = \frac{F}{A} = \frac{\text{lb}}{\text{ft}^2}$$

If force is measured in pounds and area in square inches, units of pressure will be pounds per square inch. The abbreviations *psf* for pounds per square foot and *psi* for pounds per square inch are commonly used. The standard unit for pressure in the SI system is the pascal (Pa), which is equal to 1 N/m². In refrigeration work, however, other metric units of pressure are frequently used, such as the millimeter of mercury (mm Hg; Hg is the abbreviation for mercury) and the atmosphere (atm). Appendix 2 lists conversion factors for these units.

**Example 1.5** A chilled-water storage tank used in a solar cooling system contains 3000 lb of water. The tank is 2 ft long by 3 ft wide. What is the pressure exerted on the bottom of the tank in pounds per square foot?

*Solution* A sketch of the tank is shown in Figure 1.3. Equation 1.4 is used to find the pressure. The pressure is being exerted on an area 2 by 3 ft, or 6 ft². The force acting on the bottom is the total weight of water.

$$p = \frac{F}{A} = \frac{3000 \text{ lb}}{6 \text{ ft}^2} = 500 \text{ lb/ft}^2$$

The relation between force and pressure is illustrated in Figure 1.4. In this example a force of 3000 lb is distributed over the 2 ft by 3 ft area. The pressure is the force on each of the six 1 ft by 1 ft areas, 500 lb/ft².

Pressures of liquids and gases are of great importance in refrigeration work. Some examples are the gas pressure in a compressor and the pressure developed by a pump.

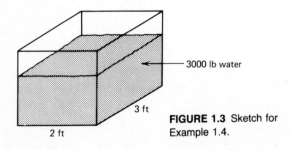

**FIGURE 1.3** Sketch for Example 1.4.

3000 lb water

3 ft

2 ft

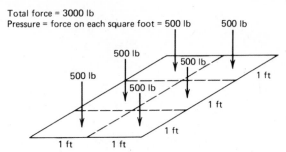

Total force = 3000 lb
Pressure = force on each square foot = 500 lb

500 lb
500 lb
500 lb
500 lb
500 lb
500 lb
1 ft
1 ft
1 ft
1 ft
1 ft

**FIGURE 1.4** Pressure exerted on the bottom of a tank. Total force is 3000 lb. Pressure, the force on each square foot, is 500 lb.

*Absolute, Gage, and Vacuum Pressure.* A space that is completely evacuated of any gas or liquid (a complete vacuum) has zero pressure. The pressure exerted by a fluid above the zero value is called its *absolute pressure*. ($p_{abs}$). This is illustrated in Figure 1.5.

The atmospheric air above the earth exerts a pressure ($p_{atm}$) because of its weight. The pressure it exerts at sea level has been measured and found to be approximately 14.7 lb/in.² absolute (psia). It varies slightly from this value according to weather conditions. The atmospheric pressure also decreases at higher elevations because there is less weight of air above. For instance the atmospheric pressure in Denver, Colorado is about 12.23 psia.

Pressure measuring instruments are usually constructed to measure the difference between the pressure of a fluid and the pressure of the atmosphere, rather than the absolute pressure of the fluid. The pressure measured above atmospheric pressure is called *gage pressure* ($p_g$). The relation between absolute, atmospheric, and gage pressures, shown in Figure 1.5, is

$$p_{abs} = p_{atm} + p_g \tag{1.5}$$

Gage pressure is convenient to use because most pressure measuring instruments are calibrated to read zero when they are subject to atmospheric pressure. Figure 1.6(a) shows the dial face of a typical *compression gage*.

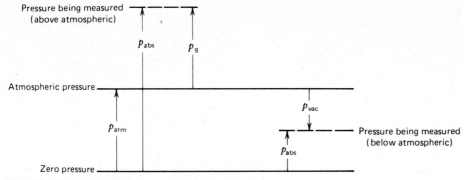

**FIGURE 1.5** Relationship between absolute, gage, and vacuum pressures.

**Example 1.6** A pressure gage connected at the discharge of a cooling tower water pump in the Trailblazers Bus Terminal in San Francisco reads 18 psi. What is the absolute water pressure at the pump discharge?

*Solution* The pressure gage reads gage pressure (above atmospheric). San Francisco is at sea level, so the atmospheric pressure is approximately 14.7 psia. Using Equation 1.5:

$$p_{abs} = p_g + p_{atm} = 18 \text{ psi} + 14.7 \text{ psi}$$
$$= 32.7 \text{ psia}$$

When a fluid exerts a pressure below atmospheric pressure, the difference from atmos-

pheric pressure is called *vacuum pressure* ($p_{vac}$). The relation between absolute, atmospheric, and vacuum pressures, shown in Figure 1.5, is

$$p_{abs} = p_{atm} - p_{vac} \qquad (1.6)$$

Some gages are constructed and calibrated to read both vacuum and gage pressure. This type, shown in Fig. 1.6(b), is called a *compound gage*.

**Example 1.7** The pressure gages connected at the suction and discharge of a refrigeration compressor read 8 in. Hg vac (inches of mercury vacuum) and 60 psig, respectively. How much is the pressure of the refrigerant increased by the compressor, in psi?

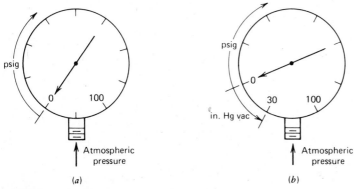

**FIGURE 1.6** Pressure gages. (*a*) Compression gage reads gage pressure only. (*b*) Compound gage reads gage and vacuum pressure.

*Solution*  Before finding the pressure increase, the two pressures must be expressed in the same units. Using the proper conversion factor (Appendix 2) to change the suction gage reading to psi

$$8 \text{ in. Hg vac} \times \frac{1 \text{ psi}}{2.04 \text{ in. Hg}} = 3.9 \text{ psi vac}$$

Because the suction pressure is below atmospheric (vacuum) and the discharge pressure is above atmospheric (gage), the pressures must be added to find the pressure increase, as shown in Figure 1.7.

$$\begin{aligned} \text{pressure increase} &= 60 \text{ psi} + 3.9 \text{ psi} \\ &= 63.9 \text{ psi} \end{aligned}$$

The answer is expressed to three significant figures. In many cases of this type it would be satisfactory to round off the result to two figures, that is, 64 psi.

Compound pressure gages are particularly useful in refrigeration work because pressures are frequently below atmospheric in the suction lines to compressors.

In the previous example we expressed one of the pressures as the height of a column of liquid (in. Hg). An explanation of how this type of unit is computed will be given in the following section.

## 1.8  Pressure of a Liquid Column

A liquid exerts a pressure because of its weight, and the weight depends on the height

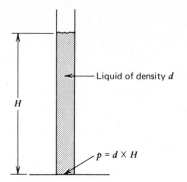

**FIGURE 1.8** Pressure exerted by a liquid column. Pressure may be expressed as "head" (height of liquid).

of the column of liquid. The relation between the pressure exerted and the height, as shown in Figure 1.8, is

$$p = d \times H \tag{1.7}$$

where

$p$ = pressure exerted by a liquid, lb/ft$^2$
$d$ = density of liquid, lb/ft$^3$
$H$ = height of liquid, ft

Other units can be used in the equation, but these are often convenient.

**Example 1.8**  A 300-ft vertical pipe in an office building is filled with chilled water. What is the pressure in pounds per square inch gage (psig) that will be exerted on a valve in the bottom of the line?

*Solution*  The density of water is approxi-

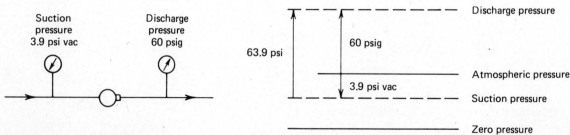

**FIGURE 1.7** Sketch for Example 1.7.

mately 62.4 lb/ft³. Using Equation 1.7,

$$p = d \times H$$

$$p = 62.4 \frac{lb}{ft^3} \times 300 \text{ ft}$$

$$= 18,720 \frac{lb}{ft^2} \times \frac{1 \text{ ft}^2}{144 \text{ in.}^2} = 130 \text{ psig}$$

The relation between pressure and height of a liquid is used in pressure measuring instruments that have a column of liquid. These are called *manometers*, an example of which is shown in Figure 1.9. In Figure 1.9(a), the pressure exerted on both legs of the manometer (atmospheric pressure) is the same, so the liquid is at the same level. In Figure 1.9(b) the pressure in the tank is above atmospheric. In Figure 1.9(c) the pressure in the tank is below atmospheric (vacuum pressure), so the liquid is higher in the leg connected to the tank.

**Example 1.9**   The evaporator in a refrigeration machine is being evacuated of gases with a vacuum pump so that it may be charged with refrigerant. The technician checks how much the pressure has been reduced, using a mercury (Hg) manometer. The reading on the manometer is 700 mm Hg vacuum. What is the absolute pressure in the evaporator expressed in the following units a) kPa b) atm c) psi?

*Solution*   The pressure reading must first be converted from vacuum to absolute reference. Atmospheric pressure is approximately 760 mm Hg (this will be discussed soon). Using Equation 1.6:

$$p_{abs} = p_{atm} - p_{vac}$$

$$p_{abs} = 760 - 700 = 600 \text{ mm Hg}$$

Converting to kilopascals (kPa):

$$p_{abs} = 60 \text{ mm Hg} \times \frac{133.3 \text{ Pa}}{1 \text{ mm Hg}}$$
$$\times \frac{1 \text{ kPa}}{1000 \text{ Pa}} = 8.00 \text{ kPa}$$

Converting to atm

$$p_{abs} = 60 \text{ mm Hg} \times \frac{1 \text{ atm}}{760 \text{ mm Hg}}$$
$$= 0.079 \text{ atm}$$

Converting to psi:

$$p_{abs} = 60 \text{ mm Hg} \times \frac{14.7 \text{ psi}}{760 \text{ mm Hg}} = 1.16 \text{ psi}$$

The *barometer* (Figure 1.10) is a special manometer used for measuring atmospheric

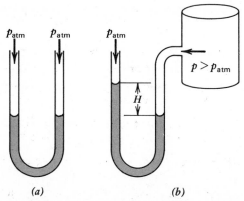

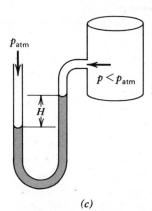

(a)                    (b)                              (c)

**FIGURE 1.9** Manometer used to measure pressure. (a) Equal (atmospheric) pressure on both legs. (b) Reading tank pressure above atmospheric. (c) Reading tank pressure below atmospheric.

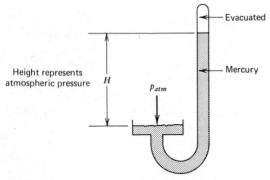

**FIGURE 1.10** A barometer (manometer used to measure atmospheric pressure).

air pressure. Mercury is the liquid used. The tube is evacuated so that no atmospheric pressure acts on the top of the mercury column. Since atmospheric pressure acts on the bottom of the mercury, the height to which the mercury column is lifted represents atmospheric pressure.

**Example 1.10**   How high would the mercury column in a barometer be, in both inches of mercury and millimeters of mercury, at the location where atmospheric pressure is 14.7 psi and the temperature 32° F (0°C).

*Solution*   Using Equation 1.7 with proper units, noting the density of mercury (Table 1.1) is $d = 849$ lb/ft$^3$ at 32° F,

$$p_{atm} = 14.7 \frac{lb}{in.^2} \times \frac{144 \text{ in.}^2}{1 \text{ ft}^2} = 2116.8 \text{ lb/ft}^2$$

$$= \frac{p}{d} = \frac{2116.8 \text{ lb/ft}^2}{849 \text{ lb/ft}^3} = 2.49 \text{ ft Hg} \times \frac{12 \text{ in.}}{1 \text{ ft}}$$

$$29.92 \text{ in. Hg} \times \frac{25.4 \text{ mm}}{1 \text{ in.}} = 760 \text{ mm Hg}$$

't is often convenient to express n units of head. *Head* is the equiva- id column height ($H$) expressed in 7. In Example 1.10, instead of he pressure of the atmosphere t could have been stated that it

was 29.92 in. Hg or 760 mm Hg. In Example 1.9 also the pressure could have been stated both ways, $p = 3.9$ psi $= 8$ in. Hg.

That is, there does not actually have to be a column of liquid to express any pressure in head units. Equation 1.7 can be used to convert to or from pressure expressed in units of head. Some of the conversions for pressure expressed as head, obtained from that equation, are also listed in Appendix 2.

**Example 1.11**   A contractor, requiring a pump that will have a discharge pressure of 42 psi, looks in a manufacturer's catalog to find a suitable pump but finds that the pump pressure ratings are listed as ft w. (feet of water). What pump head should be specified in the purchase order?

*Solution*   Using the conversion factor equality (Appendix 2) of

$$2.3 \text{ ft w.} = 1 \text{ psi}$$

$$H = 42 \text{ psi} \times \frac{2.3 \text{ ft w.}}{1 \text{ psi}}$$

$$= 96.6 \text{ ft w.}$$

## 1.9 Work, Power, and Energy

*Work* is the effect created by a force when it moves a body. It is expressed by the following equation:

$$\text{work} = \text{force} \times \text{distance} \qquad (1.8)$$

**Example 1.12**   A 6000-lb cooling tower is hoisted from the street level to the roof of the Gusher Oil Co. building 300 ft high. How much work is done in lifting it?

*Solution*   The force required is equal to the weight of the tower. Using Equation 1.8:

$$\text{work} = 6000 \text{ lb} \times 300 \text{ ft} = 1,800,000 \text{ ft-lb}$$

In the SI system the unit of work is the joule (J), the amount of work accomplished by a force of one newton (N) acting through a distance of one meter, that is $1 J = 1 N\text{-}m$.

**Power** *is the time rate of doing work.*

It is expressed by the equation

$$\text{power} = \frac{\text{work}}{\text{time}} \qquad (1.9)$$

Power is usually of more direct importance than work in industrial applications; the capacity of equipment is based on its power output or power consumption. If work is expressed in foot-pounds, some units of power that would result are foot-pounds per minute and foot-pounds per second. More commonly used units for power are the horsepower (hp) and kilowatt (kW). The standard SI unit for power is the kilowatt, equal to 1 J/sec.

**Example 1.13** If the cooling tower in Example 1.12 is lifted by a crane in four minutes, what is the minimum power required?

*Solution* Using Equation 1.9,

$$\text{power} = \frac{1,800,000 \text{ ft-lb}}{4 \text{ min}}$$
$$= 450,000 \text{ ft-lb/min}$$

From Appendix 2,

$$1 \text{ hp} = 33,000 \text{ ft-lb/min} = 0.746 \text{ kW}$$

Changing units,

$$450,000 \text{ ft-lb/min} \times \frac{1 \text{ hp}}{33,000 \text{ ft-lb/min}}$$
$$= 13.6 \text{ hp}$$
$$13.6 \text{ hp} \times \frac{0.746 \text{ kW}}{1 \text{ hp}} = 10.1 \text{ kW}$$

*Energy,* although it is a somewhat abstract concept, is sometimes defined as the ability to do work. For example we use the stored chemical energy in a fuel by burning it to create combustion gases at high pressure that drive the pistons of an engine and thus do work. Work is therefore one of the forms of energy.

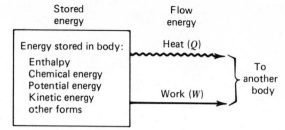

**FIGURE 1.11** Forms of energy.

Energy can exist in a number of forms. They can be grouped into those forms of energy that are *stored* in bodies or those forms of energy in *transfer* or motion between bodies. Work is one of the forms of energy in transfer between bodies. That is, one body does work on another when it moves it.

Energy can be stored in matter in many forms. Figure 1.11 is a diagram showing some types of *stored energy* and *energy in transfer.* At this time we will turn our attention to a form of energy in transfer or motion called heat. Some of the forms of stored energy will be discussed later.

## 1.10 Heat and Temperature

**Heat** *can be defined as the form of energy that transfers from one body to another due to a temperature difference.*

Figure 1.12 describes graphically this definition. In Figure 1.12($a$) heat ($Q$) flows from the higher temperature ($t_h$) body, the sun, to the lower temperature ($t_l$) body, the sunbather. Figure 1.12($b$) shows that heat will flow from the higher temperature ($t_h$) body, the warm milk, to the lower temperature ($t_l$) body, the ice, due to the temperature difference.

Note that heat can only flow naturally from a higher to a lower temperature—"downhill," so to speak. Of course if there is no temperature difference there is no heat flow.

Refrigeration is simply a special case of heat transfer—the transfer or removal of heat

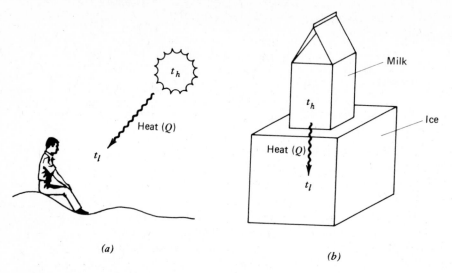

Heat (Q)

Milk

Ice

Heat (Q)

(a)

(b)

**FIGURE 1.12** Flow of heat from higher temperature body to lower temperature body.

from a body to bring it to a desired low temperature, or to keep it at a low temperature. Of course there must therefore be another body at an even lower temperature to transfer the heat to. This is what creates the need for methods of mechanical refrigeration, which is the subject of this book.

Although we ordinarily speak of "cooling" something to refer to refrigeration, what is really happening is that heat is being removed. Technically there is no meaning to words such as *cool* or *cooling*. These are only relative physical feelings that we have, reflecting the fact that some object is at an unusual low temperature, or that it is losing heat.

A common unit used to measure heat in the United States is the Btu (British thermal unit). The Btu is defined as *the quantity of heat required to raise the temperature of one pound of water one degree Fahrenheit at 59° F.*

The standard SI unit for heat is the joule. Note that it is also the SI unit for work. Because work and heat are both forms of the same physical entity—energy—it is possible to measure them in the same units. Indeed we have all seen many instances in which work,

one form of energy, is converted into another form of energy, heat, through friction. A common example is the work done by the tires of a car rubbing on the road, which through friction heats the tire.

The fact that the joule is the only unit used for all forms of energy and the kilowatt is used for all forms of rate of energy or power in the standard SI system simplifies calculations. However in refrigeration work it is still common to use the calorie (cal) and kilocalorie (kcal) for heat energy in countries using the metric system. The calorie is the quantity of heat required to raise the temperature of one gram of water one degree Celsius at 15° C.

Temperature is a property of substances that depends on the velocity of the molecules in a body. Molecules are the particles that make up the structure of substances. The greater the molecular velocity, the higher the temperature. However it is not practical to measure temperature by measuring the velocity of molecules. Our sense of touch can give us a relative comparison of temperatures, and we speak of "hot" and "cold" bodies according to our reactions. This is not adequate to develop an accurate numerical scale, however. Temperature is measured accurately by observing the change of some other physical effect due to changes in temperature. The most common temperature measuring device (the thermometer) uses the fact that liquids expand and contract as their temperature changes. A mercury thermometer consists of a narrow glass tube and bulb containing mercury. When the temperature increases, the mercury expands and rises in the bulb. By noting where the mercury is in relation to a temperature scale of numbers inscribed on the glass, the temperature can be measured.

The unit scale used in the United States for measuring temperature is the *degree Fahrenheit* (°F), in which the boiling point of water is 212°F and the freezing point of water 32°F, at atmospheric pressure. In the metric system of units the *degree Celsius* (°C) is used, in which the boiling point of water is 100°C and the freezing point is 0°C, at atmospheric pressure. The relationship between these two units is therefore

$$°F = 1.8°C + 32 \qquad (1.10a)$$

$$°C = \frac{°F - 32}{1.8} \qquad (1.10b)$$

**Example 1.14** The cooling water in a refrigerant condenser is supposed to be at a temperature of 78°F. The operating engineer checks the temperature with a thermometer that has a Celsius scale. What should be the reading on the thermometer?

*Solution* Using Equation 1.10b

$$°C = \frac{°F - 32}{1.8} = \frac{78 - 32}{1.8} = 25.6°C$$

There are also two *absolute temperature* scales. These take the value zero for the lowest temperature that can exist. They are called the *Rankine* (R) and *Kelvin* (K) temperature scales. The Rankine is used in the U.S. system, with the difference in size between each degree the same as that in the Fahrenheit system. The

Kelvin is used in the SI system with the difference between each degree equal to the difference between Celsius degrees. The relationships are

$$°R = °F + 460 \qquad (1.10c)$$

$$°K = °C + 273 \qquad (1.10d)$$

The relations between temperature scales are shown graphically in Figure 1.13.

## 1.11 Enthalpy

It has been stated that energy can be classified into energy in flow and stored energy. The total energy stored in a body includes a number of types. For instance we are well aware that a body has stored chemical energy, because we have experienced that this energy can be released from some substances by combustion. Other forms of stored energy are kinetic and potential energy. *Kinetic energy* is the stored energy in a body due to its motion, or velocity. *Potential energy* is the stored energy a body has due to its position, or elevation. Bodies also have additional energy due to their temperature and pressure. We are aware that a gas at a high pressure has energy (e.g., a

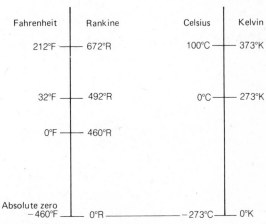

**FIGURE 1.13** Relationship between different temperature scales.

steam boiler that bursts) and water at a high temperature can give up heat energy.

*This stored energy of temperature and pressure is called **enthalpy** (H).*

(There is a more precise definition of enthalpy, but it serves no purpose in our discussion.) It is also common in the refrigeration industry to use the phrase *heat content* to mean the same as enthalpy. (Strictly speaking, heat is a form of energy that flows into or out of a body and enthalpy or heat content is a form of stored energy in a body.) Being a form of energy, enthalpy can also be measured in Btu or joules. *Specific enthalpy* (*h*) is the enthalpy per unit mass of a substance, expressed in Btu per pound in U.S. units and joules per kilogram in SI units.

It is important to distinguish temperature from enthalpy (heat content). Temperature is a measure of the thermal level of a body. When heat is added to a body its temperature rises, but the total enthalpy or heat content of a body depends on the mass of a body as well as its temperature. For example a thimbleful of molten steel at 2500°F has a much greater temperature than a large tank filled with water at 200°F but the enthalpy of the tank of water is greater. That is, there is more stored energy in the water. This is an important fact, because for many applications more heat can be obtained from the tank of water despite its lower temperature.

# REVIEW QUESTIONS

1. What is refrigeration?
2. What are the names of the two most commonly used systems of achieving refrigeration?
3. Into what groups, according to use in the economy, is refrigeration classified?
4. What is unitary equipment? Why is it desirable?
5. List five examples of refrigeration equipment found in a restaurant or supermarket.
6. What is a unit? What problem occurs in using units?
7. What is a conversion factor?
8. What are the advantages of the SI system of units?
9. Explain why it is important to report a value to a certain number of significant places.
10. Explain gage pressure, vacuum pressure, and absolute pressure. What is a compound gage?
11. What is meant by stored energy and energy in transfer? List names and give examples of each.

# PROBLEMS

1.1 List the physical characteristic measured by each of the following units: $lb/in.^2$, hp, GPM, in. Hg, m/sec, $ft^2$, kW, Btu, $kg/m^3$, $ft^3/lb$ (see Appendices 1 and 2).

1.2 List the standard SI unit and a typical U.S. unit for each of the following physical characteristics: power, pressure, velocity, mass, flow rate, energy, specific volume, and density.

1.3 Change the following quantities from the original units to the new units (see Appendix 2):
   a. 85 $lb/in.^2$ to ft w.
   b. 14.5 $ft^3/sec$ to gal/min (GPM).
   c. 83,200 Btu/hr to tons of refrigeration.
   d. 7.62 in. Hg to $lb/in.^2$.
   e. 12.6 hp to Btu/min.

1.4 The door to a walk-in refrigerator is 7 ft 6 in. high by 4 ft 3 in. wide. What is the door area in square feet?

1.5 Change the following quantities from

the U.S. units to the SI units shown:
   a. 23.7 tons (of refrigeration) to kW.
   b. 18.0 lb/in.$^2$ to kg/m$^3$.
   c. 62.4 lb/ft$^3$ to kg/m$^3$.
   d. 145 gal/min. to m$^3$/sec.

1.6 A cylinder filled with a refrigerant has a volume of 3.8 ft$^3$. The refrigerant weighs 206.0 lb. Find the density and the specific volume of the refrigerant in U.S. units. What is the density in SI units?

1.7 A tank 4.0 ft. long by 3.5 ft. wide is filled with a brine to a depth of 2.6 ft. The brine has a specific gravity of 1.20. What is the weight of brine in the tank?

1.8 Round off the following numbers to three significant figures:
   a. 234,340
   b. 7.2798
   c. 543
   d. 2.8
   e. 0.7826

1.9 Find the pressure exerted by the brine on the bottom of the tank described in Problem 1.7. Express the answer in lb/in.$^2$ and in kPa.

1.10 The absolute pressure in the suction line to a compressor is 8.3 in. Hg. What pressure would a vacuum gage calibrated in in. Hg read, if the compressor is at sea level?

1.11 The discharge gage on a compressor reads 210 psi. The compressor is located in a place where the atmospheric pressure is 12.2 psi. What is the absolute discharge pressure? Express the answer both in psi and in kPa.

1.12 A pressure gage at the suction of a compressor reads 7.4 in. Hg vacuum. A gage at the compressor discharge reads 162 psig. What is the refrigerant pressure increase in the compressor in psi?

1.13 A refrigeration system is to be evacuated of gases to a pressure of 0.06 psia. The pressure is measured on a manometer. What would be the equivalent manometer reading expressed in mm Hg?

1.14 A 24-ft.-high pipe filled with water extends from a condenser on the top floor of a building to a cooling tower on the floor above. What is the pressure exerted on the condenser in psi?

1.15 A barometer reads 705 mm Hg. What is the atmospheric pressure expressed in psi and in in. Hg?

1.16 Change the following temperature readings from the original units to the new units:
   a. 95°F to °C
   b. −10°C to °F
   c. 620°F to °R
   d. 32°C to °K
   e. 580°R to °C

# Chapter 2

## PHYSICAL PRINCIPLES 2

This chapter explains how refrigeration is accomplished and reviews additional subjects in physics that relate to refrigeration, including the states of matter, the First and Second Laws of Thermodynamics, the behavior of gases, and heat transfer. Further information on heat transfer will be included in Chapter 6. Other material relates to energy use and conservation.

## OBJECTIVES

A study of this chapter will enable you to:
1. Describe and use the energy equation.
2. Identify the relationship between temperature, pressure, heat, and enthalpy when a substance changes state between a liquid and a vapor.
3. Explain the meaning of saturated, subcooled, and superheated conditions.
4. Use the refrigerant property tables to find property values.
5. Use the sensible and latent heat equations.
6. Discuss the significance and some conclusions from the Second Law of Thermodynamics regarding energy conservation.

## 2.1 The Energy Equation (First Law of Thermodynamics)

Thermodynamics is the branch of physics that deals with the transformation between heat and work. The First Law of Thermodynamics is a principle that can be stated in many ways, for example "energy can be neither created nor destroyed," or "there is a conservation of energy in any process." We make great use of

this law in refrigeration work, especially when stated as the following energy balance:

*The energy added ($E_{in}$) to a system less the energy removed ($E_{out}$) from the system equals the energy change ($E_{ch}$) in the system.*

Written as the *Energy Equation* for any system, this becomes

$$energy\ change = energy\ added$$
$$- energy\ removed$$

$$E_{ch} = E_{in} - E_{out} \qquad (2.1)$$

The word *system* can refer to any body or group of bodies of concern. It might be the air in a room, a refrigeration evaporator, the gas flowing through a compressor, or the complete refrigeration plant—anything to which the equation is applied.

The energy that is added (in) or removed (out) from the system may be in the form of either heat or work, or both, flowing into or out of the system. Usually the *rate* of energy flow (energy per unit of time) is of interest. The following example illustrates the use of the energy equation.

*Example 2.1* The compressor shown in Figure 2.1 requires 2.6 hp to compress the refrigerant gas. There is a heat loss of 900 Btu/hr from the gas through the walls of the compressor to the surroundings. What is the rate of energy gain or loss to the gas?

*Solution* The problem is solved by applying the energy equation (2.1). The units for energy rate must all be the same, as shown in the conversion from hp to Btu/hr.

$$E_{ch} = E_{in} - E_{out}$$

$$= 2.6 \text{ hp} \times \frac{2545 \text{ Btu/hr}}{1 \text{ hp}} - 900 \text{ Btu/hr}$$

$$= 6617 \text{ Btu/hr} - 900 \text{ Btu/hr}$$

$$= 5717 \text{ Btu/hr}$$

That is, the energy of the refrigerant gas has increased by 5717 Btu/hr in the compressor.

In this example, the energy of the system (the gas) increased, as indicated by the result having a positive (plus) value. A negative (minus) value would indicate that there was a net decrease or loss of energy in the gas.

The enthalpy of the gas changed in this example. Enthalpy changes in many refrigeration processes. That is, any change in stored energy of the refrigerant is usually an enthalpy change.

Although the forms in which energy may be added to or removed from the refrigerant are heat and work, the units used for energy are interchangeable, regardless of the form of energy, whether it is heat, work, or enthalpy. The next example illustrates how the problem of units is simplified using the SI system.

**Example 2.2**  A cold storage walk-in cooler has evaporator fans that give off 420 W of heat energy. Apples stored in the room release 280 W (J/sec) from the heat of respiration. What is the rate of enthalpy change of the room air?

*Solution*  Applying Equation 2.1,

$$E_{ch} = E_{in} - E_{out}$$

$$= 420 \text{ W} + 280 \text{ W} - 0$$

$$= 700 \text{ W}$$

The enthalpy of the room air is increasing at a rate of 700 W. Note that because only one unit for energy rate is used (the watt), no unit conversions are required.

In the refrigeration industry in the United States, a unit expressing rate of heat is the *ton*

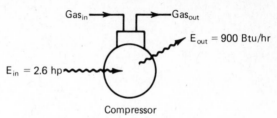

**FIGURE 2.1**  Sketch for Example 2.1

*of refrigeration.* Its equivalence is

$$1 \text{ ton} = 200 \text{ Btu/min} = 12,000 \text{ Btu/hr}$$
$$= 288,000 \text{ Btu/day}$$

The origin of this unit is based on the fact that the melting of one ton of ice releases 288,000 Btu (2000 lb × 144 Btu/lb).

## 2.2 Liquids, Vapors, and Change of State

Substances can exist in three different *states* (also called *phases*): solid, liquid, or vapor (gas). The events that occur when a substance changes state from a liquid to a vapor (boiling) or from a vapor to a liquid (condensing) is best described by an experiment, which is shown in Figure 2.2 (*a* through *f*).

Figure 2.2(*a*) shows a pot of water at room temperature. Being open, it is subject to atmospheric pressure, 14.7 psia at sea level. At (*b*) heat (*Q*) is being added to the water, and it is noted that the water temperature continually rises as heat is added. However, at some later point in time it is noted that at (*c*) the temperature stops rising (at 212°F) and even though more heat is added after that, at (*d*) the temperature does not increase for a while. What is observed now, however, is that the liquid water will change into its gas or vapor state (steam). This process is called boiling. It is a rapid evaporation. As heat is added, no further temperature increase occurs as long as some liquid remains. At (*e*), all the water is evaporated. If more heat is added it will be noted that the temperature (of the steam) will begin to rise again, above 212°F, as seen in (*f*).

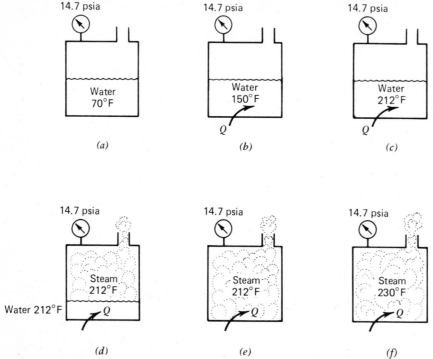

**FIGURE 2.2** Experiment showing change of state of water at atmospheric pressure (14.7 psia). (*a*) Initial condition (subcooled liquid). (*b*) Heat added, temperature increases (subcooled liquid). (*c*) Heat added, liquid reaches boiling point (saturated liquid). (*d*) Heat added, liquid changing to vapor, no temperature increase. (*e*) Heat added, all liquid vaporized (saturated vapor). (*f*) Heat added, temperature of vapor increases (superheated vapor). *Note:* Subcooled liquid is liquid below its boiling point. Saturated liquid and saturated vapor are the liquid and vapor at the boiling (condensing) point. Superheated vapor is vapor above the boiling point.

The whole series of processes just described could also be carried out in reverse. Removal of heat (cooling) from the steam in Figure 2.2 (*e*) lowers its temperature. When the cooling continues to (*f*) the temperature no longer drops, but the gas begins to condense to a liquid, at (*d*). After all of the steam is condensed, at (*c*), further removal of heat will result in a temperature drop of the liquid, (*b*) and (*a*).

A summary of all this information is shown in Figure 2.3, the temperature–enthalpy (t–h) diagram. The line shows a change in temperature of the liquid when heat is added between 32°F and 212°F, but no change in temperature when more heat is added, until all the liquid is

evaporated. When further heat is added, the temperature rises again. (The diagram also shows the change between solid and liquid state, which will be discussed later.)

## 2.3  The Dependence of Boiling Temperature on Pressure

The conclusion that can be drawn from the preceding experiment is that water changes state between a liquid and gas at 212°F and 14.7 psia. Let us conduct the same experiment with the surrounding pressure at a higher value, say 24.9 psia. Figure 2.4 represents the same heating process, or cooling if done in reverse, at the higher pressure.

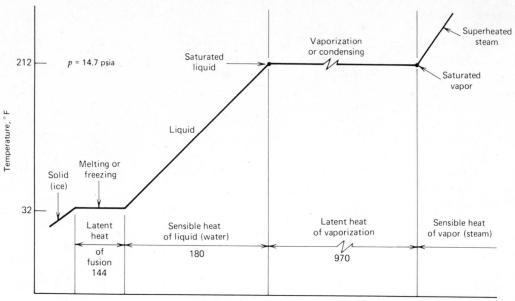

**FIGURE 2.3** Enthalpy (heat content) change of water at 14.7 psia.

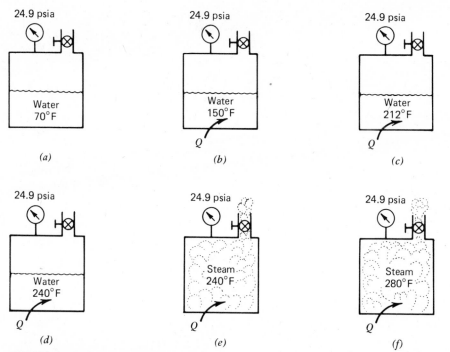

**FIGURE 2.4** Experiment showing change of state of water at 24.9 psia. (*a*) Initial condition (subcooled liquid). (*b*) Heat added, temperature increases (subcooled liquid). (*c*) Heat added, temperature increases (subcooled liquid). (*d*) Heat added, liquid reaches boiling point. (*e*) Heat added, all liquid vaporized (saturated vapor). (*f*) Heat added, temperature of vapor increases (superheated vapor).

When the water reaches 212°F, at (*c*), and more heat is added, it does not boil, but the temperature continues to rise. However when the temperature reaches 240°F, at (*d*), the boiling process begins and the temperature remains constant until the liquid has completely evaporated. This shows that the temperature at which the water boils changes with pressure. For water, the boiling point is 240°F at 24.9 psia. This means that water cannot be made to boil at a temperature below 240°F if the pressure is 24.9 psia.

If the same experiment was carried out with the pressure at 6 psia, we would find that when heat was added the boiling process would occur at 170°F. These facts show that the boiling–condensing temperature of a fluid depends on its pressure. That is, *the boiling temperature of a liquid changes with pressure.* Figure 2.5 shows a line representing these tem-

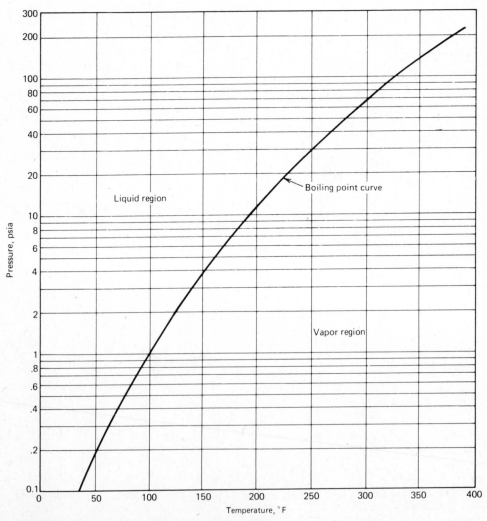

**FIGURE 2.5** Boiling point pressure–temperature curve for water, also called the vapor pressure curve.

perature–pressure values for water; it is called the *boiling point curve* or *saturation vapor pressure curve*. Water can exist at its boiling condition only at values on this line. To the left of the line it can exist only as a liquid, and to the right it can exist only as a vapor. Along the line it can exist either as a liquid about to boil, a vapor about to condense, or a mixture of the liquid–vapor.

**Example 2.3** Will water exist in the liquid state, or as steam, if its temperature is 225°F and its pressure is 25 psia?

> *Solution* Locating the pressure–temperature (*p–t*) condition on Figure 2.5, we see that this is in the liquid region. The water is in a liquid state.

This same dependence of boiling–condensing temperature on pressure holds for all fluids, except the *p–t* values are different. For example at 14.7 psia, ammonia boils at −28°F, alcohol boils at 170°F, and copper boils at 4250°F. The boiling point p–t curves for some fluids used as refrigerants are shown in Figure 2.6. The symbols R-12, R-22, and the like, are a shorthand name code for refrigerants, standardized in the industry. This numbering system avoids the problem of using trade names from different manufacturers, such as Freon, Genetron, and Isotron. It also is simpler than using the lengthy chemical names. One group of refrigerants, of which R-12, R-22, R-502, and a number of others are members, are called fluorocarbons. We will discuss refrigerants in detail in Chapter 9.

**Example 2.4** Refrigerant R-22 is to be used at an evaporating (boiling) temperature of 25°F. What will be its pressure?

> *Solution* From the boiling point curve for R-22 in Figure 2.6, the evaporation pressure corresponding to 25°F is approximately 63 psia.

Later on we will introduce tables that list the corresponding *p–t* values at the boiling point. These have the advantage that they can be read more accurately than curves.

Note from Figure 2.6 that the higher the pressure is on a liquid, the higher the boiling temperature is; and the lower the pressure the lower the temperature at which it will boil.

## 2.4 The Molecular (Kinetic) Theory of Liquids and Gases

The process of boiling and the dependence of boiling point temperature on surrounding pressure can be explained by referring to the molecular (kinetic) theory of liquids and gases. All matter is composed of particles called molecules. The molecules in a substance are constantly in motion. They are also attracted to each other by forces. The closer the molecules are to each other, the greater the attractive forces.

When a substance is in the liquid state, the molecules are closer together than when it is in its gaseous state, and therefore the attractive forces are greater. Also molecules in the gaseous state move more rapidly than molecules in the liquid state, and therefore they have more energy. This is why heat is required to boil a liquid. The heat energy is required to overcome the attractive forces holding the molecules relatively close together, so that they move further apart and change state to a gas.

The temperature of a substance is a measure of the average velocity of its molecules. The higher the average velocity, the higher the temperature. However, not all molecules move at the average velocity—some are moving faster, some slower.

Figure 2.7 shows an open vessel of water at 70°F, surrounded by air at 14.7 psia. The water is therefore in a liquid state. The average velocity of the molecules is not great enough for them to rapidly escape. However a small fraction of molecules have velocities well

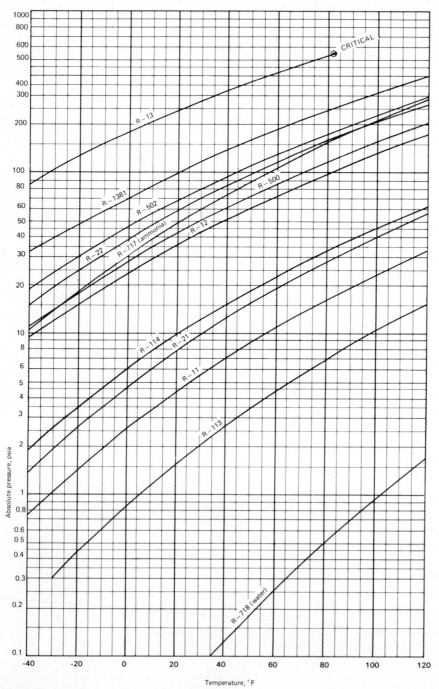

**FIGURE 2.6** Boiling point pressure–temperature curves for some refrigerants.

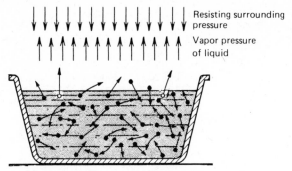

Resisting surrounding pressure

Vapor pressure of liquid

**FIGURE 2.7** Slow evaporation of liquid. Escape of some molecules through surface causes a vapor pressure.

above the average. If some of these molecules are near the surface they will escape. That is, there will be very slow evaporation from the surface. This leaves the remaining molecules at a slower average velocity, and therefore at a lower temperature. A slight cooling effect of the liquid has occurred as a result of the evaporation. We have all noticed this effect when alcohol is rubbed on the skin. It gradually evaporates and cools itself and the skin.

The molecules escaping from the surface of a liquid create vapor. The pressure exerted by the vapor at the surface of the liquid is called the *vapor pressure*. If the pressure exerted by a surrounding gas is above the vapor pressure, then the liquid cannot rapidly evaporate. However if the temperature of the liquid is increased, the molecular velocity increases to a point at which the molecules break the bonds holding them together as a liquid and the liquid boils. The vapor pressure of the liquid has been increased to a value greater than the surrounding resisting pressure. Of course if the resisting pressure is higher, the temperature of the liquid must be increased further to reach the boiling point.

While the boiling process is occurring, the heat applied is breaking the bonds by overcoming forces that hold the molecules close together. It is not increasing the velocity of the molecules. That is why the temperature does not increase during boiling.

It is of importance to note what happens if the pressure exerted by a gas above a liquid is reduced to a value below the vapor pressure exerted by the liquid. In this case the liquid will suddenly boil, because the surrounding pressure is now less than the vapor pressure exerted by the liquid. The energy of the molecules is great enough to overcome the reduced resistance, and they rapidly escape. This cools the remaining liquid, because energy is removed. *Boiling has been achieved by a lowering of pressure.* This process is essential in refrigeration, as will be seen later.

## 2.5 Saturated, Subcooled, and Superheated Conditions

The pressure and temperature condition at which boiling occurs is called the saturated condition, and the boiling point is technically known as the saturation temperature and saturation pressure. As seen from our experimental description, the substance can exist as a liquid, a vapor, or a mixture of liquid and vapor at the saturated condition. At saturation, the liquid is called saturated liquid and the vapor is called a saturated vapor.

> *Saturated vapor* is vapor at the boiling temperature, and *saturated liquid* is liquid at the boiling temperature. When the vapor is above its saturation temperature (boiling point) it is called a *superheated vapor*. When the liquid is below its saturation temperature it is called a *subcooled liquid*.

Figure 2.8, a typical boiling point curve, illustrates this. Note that a substance can exist as a subcooled liquid or superheated vapor at many temperatures for a given pressure, but it can exist as a saturated liquid or vapor at only one temperature for a given pressure.

## 2.6 Sensible and Latent Heat

When heat added to or removed from a substance results in a temperature change and no change of state, then the enthalpy change in

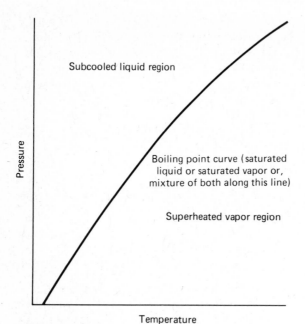

**FIGURE 2.8** Typical boiling point curve showing saturated liquid, saturated vapor, or a mixture (on curve), and subcooled liquid and superheated vapor regions.

the substance is called a *sensible heat* change. When heat added to or removed from a substance results in a change of state (at constant temperature), then the enthalpy change in the substance is called a *latent heat* change. The enthalpy increase as it changes from a liquid to a vapor is called the *latent heat of vaporization*. The opposite effect, the enthalpy decrease as it changes from a vapor to a liquid is called the *latent heat of condensation*. It is equal to the latent heat of vaporization.

## 2.7 Saturated Property Tables

Tables have been prepared for many substances that list the saturation temperatures and corresponding pressures as well as other properties at saturation conditions. For water the tables are commonly called the saturated steam tables. Appendix 3 is an abbreviated saturated properties table for water. The fol-

lowing examples illustrate some uses of these tables.

***Example 2.5*** At what temperature will water boil at a pressure of 11.5 psia?

*Solution* From Appendix 3, we read the saturation temperature (boiling point) at 11.5 psia to be 200°F.

***Example 2.6*** Use the steam tables to determine if water is in a liquid or gas state at 300°F and 150 psia.

*Solution* Using Appendix 3, the saturation (boiling) temperature at 150 psia is about 360°F. The actual temperature is less, therefore the water will be in a liquid state (subcooled liquid).

## 2.8 Refrigeration by Evaporation

That matter has a molecular nature explains how a sudden lowering of the pressure surrounding a liquid can cause the liquid to boil, resulting in refrigeration.

When a substance is in a liquid state, if the surrounding pressure is suddenly lowered to a value below the saturation pressure, the liquid will begin to vigorously boil off to a gas. The velocity of the molecules is great enough for them to rapidly escape at the lower pressure, but not at the higher original pressure. The boiling will cool the substance to the saturation temperature corresponding to the lower pressure. When the liquid boils it absorbs its latent heat of vaporization from any surrounding body, thus it cools. Refrigeration has been accomplished. In chapter 3 we will discuss how this is achieved in a practical way.

Even the boiling of water can be used to achieve refrigeration, if the pressure can be lowered enough, as seen in the following example.

***Example 2.7*** The boiling of water is to be used to accomplish refrigeration at 50°F. To what value should the surrounding pressure be lowered?

*Solution*  From Appendix 3, the saturation pressure of water at 50°F is 0.178 psia. If the pressure is reduced below this value the water will boil. This requires (latent) heat. Heat will flow to the water from any surrounding body at a higher temperature, thus cooling the body.

Some absorption refrigeration systems use the boiling (evaporation) of water at very low pressures to achieve refrigeration (see Chapter 13).

Many other fluids besides water are used as refrigerants, of course. Tables listing properties at saturation conditions for a number of refrigerants may be found in the Appendices, in both U.S. and SI units. The student should become thoroughly familiar with these tables, since we will frequently use them.

**Example 2.8**  At what temperature will refrigerant R-12 boil (evaporate) if the surrounding pressure is 31.8 psia?

*Solution*  Using Appendix 5, the saturation temperature (boiling point) of R-12 at 31.8 psia is 14°F.

**Example 2.9**  R-717 (ammonia) is at a temperature of 110°F and a pressure of 192.7 psia. What is its state?

*Solution*  Using Appendix 8, at 192.7 psia the corresponding saturation temperature (boiling point) is 94°F. The actual temperature is greater than this, therefore the refrigerant is a superheated vapor. That is, it is above its boiling point.

The following example illustrates a point made previously, that a reduction in pressure surrounding a liquid can cause it to boil.

**Example 2.10**  Refrigerant R-502 is at 90°F and 215 psia. The pressure is suddenly dropped to 65 psia. What is its initial condition, and what will happen when the pressure is decreased?

*Solution*  Appendix 7 lists the properties at saturation for R-502. At 215 psia the saturation temperature is approximately 95°F. The actual temperature is 90°F, therefore initially it is a subcooled liquid.

The saturation pressure corresponding to 90°F is approximately 200 psia. If the pressure is dropped to 65 psia, that is, below the lowest pressure which would prevent it from boiling (200 psia), the refrigerant liquid will immediately boil vigorously when the pressure is reduced.

We can further point out in this example that at the reduced pressure, 65 psia, the saturation temperature is 18°F. The refrigerant will therefore boil off at this temperature. The (latent) heat required for the evaporation will flow from any surrounding substance above 18°F. That is, refrigeration or cooling of the substance is achieved. A more complete explanation of this process is presented in Chapter 3.

In reading values from the saturated property tables, note that pressures below atmospheric are often given in units of in. Hg vacuum rather than psi. To remind the reader, these values are marked with an asterisk.

Tables of properties of the superheated gas are available for many refrigerants. Diagrams are available that show superheated and subcooled properties. These are called $p–h$ (pressure–enthalpy) diagrams. They are introduced in Chapter 3. Because these diagrams also aid in understanding and analyzing refrigeration processes, we will frequently use them.

The enthalpy and specific volume of a liquid depend almost completely on temperature and not pressure. For this reason the saturated property tables can be used to find these properties for subcooled liquids. For instance, the enthalpy of liquid water at 220°F in either the subcooled or saturated condition is 188.2 Btu/lb, as seen from Appendix 3.

Many tables list for convenience both absolute and gage pressure. The gage pressure listings are based on an assumed atmospheric pressure of 14.7 psi. If the actual atmospheric pressure in a given situation is significantly different from this, such as at high altitudes, the gage pressure listings will be incorrect. To avoid any error or misunderstanding, it is a good rule in any problem work to always use absolute pressure.

## 2.9 Determining the Amount of Heat Added or Removed

The Energy Equation (2.1) can be used to find how much heat must be added to or removed from a substance to change it from one condition to another. The changes in conditions that liquids and gases undergo are called processes. In most refrigeration processes when heat is added or removed, the enthalpy of the substance changes. In this case the Energy Equation becomes

Heat added or removed = enthalpy change
$$Q = m\,(h_2 - h_1) \quad (2.2)$$

where
$Q$ = net rate of heat added or removed from the substance, Btu/hr
$m$ = mass flow rate of substance, lb/hr
$h_2 - h_1$ = specific enthalpy change of substance, Btu/lb

Property tables or diagrams can be used with Equation 2.2 to calculate the heat added or removed. Note that the saturated property tables list specific enthalpies of both the saturated liquid ($h_f$) and saturated vapor ($h_g$). The saturated liquid values in the table can

also be used for subcooled liquids with no significant loss in accuracy. However these tables cannot be used for superheated vapors. We will use diagrams for this later.

The actual enthalpy of a substance would have a value of zero only when it is at the lowest temperature that could exist, absolute zero ($-460$°F), because at that temperature no molecular motion would occur. For all problems in refrigeration we are only interested in the change in enthalpy from one temperature to another, therefore the temperature for the zero value of specific enthalpy can be arbitrarily chosen. For water, it is usually selected at 32°F for the saturated liquid, and for refrigerants at $-40$°F for the saturated liquid.

**Example 2.11**  A water chiller cools 80 GPM (gallons per minute) of water from 60°F to 45°F. What is the cooling capacity of the chiller, in Btu/hr, tons of refrigeration, and kW?

*Solution*  Use Equation 2.2, after changing units and reading the initial and final enthalpies from Appendix 3 for water.

$$m = 80 \text{ GPM} \times \frac{500 \text{ lb/hr}}{1 \text{ GPM}}\text{water}$$
$$= 40{,}000 \text{ lb/hr}$$

From Appendix 3

$$h_1 - h_2 = 28.06 - 13.04 = 15.02 \text{ Btu/lb}.$$

(Note $h_1 - h_2$ was used rather than $h_2 - h_1$ to avoid having a negative sign in the answer). Using Equation 2.2,

$$\begin{aligned}
Q &= m\,(h_1 - h_2) \\
&= 40{,}000 \text{ lb/hr} \times 15.02 \text{ Btu/lb} \\
&= 601{,}000 \text{ Btu/hr} \\
&= 601{,}000 \text{ Btu/hr} \times \frac{1 \text{ ton}}{12{,}000 \text{ Btu/hr}} \\
&= 50 \text{ tons} \\
&= 601{,}000 \text{ Btu/hr} \times \frac{1 \text{ kW}}{3410 \text{ Btu/hr}} \\
&= 176 \text{ kW}
\end{aligned}$$

2 Saturated R-502 vapor at ̣ensed and then cooled to 80°F. ̣ neat is removed per pound?

*Solution* The initial enthalpy is that of the saturated vapor at 110°F and the final enthalpy is that of the liquid at 80°F. Using Table A.7,

$$Q = h_1 - h_2 = 87.26 - 31.59$$
$$= 355.67 \text{ Btu/lb}$$

## 2.10 Specific Heat: The Sensible Heat Equation

Although the property tables can be used to find the enthalpy change of a refrigerant liquid, another method is available, which can be used without tables. This method also adds to the understanding of processes, and therefore will be discussed here.

*The **specific heat** (c) of a substance is defined as the amount of heat in Btus required to change the temperature of one pound of the substance by one degree °F (U.S. units), at 59°F.*

The specific heat of water is 1 Btu/lb − °F (U.S. units). Specific heats for a few substances are listed in Table 1.1.

***Sensible Heat Equation.*** It follows from the definition of specific heat that the amount of heat required to change $m$ pounds of a substance from one temperature to another is

$$Q = m \times c \times TC = m \times c \times (t_2 - t_1) \quad (2.3)$$

where

$Q$ = net rate of heat added or removed, Btu/hr
$m$ = mass flow rate of substance, lb/hr
$TC = t_2 - t_1$ = temperature change of substance, °F

This equation is called the *sensible heat equation*, because it applies to a heating or cooling process where the temperature of the substance changes, but there is no change of state.

***Example 2.13*** Solve Example 2.11, using Equation 2.3.

*Solution* Using the values for $m$, $t_1$, and $t_2$ from Example 2.11,

$$Q = m \times c \times TC$$
$$= 40{,}000 \ \frac{\text{lb}}{\text{hr}} \times 1 \ \frac{\text{Btu}}{\text{lb} - °\text{F}} \times (60 - 45) \ °\text{F}$$
$$= 600{,}000 \text{ Btu/hr}$$

Note that the result agrees very closely with that found from using the property tables. Actually the property tables are more accurate because the specific heat of substances varies slightly with temperature.

When there is a change of state, the sensible heat equation does not apply, of course. In that case the tables are used. Note that the saturated property tables usually list the latent heat of evaporation ($h_{fg}$), which by definition is the difference between the enthalpy of the saturated vapor ($h_g$) and saturated liquid ($h_f$).

It is convenient to express the sensible heat equation with units of GPM for flow rate and tons of refrigeration for rate of heat, particularly when dealing with water chilling applications. Using the conversions,

12,000 Btu/hr = 1 ton
1 GPM = 500 lb/hr of water

$$(1 \ \frac{\text{gal}}{\text{min}} \times \frac{8.34 \text{ lb}}{\text{gal}} \times \frac{60 \text{ min}}{1 \text{ hr}} = 500 \text{ lb/hr})$$

and with the specific heat of water $c = 1$ Btu/lb − °F, if these values are substituted in Equation 2.3, the equation becomes

$$\text{Tons} = \frac{\text{GPM} \times \text{TC}}{24} \quad (2.4)$$

where tons = rate of heat removed, tons of refrigeration
GPM = chilled water flow rate, GPM
TC = temperature change of water, °F

## 2.11 Latent Heats of Fusion and Sublimation

The change of state of a substance from liquid to gas involves gaining the latent heat of vaporization. A substance in a solid state will increase in temperature when heat is added to it (sensible heat) but when a certain temperature is reached its temperature will no longer increase when more heat is added; however the substance will begin to change state to a liquid—it will melt. If the reverse process is carried out, heat is removed from a liquid, its temperature will drop but eventually it will freeze into a solid.

*The heat accompanying the melting or freezing process is called the* **latent heat of fusion.**

For water the latent heat of fusion is 144 Btu/lb. When there is a sensible heat change (temperature change) of a solid, the sensible heat equation (2.3) can be used.

At very low pressures and temperatures it is possible to change some substances directly from the solid to the gaseous state. This process is called *sublimation*. It is used in freeze-drying foods to maintain good flavor and appearance. First the food is frozen and then the ice in the food is evaporated directly to vapor, at a very low pressure.

## 2.12 The Perfect (Ideal) Gas Law

Under certain conditions the pressure, volume, and temperature of gases are related by an equation called the *perfect* or *ideal gas* law. The perfect gas equation can be expressed

$$pV = mRT \qquad (2.5)$$

where

$p$ = pressure, lb/ft$^2$ absolute
$V$ = volume, ft$^3$
$m$ = weight of gas, lb
$R$ = a gas constant
$T$ = absolute temperature, °R

By rearranging the terms in the equation, for two different conditions of the gas, 1 and 2,

the following equation results:

$$\frac{p_2 V_2}{T_2} = \frac{p_1 V_1}{T_1} \qquad (2.6)$$

The gas law is useful in finding changes in $p$, $V$, and $T$ for changed conditions. If only two of these three variables change, the equation simplifies. If the temperature is constant,

$$\frac{p_2}{p_1} = \frac{V_1}{V_2} \qquad (2.7)$$

If the volume is constant,

$$\frac{p_2}{p_1} = \frac{T_2}{T_1} \qquad (2.8)$$

If the pressure is constant,

$$\frac{V_2}{V_1} = \frac{T_2}{T_1} \qquad (2.9)$$

For the conditions that exist in many refrigeration systems, refrigerant gases often do not behave as perfect gases. In these circumstances the properties must be found from tables or charts. However when we study the refrigeration compression process (Chapter 5) we will find that equations relating pressure, temperature, and volume will be helpful in understanding performance of compressors.

## 2.13 Energy Utilization (Second Law of Thermodynamics)

We have seen how the First Law of Thermodynamics can be used, in the form of the Energy Equation, to solve problems in refrigeration, and we will use it even further. Basically, it tells us how much energy is used for a given task (the power to drive a compressor, the capacity of a refrigeration machine, and similar information). However, it tells us nothing about the answers to such questions as "How do I reduce the energy consumption of a refrigeration system?"

An understanding and application of the

Second Law of Thermodynamics will enable us to investigate problems of more efficient energy utilization. Energy conservation has become of great interest and concern. Unfortunately, efforts in this area have sometimes been haphazard, partly due to a lack of understanding of the Second Law.

Although the Second Law may be expressed as an equation, it is not simple to use in energy utilization analysis. Therefore, I will state some principles derived from the Second Law. Throughout the book I will suggest energy conservation steps, many based on these conclusions. Some of the conclusions that can be drawn from the Second Law are:

1. Whenever heat energy is used to do work, some must be lost, and it is never all available for a useful purpose. For instance, if we are using an engine to drive a refrigeration compressor, only part of the energy in the fuel can be used, the rest will be wasted.

2. The maximum possible amount of energy that can be made available in a power producing device such as an engine or turbine can be calculated. That is, we can determine the best efficiency possible, and compare it to an actual installation.

3. The minimum possible amount of energy required to produce a given amount of refrigeration can be calculated, and this can be compared to the actual system.

A number of irreversible physical effects cause a loss of energy available for doing work, or cause an increase in energy required to produce a given amount of refrigeration. Examples of how these factors can effect the performance of refrigeration systems will be pointed out when appropriate. Such effects cannot be avoided, but should be reduced to a minimum. Included among them are:

1. *Temperature difference.* Greater temperature differences cause greater losses during heat transfer, therefore temperature difference should be kept as small as practical, in, for example, evaporators and condensers.

2. *Friction.* Friction causes loss of useful energy, and therefore should be minimized. For example, regular cleaning of tube walls prevents scale build-up. Fluid friction will be less, and less energy will be lost in pumping power.

3. *Rapid expansion.* The sudden expansion of a high pressure fluid to a low pressure, sometimes called throttling, is a process that wastes some energy available in the high pressure fluid that could have been used to do work. The throttling process, important in refrigeration systems, will be discussed later.

4. *Mixing.* Mixing of fluids will result in a loss of the useful energy available for work.

Any process that occurs without any of these effects is called a reversible process. Although a reversible process is an ideal case that is impossible to achieve, we always try to minimize irreversible effects in the interests of energy conservation.

*Entropy* is a physical property of substances related to energy utilization and conservation. It is defined as the ratio of the heat added to a substance to the temperature at which it is added. However, this definition is not useful here. However, it is important to understand that entropy is a measure of the energy that is *not available* to do work.

For any process that requires work, such as driving a refrigeration compressor, the least amount of work is required if the entropy of the fluid does not change. This is called a constant entropy, or *isentropic* process. In a constant entropy process no heat is added to or removed from the substance (called an *adiabatic* process) and there are no irreversible effects (e.g., friction).

A constant entropy process is an ideal reversible process that can never really occur. However, studying it gives us a goal to aim for. In any real process where work is required, the entropy increases, and we try to minimize this increase.

Practical applications of the First and Second Laws are discussed in much greater detail in later chapters.

**Example 2.14** A mechanical contractor has a choice of using copper tubing or steel piping of the same diameter in a chilled-water system. Which would be the best choice to minimize energy consumption in the pump?

*Solution* Copper tubing has a smoother surface and therefore has less frictional resistance than steel. Less energy will be required in the pump if copper tube is used, according to the Second Law.

## 2.14 Heat Transfer

Heat has already been defined as a form of energy that flows or transfers from one body to another due to a temperature difference between the bodies. Heat transfer is the study of how heat flows and of the procedures for calculating the rate of heat transfer, an important requirement in refrigeration.

Heat transfer can occur in three possible ways; *conduction, convection,* and *radiation.* In *conduction* heat is transferred through a sub-

stance without any movement of the substance. Energy is transferred by motion of molecules internally. This usually occurs in solids. The heat transfer through the walls of a refrigeration warehouse is an example.

In *convection* heat is transferred by the movement of a fluid, either a liquid or a gas. In *natural convection* the circulation of the fluid occurs due to differences in density of the fluid resulting from temperature differences. A higher temperature fluid will have a lighter density and will therefore rise. For example, in a natural convection air cooled condenser, the ambient air near the condenser is heated by the hot refrigerant. This air, now warmer than air further away, will rise, carrying heat with it. Cooler air will then flow to take its place (Figure 2.9.)

In *forced convection* the circulation of the fluid is mechanically forced, usually by means of a pump or fan.

*Radiation* is the form of heat transfer between objects that occurs through space by means of wave motion, without warming the space between, such as radiation from the sun to the earth.

Heat transfer will be discussed in more detail when we study such equipment as evaporators and condensers, and when we study the refrigeration load.

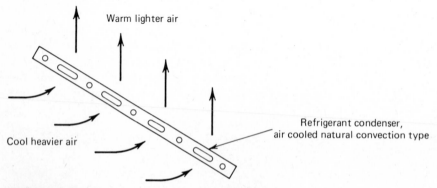

**FIGURE 2.9** Natural convection heat transfer from refrigerant in air cooled condenser.

# REVIEW QUESTIONS

1. List all of the comments you would make about the statement "water boils at 212°F."

2. What are the three common states (phases) in which matter can exist?

3. What names are used to refer to changes of state from liquid to gas and from gas to liquid?

4. Define *saturated condition, superheated condition,* and *subcooled condition.*

5. Explain what is meant by a sensible heat change and a latent heat change.

6. How can boiling produce refrigeration?

7. Explain the three means by which heat can be transferred. Give two examples of each from your own experience (not from technical processes).

8. What is the importance of the concept of entropy?

# PROBLEMS

2.1 What is the boiling point (saturation) temperature of water at pressures of 7.5 psia and 67.0 psia?

2.2 Is water liquid or vapor at 270°F and 50 psia?

2.3 Determine the following for R-22, in U.S. units:
   a. Evaporating (boiling) temperature at 83.2 psia.
   b. Condensing temperature at 250 psia.
   c. State (liquid or vapor) at 20°F and 60 psia.
   d. State (liquid or vapor) at 171 psia and 90°F.
   e. Saturation pressure at 116°F.

2.4 Determine the following for R-12, in SI units:

a. Evaporating temperature at 252 kPa.
b. Condensing temperature at 706 kPa.
c. Saturation pressure at 12°C.
d. State (liquid or vapor) at 35°C and 760 kPa.
e. State (liquid or vapor) at 410 kPa and −10°C.

2.5 Determine the following for R-717, in U.S. units:
   a. Condensing temperature at 172 psia.
   b. Evaporating temperature at 16 psia.
   c. Saturation pressure at 37°F.
   d. State (liquid or vapor) at −36°F and 9.5 psia.

2.6 A water chiller cools 110 GPM of water from 55°F to 42°F. Find the cooling capacity of the chiller in Btu/hr, tons of refrigeration, and kW.

2.7 A water chiller with a capacity of 150 tons of refrigeration cools 320 GPM of water entering the chiller at 52°F. At what temperature does the water leave the chiller?

2.8 Determine the following for R-502, in U.S. units:
   a. Enthalpy of saturated liquid and saturated vapor at 84°F.
   b. Latent heat of vaporization at 44°F.
   c. Enthalpy of saturated liquid and saturated vapor, and latent heat of vaporization, at −8°F.

2.9 Determine the following for R-12, in SI units:
   a. Enthalpy of saturated liquid and saturated vapor at −12°C.
   b. Latent heat of vaporization at 26°C.
   c. Enthalpy of saturated liquid and saturated vapor, and latent heat of vaporization, at 40°C.

2.10 A refrigeration unit has a cooling capacity of 327,000 Btu/hr. Express this capacity in tons of refrigeration and in kW.

# Chapter 3

## THE VAPOR COMPRESSION REFRIGERATION SYSTEM: PRESSURE–ENTHALPY DIAGRAMS

The most widely used method of producing mechanical refrigeration is called the vapor compression refrigeration system. In this chapter we will explain how refrigeration is accomplished by this method, and what equipment is required for it. Some of the basic calculations used in determining the performance of the system will also be introduced.

### OBJECTIVES

A study of this chapter will enable you to:
1. Identify the processes in the vapor compression refrigeration system.
2. Sketch and name the components and piping in the vapor compression refrigeration system.
3. Explain the construction of the $p$–$h$ diagram.
4. Use the $p$–$h$ diagram to read property values.
5. Explain quality and how it is found on the $p$–$h$ diagram.
6. Use the $p$–$h$ diagram to find latent heat of vaporization and superheat.
7. Use the $p$–$h$ diagram to show processes and determine changes in properties.

### 3.1 Refrigeration by Vaporization of a Liquid

A brief explanation of how the vaporization of a liquid results in refrigeration was given in Chapter 2. A more detailed analysis will be presented here, using a specific example. Consider a tank filled with liquid refrigerant R-12 at a relatively high pressure of 200 psia and an ambient temperature of 80°F, as shown in Figure 3.1. Note that the refrigerant must be in a liquid state, since the saturation (boiling) temperature at 200 psia is about 132°F. The tank outlet is connected at A through a valve to some tubing B–C. The surrounding pressure is atmospheric, say 14.7 psia. When the valve is opened, the refrigerant will, of course, flow through the tubing, due to the higher pressure in the tank. The apparatus arrangement also provides for the circulation of a fluid over the outside surface of the tubing, for example, air or water. This fluid is the substance that is to be cooled.

***The Expansion Process.*** As soon as the liquid refrigerant flows from the tank through the small, restricted opening in the valve, its pressure drops immediately and sharply at B to approximately the pressure to which the tube is exposed at C, 14.7 psia. This pressure is far lower than the saturation pressure for R-12 at a temperature of 80°F. (The saturation pressure at 80°F is about 99 psia, as seen from Appendix 5). The refrigerant will therefore begin to boil rapidly, that is, it will begin to flash into a gas. This happens because the new pressure (14.7 psia) is not great enough to prevent the rapid escape of the molecules from the liquid.

When the liquid begins to boil it absorbs heat—the latent heat of vaporization. The

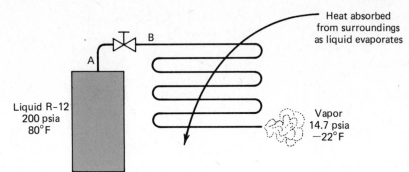

Liquid R-12
200 psia
80°F

B

A

Heat absorbed
from surroundings
as liquid evaporates

Vapor
14.7 psia
−22°F

**FIGURE 3.1** Refrigeration achieved by vaporization (boiling) of a liquid.

heat is obtained from the refrigerant itself, which is at a relatively high temperature entering the valve. The result is that the refrigerant cools to the saturation temperature corresponding to the lower pressure by the time it leaves the valve. In this case, that is approximately −22°F, at 14.7 psia. That portion of the refrigerant that vaporizes as it flows through the valve is called the *flash gas*. The proportion that flashes is the amount required to cool the total mixture of liquid and vapor to the evaporating temperature. This is how the low temperature required for refrigeration is achieved.

Because the refrigerant flows at a very rapid rate through the valve, and, furthermore, because the valve has a very small surface area exposed to the surroundings, there is practically no heat transfer to the refrigerant from the external surroundings as it flows through the valve. That is, the process A–B is adiabatic. Because there is no heat transfer to or from the refrigerant, the enthalpy of the refrigerant does not change as it goes through the valve. That is, the process A–B is one of constant enthalpy. This conclusion follows from our understanding of the energy balance. No energy is added to or removed from the refrigerant, therefore its stored energy content, including the enthalpy, remains the same.

***The Evaporation Process.*** The actual useful refrigeration occurs in the tubing B–C. The surrounding fluid passing across the outside

of the tubes is at a temperature higher than that of the refrigerant. Heat will therefore flow from the fluid through the tube walls, cooling the fluid. The desired refrigeration has been achieved. The refrigerant at B is mostly still liquid, except for the flash gas. The heat that the liquid refrigerant gains causes it to evaporate as it travels through the tubing. The tubing or other similar equipment is called an evaporator. In an actual system the refrigerant usually leaves the evaporator either as a saturated or superheated vapor.

## 3.2 Recovery of the Refrigerant

The arrangement shown in Figure 3.1 will produce refrigeration but it has some unacceptable weaknesses. Obviously once the refrigerant has escaped into the surroundings it cannot be recovered. Replenishing of the supply would be possible but the cost would be prohibitive. Furthermore, the evaporating temperature is limited to the saturation temperature of the refrigerant at atmospheric pressure, which will limit the temperatures at which it is desired to cool the refrigerated substance. A means must be found for recovering the refrigerant for continued reuse. The first thought on how this might be accomplished is simply to collect the refrigerant gas from the evaporator in a container, and then to condense it back to its original liquid state. In order to condense the gas, heat must be removed from it. But the gas leaving the evaporator has a condensing–evaporating temperature of approximately −22°F at 14.7 psia. Therefore, to remove heat from it there must be available some substance at a temperature lower than −22°F to which the heat would flow. This is extremely unlikely; besides, if there were a substance available at that low temperature it could have been used to do the cooling in the first place, eliminating the need for the equipment described!

*The Compressor and Condenser.* The failure of the method just described suggests a practical solution to the problem. As explained in Chapter 2, the saturation (condensing) temperature of fluids increases with an increase in pressure. The solution is therefore to raise the pressure and temperature of the gas to a sufficiently high level and then to remove heat from it using a cooling medium such as air or water at a temperature available from the

natural surroundings. The compressor is used to raise the pressure of the refrigerant gas. The high pressure gas is then delivered to the condenser. The condenser is used to remove heat from the refrigerant, which causes it to condense. The refrigerant is then in its original condition, ready for reuse. We now explain how each piece of equipment functions with the other as a complete system for continued operation.

## 3.3 The Vapor Compression Refrigeration System

The equipment arrangement and interconnecting piping for the basic vapor compression system is shown in Figure 3.2. Typical operating conditions have been selected in order to make the discussion more practical.

The four basic components of the system are the *expansion device* (also called the *flow*

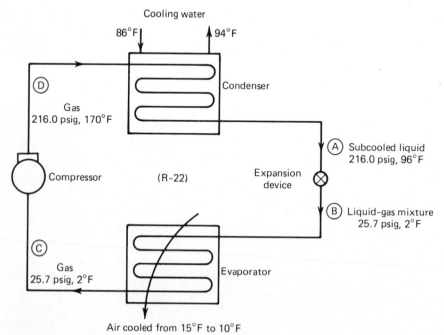

**FIGURE 3.2** Basic vapor compression refrigeration system with example of possible operating conditions.

control device), *evaporator, compressor,* and *condenser.*

**The Process A–B through the Flow Control Device.** Liquid refrigerant R-22 at 216.0 psig (gage pressure) and 96°F enters the expansion device, point A. There are various types of expansion devices; an expansion valve or capillary tube are two common types. (Expansion devices are discussed in detail in Chapter 8.) In all cases the flow control has a narrow opening, which results in a large pressure loss as the refrigerant flows through it. The refrigerant leaves at point B at 25.7 psig. Because this pressure is below the saturation pressure corresponding to 96°F, some of the liquid refrigerant immediately flashes to gas. The portion of the liquid that evaporates takes the latent heat required for its evaporation from the flowing mixture, thus cooling it. The refrigerant leaves the valve as a liquid–vapor mixture in the saturated state. The saturation temperature for R-22 at 25.7 psig is 2°F; therefore this will be the refrigerant temperature at B.

**Example 3.1** Refrigerant R-502 enters the flow control device in a refrigeration system at 231 psia and 94°F. The pressure leaving the flow control is 67 psia. What is the state of the refrigerant at the inlet and outlet of the flow control device? What is the evaporating temperature?

*Solution* Referring to Appendix 7, the saturation temperature at 231 psia is 100°F. The refrigerant at 94°F is therefore a subcooled liquid before entering the flow control.

The saturation pressure at 94°F is 213 psia. The pressure leaving the flow control is 67 psia, far below the saturation pressure corresponding to 94°F; therefore the refrigerant will begin to flash into a gas. The state at the outlet of the flow control will be a mixture of liquid and vapor.

From Appendix 7, at 67 psia the evaporating temperature is 20°F.

**The Process B–C through the Evaporator.** The refrigerant flows through the evaporator tubing from B to C. The substance to be cooled, usually air or a liquid, flows over the outside of the tubes. It is at a temperature higher than the refrigerant in the evaporator, therefore heat will flow from it through the tube wall to the refrigerant. In the case we have chosen, air is cooled from 15°F to 10°F. Because the liquid refrigerant in the evaporator is already at its saturation temperature (its boiling point) the heat that it gains will cause it to evaporate as it travels through the evaporator. The refrigerant generally leaves the evaporator either as a saturated vapor or a superheated vapor.

**The Process C–D through the Compressor.** The compressor draws the vapor into its suction side and then compresses it to a suitable high pressure for condensing. This pressure will be approximately that at which it entered the flow control device, 216.0 psig. (The pressure is actually slightly higher than this, as will be explained shortly). Work is required to compress the gas, coming from a motor or engine that drives the compressor. This work is converted into an increase in stored energy of the compressed vapor, resulting in a rise in its temperature. The refrigerant leaves the compressor at 170°F in this example, at point D, in a superheated condition.

**Example 3.2** Refrigerant R-11 is discharged from a centrifugal compressor at 22.64 psia and 120°F. How many degrees is it superheated above its saturation temperature?

*Solution* From Appendix 4, the saturation temperature at 22.64 psia is 98°F. The refrigerant is superheated $120 - 98 = 22$°F.

*The Process D–A through the Condenser.* The high pressure gas discharged from the compressor flows through the condenser tubing, from D to A. A fluid such as air or water flows over the outside of the tubing. In this example water is used, available at a temperature of 86°F. Heat will flow from the higher temperature refrigerant through the tube walls to the cooling water. Since the refrigerant is superheated when it enters the condenser it will at first be cooled, until it reaches its saturation temperature, which at 216.0 psig is 106°F. Further removal of heat results in gradual condensation of the refrigerant, until it is all liquified. The refrigerant may leave the condenser as a saturated liquid or it may be subcooled. In this example we assumed it was subcooled to 96°F before entering the flow control device.

## 3.4 The High Side and the Low Side

The pressure from the compressor discharge to the flow control device inlet is called the high side pressure or condensing pressure. The pressure from the flow control device outlet to the compressor suction inlet is called the low side pressure or evaporator pressure. Often the terms *low side* and *high side* are used to refer to these two parts of the system.

Actually the pressure is not exactly constant on either the high side or low side; for instance, a slight pressure drop as a result of friction in the piping is unavoidable. For the time being, however, we will assume that there are only the two pressures in the system. The small variations that really occur will be discussed later.

*Example 3.3* The high-side pressure in a refrigeration system using R-717 is supposed to be maintained no higher than 172 psia. Cooling water is available at 90°F. Can the high side pressure be maintained?

*Solution* From Appendix 8 the saturation (condensing) pressure at 172 psia is 87°F.

Cooling water for condensing must be at a lower temperature than this, so the pressure cannot be maintained. (It will rise to a value somewhat above that corresponding to 90°F, since there must be a temperature difference between the refrigerant and water for the heat to flow).

Note that in the case shown in Figure 3.2 the evaporator pressure is not at atmospheric pressure as it was in the case where the tank of refrigerant discharged through the tubing to the surrounding atmosphere. The action of the compressor in drawing the refrigerant into its suction side, along with the ability to adjust the flow control device opening, makes it possible to control the evaporator pressure, and therefore temperature, to a desired value.

The evaporator and condenser for this example were constructed in a tubular coil-shaped arrangement, through which the refrigerant flows. Although this construction is quite common, especially when air is being cooled or is used as the condenser cooling medium, it is by no means the only construction available. Many other types of evaporators and condensers will be discussed in detail. However it is worth noting now that in all cases they are simply heat exchangers in which one substance is cooled and another is heated.

## 3.5 The System Piping and Receiver

The piping connections between the main equipment components in a system, with a receiver included, are shown in Figure 3.3.

A *receiver* is a tank used to store the excess refrigerant charge that is not circulating through the system. It can also serve to collect all the refrigereant so that any piece of equipment can be removed for service without having to remove all the refrigerant from the plant. A separate receiver is not always needed in a system, since some types of condensers can be used to store refrigerant. In some cases

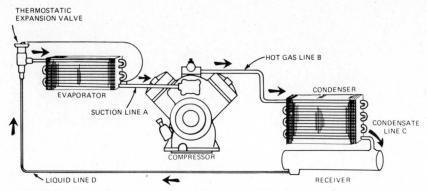

**FIGURE 3.3** Example of vapor compression system equipment and piping arrangement.

a receiver is even undesirable, a point which will be discussed later.

The piping from the evaporator to the compressor (A) is called the *suction line*. The piping from the compressor to the condenser (B) is called the *hot gas line* or *discharge line*. The piping from the condenser to the receiver (C) is called the *condensate line*. The piping from the receiver (or condenser, if no receiver is used) to the flow control device (D) is called the *liquid line*.

Manual service (shut-off) valves are located at the compressor inlet and outlet as shown, except on certain small units. A manual liquid shut-off valve is also located at the receiver outlet. Additional valves and accessories such as strainer, sight glass, and oil separator are not shown in Figure 3.3. The use of these items will be discussed later.

## 3.6 The Pressure–Enthalpy (Mollier) Diagram

The properties of refrigerants can be listed in tables or they can be shown in a graph. An example of the tabular form are the tables of properties at saturated conditions. There are a number of types and arrangements of property diagrams. The one that is most useful and used most often in refrigeration work is called the *pressure–enthalpy (p–h)* or Mollier diagram.

It is called the *p–h* diagram because the properties of pressure and enthalpy are shown on the vertical and horizontal axes, respectively. Other property diagrams that are sometimes used are the temperature–entropy and enthalpy–entropy diagrams. They will not be discussed further.

Before studying how the *p–h* diagram is used to represent the refrigeration cycle, it is necessary to learn how it is constructed and how to read values of properties from it. Pressure–enthalpy diagrams for a number of refrigerants are shown in the Appendices. We will first explain each of the main features of *p–h* diagrams.

***The Saturation Line and the Liquid and Vapor Regions.*** A sketch of the basic construction of pressure–enthalpy diagrams is shown in Figure 3.4. Values of pressure are located on the vertical scale and enthalpy values are located on the horizontal scale.

An important concept to understand is that a point on the diagram represents the complete condition of the refrigerant. That is, if we know a point on the diagram, we can determine all the properties of the refrigerant at that particular condition.

The heavy-dome-shaped curve on the diagram represents all the saturated liquid and saturated vapor conditions of the refrigerant.

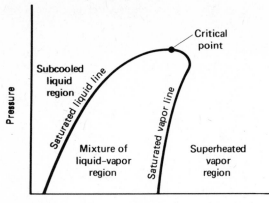

**FIGURE 3.4** Form of a pressure–enthalpy ($p$–$h$) diagram, indicating liquid and vapor regions.

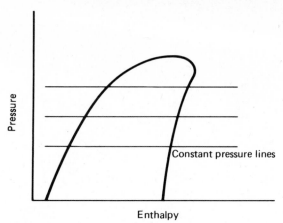

**FIGURE 3.5** Lines of constant pressure on $p$–$h$ diagram.

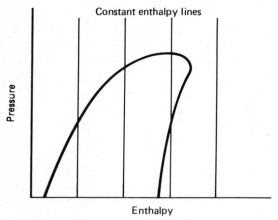

**FIGURE 3.6** Lines of constant enthalpy on $p$–$h$ diagram.

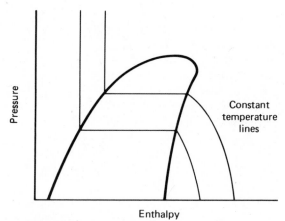

**FIGURE 3.7** Lines of constant temperature on $p$–$h$ diagram (note changes in direction).

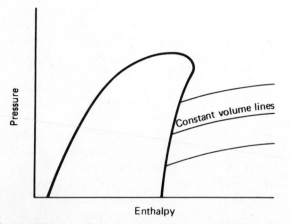

**FIGURE 3.8** Lines of constant volume on $p$–$h$ diagram.

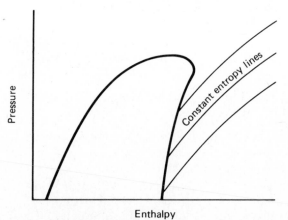

**FIGURE 3.9** Lines of constant entropy on $p$–$h$ diagram.

The left part of the curved line indicates saturated liquid conditions and the right part indicates saturated vapor conditions. The saturated liquid line and saturated vapor line are separated by the *critical point.*

The region inside the dome represents all the possible conditions of mixtures of saturated liquid and vapor. The region to the left of the saturated liquid line represents all the conditions at which subcooled liquids can exist, and the region to the right of the saturated vapor line represents all the conditions of superheated vapor. The *critical point* is a limit of temperature and pressure above which the refrigerant exists in a state where liquid and vapor are not distinguished. The critical point is never reached in refrigeration processes.

### 3.7 Property Lines on the Pressure–Enthalpy Diagram

The properties that are shown in *p–h* diagrams are pressure, enthalpy, temperature, entropy, and volume. Some diagrams also show quality.

> **Quality** *is the percentage of vapor by mass in a liquid–vapor mixture.*

Figure 3.5 shows lines of constant pressure values, which are horizontal lines, and Figure 3.6 shows lines of constant specific enthalpy values, which are vertical lines. Note that lines of constant value of the properties are always perpendicular to the scale.

Figure 3.7 shows lines of constant temperature. Note that these lines change in direction. In the superheated vapor region they are slightly curved, steeply vertical lines. In the liquid–vapor mixture region, constant temperature lines are horizontal. Note that this agrees with the fact that when a substance changes state between a liquid and a vapor at constant pressure its temperature does not change. That is, in the saturated region a

constant temperature line is also a constant pressure line (horizontal) on the *p–h* diagram.

In the subcooled liquid region constant temperature lines are almost exactly vertical. Some charts do not show temperature lines in this region. Then constant enthalpy lines can be used as a vertical guide without any significant loss in accuracy.

Lines of constant specific volume are shown in Figure 3.8. These lines slope slightly from lower left to upper right in the superheated vapor region. Values are not shown in other regions, because the saturated property tables can be used there.

Lines of constant specific entropy are shown in Figure 3.9. These lines slope steeply from lower left to upper right in the superheated vapor region.

A summary of each of the constant property lines is shown in Figure 3.10.

### 3.8 Change of State on the Pressure–Enthalpy Diagram

Note that the construction of the pressure–enthalpy diagram confirms our explanation in Chapter 2 of the behavior of a fluid when heat is added to or removed from it. Referring to

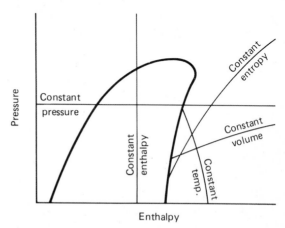

**FIGURE 3.10** *P–h* diagram showing typical constant property lines of each property.

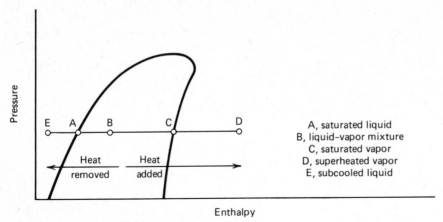

**FIGURE 3.11** Change of state at constant pressure shown on the *p–h* diagram.

Figure 3.11, consider a refrigerant in the saturated liquid state A. When heat is added, its enthalpy increases but its pressure and temperature remain constant. Therefore the change in the condition must be toward point B. In this condition we note that some of the refrigerant is a vapor; that is, some of it has boiled. If we continue adding heat, the condition moves farther to the right (increased enthalpy) until it reaches C, a saturated vapor, still at the saturation temperature and pressure.

If more heat is now added, at the same pressure, the enthalpy increases to D, and the temperature also increases—the refrigerant is a superheated vapor. Note that this agrees with the diagram; D is in the superheat region.

If heat is removed from the saturated liquid initially at A, without changing its pressure, the enthalpy decreases, and the new condition is at E. Note that point E is in the region that indicates that the refrigerant is a subcooled liquid, which we would expect.

## 3.9 Construction of an Actual Pressure–Enthalpy Diagram

After describing the general regions and each of the property lines on the *p–h* diagram it is advisable to study how all of this information is

assembled on an actual diagram. Let us use the example for refrigerant R-22, Figure A.3.

There are some features relating to units and values that should be noted. Pressure is shown in absolute units: psia (or kPa absolute in SI units). Enthalpy is in Btu/lb (kJ/kg). A value of zero is chosen for the enthalpy of saturated liquid at −40°F. This is an arbitrary choice but is not of concern because in practical problems the *change* in enthalpy is important. In SI unit diagrams (and tables) used here a value of 0 kJ/kg is chosen for the enthalpy of saturated liquid at −40°C.

Note that the values of temperature are marked along the saturation curves. In those cases where the constant temperature lines are not shown in the subcooled liquid region, vertical lines can be drawn from the saturated liquid line temperature values to make approximate lines of constant temperature. (The enthalpy lines can be used for this purpose, but of course not the enthalpy scale.)

Note that the enthalpy scale values change distance on the left and right sides of the diagram. Watch this when counting between numbered values. For any property, values should always be interpolated between lines as accurately as can be estimated.

Remember that changes in value are perpendicular to constant value lines of a property. When reading values, always interpolate between numbers to the best estimate you can make that is reasonable. For instance, it appears that temperatures in the superheated vapor region can be estimated to the nearest 5°F.

## 3.10 Locating Conditions on the Pressure–Enthalpy Diagram

The $p–h$ diagram can be used to determine properties of a refrigerant at any condition. The condition of the refrigerant can be located when any two independent properties are known. The condition is the point on the diagram representing the known values of both properties. Graphically, this is found by drawing or following the constant value lines of the two properties to the point where they intersect. A few examples will illustrate the procedure.

**Example 3.4**  Refrigerant R-22 is discharged from a compressor at 250 psia and 180°F. What is the state of the refrigerant? Determine its enthalpy and specific volume.

*Solution*  Using Figure A.3, the condition point is located at the intersection Point A of the constant pressure and constant temperature line values given, as seen in Figure 3.12.

At this point the refrigerant is in the superheated gas region. The enthalpy and specific volume values are read by interpolation between numbered values as

$$h = 127 \text{ Btu/lb}; \quad v = 0.27 \text{ ft}^3/\text{lb}$$

**Example 3.5**  Refrigerant R-12 enters a compressor suction at a pressure of 300 kPa (0.3 MPa) and density of 15 kg/m$^3$. Find its temperature and enthalpy.

*Solution*  Using Figure A.6, the condition point is located at the intersection point A of the constant pressure and constant specific

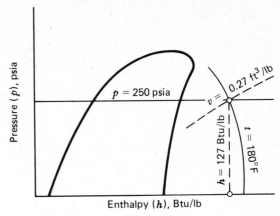

FIGURE 3.12 Sketch for Example 3.4.

volume line values given, as seen in Figure 3.13. At this point

$$t = 300 \text{ K}; \quad h = 590 \text{ kJ/kg}$$

**Example 3.6**  Refrigerant R-502 is at a pressure of 250 psia and temperature of 80°F at the inlet to an expansion valve. What is the state of the refrigerant? Determine its enthalpy.

*Solution*  Using Figure A.4, the condition point is located at the intersection point A of the constant pressure and constant temperature line values known, as seen in Figure

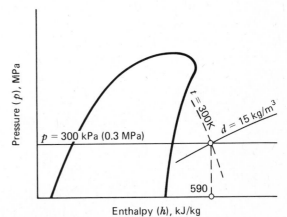

FIGURE 3.13 Sketch for Example 3.5.

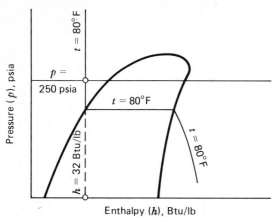

**FIGURE 3.14** Sketch for Example 3.6.

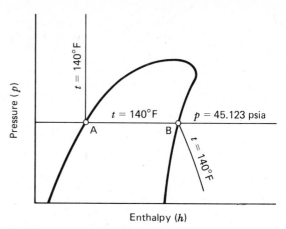

**FIGURE 3.15** Sketch for Example 3.7.

3.14. This point is in the subcooled liquid region. The enthalpy reading is 32 Btu/lb.

## 3.11 Locating Saturated Conditions on the Pressure–Enthalpy Diagram

It was stated previously that two independent properties must be known in order to determine the condition of the refrigerant, and then from this any other properties are found. Under certain circumstances two properties may not be independent; if this is so they are not sufficient to determine the condition. A case where this may occur in using the p–h diagram is when the refrigerant is in a saturation state. If the two properties known are pressure and temperature, we cannot locate a point on the diagram. This is because the saturation temperature is dependent on pressure. Or, to express it another way, the boiling temperature depends on pressure, a fact that we have already discussed.

An examination of any p–h diagram shows that if we know only the pressure and temperature at saturation, the refrigerant may be a saturated liquid, saturated vapor, or any mixture of liquid and vapor in between. The following example illustrates this.

***Example 3.7*** Refrigerant R-11 is at 140°F and 45.123 psia. Determine its state. Try to locate

the condition of the refrigerant on the p–h diagram.

*Solution* From Appendix 4 it is seen that the refrigerant is in a saturated condition. Using Figure A.1, we see that the condition can be any of the points along the line A–B noted in Figure 3.15.

## 3.12 Mixtures of Liquid and Vapor: Quality

In order to determine the condition point of the refrigerant when it is at saturation, another property in addition to the pressure or temperature must be known.

***Example 3.8*** Refrigerant R-12 is at a pressure of 0.15 MPa and enthalpy of 500 kJ/kg. Locate the condition point on the p–h diagram. What is the state of the refrigerant?

*Solution* Using Figure A.6, the condition is at the intersection point A (Figure 3.16) of the constant property lines for the two known properties. The refrigerant is a mixture of saturated liquid and vapor in this region.

Once the condition point has been located for a liquid–vapor mixture, the percentages by mass of vapor and liquid in the mixture can

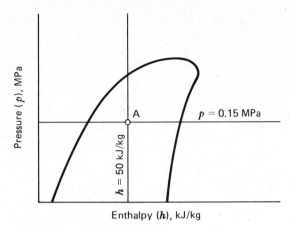

**FIGURE 3.16** Sketch for Example 3.8.

be determined. The percentage of vapor in the mixture by mass is called quality, $x$. The quality can be found by the following equation, as illustrated in Figure 3.17:

$$x = \frac{h_x - h_f}{h_g - h_f} \times 100 \qquad (3.1)$$

***Example 3.9*** Find the quality and percentage of liquid in the mixture for refrigerant R-22 at a pressure of 25 psia and enthalpy of 15.0 Btu/lb.

*Solution* The condition point is first located in the $p$–$h$ diagram (Figure 3.18), and it is seen that it is in the liquid–vapor mixture region. Using Equation 3.1, the quality is:

$$x = \frac{15.0 - 5.3}{102.8 - 5.3} \times 100 = 10\%$$

The percentage of liquid by mass is therefore $100 - 10 = 90$ percent. That is, for every 1 lb of refrigerant, 0.1 lb is vapor, and 0.9 lb is liquid.

*Note:* the values of the enthalpies at points $f$ and $g$, for the saturated liquid and vapor, can be taken from the saturation tables, rather than from the $p$–$h$ diagram, for improved accuracy.

Some pressure–enthalpy diagrams show a quality scale. Then, of course, the calculation is not required.

## 3.13 Latent Heat of Vaporization or Condensation

The *latent heat of vaporization* or *condensation* of a fluid is defined as the change in enthalpy between the saturated liquid and saturated vapor states, at constant pressure and temper-

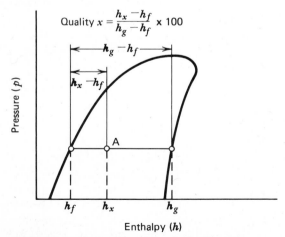

**FIGURE 3.17** Finding the quality of a liquid–vapor mixture.

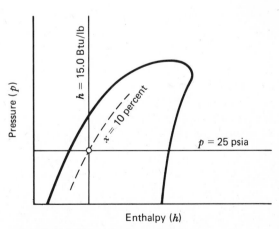

**FIGURE 3.18** Sketch for Example 3.9.

ature (Chapter 2). The pressure–enthalpy diagram shows the latent heat, as seen in the following example.

**Example 3.10**  Use the $p$–$h$ diagram to find the latent heat of condensation of R-502 at 80°F. Compare the result to that found from using the saturated property tables.

*Solution*  The enthalpies of the saturated liquid ($h_f$) and saturated vapor ($h_g$) at 80°F are read from Figure A.4. By definition the difference between them is the latent heat of condensation ($h_{fg}$). Figure 3.17 illustrates the solution.

$$h_{fg} = h_g - h_f = 85 - 31 = 54 \text{ Btu/lb}$$

From Appendix 7, the result is

$$h_{fg} = h_g - h_f = 85.35 - 31.59$$
$$= 53.76 \text{ Btu/lb}$$

Note that the result can be read more accurately by using the tables.

## 3.14 Superheat

The refrigerant often leaves the evaporator in a real refrigeration system in a superheated vapor condition. The reasons for this will be discussed later.

*The term degrees of superheat, or more simply superheat, is defined as the number of degrees above saturation temperature of the superheated vapor.*

**Example 3.11**  The evaporator pressure in an R-12 system is 43 psia. The refrigerant leaves the evaporator at 38°F. How many degrees of superheat does it have?

*Solution*  From the saturated property Appendix 5 for R-12 the evaporating (saturation) temperature corresponding to 43 psia is 30°F. The refrigerant therefore has 38 − 30 = 8°F superheat.

## 3.15 Processes on the Pressure–Enthalpy Diagram

Processes are the changes in the conditions of the refrigerant that occur as it flows through equipment. Processes result from some effect being imposed on the refrigerant; for example, adding heat to it.

The pressure–enthalpy diagram can be used to show processes and therefore changes in values of properties. This is a very powerful use of the $p$–$h$ diagram. It aids in understanding how the vapor-compression system functions. It also assists in analyzing system operating problems, selecting equipment, and in making decisions concerning energy conservation.

A process on the pressure–enthalpy diagram is represented by a line connecting the initial condition point of the refrigerant to its final condition. Many (but not all) processes are of the type in which the value of one property does not change. Thus we speak, for example, of a "constant enthalpy" or "constant pressure" process.

**Example 3.12**  Refrigerant R-502 enters a condenser at 250 psia and 180°F. There is no pressure change as the refrigerant flows through the condenser. The cooling medium removes enough heat from the refrigerant so that it leaves the condenser as a saturated liquid. Draw the process line on the $p$–$h$ diagram and determine the amount of heat removed per pound of refrigerant flowing.

*Solution*  The condition of the refrigerant entering the condenser at the known pressure and temperature is point A, as seen in Figure 3.19. The process is at constant pressure, therefore the line representing the process is horizontal, at 250 psia. The refrigerant leaves the condenser as a saturated liquid, therefore point B represents this condition. The process line is A-B.

According to the Energy Equation, the heat

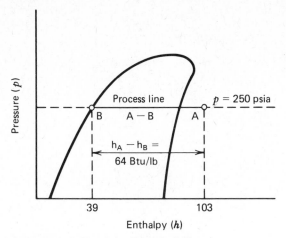

**FIGURE 3.19** Sketch for Example 3.12.

removed from the refrigerant is equal to the decrease in its enthalpy from A to B.

$$\text{heat removed} = h_A - h_B = 103 - 39$$
$$= 64 \text{ Btu/lb}$$

In Chapter 4 we use the $p–h$ diagram to describe each of the processes that occur in the vapor compression refrigeration system.

## REVIEW QUESTIONS

1. What is the name of the most widely used method of accomplishing refrigeration?

2. Name the four processes that occur in the vapor compression system, and the corresponding items of equipment in which they occur.

3. What happens to liquid refrigerant when the surrounding pressure is suddenly decreased?

4. Why does the temperature of a refrigerant drop when it undergoes the expansion process?

5. What physical property remains constant during the expansion process?

6. In the ideal cycle, what is the condition of the refrigerant entering and leaving (a) the flow control device, (b) the evaporator, (c) the compressor, and (d) the condenser?

7. Why is it not practical to condense the refrigerant after it leaves the evaporator?

8. What is the purpose of a receiver?

9. Name the piping lines and their locations.

10. Name two major purposes of using the $p–h$ diagram.

11. Sketch a $p–h$ diagram showing the saturation line. Identify liquid, vapor, and mixture regions and the saturated liquid and saturated vapor conditions.

12. Sketch a $p–h$ diagram and draw typical lines of pressure, enthalpy, temperature, specific volume, and entropy.

13. Define *quality*. Show on a sketch of a $p–h$ diagram how it is found.

## PROBLEMS

3.1 Refrigerant R-22 enters a flow control device in a refrigeration system at 241 psia and 100°F. The pressure leaving the flow control is 74.8 psia. What is the state of the refrigerant at the inlet and outlet of the flow control device? What is the evaporating temperature?

3.2 R-11 is discharged from a centrifugal compressor at 27.9 psia and 135°F. How many degrees is it superheated above its saturation temperature?

3.3 R-502 enters a compressor suction at a pressure of 40 psia and a temperature of 20°F. Determine its enthalpy, specific volume, and superheat.

3.4 R-22 is discharged from a compressor at 289 psia and 170°F. Determine the enthalpy, specific volume, and superheat of the refrigerant.

3.5 R-12 is at a pressure of 32 psia and has an enthalpy of 25.0 Btu/lb. Find the quality and percentage of liquid of the mixture.

3.6 A mixture of 15 percent liquid and 85

percent vapor of R-717 is at a temperature of −20°F. Determine its enthalpy and pressure.

3.7 Using the $p$–$h$ diagram, find the latent heat of vaporization of R-11 at 40°F. Compare the result to that found from using the saturated property tables.

3.8 R-12 enters a compressor suction at a pressure of 506 kPa and a temperature of 25°C. Determine its enthalpy, specific volume, and superheat.

3.9 R-717 is at a pressure of 150 kPa and has an enthalpy of 260 kJ/kg. Find the quality and percentage of liquid in the mixture.

# Chapter 4

# THERMODYNAMICS OF THE VAPOR COMPRESSION REFRIGERATION CYCLE

In Chapter 3 we described how the vapor compression refrigeration system functions and introduced the pressure–enthalpy diagram. In this chapter we will study in more detail the processes occurring in the system, with the aid of the pressure–enthalpy diagram. Our goal will be to analyze the performance of the vapor compression system. The data included are used to select equipment, to aid in service analysis, and as a guide in energy conservation policies. Throughout the text we will be referring to the material presented here. It cannot be overstressed that the information presented in this chapter is the key to a useful knowledge of refrigeration principles.

## OBJECTIVES

A study of this chapter will enable you to:
1. Draw and identify the ideal vapor compression cycle processes on the $p$–$h$ diagram.
2. Find graphically the refrigeration effect, heat of compression, and heat of rejection.
3. Determine the mass flow rate, required theoretical compressor displacement, and horsepower.
4. Calculate the COP and EER.
5. Show and explain the effects in cycle performance of changing evaporating or condensing temperature.
6. Find the effect of superheat or subcooling on cycle performance.

7. Explain the reason for using a liquid-suction heat exchanger and sketch its piping arrangement in the system.
8. Suggest some energy conservation measures for the vapor compression cycle.

## 4.1 System Performance and the Thermodynamic Refrigeration Cycle

It is essential to be able to determine the refrigeration system's performance. Some of the performance characteristics that are of concern are the cooling (refrigeration) capacity, the power required for the compressor, the refrigerant flow rate, and the rate of heat rejected (removed) in the condenser.

The system performance is determined by examining its thermodynamic cycle. The thermodynamic cycle is the complete series of physical changes or processes that the refrigerant undergoes in the system. In each piece of equipment in the plant, some of the physical properties of the refrigerant change; that is, its condition changes. These changes are called *processes*. Because the refrigerant is circulating in a closed loop, the series of changes is called a *cycle*. That is, when the refrigerant returns to the same place in the system it has also returned to the same physical condition. This situation is called a *steady-state* operation. The refrigerant is flowing at a constant rate, and its properties at any point are always the same. If some disturbance occurs, such as a change in load or adjustment of a valve, the operation may become unsteady for a short time. The flow rate changes, properties change. After a brief period, however, a new set of steady conditions exist.

## 4.2 The Ideal Saturated Vapor Compression Refrigeration Cycle

In Chapter 3 we described how the vapor compression refrigeration system functions. In the present section we describe the thermodynamic changes that occur to the refrigerant in each piece of equipment. The cycle described is a theoretical ideal which never actually exists. Despite this, there are reasons why it is useful to examine this ideal case. First, we can still draw some general conclusions about a real system's performance, particularly how it is affected by changing conditions. Also it is simpler to study and understand the ideal cycle. The differences that exist in real cycles and their effects will be explained later.

In the ideal cycle, it is assumed that there is no pressure drop resulting from friction as the refrigerant flows through the piping and equipment. This is not true in a real system.

It is also assumed in the ideal cycle that no other effects occur in the piping between equipment. That is, not only is there no pressure drop in the piping, but there is no heat exchange with the surroundings as the refrigerant flows through the piping. Practically, these assumptions mean that the condition of the refrigerant leaving each piece of equipment is the same as it is entering the next component.

An ideal vapor compression refrigeration cycle is shown in the $p$–$h$ diagram, Figure 4.1. A corresponding sketch of the system is shown, with locations labeled. The cycle consists of four processes, labeled A–B, B–C, C–D, and D–A. These processes are of the following types:

| Line | Thermodynamic Process | Equipment in Which It Occurs |
|------|------------------------|------------------------------|
| A–B | Constant enthalpy | Flow control (expansion) device |
| B–C | Constant pressure | Evaporator |
| C–D | Constant entropy | Compressor |
| D–A | Constant pressure | Condenser |

Each of these processes will be discussed in detail. In order to make the discussion more practical, a specific set of conditions has been chosen, using refrigerant R-22, as follows:

Evaporating temperature $t_e = 20°F$
Condensing temperature $t_c = 100°F$

This set of conditions is arbitrary of course, and another would have been suitable for our example.

## 4.3 The Process in the Flow Control Device (Constant Enthalpy)

Point A (Figure 4.1) is the condition of the refrigerant leaving the condenser and entering the flow control device, since it is assumed that no changes take place in the piping. The refrigerant leaves the condenser and enters the flow control device as a saturated liquid at the condensing temperature. The corresponding condensing pressure (high-side pressure) is 210.6 psia.

When the refrigerant flows through the restriction in the flow control device its pressure drops suddenly to the low-side pressure, at B. This process is sometimes called *throttling* or *expansion*. Because the refrigerant flows so rapidly and because the flow control device has such a small surface there is practically no heat exchange between the refrigerant and the surroundings. Since there is no heat transfer to or from the refrigerant, its enthalpy does not change. This follows from the En-

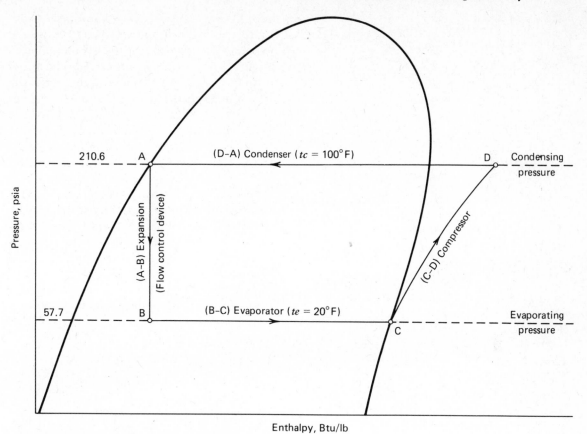

**FIGURE 4.1** Ideal vapor compression refrigeration cycle shown on the *p–h* diagram.

ergy Equation 2.2. We can thus conclude that:

*The ideal cycle process through the flow control device is a constant enthalpy process.*

The process line A–B is therefore a vertical line (no enthalpy change) downward to the evaporating pressure (low-side pressure) corresponding to the evaporating temperature. This pressure is the saturation pressure at 20°F, which is 57.7 psia for R-22.

The refrigerant entering the flow control device is a saturated liquid at a relatively high temperature, 100°F (point A). Leaving the flow control device it is at a low temperature, 20°F, and is a mixture of liquid and vapor

(point B). Since the refrigerant does not lose any heat to the surroundings and has the same enthalpy, you might wonder how it became cooled. The answer to this is that some of the liquid evaporates due to the sudden drop in pressure. The latent heat of evaporation required for this is taken from the mixture itself, cooling it. Expressed in a different way, the sensible heat (and therefore temperature) of the refrigerant has decreased while its latent heat has increased by the same amount.

Note that the location of point B on the *p–h* diagram confirms that some of the refrigerant has evaporated in the expansion process. This vapor is called the *flash gas*. The percentage of

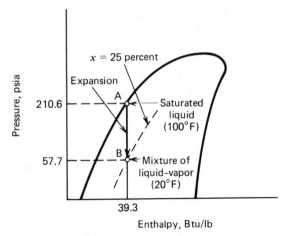

**FIGURE 4.2** Ideal cycle expansion (throttling) process, A–B, constant enthalpy.

flash gas by mass is called the *quality* of the mixture and is found as explained in Section 3.12.

*Example 4.1* Determine the percentage of flash gas for R-22 for the ideal vapor compression cycle with saturated liquid at 100°F entering the flow control device and at an evaporation temperature of 20°F.

*Solution* Using Figure A.3, the process line A–B is drawn (Figure 4.2). The percentage of flash gas at B can be read directly if quality lines are shown, or Equation 3.1 can be used. Using the quality lines, the result is

Percentage flash gas = 25 percent

## 4.4 The Process in the Evaporator (Constant Pressure)

In the ideal cycle the condition at point B, leaving the flow control device, is assumed to be the condition entering the evaporator. It is also assumed that there is no pressure drop through the evaporator.

*The ideal cycle process through the evaporator is a constant pressure process.*

The load to be cooled is at a higher tempera-

ture than that of the refrigerant in the evaporator; therefore heat will flow through the evaporator tube walls from the load to the refrigerant. Since the liquid refrigerant in the evaporator is already in a saturated state, the heat gained causes it to evaporate as it flows through the evaporator.

The process line B–C in the evaporator is therefore a horizontal line (constant pressure) to the right, since the refrigerant gains heat and increases in enthalpy. The refrigerant leaves the evaporator as a saturated vapor (point C) in the ideal cycle (Figure 4.3). This is the usual condition in a flooded type evaporator. In direct expansion type evaporators the refrigerant generally leaves the evaporator in a superheated vapor state. Descriptions of these types of evaporators and reasons for their leaving conditions being different will be explained later.

## 4.5 The Refrigeration Effect

*The increase in enthalpy of the refrigerant in the evaporator is called the* **refrigeration effect** *(R.E.), expressed in Btu/lb or kJ/kg.*

It is called the refrigeration effect because it is also the amount of heat removed from the

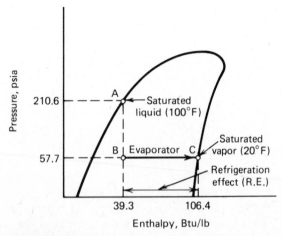

**FIGURE 4.3** Ideal cycle evaporator process, B–C, constant pressure.

medium to be cooled, for each pound or kilogram of refrigerant flowing. This follows from the Energy Equation. That is

$$\text{R.E.} = h_c - h_b = h_c - h_a \qquad (4.1)$$

where

R.E. = refrigeration effect, Btu/lb
$h_c$ = enthalpy of refrigerant leaving evaporator, Btu/lb
$h_b = h_a$ = enthalpy of refrigerant entering evaporator, Btu/lb

Note that the value of the enthalpy entering the evaporator, $h_b$, is the same as the value entering the flow control device, $h_a$. This is true because the process A–B is at constant enthalpy. For this reason both $h_c$ and $h_a$ can be read from the saturation tables rather than from the p–h diagram, for better accuracy, as seen in the following example.

**Example 4.2** What is the refrigeration effect for the R-22 ideal cycle shown in Figure 4.3, operating at evaporating and condensing temperatures of 20°F and 100°F?

*Solution* Using Equation 4.1, with the values of $h_c$ and $h_a$ read from the saturated property tables for R-22,
$h_c$ = 106.4 Btu/lb (saturated vapor at 20°F)
$h_a = h_b$ = 39.3 Btu/lb (saturated liquid at 100°F)
R.E. = 106.4 − 39.3 = 67.1 Btu/lb

## 4.6 Refrigerant Mass Flow Rate

The refrigerant mass flow rate circulating through a system to produce a given refrigeration capacity can be found as follows:

$$m = \frac{Q_e}{\text{R.E.}} \qquad (4.2)$$

where

$m$ = mass flow rate, lb/min

$Q_e$ = system refrigeration capacity, Btu/min
R.E. = refrigeration effect, Btu/lb

In order to compare performance of systems operating at different conditions, it is useful to find the refrigerant flow rate per ton of refrigeration capacity. In this case, since 1 ton = 200 Btu/min, Equation 4.2 becomes

$$m = \frac{200}{\text{R.E.}} \qquad (4.3)$$

where

$m$ = mass flow rate, lb/min per ton

**Example 4.3** What is the refrigerant mass flow rate for the R-22 ideal cycle system operating at evaporating and condensing temperatures of 20°F and 100°F, described in Example 4.2, if the system is to have a 20-ton refrigeration capacity?

*Solution* Equation 4.2 is used, with the refrigeration capacity expressed in Btu/min.

$$Q_e = 20 \text{ tons} \times \frac{200 \text{ Btu/min}}{1 \text{ ton}}$$
$$= 4000 \text{ Btu/min}$$

From Example 4.2,

R.E. = 67.1 Btu/lb

$$m = \frac{Q_e}{\text{R.E.}} = \frac{4000 \text{ Btu/min}}{67.1 \text{ Btu/lb}} = 59.6 \text{ lb/min}$$

## 4.7 The Process in the Compressor (Constant Entropy)

In the ideal cycle it is assumed that there are no changes, such as pressure drop or heat exchange, in the suction line. Therefore the refrigerant condition C leaving the evaporator is also the condition entering the compressor.

In the ideal compression process there is no heat exchange between the refrigerant and the surroundings (called an *adiabatic* process);

furthermore, there is no friction. It can be shown that in an adiabatic frictionless process there will be no change in the entropy of the gas as it is compressed. A constant entropy process is also called an *isentropic* process.

*The ideal cycle process through the compressor is a constant entropy (isentropic) process.*

The constant entropy compression process line C–D is shown on the *p–h* diagram in Figure 4.4. From point C, the condition entering the compressor, a constant entropy line is drawn. The discharge pressure from the compressor is at the condensing pressure. Point D, the condition leaving the compressor, is therefore located at the intersection of the constant entropy line and the condensing pressure line.

## 4.8 The Heat of Compression and Work of Compression

When the refrigerant is compressed, its pressure, temperature, and enthalpy all increase.

*The **heat of compression (H.C.)** is defined as the increase in enthalpy of the refrigerant as the result of the compression.*

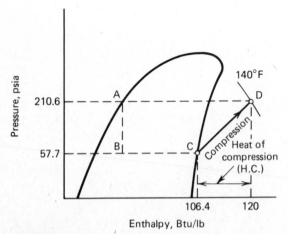

FIGURE 4.4 Ideal cycle compression process, C–D, constant entropy.

As seen from Figure 4.4, this is

$$\text{H.C.} = h_d - h_c \quad \text{in Btu/lb} \quad (4.4)$$

***Example 4.4*** Determine the heat of compression and discharge temperature for the R-22 ideal cycle operating at evaporating and condensing temperatures of 20°F and 100°F (Figure 4.4).

*Solution* Using the *p–h* diagram for R-22, from point C, the condition entering the compressor, a line parallel to the nearest constant entropy line is drawn. Point D is located where the entropy line intersects with the discharge (condensing) pressure line. Reading the values of $h_c$ and $h_d$ and using Equation 4.4;

$$\text{H.C.} = h_d - h_c = 120 - 106.4$$
$$= 13.6 \text{ Btu/lb}$$

The temperature at point D reads 140°F.

Work is required to drive the compressor in order to compress the refrigerant vapor. It follows from the Energy Equation that the energy added to the gas, in the form of work, increases the energy content of the refrigerant, in the form of enthalpy, by the same amount. That is, *the work of compression is equal to the heat of compression, expressed in the same units.*

$$W = \text{H.C.} = h_d - h_c \quad (4.5)$$

where

$W$ = work of compression, Btu/lb
$h_d - h_c$ = increase in enthalpy of refrigerant in compressor, Btu/lb

## 4.9 Required Theoretical Compressor Power

It is usually more valuable to determine how much power is needed to drive the compressor, rather than the work required. This can be found from the work of compression and the mass flow rate, using the following equation:

$$P = W \times m \qquad (4.6)$$

where

$P$ = compressor required theoretical power, Btu/min
$W$ = work (heat) of compression, Btu/lb
$m$ = mass flow rate, lb/min

The compressor power is more conveniently expressed in units of horsepower rather than Btu per minute. It is also useful to determine the required power in horsepower per ton of refrigeration, in order to compare the effect of operating at different conditions. The following example illustrates this.

*Example 4.5* Find the horsepower per ton required for the ideal cycle system using R-22, operating with evaporating and condensing temperatures of 20°F and 100°F, with saturated vapor entering the compressor.

*Solution* The work of compression, equal to the heat of compression, and the refrigeration effect, have been found in Examples 4.4 and 4.2, respectively. They are

$$W = h_d - h_c = 13.6 \text{ Btu/lb}$$
$$\text{R.E.} = h_c - h_a = 67.1 \text{ Btu/lb}$$

where

$W$ = work of compression

The refrigerant mass flow rate, using Equation 4.3, is

$$m = \frac{200}{\text{R.E.}} = \frac{200}{67.1} = 2.98 \text{ lb/min per ton}$$

The required compression power is

$$P = W \times m = 13.6 \, \frac{\text{Btu}}{\text{lb}} \times 2.98 \, \frac{\text{lb}}{\text{min}}$$
$$\text{per ton} = 40.5 \text{ Btu/min per ton}$$

Expressed in units of hp or kW,

$$P = 40.5 \text{ Btu/min per ton} \times \frac{1 \text{ hp}}{42.4 \text{ Btu/min}}$$
$$= 0.96 \text{ hp/ton}$$
$$= 40.5 \text{ Btu/min per ton} \times \frac{1 \text{ kW}}{56.9 \text{ Btu/min}}$$
$$= 0.71 \text{ kW/ton}$$

The power required to drive the compressor in the ideal cycle is called the theoretical power. A very important fact concerning this power is:

*The minimum theoretical power required to drive the compressor occurs in the ideal cycle, for any given conditions.*

The importance of this is that the power required for an actual system can be measured and compared to the best possible situation—the ideal cycle. This provides a goal for purposes of minimizing energy consumption. This goal can never be reached, but it provides a good frame of reference.

The minimum power is required because the compression is an isentropic (adiabatic and frictionless) process. The proof of this can be found in a thermodynamics textbook.

### 4.10 Required Theoretical Compressor Displacement

After the mass flow rate of refrigerant is determined, the volume flow rate can be calculated. The volume flow rate will vary, depending on where in the system it is determined, since the specific volume of the refrigerant varies. Usually the volume flow rate is calculated at the compressor suction inlet.

*The volume of gas that the compressor must be capable of handling in the ideal cycle is called the **theoretical compressor displacement**.*

It is found from the following equation:

$$V_t = v \times m \qquad (4.7)$$

where

$V_t$ = theoretical compressor displacement, ft³/min

$v$ = specific volume of refrigerant at compressor suction, ft³/lb

$m$ = mass flow rate of refrigerant, lb/min

**Example 4.6.** Determine the required theoretical compressor displacement for a 20-ton-capacity R-22 ideal cycle system, operating at evaporating and condensing temperatures of 20°F and 100°F, with saturated vapor entering the compressor.

*Solution.* Equation 4.7 is used. The mass flow rate was previously calculated for these conditions in Example 4.3. Because the compressor displacement is required, the specific volume of the saturated vapor at 20°F, the compressor suction, is used.

$$V_t = v \times m = 0.936 \text{ ft}^3/\text{lb} \times 59.6 \text{ lb/min}$$
$$= 55.8 \text{ ft}^3/\text{min}$$

The required compressor displacement for the ideal cycle is called the theoretical displacement because it is the minimum possible displacement. The actual displacement of a compressor is always greater, for reasons that will be explained in Chapter 5.

## 4.11 The Process in the Condenser (Constant Pressure)

In the ideal cycle it is assumed that there is no pressure drop or heat exchange in the hot gas discharge line. Therefore, the refrigerant condition D leaving the compressor is also the condition entering the condenser. It is also assumed that there is no pressure drop through the evaporator.

*The ideal cycle process through the condenser is a constant pressure process.*

Heat is removed from the superheated refrigerant vapor entering the condenser to first reduce its temperature to the saturation point and then to condense it. A cooling fluid at a temperature lower than the saturation temperature is provided for this. The refrigerant leaves the condenser as a saturated vapor, point A. In many systems the refrigerant is further subcooled below the saturation temperature, a case that will be discussed later.

The process line D–A in the condenser (Figure 4.5) is therefore a horizontal line on the $p$–$h$ diagram from right to left (heat removal) at the high-side (condensing) pressure. The refrigerant has completed its cycle and is back at the same condition and location as when the analysis was begun.

### The Heat of Rejection.

*The heat of rejection (H.R.) is defined as the amount of heat removed from the refrigerant in the condenser, per pound.*

As seen from Figure 4.5, this is equal to the decrease in enthalpy of the refrigerant

$$\text{H.R.} = h_d - h_a \qquad (4.8)$$

The total rate of heat rejection from the con-

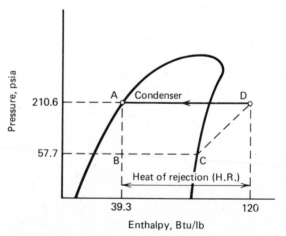

**FIGURE 4.5** Ideal cycle condenser process, D–A, constant pressure.

denser ($Q_c$) in Btu/min, is

$$Q_c = m\,(h_d - h_a) \qquad (4.9)$$

## 4.12 The Energy Equation and the Refrigeration Cycle

From Figure 4.5 it is apparent that the heat of rejection is the sum of the refrigeration effect and the heat of compression. This is the algebraic sum

$$\text{R.E.} + \text{H.C.} = \text{H.R.} \qquad (4.10)$$

Equation 4.10 is an application of the Energy Equation (2.1). Because there is no change in the energy of the refrigerant when it completes a cycle, the energy added to the system (the refrigeration effect plus the work of compression) equals the energy removed from the system (the heat of rejection).

**Example 4.7** Find the heat of rejection for an R-22 ideal cycle operating at evaporating and condensing temperatures of 20°F and 100°F, with saturated vapor entering the compressor.

*Solution* Using Equation 4.8,

H.R. = $h_d - h_a$ = 120 − 39.3 = 80.7 Btu/lb

The same result would be found from Equation 4.10 by adding the refrigeration effect and the heat of compression, using the values of these from Examples 4.2 and 4.5.

R.E. + H.R. = 67.1 + 13.6 = 80.7 Btu/lb

The Energy Equation can also be applied to the refrigeration system in terms of rate of energy added or removed, rather than per pound of refrigerant. Since the rate of energy added equals the rate of energy removed, the equation is written

$$Q_c = Q_e + P \qquad (4.11)$$

where

$Q_c$ = heat rejected in condenser
$Q_e$ = heat gained in evaporator

$P$ = heat equivalent of power required to compress refrigerant

All terms must be in the same units in Equation 4.11. Note that this equation tells us that if the rate of energy transfer in any two of the components is known, the rate of energy transfer in the third is fixed.

**Example 4.8** A refrigeration system operating with a 10-ton cooling load requires 9 kW of power to compress the gas. What must be the capacity of the condenser that is used?

*Solution* 4.8. After changing all units to Btu/min, Equation 4.11 is used.

$$Q_e = 10 \text{ tons} \times \frac{200 \text{ Btu/min}}{1 \text{ ton}}$$

$$= 2000 \text{ Btu/min}$$

$$P = 9 \text{ kW} \times \frac{42.4 \text{ Btu/min}}{1\text{hp}} \times \frac{1 \text{ hp}}{0.746 \text{ kW}}$$

$$= 512 \text{ Btu/min}$$

$$Q_c = Q_e + P = 2000 + 512$$

$$= 2512 \text{ Btu/min}$$

## 4.13 Complete Ideal Cycle Performance Analysis

A review of each of the individual performance characteristics described in the last few sections is perhaps best shown by an example in which the complete cycle performance is analyzed.

**Example 4.9** An ideal cycle vapor compression refrigeration system using R-12 operates with an evaporating temperature of 0°F and condensing temperature of 120°F. The refrigerant leaves the condenser as a saturated liquid and leaves the evaporator as a saturated vapor. Calculate the percentage of flash gas, refrigeration effect, mass flow rate, heat of compression, heat of rejection, compressor theoretical power, and compressor theoretical displacement.

*Solution*  Appropriate values are read from Appendix 5 and Figure A.2. The results are indicated on the sketch in Figure 4.6. Using Equation 3.1, the percentage of flash gas is

$$x = \frac{h_b - h_f}{h_c - h_f} \times 100 = \frac{36.0 - 8.5}{77.3 - 8.5}$$

$$\times 100 = 40 \text{ percent}$$

Using Equation 4.1, the refrigeration effect is

$$\text{R.E.} = h_c - h_a = 77.3 - 36.0$$
$$= 41.3 \text{ Btu/lb}$$

Using Equation 4.3, the mass flow rate per ton of refrigeration is

$$m = \frac{200}{\text{R.E.}} = \frac{200 \text{ Btu/min per ton}}{41.3 \text{ Btu/lb}}$$

$$= 4.84 \text{ lb/min per ton}$$

Using Equation 4.4, the heat of compression is

$$\text{H.C.} = h_d - h_c = 92.5 - 77.3$$
$$= 15.2 \text{ Btu/lb}$$

Using Equations 4.8 and 4.9 the heat of rejection is

$$\text{H.R.} = h_d - h_a = 92.5 - 36.0 = 56.5 \text{ Btu/lb}$$

$$Q_c = 4.84 \text{ lb/min per ton}$$
$$\times 56.5 \text{ Btu/lb}$$

$$= 273.5 \text{ Btu/min per ton}$$

Using Equation 4.6, the compressor theoretical power requirement is

$$P = W \times m$$
$$= 15.2 \text{ Btu/lb} \times 4.84 \text{ lb/min per ton}$$

$$= 73.6 \text{ Btu/min per ton} \times \frac{1 \text{ hp}}{42.4 \text{ Btu/min}}$$

$$= 1.74 \text{ hp/ton}$$

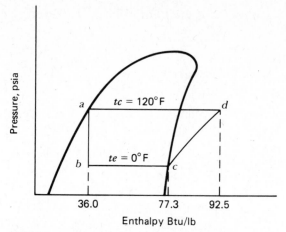

**FIGURE 4.6** Sketch for Example 4.9.

Using Equation 4.7, the compressor theoretical displacement per ton is

$$V_t = v \times m$$
$$= 1.61 \text{ ft}^3/\text{lb} \times 4.84 \text{ lb/min per ton}$$

$$= 7.79 \text{ ft}^3/\text{min per ton}$$

## 4.14 The Coefficient of Performance

It is useful to have a single measurement that describes how effectively a refrigeration machine is performing. The *coefficient of performance* (COP) serves this purpose. It is defined as

$$\text{COP} = \frac{\text{refrigeration capacity} (Q_e)}{\substack{\text{net power input} (P), \\ \text{in same units}}} \quad (4.12)$$

In this equation the refrigeration capacity of the system, $Q_e$, and the net power input to the compressor, $P$ must be expressed in the same units. For example, if the refrigeration capacity is expressed in Btu per hour then the power input must also be expressed in Btu per hour.

The COP provides a measurement of the energy use efficiency of the system. Because we always wish to have the largest refrigeration capacity with the smallest expenditure of power, the largest practical value of the COP is desirable. The COP can also be expressed in terms of the units used in the thermodynamic cycle of the vapor compression system. In this case it is

$$COP = \frac{\text{refrigeration effect}}{\text{heat of compression}} \quad (4.13)$$

The units of both terms must still be the same, such as Btu/lb or kJ/kg.

It should be understood that Equation 4.12 is also the definition of the COP for any refrigeration system, regardless of how the refrigeration is accomplished. The definition is valid for an absorption system as well as a vapor compression system. Equation 4.13 is simply the expression of the COP for the case of the vapor compression cycle.

**Example 4.10.** Find the coefficient of performance for an R-12 ideal vapor compression cycle operating at evaporating and condensing temperatures of 0°F and 120°F, with saturated vapor entering the compressor.

*Solution* Use Equation 4.13. The refrigeration effect and heat of compression have already been determined for the same conditions, in Example 4.9. Using these values,

$$COP = \frac{R.E.}{H.C.} = \frac{41.3 \text{ Btu/lb}}{15.2 \text{ Btu/lb}} = 2.72$$

The COP of real systems is always less than that of ideal cycles, due to unavoidable losses such as friction.

It is possible to determine the maximum possible COP for any given evaporating and condensing temperatures. This value is even greater than that for the ideal vapor compression cycle. This is discussed in detail later in this chapter. Another performance factor similar to the COP, called the energy efficiency ratio (EER), which is now widely used, is also discussed later.

## 4.15 Change of Evaporating Temperature

It is useful to know what effect, if any, changes in either evaporating or condensing conditions have on the performance requirements of a refrigeration system. An examination of the *p–h* diagram and a few calculations will show any effects on the ideal cycle. Generally the same conclusions can be drawn for a real system, although the values may be different.

Figure 4.7 shows the change in the ideal cycle on the *p–h* diagram when the evaporating temperature is *increased*, with a constant condensing temperature. It is clear from the sketch that the refrigeration effect *increases* (B′–C′ instead of B–C) and the heat of compression *decreases* (C′–D′ instead of C–D).

The effect that changing evaporating temperature has on the performance characteristics is shown in Figure 4.8 for an ideal cycle using R-12.

An inspection of Figures 4.7 and 4.8 leads to the following conclusions for an increase in evaporating temperature:

1. The refrigeration effect increases. Less flash gas is required to cool the refrigerant to a higher evaporating temperature, leav-

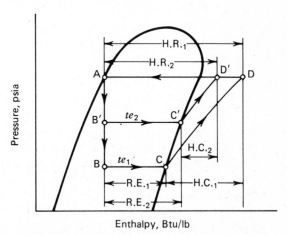

**FIGURE 4.7** Effect of changing evaporating temperature on R.E., H.C., and H.R. for ideal cycle.

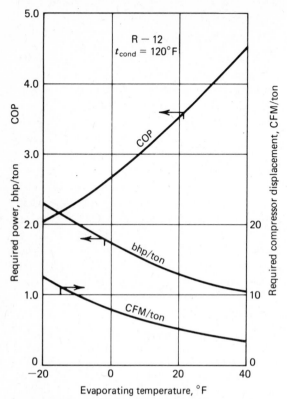

**FIGURE 4.8** Effect of changing evaporating temperature on hp/ton, CFM/ton, and COP for ideal cycle.

5. The required compressor displacement per ton decreases. This is because both the mass flow rate of refrigerant decreases and its specific volume decreases.

6. The required power per ton decreases. This is because both the work of compression decreases and the flow rate decreases.

7. The coefficient of performance increases, because the refrigeration effect increases and the heat of compression decreases.

Although these effects are for the ideal cycle, the same type of effect occurs and should be considered when planning real systems, and is of great importance for energy conservation. An increase in evaporating temperature results in less power being required per ton of refrigeration capacity. Of course the evaporating temperature is limited by the temperature at which it is necessary to maintain the load. Within practical limits however, evaporating temperatures should be kept as high as is reasonable.

It is also noted that a higher evaporating temperature results in a smaller required compressor displacement (a smaller compressor can be used). It can be seen from Figure 4.8 that *decreasing* the evaporating temperature has an effect opposite that of the conclusions noted previously.

The *required* power to produce a given capacity, as discussed here, is different from the question of how an actual compressor will perform once it is selected and operating. This subject is discussed later in this chapter as well as in Chapter 5.

ing a greater proportion of liquid for useful refrigeration in the evaporator.

2. The mass flow rate per ton of refrigeration capacity decreases, because the refrigeration effect increases.

3. The heat of compression decreases because less work is required to compress the gas over a smaller pressure range.

4. The rate of heat rejected in the condenser per ton decreases. Note that the heat rejection per pound of refrigerant circulating does not change much. This is because, although the refrigeration effect increases, the heat of compression decreases. However, the decrease in the mass flow rate results in a decrease in the total rate of heat rejected.

## 4.16 Change of Condensing Temperature

Figure 4.9 shows the change in the ideal cycle on the *p–h* diagram when the condensing temperature is *decreased*, with a constant evaporating temperature. It is clear from the sketch that the refrigeration effect *increases* (B′–C instead of B–C), the heat of compres-

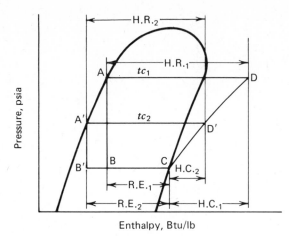

**FIGURE 4.9** Effect of changing condensing temperature on R.E., H.C., and H.R. for ideal cycle.

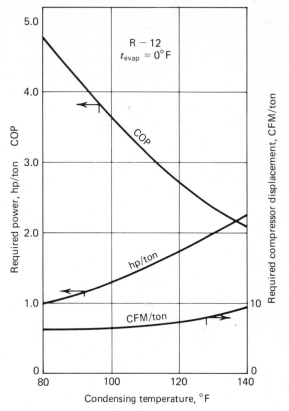

**FIGURE 4.10** Effect of changing condensing temperature on hp/ton, CFM/ton, and COP for ideal cycle.

sion *decreases* (C–D′ instead of C–D), and the heat of rejection *decreases* (D′–A′ instead of D–A).

The effect that changing condensing temperature has on each of the performance characteristics is shown by the calculated values in Figure 4.10 for an ideal cycle using R-12.

An inspection of Figures 4.9 and 4.10 leads to the following conclusions for a decrease in condensing temperature:

1. The refrigeration effect increases. This is because the refrigerant requires less cooling from the lower condensing temperature (A′–B′ instead of A–B), leaving more liquid refrigerant available for useful refrigeration.

2. The mass flow rate per ton of refrigeration capacity decreases because the refrigeration effect increases.

3. The heat of compression decreases because less work is required to compress over a smaller pressure range.

4. The rate of heat rejected in the condenser decreases. Note that the heat rejection per pound of refrigerant circulating does not change much. This is because, although the

refrigerant effect increases, the heat of compression decreases. However, the decrease in the mass flow rate results in a decrease in the rate of heat rejected.

5. The required compressor displacement per ton decreases. This is because the mass flow rate of refrigerant decreases. The specific volume at the compressor suction does not change.

6. The required power per ton decreases. This is because both the work of compression and the flow rate decrease.

7. The coefficient of performance increases, because the refrigeration effect increases and the heat of compression decreases.

An increase in condensing temperature will have effects opposite these.

The same type of energy effects occur for real cycles when condensing temperature is changed. Lower condensing temperatures result in significant reduction in energy use. One simple and practical method to maintain low condensing temperatures is to keep condenser tubing clean. This subject is discussed in Chapter 7.

***Requirements Versus Actual Performance of Existing Compressors.***   The trends shown in the curves of Figures 4.8 and 4.10 are of use in energy decisions when considering equipment size and operating conditions for a *new* installation. They do not, however, indicate what total power is used in an existing system with a fixed displacement compressor, when evaporating and condensing temperatures change. Indeed, when evaporating temperature increases with an existing (fixed displacement) compressor, the total actual power requirement increases. This is because the system refrigeration capacity (tons) increases so rapidly that, even though the horsepower per ton is lower, the total horsepower increases.

These effects in an existing system with a fixed displacement compressor are explained in Chapter 5, where actual compressors are considered in detail (e.g., see Figures 5.18 and 5.19). An interesting point, however, is that for systems with multiple compressors or variable displacement compressors (e.g., unloaders, guide vanes) the energy efficiency trends discussed here might be considered in operating procedures.

## 4.17 Superheat in the Evaporator

In evaporators of the flooded chiller type, the refrigerant usually leaves the evaporator in a saturated vapor condition. This case has already been examined. In direct-expansion-type evaporators the refrigerant is usually superheated before it leaves the evaporator.

This provides a good means of controlling refrigerant flow rate when a thermostatic expansion valve is used (Chapter 8). It also aids in ensuring that no liquid enters the compressor.

The performance with superheat in the evaporator is calculated in the following example.

***Example 4.11***   A cycle using R-12 operates between evaporating and condensing temperatures of 0°F and 120°F, with 10°F superheat in the evaporator. Calculate the cycle performance characteristics.

*Solution*   Figure 4.11 shows the cycle. Using the property tables and $p$–$h$ diagram

$$\text{R.E.} = h_c - h_a = 78.5 - 36.0$$
$$= 42.5 \text{ Btu/lb}$$

$$m = \frac{200}{\text{R.E.}} = \frac{200}{42.5} = 4.71 \text{ lb/min}$$
$$\text{per ton}$$

$$\text{H.C.} = h_d - h_c = 94 - 78.5$$
$$= 15.5 \text{ Btu/lb}$$

$$\text{H.R.} = h_d - h_a = 94 - 36.0$$
$$= 58.0 \text{ Btu/lb}$$

$$Q_c = m \times \text{H.R.} = 4.71 \times 58.0$$
$$= 273.2 \text{ Btu/min per}$$
$$\text{ton}$$

$$P = W \times m$$
$$= 15.5 \times 4.71 = 73.0 \text{ Btu/min per ton}$$
$$= 73.0 \text{ Btu/min per ton} \times \frac{1 \text{ kW}}{56.9 \text{ Btu/min}}$$
$$= 1.28 \text{ kW/ton}$$

$$\text{COP} = \frac{\text{R.E.}}{\text{H.C.}} = \frac{42.5}{15.5} = 2.74$$

$$V_t = v \times m = 1.6 \times 4.71$$
$$= 7.54 \text{ ft}^3\text{/min per ton}$$

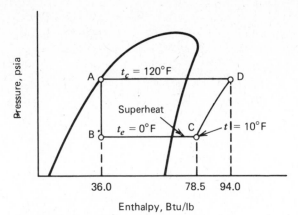

**FIGURE 4.11** Effect of superheat in evaporator (Example 4.11).

pansion type evaporators. Typical control superheat temperatures range from 5 to 14°F.

## 4.18 Superheat in the Suction Line

When the suction gas line is of significant length, possible additional superheat effects in it may occur. If the line passes through an unrefrigerated warm space the amount of superheat might be significant and should be considered when analyzing the cycle on the $p$–$h$ diagram. However, no useful cooling is achieved in this case. Furthermore, the cycle performance is poorer, as seen from the following example and discussion.

The differences in performance between the cycle with and without superheat in the evaporator can be seen by comparing the results of Examples 4.9 and 4.11. For the 10°F superheat used in the example, there is a small increase in the refrigeration effect. The compressor displacement decreases because of the reduction in mass flow rate. This slight apparent improvement in performance is not the reason why the refrigerant is superheated in the evaporator. The primary reason is that it provides an excellent means of controlling the refrigerant flow rate when a thermostatic expansion valve is used (Chapter 8). In addition, superheat ensures that no refrigerant liquid reaches the compressor suction; this could result in damage to the compressor.

In reality a penalty is paid for superheating the refrigerant in the evaporator. The evaporator surface must be increased in size to provide the extra heat transfer to superheat the vapor. Heat transfer to a vapor is poorer than transfer to an evaporating liquid. If the extra surface had been used for evaporation, the evaporating temperature could have been raised, improving the system performance, as shown previously. Nevertheless, for purposes of control, the refrigerant is usually superheated in the evaporator with direct ex-

*Example 4.12* A cycle using R-12 operates between evaporating and condensing temperatures of 0°F and 120°F. The suction line passes through an unrefrigerated warm space, with 60°F of superheat resulting. Compare the cycle performance to that if no superheat occurred.

*Solution* Figure 4.12 shows the cycle. The calculations are as follows.

$$\text{R.E.} = h_c - h_a = 77.3 - 36.0$$

$$= 41.3 \text{ Btu/lb}$$

$$m = \frac{200}{\text{R.E.}} = \frac{200}{41.3}$$

$$= 4.84 \text{ lb/min per ton}$$

$$\text{H.C.} = h_d - h_{c'} = 104 - 86 = 18 \text{ Btu/lb}$$

$$\text{H.R.} = h_d - h_a = 104 - 36.0$$

$$= 68 \text{ Btu/lb}$$

$$Q_c = 68 \text{ Btu/lb} \times 4.84 \text{ lb/min per ton}$$

$$= 329.1 \text{ Btu/min per ton}$$

$$P = W \times m$$

$$= 18 \text{ Btu/lb} \times 4.84 \text{ lb/min per ton}$$

$$= 87.1 \text{ Btu/min per ton} \times \frac{1 \text{ hp}}{42.4 \text{ Btu/min}}$$

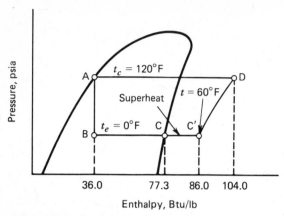

**FIGURE 4.12** Effect of superheat in suction line outside refrigerated space (Example 4.12).

$$= 2.05 \text{ hp/ton}$$

$$V_t = v \times m$$

$$= 1.8 \text{ ft}^3/\text{lb} \times 4.84 \text{ lb/min per ton}$$

$$= 8.71 \text{ ft}^3/\text{min per ton}$$

$$COP = \frac{R.E.}{H.C.} = \frac{41.3 \text{ Btu/lb}}{18 \text{ Btu/lb}} = 2.29$$

The performance with superheat in the suction line that does not produce useful cooling is compared in Table 4.1 to the case without this effect. Superheat in the suction line that does not produce useful cooling has the following results:

1. The heat of compression increases.

**TABLE 4.1** Effect of Nonuseful Suction Line Superheat of 60°F on Ideal Cycle Performance (R-12, $t_e$ = 0°F, $t_c$ = 120°F)

| Performance Factors | Superheat | |
|---|---|---|
|  | 0°F | 60°F |
| R.E. (Btu/lb) | 41.3 | 41.3 |
| m (lb/min per ton) | 4.84 | 4.84 |
| H.C. (Btu/lb) | 15.2 | 18.0 |
| Required power (hp/ton) | 1.74 | 2.05 |
| COP | 2.72 | 2.29 |
| Required displacement (CFM/ton) | 7.79 | 8.71 |

2. The heat of rejection increases. In addition to the increased heat of compression, the added superheat must be removed.

3. The required compressor power per ton increases, due to the increased heat of compression.

4. The coefficient of performance decreases, due to the increased heat of compression.

5. The required compressor displacement increases because the specific volume increases.

The suction line can be insulated to reduce any undesired superheat. This has the added benefit of preventing condensation of moisture on the piping. At higher evaporating temperatures (in the air conditioning range) the suction line might not be insulated if the benefit is not significant and if excessive superheating does not occur.

From an energy conservation viewpoint, suction line insulation can reduce power requirements by 10 to 15 percent in low temperature applications.

Excessive superheating of the refrigerant gas may cause temperatures in the compressor to be unacceptably high, leading to lubrication problems and possibly even to damage to valves (Chapter 5).

If the suction line is in the refrigerated space, then the suction gas superheat produces an additional useful refrigeration effect and the performance is not adversely affected.

## 4.19 Subcooling of the Refrigerant

The refrigerant liquid may be subcooled either in the condenser or in an additional heat exchanger. The cycle diagram is shown in Figure 4.13. It is apparent from the diagram that the refrigeration effect increases with subcooling and that there is less flash gas. Table 4.2 compares performance characteristics of a cycle with 20°F subcooling to one without subcooling, for the conditions shown.

Subcooling results in a lower required com-

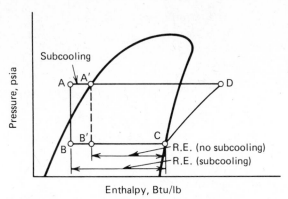

**FIGURE 4.13** Effect of subcooling on refrigeration effect.

pressor power per unit capacity and a higher coefficient of performance. The required compressor displacement also decreases. Clearly, then, subcooling is desirable, and therefore it is common practice. From an energy conservation viewpoint, subcooling can easily reduce power consumption by 5 to 15 percent. Other than using a larger condenser there are a number of ways of achieving subcooling. We discuss those related to condenser construction and operation in Chapter 7. Another method is discussed in the following section.

An additional advantage of subcooling is that it reduces the possibility of liquid refrigerant flashing in the liquid line before it reaches the flow control device. This would happen if

there were an excessive pressure drop in the liquid line. Since the flash gas has a higher specific volume than the liquid, the mass flow rate would be reduced, affecting the system performance adversely.

## 4.20 Liquid-Suction Heat Exchangers

It would seem reasonable to take advantage of the cold suction gas in order to subcool the warm liquid refrigerant leaving the condenser, while also providing any additional required superheat to the suction gas to prevent liquid from entering the compressor. The simplest way of doing this is to place the liquid and suction lines in contact along their length. To increase the heat exchange they may be soldered and insulated from the surrounding air.

If the lines are too short, improved heat exchange is accomplished by a liquid-suction heat exchanger. The circuiting when a heat exchanger is used is shown schematically in Figure 4.14. Their construction is discussed in Chapter 11.

When compared to suction gas superheat outside the refrigerated space, which was shown to reduce performance, using this heat to produce the desired subcooling is usually a worthwhile energy saving advantage at lower temperatures. At suction temperatures corresponding to air conditioning applications, however, the use of a heat exchanger is generally not justified for the possible slight increase in performance. In any case it is usually not desirable with R-22 and ammonia systems. With these refrigerants the high suction temperatures could result in excessive hot gas discharge temperatures that might overheat the compressor.

## 4.21 Pressure Drop in Lines

The effect of friction on the flow of any fluid in a pipe results in a pressure drop in the direction of flow. We neglected this real effect

**TABLE 4.2** Effect of Liquid Subcooling of 20°F on Ideal Cycle Performance (R-12, $t_e$ = 0°F, $t_c$ = 120°F)

| Performance Factors | Subcooling | |
|---|---|---|
| | 0°F | 20°F |
| R.E. (Btu/lb) | 41.3 | 46.0 |
| m (lb/min per ton) | 4.85 | 4.35 |
| H.C. (Btu/lb) | 15.2 | 15.2 |
| Required power (hp/ton) | 1.74 | 1.56 |
| COP | 2.72 | 3.03 |
| Required displacement (CFM/ton) | 7.79 | 7.00 |

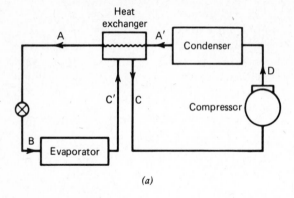

*(a)*

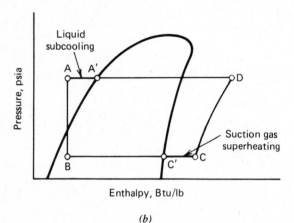

*(b)*

**FIGURE 4.14** Use of liquid-suction heat exchanger to superheat suction gas and subcool liquid. (*a*) Equipment arrangement. (*b*) Cycle diagram (note enthalpy change $h_{a-a'} = h_{c'-c}$).

when we defined and analyzed the ideal cycle. Generally these effects should be considered if an accurate cycle analysis is to be carried out.

It is common practice in the refrigeration industry to express the piping pressure drop as an *equivalent drop in saturation temperature* (called the *equivalent pressure drop*). This is convenient because the conditions at the compressor inlet and outlet are usually expressed as saturated suction and discharge temperatures (even though the gas is actually superheated) and compressors are rated at these saturated conditions.

*The **saturated suction temperature** is defined as the saturation temperature corresponding to the pressure at the compressor suction inlet.*

Compressor ratings are discussed in Chapter 5.

Pipe lines are sized according to specified pressure drops that are found to result in good performance and reasonable cost (see Chapter 11). For example, suction lines are often sized to have a pressure drop "equivalent to a 2°F drop in saturation temperature." An example illustrates this method.

**Example 4.13** A refrigeration system using R-502 is operating at an evaporating temperature of 40°F. The suction line has a pressure drop equivalent to 2°F. What is the suction-line pressure drop and saturated suction temperature at the compressor inlet?

*Solution* The saturated suction temperature is $40 - 2 = 38°F$. Using Appendix 7, the saturation pressures at 40°F and 38°F are noted, and the calculations are as follows:

| | Temperature | Pressure |
|---|---|---|
| Saturated refrigerant | 40°F | 95.2 psia |
| Suction line "equivalent pressure drop" | − 2°F | |
| Saturated suction conditions at compressor inlet | 38°F | 92.1 psia |
| Suction line pressure drop | | 3.1 psia |

It should be noted that when the pressure drop in the hot gas line is accounted for, the equivalent temperature should be *added* to the saturated condensing temperature to find the saturation temperature at the compressor discharge. This follows from the fact that the

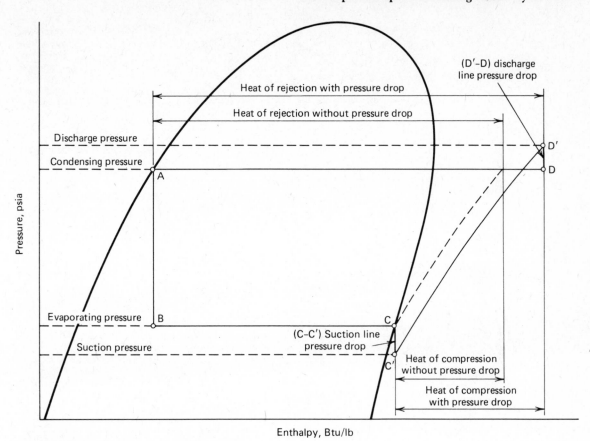

**FIGURE 4.15** Effect of suction and discharge line pressure drop.

pressure at the compressor discharge is higher than that at the condenser inlet; the reverse is true in relation to the compressor inlet and evaporator, as seen in Figure 4.15.

The refrigerant cycle with pressure drop in the suction and discharge lines is shown in Figure 4.15. The effect of each is shown separately to clarify the explanation. Note that the heat of compression and heat of rejection increase due to the pressure drop in suction and discharge lines. Since the refrigeration effect does not change, it follows that both the power required per unit capacity increases and the coefficient of performance decreases as a result of the pressure drops. This would

be expected because the pressure range through which the gas must be compressed increases.

Note that the pressure drops in the lines are assumed to be at constant enthalpy (vertical lines); that is, it is assumed that there is negligible heat transfer between the gas and the surroundings. This is usually a satisfactory approximation.

Pressure drop in the evaporator and condenser will also occur as a result of friction. As with any pressure loss, there is an undesirable effect on cycle performance. In many cases, however, the evaporator and condenser pressure drop are neglected in analysis, be-

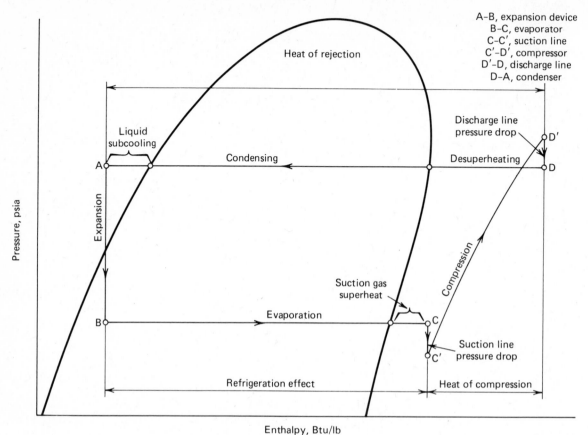

**FIGURE 4.16** Vapor compression cycle with liquid subcooling, suction gas superheat, and pressure drop.

cause the effect is often small. Manufacturers will adjust their evaporator ratings when the pressure drop is high.

A cycle diagram showing all the effects we have discussed is shown in Figure 4.16. A performance analysis would be carried out in the same manner that we have already used.

Friction losses in the compression process result in an increase in entropy and an increase in hot gas discharge temperature. This effect can be found by actual compressor test, and is discussed in Chapter 5.

## 4.22 Energy Conservation

A summary of cycle effects that result in reduced energy consumption per unit of refrig-

eration capacity are listed here. In some cases suggestions of how to achieve these benefits will be postponed to a more appropriate place.

1. Operate at low condensing temperatures. This can be achieved by using large condensers and maintaining clean heat transfer surfaces. (It will be explained later that an extremely low condensing temperature may cause erratic system performance.)

2. Operate at high evaporating temperatures. This can be achieved by using large evaporators.

3. Size refrigerant pipe lines for reasonably low pressure drops.

4. Design and operate the system to provide

significant liquid subcooling in the condenser.

5. Use a liquid-suction heat exchanger if analysis shows it improves cycle performance significantly, but do not use with a refrigerant where the hot gas discharge temperature would be too high.

## 4.23 The Energy Efficiency Ratio (EER)

Another measure of efficiency of performance of refrigeration equipment, other than the COP, is the energy efficiency ratio (EER). It is expressed by the following equation:

$$EER = \frac{Q_e}{P} = \frac{\text{useful cooling capacity, Btu/hr}}{\text{power input, W}} \quad (14.14)$$

The EER has the same two terms as the equation for the COP has, and therefore it measures the same efficiency use of energy. However, the units in the equation differ, and therefore the numerical values of the EER will differ from these of the COP for the same conditions. The EER has been developed because it is easier for the consumer to understand and use. Labeling of air conditioning and refrigeration equipment with EER values at a standard set of conditions is legally required in certain places and circumstances. Since the EER (and COP) change with conditions, it is often difficult to obtain a realistic EER under varying operating conditions. One attempt to accomplish this is by use of the Seasonal Energy Efficiency Ratio (SEER), which tries to measure the average EER of equipment for a cooling season.

***Example 4.14*** An air conditioning unit has an EER rating of 7.7 (at standard conditions) and a rated capacity of 9200 Btu/hr. What would be the expected power use at standard conditions?

*Solution* Equation 14.14 is used, solving for the power input:

$$P = \frac{Q_e}{EER} = \frac{9200}{7.7} = 1200 \text{ W}$$

Recommended energy conservation standards for air conditioning and refrigeration equipment can be found in the ASHRAE (American Society of Heating, Refrigerating and Air-Conditioning Engineers) Standard 90-80 publication.

## 4.24 Maximum Coefficient of Performance

It can be shown from the Second Law of Thermodynamics that a refrigeration system has a maximum possible coefficient of performance. The equation expressing this is:

$$COP_m = \frac{T_1}{T_2 - T_1} \quad (4.15)$$

where $COP_m$ = maximum possible COP for a refrigeration system
$T_1$ = temperature at which heat is absorbed from cooling load
$T_2$ = temperature at which heat is rejected to heat sink

The derivation of this equation can be found in a thermodynamics textbook. Temperatures in the equation must be expressed in absolute units, Kelvin (K), or Rankine (R).
The value of Equation 4.15 is that it shows the upper limit of efficiency. In reality, the COP of real machines is always considerably less than the maximum possible, due to friction and other losses.

## REVIEW QUESTIONS

1. List some of the refrigeration system performance characteristics that are of importance.

2. Explain the terms *process, cycle,* and *steady state operation.*

3. What are the differences between the ideal refrigeration cycle and real cycles? Why is it useful to study the ideal cycle?

4. Sketch a p–h diagram showing the ideal vapor compression cycle. Label each point on the diagram and show the comparable location on a sketch of the refrigeration system plant.

5. What property remains constant in each of the processes in the ideal cycle?

6. Sketch a p–h diagram and ideal cycle and show the refrigeration effect, heat of compression, and heat of rejection. What is their arithmetic relationship?

7. Explain what causes the refrigerant to drop in temperature when it passes through the flow control device.

8. What is the importance of calculating the performance of the theoretical compression cycle?

9. Describe the effect of changing evaporating temperature in system performance characteristics. Explain the causes in each case. Use a sketch of the p–h diagram as an aid.

10. Describe the effect of changing condensing temperatures on system performance characteristics. Explain the causes in each case. Use a sketch of the p–h diagram as an aid.

11. What is superheat? What are the effects of superheat in:
    a. The evaporator.
    b. The suction line in the refrigerated space.
    c. The suction line outside the refrigerated space?

12. What is subcooling? What are the effects of subcooling?

13. What are the functions of a liquid suction heat exchanger? Draw a sketch of the refrigeration system with one.

14. Explain the term *equivalent pressure drop*.

15. What are the effects of pressure drop in the suction and discharge lines?

16. Explain the meaning of the COP, maximum COP, and EER. Why is it useful to know their values?

17. List some ways of conserving energy in:
    a. Designing.
    b. Operating refrigeration systems.

## PROBLEMS

4.1 An ideal vapor compression refrigeration cycle using R-502 operates at evaporating and condensing temperatures of 4°F and 100°F. Refrigerant leaves the evaporator as a saturated vapor. Determine:
   a. Refrigeration effect, Btu/lb.
   b. Mass flow rate, lb/min.
   c. Heat of compression, Btu/lb.
   d. Heat of rejection, Btu/lb.
   e. Theoretical compressor power, hp/ton.
   f. Theoretical compressor displacement, ft$^3$/min.
   g. Percentage flash gas.
   h. Coefficient of performance.

4.2 Find the quantities listed in Problem 4.1 for an ideal refrigeration cycle using R-717 operating at evaporating and condensing temperatures of 10°F and 96°F.

4.3 Find the quantities listed in Problem 4.1 for an ideal refrigeration cycle using R-12 operating at evaporating and condensing temperatures of 30°F and 120°F.

4.4 A refrigeration unit is operating with a cooling capacity of 34 tons of refrigeration. The compressor is using 40 kW of power to compress the gas. What is the rate of heat rejection in the condenser, in Btu/min? What is the coefficient of performance of the unit?

4.5 A water chiller is cooling 64 GPM of water from 55°F to 42°F. It has a water cooled condenser that uses 100 GPM of water entering at 85°F and leaving at 95°F. What is the net power in kW used in the compressor? What is the coefficient of performance? What is the hp/ton?

4.6 Find the coefficient of performance for an ideal cycle system using R-12 for the following conditions:

| | Evaporating Temperature (°F) | Condensing Temperature (°F) |
|---|---|---|
| a. | 26 | 94 |
| b. | 32 | 94 |
| c. | 26 | 106 |

Explain the significance of the results for energy conservation.

4.7 A refrigeration cycle using R-502 operates at evaporating and condensing temperatures of 4°F and 100°F. Refrigerant leaves the evaporator with 20°F superheat. Find the refrigeration effect, mass flow rate, heat of compression, heat of rejection, theoretical compressor power, theoretical compressor displacement, and coefficient of performance. Prepare a table comparing the results to those found in Problem 4.1 and explain their significance in terms of energy use.

4.8 For the same refrigeration cycle and conditions described in Example 4.7, except that the refrigerant leaves the condenser with 15°F subcooling, find the quantities requested in Example 4.7. Prepare a table comparing the results and explain their significance in terms of energy use.

4.9 A refrigeration system using R-22 operates at an evaporating temperature of 32°F. The suction line has a pressure drop equivalent to 2°F. Find the suction-line pressure drop and saturated suction temperature at the compressor inlet.

4.10 An ideal vapor compression refrigeration cycle using R-22 operates at an evaporating temperature of −2°C and a condensing temperature of 42°C. Refrigerant leaves the evaporator as a saturated vapor. Find the

a. Refrigeration effect, kJ/kg.
b. Mass flow rate.
c. Heat of compression, kJ/kg.
d. Heat of rejection, kJ/kg.
e. Theoretical compressor power, kW/kW.
f. Theoretical compressor displacement, m³/min.
g. Coefficient of performance.

4.11 R-717 is used in an ideal vapor compression system operating at evaporating and condensing temperatures of −12°C and 40°C, respectively. Refrigerant leaves the evaporator as a saturated vapor. Find the quantities requested in Problem 4.10.

# Chapter 5

## RECIPROCATING, ROTARY, AND SCREW COMPRESSORS

In this chapter we examine some types of compressors and their construction, performance, and selection. Our emphasis is on modern compressors and their features, including energy conservation factors. Compressors of the type that are no longer manufactured or are rarely encountered will not be discussed.

## OBJECTIVES

A study of this chapter will enable you to:
1. Describe the basic operation and identify the parts of each type of positive displacement compressor.
2. Identify the major differences between open and hermetic compressors and their relative advantages.
3. Explain slugging, floodback, and refrigerant migration, and their causes.
4. Describe different methods of reciprocating compressor capacity control and their features.
5. Calculate compressor displacement.
6. Select a compressor for a given application.
7. Show and explain the effect that changing conditions have on the performance of a given compressor.
8. Suggest some energy conservation measures in the selection and operation of compressors.

## 5.1 Purpose of Compressors

The primary function of a refrigeration compressor is to increase the pressure of the refrigerant gas from the evaporating pressure to a pressure at which the gas can be condensed. As explained in Chapter 3, the pressure must be raised to the saturation pressure corresponding to the condensing temperature.

The primary compressor function (the pressure increase) results in some secondary, yet necessary, functions. The high discharge pressure provides the energy required to circulate the refrigerant against frictional resistance through the piping and equipment. In addition, the large pressure differential created provides for the sudden expansion in the flow control device, causing a temperature drop.

## 5.2 Compressor Types

Refrigeration compressors can be classified into two main groups in relation to how the increase in gas pressure is accomplished; one group is called *positive displacement* compressors, the other is called *dynamic* compressors. There are three types of positive displacement compressors: *reciprocating*, *rotary*, and *helical rotary* (*screw*). There is only one dynamic type used in refrigeration work, called the *centrifugal* compressor. Other dynamic types, such as the axial flow compressor, are not used in refrigeration systems.

All positive displacement compressors raise the gas pressure by taking a given quantity of the gas into a confined volume, and then decreasing this volume. Decreasing the volume of a gas causes its pressure to increase (unless it is cooled).

Centrifugal compressors are discussed in Chapter 10.

# RECIPROCATING COMPRESSORS

## 5.3 Operation and Construction

Reciprocating compressors are similar in construction to reciprocating automotive type engines, having cylinders, pistons, a drive shaft, and suction and discharge valves. The compressor may have one or more cylinders.

The basic operation of the compressor is shown in Figure 5.1. The piston is driven through the linkage from an electric motor or engine. When the piston moves down on its suction stroke, the increasing volume in the cylinder results in a decrease in pressure below that in the suction line. The pressure difference forces the suction valve to open and refrigerant gas flows into the cylinder. The

discharge valve is closed because of the higher pressure in the discharge line.

When the piston moves up on its compression stroke, the decrease in volume causes the gas pressure to increase. This forces the suction valve closed. Near the end of the stroke, the gas pressure has increased above the pressure in the discharge line, forcing the discharge valve open and the compressed gas flows into the discharge line to the condenser. Note that the compressor completes the suction and compression of the gas once for every revolution of the crankshaft.

This compressor operation is called single acting because compression takes place only in one end of the cylinder. An alternate compressor construction, in which the gas is compressed on both ends of the cylinder (double acting) was available in older, slow-speed compressors.

## 5.4 Open Compressors

In an *open* compressor, the shaft extends through the crankcase housing (Figure 5.2).

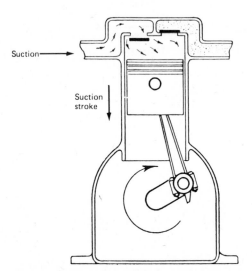

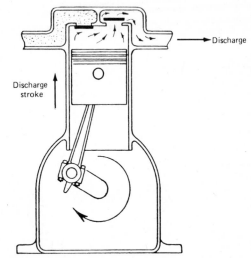

**FIGURE 5.1** Operation of reciprocating compressor. (*a*) Suction stroke. Increasing volume reduces pressure in the cylinder. Pressure in the suction line forces the suction valve open. Pressure in the discharge line holds the discharge valve closed. (*b*) Discharge stroke. Decreasing volume raises pressure in the cylinder, forcing the discharge valve open. Pressure in cylinder holds the suction valve closed.

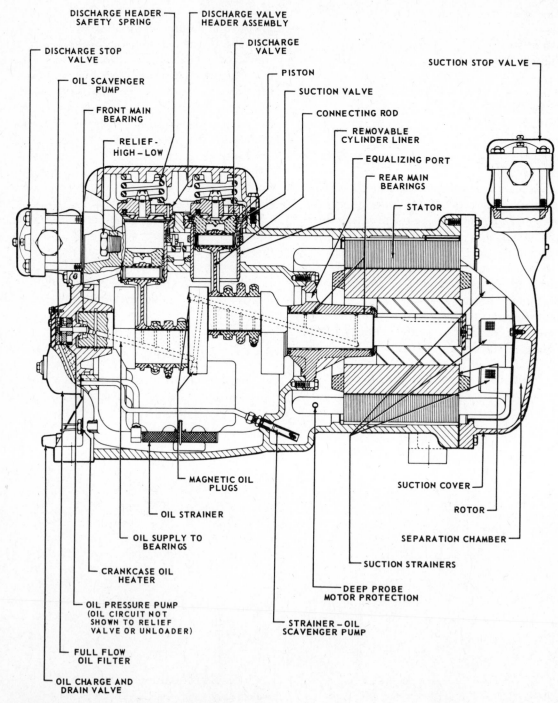

DISCHARGE HEADER
SAFETY SPRING

DISCHARGE VALVE
HEADER ASSEMBLY

DISCHARGE
VALVE

PISTON

SUCTION VALVE

CONNECTING ROD

REMOVABLE
CYLINDER LINER

EQUALIZING PORT

REAR MAIN
BEARINGS

STATOR

SUCTION STOP VALVE

DISCHARGE STOP
VALVE

OIL SCAVENGER
PUMP

FRONT MAIN
BEARING

RELIEF-
HIGH-LOW

MAGNETIC OIL
PLUGS

OIL STRAINER

OIL SUPPLY TO
BEARINGS

CRANKCASE OIL
HEATER

OIL PRESSURE PUMP
(OIL CIRCUIT NOT
SHOWN TO RELIEF
VALVE OR UNLOADER)

FULL FLOW
OIL FILTER

OIL CHARGE AND
DRAIN VALVE

STRAINER–OIL
SCAVENGER PUMP

DEEP PROBE
MOTOR PROTECTION

SUCTION STRAINERS

SEPARATION CHAMBER

ROTOR

SUCTION COVER

**FIGURE 5.2** An open reciprocating compressor.

74

The compressor may be either *direct-driven* or *belt-driven*. If direct-driven, the compressor shaft is usually connected to the driver shaft by a flexible coupling. The coupling serves to absorb excess vibration and shock and provides a simple method of aligning the two shafts. If the driver is an electric motor, the direct driven speed used for 60-Hz current is about 1750 or 3500 RPM. Belt-driven compressors utilize a pulley on each shaft, connected by belts. Compressor speeds may be changed by using different diameter pulleys.

It is common for manufacturers to furnish a complete compressor unit, with the compressor, motor, and sometimes starter mounted on a common base plate (Figure 5.3), already connected and aligned. This is a convenience and usually reduces installation costs.

Because of the temperatures and heat generated during compression, ammonia compressors often require cooling. This is usually provided by a built-in water jacket construction similar to automobile engines.

## 5.5 Hermetic Compressors

A *hermetic*-type compressor is one in which the compressor and motor are integral on one shaft and they are both contained in a pressure sealed housing. Hermetic-type compressors are manufactured either as fully her-

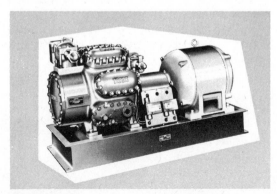

**FIGURE 5.3** A compressor unit, with motor and base. (The Trane Co.)

metic or *semihermetic* (also called serviceable or accessible hermetic). The hermetic compressor has a sealed welded housing (Figure 5.4), and cannot be serviced in the field. It is compact in size, quiet, and low in cost. These features make it very popular in domestic refrigerators and other small unitary equipment. The semihermetic compressor (Figure 5.5) has a bolted removable housing so that it may be serviced in the field.

The main advantage of a hermetic compressor is that, because there is no shaft extending externally through a housing, there is no problem of refrigerant gas leakage. With an open compressor, a shaft seal is required to prevent or minimize leakage of refrigerant between the shaft and housing.

The motor in a hermetic-type compressor is cooled by the refrigerant suction gas. The allowable power output (rating) of a motor decreases with an increase in temperature of the motor windings, to prevent overheating. The cool suction gas flowing rapidly over the windings allows the motor to take more current and thus deliver more power than it would if it were cooled only by ambient, still air, as with an open motor. The result is that a smaller, less costly motor can be used with hermetic compressors. However, adding the motor heat to the suction gas results in the compressor power being slightly greater than that in an open machine.

Because of the sealed compressor–motor assembly, hermetic units usually have a noise level lower than that of comparable open units.

Hermetic compressors using 60 Hz current are operated at either approximately 1750 RPM (four-pole motor) or 3500 RPM (two-pole motor).

At low temperatures (below 0°F) the density of suction gas may not be adequate to cool hermetic units, and a fan may be required.

Compressors are not made in hermetic design for use with ammonia because this refrigerant chemically reacts with motor materials.

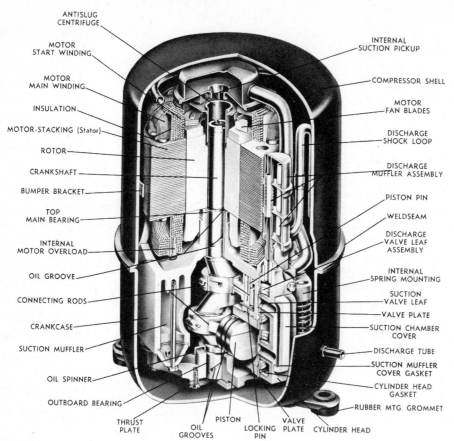

**FIGURE 5.4** A hermetic reciprocating compressor.
(Tecumseh Products Co.)

## 5.6 Compressor Seals

With older, open compressors, designed to operate at slow speeds, a soft packing around the shaft was an adequate seal to prevent gas leakage. Modern compressors are designed to operate at high speeds so that a smaller compressor is needed for a given capacity, reducing costs. Packing would wear out rapidly under these conditions.

*Mechanical seals* are used in all modern compressors. The essential feature is that two hard surfaces, one stationary and one rotating, mate tightly to form a leak-proof seal. The *rotary seal* has a carbon ring attached to the shaft; the face of this ring is held against a stationary ring by a spring (Figure 5.6). There are other designs of mechanical seals, but the rotary seal is one of the most popular because of its low cost and reliability.

## 5.7 Valves

Two basic types of suction and discharge valves are used in reciprocating refrigeration compressors. One is the *flapper, reed,* or *flexing* type. It consists of a thin piece of flexible spring steel clamped on one end or at the middle, usually shaped like a reed. The valve may consist of one or more reeds, covering

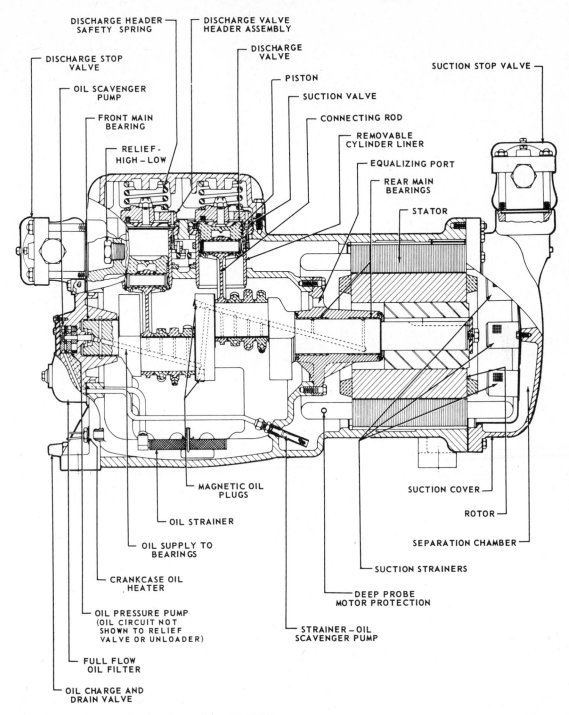

DISCHARGE HEADER
SAFETY SPRING

DISCHARGE VALVE
HEADER ASSEMBLY

DISCHARGE STOP
VALVE

DISCHARGE
VALVE

OIL SCAVENGER
PUMP

PISTON

FRONT MAIN
BEARING

SUCTION VALVE

RELIEF-
HIGH–LOW

CONNECTING ROD

REMOVABLE
CYLINDER LINER

SUCTION STOP VALVE

EQUALIZING PORT

REAR MAIN
BEARINGS

STATOR

MAGNETIC OIL
PLUGS

OIL STRAINER

OIL SUPPLY TO
BEARINGS

CRANKCASE OIL
HEATER

OIL PRESSURE PUMP
(OIL CIRCUIT NOT
SHOWN TO RELIEF
VALVE OR UNLOADER)

FULL FLOW
OIL FILTER

OIL CHARGE AND
DRAIN VALVE

SUCTION COVER

ROTOR

SEPARATION CHAMBER

SUCTION STRAINERS

DEEP PROBE
MOTOR PROTECTION

STRAINER–OIL
SCAVENGER PUMP

**FIGURE 5.5** An accessible (semihermetic) compressor.

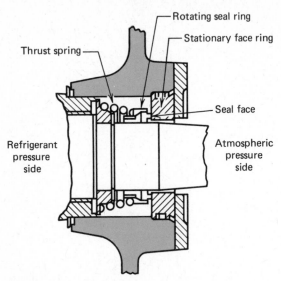

FIGURE 5.6 A rotary mechanical compressor seal.

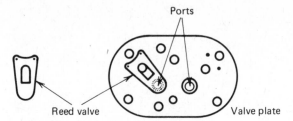

**FIGURE 5.7** Compressor valve, reed type.

holes in a valve plate (Figure 5.7). The pressure differential will force the free end of the valve away from the hole. When the pressure is not acting, the strip springs back to its natural position.

For larger compressors a more rugged type, called a *ring valve*, is often preferred. The valve is a ring-shaped plate that covers holes in the valve plate (Figure 5.8). The valve is held against the plate by small coil springs.

On some compressor designs, a heavy coil spring is provided between the compressor head and discharge valve assembly to help protect the compressor valves against damage from liquid slugging. If liquid is trapped in the cylinder on the discharge stroke, the valve assembly will lift and relieve pressure (Figure 5.9).

## 5.8 Lubrication System

The compressor lubrication system may be either the *splash* or *forced feed* type, or both. The splash type uses dippers on the bottom of the connecting rod which pick up oil from the

**FIGURE 5.8** Compressor valve, ring plate type. (The Trane Co., La Crosse, WI)

**FIGURE 5.9** The discharge header safety spring relieves pressure from trapped liquid. (The Trane Co., La Crosse, WI)

crankcase and splash it onto wearing surfaces. The forced feed system has an oil pump that forces oil to the bearings through drilled holes in the crankshaft.

Most forced feed compressors use positive displacement oil pumps of the gear or vane type driven from the crankshaft. A spring-loaded pressure relief valve at the pump discharge opens if there is excess pump pressure, bypassing oil to the crankcase. The pumps are usually designed so that they will function in either direction of rotation, since compressors often may be run in either direction. Some small welded hermetic compressors use centrifugal pumps.

Oil entrained with the refrigerant lubricates the cylinder walls and is carried through the system. In order to return this oil to the crankcase an oil port is provided in the compressor, between the suction and the crankcase. A check valve is provided in the oil return port to prevent a sudden surge of oil loss from the crankcase when the compressor is started. (The cause of this problem is explained later.)

A suction screen (strainer) is located in the suction line to catch oil and refrigerant droplets as well as foreign matter. A large separation chamber is also sometimes incorporated

in the suction as an oil trap, before the oil returns through the oil port.

*Service valves* are generally furnished at the compressor suction and discharge, for isolating the compressor for maintenance and repair. They usually are of the back-seating type (Chapter 11).

## 5.9 Liquid Refrigerant–Oil Problems

Great care must be taken to prevent excess liquid refrigerant from entering reciprocating compressors. A liquid is incompressible, and if a large amount is trapped in the cylinder at the end of the discharge stroke the force could easily break valves and even connecting rods (Figure 5.10).

A related problem is excess dilution of the lubricating oil by the refrigerant. This may result in ineffective lubrication and rapid wear of bearings or the piston and cylinder (Figure 5.11).

Modern compressors have numerous features to lessen the occurrence of these problems, and to protect the compressor if they do occur. Certain operating procedures should also be carried out to decrease the possibility of problems happening. The refrigeration

**FIGURE 5.10** Connecting rod broken as a result of liquid slugging. (The Trane Co., La Crosse, WI)

piping system must be designed and installed in a way that prevents liquid refrigerant from entering the compressor and enhances good oil return to the crankcase. Piping systems and oil return problems are discussed in Chapter 11.

When liquid refrigerant enters the compressor from the evaporator continually during operation, it is called *floodback*. When large quantities of liquid suddenly enter the compressor for a short period of time it is called *slugging*. Liquid slugging tends to occur when there is a sudden change in load or on start-up. Flooding tends to cause oil dilution and subsequent excess wear, and slugging causes damage to compressor parts. We will discuss causes of both.

**FIGURE 5.11** Piston damage from lack of lubrication. (The Trane Co., La Crosse, WI)

*Refrigerant migration.* This term refers to the migration of refrigerant vapor from the evaporator to the oil crankcase. When the system is shut down, the vapor pressure of the refrigerant in the evaporator will drive it to the crankcase. Most refrigerants are soluble in oil, and when the refrigerant reaches the crankcase and dissolves in the oil, this reduces the crankcase vapor pressure, causing a further pressure difference that enhances the migration.

When the compressor starts, the pressure in the crankcase (suction pressure) will suddenly drop. The drop in pressure causes the refrigerant to boil rapidly out of the oil. The vapor bubbles formed cause a foaming or surge of oil and liquid refrigerant out of the crankcase. This may result in liquid slugs entering the compressor on start-up, possibly causing damage. Even if this does not occur, either the loss of oil from the crankcase or the foaming vapor may starve the oil pump, resulting in insufficient lubrication.

We have already described how the check valve in the oil return port is used to reduce the surge of oil from entering the compressor suction. To reduce migration of refrigerant, a crankcase heater is used. The oil temperature is kept high enough to evaporate and drive off any migrating refrigerant. The heater is an electric heating element, inserted in the crankcase in larger compressors. On small hermetic units it may be externally strapped around the shell. Care must be taken that the oil temperature is not high enough to cause carbonization (Chapter 9), which reduces the lubricating quality of the oil.

Liquid slugging of refrigerant may occur directly from the evaporator to the compressor. This could occur on start-up if sufficient liquid has collected in the evaporator during the off period. It could also occur where the compressor has been running unloaded because the coils are being defrosted, resulting in liquid refrigerant collecting in the evaporator.

The use of the suction screen in the compressor to reduce liquid flow to the compressor was discussed previously. Sometimes a separate liquid trap, called a *suction accumulator,* is installed in the suction line, especially with heat pumps (see Chapter 11).

There are further means and devices used to protect against liquid slugging on start-up. For example the refrigerant may be pumped out of the evaporator on shut-down; this is called the *pumpdown cycle* (Chapter 16).

In addition to the problems discussed here, flood-back of refrigerant from the evaporator can occur as a result of improper design and installation. For example excess refrigerant may be charged into the system, or the thermostatic expansion valve may be the incorrect type, or may be installed improperly (see Chapter 8 for a discussion of this problem).

## 5.10 Accessories

Some items are usually offered as options with the compressor, to be used when required and installed separately. Among these are:

*Mufflers.* These are used in suction and discharge lines for reducing noise from gas pulsations. On some small hermetic units they are standard items.

*Suction, discharge, and oil pressure gages.* Used for checking performance.

*Vibration isolator springs.* The compressor is mounted on these, to reduce transmission of compressor vibrations to the building or piping. On small hermetic units the compressor–motor is mounted on springs attached to the inside of the shell.

Compressors are often furnished from the factory as a unit with motor, starter, and electrical controls mounted and wired, if desired.

## 5.11 Capacity Control

A compressor is generally chosen to have a displacement capacity adequate to handle the maximum refrigeration load of a system. In most applications the load fluctuates, and the system will be at part load much of the time. For example, in commercial refrigeration, the load is very high when cooling a new supply of warm food products, but is less after the product has been cooled. Some method of compressor capacity control is usually required when there is a variation in system load, for reasons that will now be discussed.

When the load decreases the evaporator flow control device usually throttles the refrigerant mass flow rate. The compressor, however, being a constant displacement device, pumps a constant volume of gas. With a smaller mass quantity of refrigerant gas entering the suction, its pressure and temperature drop. The space or product temperature may then fall to unacceptable levels.

In some situations the drop in suction pressure may result in the evaporating temperature unintentionally falling below 32° F, with ice forming on an air cooling coil. This reduces heat transfer, causing a further drop in evaporating temperature and suction pressure. With a water chiller the water may freeze and cause damage to equipment.

Two other problems may occur at part load, resulting from the reduced refrigerant flow rate. These are:

1. There may not be enough refrigerant flow to adequately cool the motor in a hermetic unit, and the motor may overheat.

2. The lower refrigerant velocity may not be adequate to carry oil back to the compressor, resulting in loss of lubrication.

These problems should be kept in mind when comparing different methods of compressor capacity control. Depending on the application, one method may be superior to another in preventing these problems from occurring. Also, some capacity control methods result in reduced energy use at part loads, however, others do not.

All methods of compressor capacity control function by reducing the amount of compressed refrigerant delivered to the condenser. Less liquid is therefore available to the evaporator, and system capacity is reduced. There are four methods of controlling reciprocating compressor capacity.

1. On–off control.
2. Speed variation.
3. Cylinder unloading.
4. Hot gas by-pass.

*On–Off Control.* This refers to simply starting and stopping the compressor in response to the need. This method may be satisfactory with small compressors and where the partial load is not very light or frequent. With frequent light loads short cycling may occur—the compressor cycles on and off too often. This shortens the life of compressor, motor, and starter.

If a system is large enough to have multiple compressors, operation of less than the full number of compressors, in sequence, can be considered a variation of on–off control.

The signal to automatically control the compressor may come directly from a suction pressure controller or from a space thermostat. This applies to on–off control and the other methods of capacity control.

*Speed Variation.* This refers to changing the speed of the compressor in response to the load. Compressor displacement varies directly with speed, of course. If an engine is used to drive the turbine, this is a convenient method. With an electric motor, one can use a two speed motor, but this increases motor cost, and only gives one step of capacity reduction. This is one reason speed reduction is not often used. However, the availability of modern solid state motor speed controls is leading to increased use of compressor capacity control by speed variation. See Chapters 15 and 16 for a discussion of motor speed control.

One important advantage of speed variation is that the power requirements decrease considerably with capacity when compressor speed is reduced.

*Cylinder Unloading.* This is the most widely used method of controlling capacity of multicylinder reciprocating compressors. The operation of one or more cylinders is controlled so that the refrigerant vapor is not compressed and pumped out of the unloaded cylinders to the condenser, even though the pistons continue to go through their strokes. This reduces the quantity of liquid refrigerant going to the evaporator, reducing compressor capacity.

Unloading of a cylinder can be accomplished by holding open the suction valve or by providing, in the compressor, a passage or port from the discharge to the suction chamber, which bypasses the normal path through the discharge valves and discharge line. In either case, the suction gas is not compressed; it is circulated around in the suction chamber or bypass passages.

Two types of actuators are commonly used to hold open the suction valve or to open the bypass port. One has an electric solenoid valve that operates mechanical parts. The assembly is an integral part of the compressor head. The other type is a hydraulic system in which oil pressure is used to open the valves. There is some variation in the physical construction of unloader components among manufacturers. Two are explained in the following discussion. In all types, the unloader actuators can be operated from thermostats or pressure controllers, either electric or pneumatic.

Figure 5.12 illustrates the arrangement of a hydraulic-type unloader that functions by holding open the suction valve of a cylinder to be unloaded. When the compressor is running, oil is fed under pressure into the three-way electric solenoid valve from the compressor lubrication oil pump. The outlet ports from the solenoid valve are either to the un-

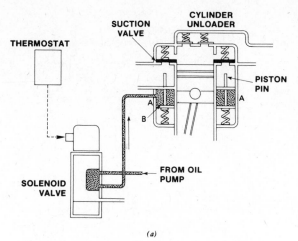

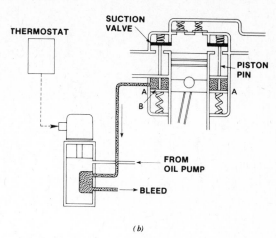

**FIGURE 5.12** Compressor unloader capacity control, hydraulic pressure operated to hold open suction valve.

(a) Loaded operation. (b) Unloaded operation, suction valve held open. (The Trane Co., La Crosse, WI)

loader cylinder A or a bleed back to the oil pump.

The solenoid valve is normally deenergized. If the thermostat calls for cooling, the solenoid is energized and the valve position moves to close the bleed port and open the unloader port, as in Figure 5.12(a). Oil pressure is now exerted in the unloader cylinder A. This forces the unloader piston and its pin B down and away from the suction valve. The valve can now close and open in the normal operating manner—the cylinder is loaded.

When the thermostat is satisfied it deenergizes the solenoid valve and its mechanism moves to open the bleed port, as in Figure 5.12(b). This relieves the oil pressure in the unloader cylinder and the unloader piston spring forces the stem up against the suction valve, holding the valve away from its seat—the cylinder is unloaded.

This arrangement provides for unloaded starting, since oil pressure is required to load, and is not available for a brief period after the compressor is started. This means that a higher starting torque, and thus a more expensive motor, is not required. Furthermore, the starting power demand is less. Since the starting power of a motor under load is much

higher than both starting power unloaded and power when running (see Chapter 15), this can reduce electric power costs. Utility companies generally impose a separate charge (a demand charge), on a customer, proportional to the peak power use.

A mechanical-type unloader directly operated by a solenoid valve is illustrated in Figure 5.13. The assembly is an integral part of the compressor head. Note the unloading ports that provide a passage from the compressor cylinder to the suction manifold. On a signal from a controller, the solenoid valve is energized. This opens the high pressure port from the compressor discharge manifold through the solenoid valve to the unloader piston cylinder, as in Figure 5.13(a). The high pressure gas forces the unloader piston down against the closure plate, closing the unloading ports, and the compressor cylinder operates in its normal loaded manner.

When the controller (e.g., thermostat, suction pressure controller) is satisfied the solenoid is deenergized and its valve moves to close the high pressure port and open the port to the suction manifold, as in Figure 5.13(b). Since only low suction pressure is now exerted in the top of the unloader cylinder, the un-

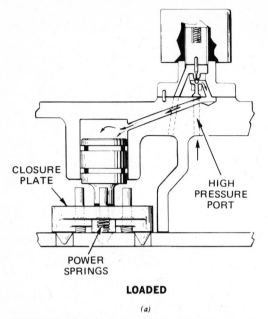
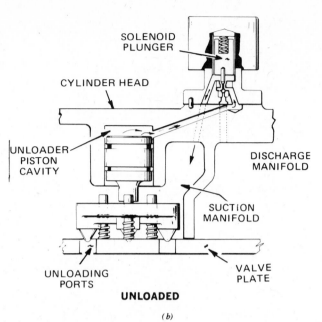

**LOADED**

(a)

**UNLOADED**

(b)

**FIGURE 5.13** Compressor unloader capacity control, electric solenoid operated to bypass discharge gas to suction. (a) Cylinder loaded. Unloading port closed. (b) Cylinder unloaded. Unloading ports opened. (Courtesy Dunham–Bush, Inc.)

loader springs force the closure plate up and opens the unloading ports. The suction gas is not compressed and the cylinder is unloaded.

With this type of unloader, the solenoids are deenergized at start up and the compressor can start unloaded long enough to reduce starting torque.

Unloaders and their controllers can be arranged to unload one or more cylinders in sequence, according to the need and the number of cylinders in the compressor. Caution must be observed not to reduce capacity to the point where refrigerant flow through the system is inadequate for hermetic motor cooling or oil return. When very low capacities are required, hot gas bypass may be used.

Unloading control results in about a 35-percent reduction in power use for a 50-percent reduction in refrigeration capacity. The reason there is not an equal reduction is that some power is required to overcome the friction and gas turbulence in the idling cylinders.

Unloading can also be achieved by shutting off the suction gas with a control valve in the suction line. Since no suction gas is recirculated in the compressor, this method is claimed to save even more energy at part loads than methods described previously.

***Hot Gas Bypass.*** This refers to bypassing the compressor hot gas discharge around the condenser. This keeps suction pressure from falling below a set value.

The hot gas bypass may be to the evaporator inlet or to the suction line. An arrangement for the first scheme is shown in Figure 5.14. A hot gas bypass valve opens in response to falling suction pressure. A modulating valve can be used so that just enough hot gas is bypassed to maintain constant suction pressure. (The solenoid valve shown is used for pumpdown, to be discussed later).

When hot gas is bypassed to the evaporator inlet, the thermostatic expansion valve feeding refrigerant to the evaporator responds to

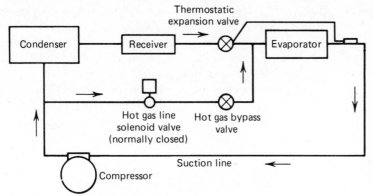

**FIGURE 5.14** Capacity control with hot gas bypass to evaporator inlet.

its control by feeding more refrigerant (Chapter 8). The refrigerant flow rate and suction temperature therefore remain relatively constant; oil return is maintained and compressor overheating does not occur. Because the compressor must always compress the full amount of gas, the power requirement remains high even at low loads.

If the evaporator is very far from the condenser, or if the system has multiple evaporators, bypassing to each evaporator inlet would be too expensive because of the extensive piping and valves required. In this situation bypassing to the suction line is used. But then the compressor can overheat. This is prevented by feeding a small amount of liquid refrigerant to the suction line when required, through a desuperheating expansion valve. (Figure 5.15)

Hot gas bypass is also used to start the compressor in an unloaded condition. This reduces the starting torque required and the

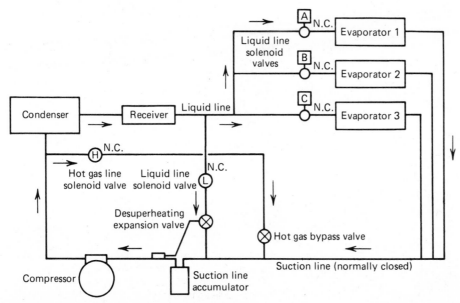

**FIGURE 5.15** Capacity control with hot gas bypass to suction line and desuperheating expansion valve.

inrush current. It is often used on ammonia compressors.

## 5.12 Safety Controls and Devices

Compressors can be furnished with a number of safety controls or devices:

*Low pressure* and *high pressure* safety cutout controls stop the compressor on low suction pressure or high discharge pressure. The two are often combined in one device.

An *oil pressure* safety control stops the compressor when the oil pump pressure differential falls below a safe value.

A refrigerant *pressure relief valve* opens on excess discharge pressure to bypass refrigerant to the suction chamber.

A *discharge temperature thermostat* stops the compressor on excess refrigerant discharge temperature.

## 5.13 Compressor Displacement and Volumetric Efficiency

*The **displacement** of a compressor is the volume swept through by the pistons. It is usually expressed per unit of time, such as CFM.*

In Chapter 4 it was shown how to determine the required volume flow rate of refrigerant gas at the compressor suction inlet that must be circulated for a given system refrigeration capacity. This is called the *theoretical displacement* ($V_t$), or compressor *capacity*. That is, the required compressor capacity is equal to the system capacity. The *actual* displacement of a compressor, however, must be greater than the theoretical value, for a number of reasons.

In order to prevent the piston from striking the valve plate, a *clearance volume* must be allowed at the end of the piston compression stroke. Manufacturing design tolerances require this and it allows for reasonable bearing wear, which would effectively lengthen the

stroke. The clearance volume is shown in Figure 5.16.

The effect of the clearance volume is that a small amount of gas in the cylinder is not discharged, but remains in the cylinder at the end of the compression stroke. This gas reexpands on the next suction stroke, occupying space in the cylinder volume. The result is that less suction gas is drawn in on each stroke than would be if there were not already some gas remaining. So the compressor volumetric displacement must be greater than the volume of gas to be drawn in.

There is also space between the bottom and top of the valve assembly where gas will remain; this increases the clearance volume.

Other factors cause a reduction in compressor capacity. Pressure drop through valves (called *wiredrawing*) reduces the amount of gas drawn in or discharged. Gas leaks around closed valves or past the piston. Refrigerant may evaporate out of oil in the cylinder, occupying space otherwise filled by new suction gas. The suction gas will be heated by the cylinder walls, increasing its specific volume,

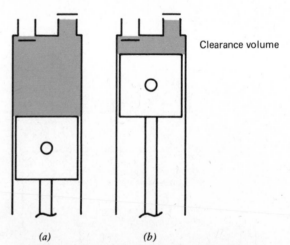

Clearance volume

**FIGURE 5.16** Clearance volume in a reciprocating compressor. (*a*) Piston at end of suction stroke. Cylinder completely filled with gas. (*b*) Piston at end of discharge stroke. Some compressed gas is not discharged, but remains in clearance volume.

so that less mass will be pumped. The effect of all these losses are combined into one term called the *volumetric efficiency* ($E_v$) It is defined as

$$E_v = \frac{V_t}{V} \times 100 \qquad (5.1)$$

where

$E_v$ = volumetric efficiency, percent
$V_t$ = theoretical compressor displacement
$V$ = actual compressor displacement

The volumetric efficiency is found by actual test of compressors. Figure 5.17 shows some typical values, at the conditions shown, for different compression ratios. From the volumetric efficiency and the theoretical displacement, the compressor displacement can be determined from Equation 5.1.

The **compression ratio** *is defined as the ratio of discharge to suction pressure at saturated conditions, expressed in absolute units, such as psia.*

That is

$$CR = \frac{P_d}{P_s} \qquad (5.2)$$

where

CR = compression ratio
$P_d$ = saturated discharge pressure, psia
$P_s$ = saturated suction pressure, psia

In Chapter 4 the theoretical displacement (required volume flow rate of refrigerant at the compressor suction) was found to be

$$V_t = v \times m$$

and the required mass flow rate of refrigerant $m$ was found to be

$$m = \frac{Q_e}{R.E.}$$

Substituting for $m$ in the first equation results

in a useful expression for calculating $V_t$

$$V_t = \frac{v \times Q_e}{R.E.} \qquad (5.3)$$

where

$V_t$ = theoretical displacement, CFM
$v$ = specific volume of refrigerant at compression suction, ft$^3$/lb
$Q_e$ = refrigeration capacity, Btu/min
R.E. = refrigeration effect, Btu/lb

An example illustrates how to determine the required compressor displacement for a given application.

***Example 5.1*** A refrigeration system using R-502 operates with an evaporating temperature of 20°F and condensing temperature of 105°F. The system capacity required is 45 tons. Assuming a compressor is used of the type whose volumetric efficiency is shown in Figure 5.17, determine the required compressor displacement. Assume ideal cycle conditions, except that suction gas is superheated to 65°F.

*Solution* The volumetric efficiency is determined first, then the compressor displacement is calculated using Equation 5.2. Using the saturation table for R-502,

$P_s$ = 67.2 psia (20°F)
$P_d$ = 246.4 psia (105°F)

$$CR = \frac{246.4}{67.2} = 3.67$$

From Figure 5.17,

$E_v$ = 71 percent

$$V_t = \frac{v \times Q_e}{R.E.}$$

$$= \frac{0.7 \text{ ft}^3/\text{lb} \times 45 \text{ tons} \times 200 \text{ Btu/min-ton}}{40.7 \text{ Btu/lb}}$$

$$= 154.8 \text{ CFM}$$

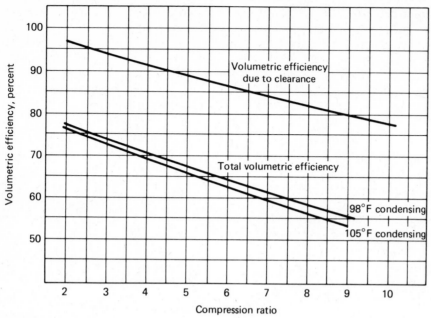

**FIGURE 5.17** Typical compressor volumetric efficiency curves, 3.8 percent clearance, 65°F gas temperature.

Using Equation 5.1, the compressor displacement is

$$V = \frac{V_t \times 100}{E_v} = \frac{154.8 \times 100}{71} = 218.0 \text{ CFM}$$

## 5.14 Displacement and Compressor Specifications

The displacement of a compressor is a function of the piston diameter (called *bore*) and stroke, number of cylinders, and speed. It is determined from the following equation

$$V = \frac{\pi \times D^2 \times L \times N \times \text{rpm}}{4 \times 1728} \quad (5.4)$$

where

$V$ = compressor displacement, CFM
$D$ = piston diameter (bore), in.
$L$ = piston stroke, in.
$N$ = number of cylinders
rpm = speed, revolutions per minute

***Example 5.2*** Determine the displacement of a four-cylinder compressor with a 3-in. bore and 2.5 in. stroke, operating at 1750 rpm.

*Solution* Using Equation 5.4,

$$V = \frac{\pi \times D^2 \times L \times N \times \text{rpm}}{4 \times 1728}$$

$$= \frac{\pi = 3^2 \times 2.5 \times 4 \times 1750}{4 \times 1728}$$

$$V = 71.5 \text{ CFM}$$

## 5.15 Compressor Ratings and Selection

Although the procedures described in the last two sections could be used to select a compressor of the proper size for a given application, it is not ordinarily done in this manner. There are so many different possible combinations of compressor dimensions, volumetric efficiencies, and other variables that these procedures would be too time consuming and perhaps not result in the most economical choices. The reason we have discussed these ideas however, is that they give us an understanding of compressor performance and how it is affected by changing conditions, a subject to be discussed further.

Manufacturers usually present the performance data (ratings) of their compressors in a form that makes selection of the proper compressor relatively simple. Table 5.1 is an example of such rating tables. These data come from actual tests of compressors.

The table lists compressor capacity in tons of refrigeration. This, of course, is the system cooling capacity. For a required capacity, the properly chosen compressor will have an adequate displacement. The bhp is the brake horsepower required to drive the compressor.

A few points need to be clarified concerning the use of these tables.

1. A separate table is required for each refrigerant, as performance changes with the refrigerant used.

2. Each table applies to only one compressor speed, since performance changes with speed. This table is for operation at 1750 rpm.

3. The ratings are listed for *saturated suction temperature* (SST) and *saturated discharge temperature* (SDT). The saturated suction temperature is the saturation temperature corresponding to the pressure at the compressor suction inlet; it is not the actual suction gas temperature. The saturated discharge temperature has the same meaning in reference to the compressor discharge.

   These temperatures would of course be different from the evaporating and condensing temperatures, taking into account pressure drop in the suction and discharge lines.

4. Although the ratings are based on saturated suction and discharge temperatures,

with R-12 and R-502 the compressor capacity is corrected for the actual suction (return) gas temperature. Correction factors for R-12 are shown in Table 5.2. Suction gas temperature is taken at the point it leaves the conditioned space. Any further increase in temperature outside the space does not contribute to the cooling capacity.

5. Subcooling increases refrigeration capacity. Corrections for the amount of subcooling are shown in Table 5.3.

***Example 5.3*** Select a compressor operating at 1750 rpm and for a 14.5-ton capacity using R-12. Saturated suction and discharge temperatures are 20°F and 115°F, respectively. Actual suction gas temperature is 65°F. Liquid subcooling is 10°F.

*Solution* Table 5.1 will be used. Corrections must be made for liquid subcooling. The required capacity is

$$14.5 \text{ tons} \times \frac{12,000 \text{ Btu/hr}}{1 \text{ ton}} = 174,000 \text{ Btu/hr}$$

At the specified SST and SDT, the capacity of a size 258DHN compressor is 170,000 Btu/hr. According to Table 5.2, no correction is necessary for a 65°F actual suction gas temperature. However, according to Table 5.3 a correction factor of 1.05 for subcooling is required.

$$\text{Capacity} = 170,000 \times 1.05$$
$$= 178,500 \text{ Btu/hr}$$

The 258DHN compressor is therefore satisfactory. The compressor requires 25.3 bhp.

## 5.16 Factors Affecting Compressor Performance

The performance of a compressor (the capacity and bhp) is influenced by the following direct factors:

1. Compressor speed.
2. Suction pressure.

**TABLE 5.1** Compressor Capacity Ratings for R-12 at 1750 rpm

| | 207DHN | | | | | | | | | | 258DHN | | | | | | | | | |
|---|---|---|---|---|---|---|---|---|---|---|---|---|---|---|---|---|---|---|---|---|
| | SDT = Saturated Discharge Temperature °F | | | | | | | | | | SDT = Saturated Discharge Temperature °F | | | | | | | | | |
| SST | 95° | | 105° | | 115° | | 125° | | 135° | | 95° | | 105° | | 115° | | 125° | | 135° | |
| | MBH | HP | MBH | HP | MBH | HP | MBH | HP | MBH | HP | MBH | HP | MBH | HP | MBH | HP | MBH | HP | MBH | HP |
| 0° | 106 | 14.1 | 97 | 14.7 | 88 | 15.9 | 79 | 16.5 | 72 | 17.7 | 118 | 16.2 | 110 | 17.4 | 100 | 18.3 | 90 | 19.5 | 82 | 20.4 |
| 5° | 118 | 15.6 | 110 | 16.5 | 100 | 17.4 | 92 | 18.3 | 82 | 19.5 | 137 | 18.3 | 124 | 19.2 | 116 | 20.1 | 106 | 21.3 | 96 | 22.5 |
| 10° | 134 | 17.1 | 124 | 18.0 | 113 | 19.2 | 107 | 20.1 | 96 | 21.3 | 151 | 19.5 | 141 | 10.7 | 131 | 21.9 | 121 | 23.1 | 110 | 24.6 |
| 15° | 149 | 18.6 | 139 | 19.5 | 129 | 20.7 | 118 | 21.3 | 108 | 23.1 | 172 | 21.0 | 160 | 21.6 | 149 | 23.7 | 137 | 24.9 | 127 | 26.4 |
| 20° | 170 | 19.5 | 158 | 21.0 | 147 | 22.2 | 134 | 23.4 | 123 | 24.6 | 196 | 22.2 | 183 | 23.7 | 170 | 25.3 | 158 | 26.7 | 144 | 28.8 |
| 25° | 191 | 21.3 | 178 | 22.2 | 164 | 23.7 | 151 | 24.9 | 139 | 26.1 | 219 | 23.4 | 206 | 25.2 | 193 | 26.7 | 180 | 28.5 | 168 | 30.3 |
| 30° | 216 | 22.5 | 203 | 23.7 | 188 | 25.2 | 172 | 26.4 | 158 | 27.9 | 247 | 24.6 | 232 | 26.4 | 219 | 27.9 | 206 | 30.0 | 191 | 31.8 |
| 35° | 242 | 23.4 | 230 | 24.9 | 211 | 26.4 | 195 | 27.9 | 178 | 28.8 | 278 | 25.5 | 261 | 27.6 | 244 | 29.4 | 232 | 31.2 | 216 | 33.3 |
| 40° | 271 | 24.3 | 254 | 25.8 | 236 | 27.6 | 219 | 29.1 | 201 | 30.9 | 309 | 26.1 | 291 | 28.5 | 275 | 30.3 | 261 | 32.7 | 242 | 34.8 |
| 45° | 302 | 24.9 | 283 | 26.7 | 263 | 28.5 | 243 | 30.3 | 224 | 32.1 | 345 | 26.7 | 324 | 29.1 | 306 | 31.5 | 290 | 33.0 | 275 | 36.3 |
| 50° | 333 | 25.5 | 312 | 27.3 | 288 | 29.4 | 271 | 31.2 | 247 | 33.3 | 384 | 27.0 | 360 | 29.7 | 340 | 31.9 | 322 | 33.9 | 299 | 37.2 |
| 55° | 366 | 25.8 | 340 | 33.6 | 319 | 30.3 | 296 | 32.1 | 273 | 33.9 | 422 | 27.3 | 367 | 30.0 | 376 | 32.7 | 353 | 35.1 | 330 | 38.1 |

| | 309DHN | | | | | | | | | | 361DHN | | | | | | | | | |
|---|---|---|---|---|---|---|---|---|---|---|---|---|---|---|---|---|---|---|---|---|
| | SDT = Saturated Discharge Temperature °F | | | | | | | | | | SDT = Saturated Discharge Temperature °F | | | | | | | | | |
| SST | 95° | | 105° | | 115° | | 125° | | 135° | | 95° | | 105° | | 115° | | 125° | | 135° | |
| | MBH | HP | MBH | HP | MBH | HP | MBH | HP | MBH | HP | MBH | HP | MBH | HP | MBH | HP | MBH | HP | MBH | HP |
| 0° | 134 | 17.1 | 124 | 18.6 | 113 | 20.1 | 103 | 21.6 | 93 | 22.8 | 155 | 20.1 | 144 | 21.6 | 134 | 23.4 | 121 | 24.6 | 110 | 26.1 |
| 5° | 151 | 19.2 | 141 | 20.7 | 129 | 21.3 | 118 | 23.7 | 108 | 25.2 | 178 | 22.2 | 165 | 24.0 | 155 | 25.8 | 147 | 27.0 | 129 | 28.5 |
| 10° | 172 | 21.0 | 160 | 22.8 | 147 | 24.3 | 137 | 26.1 | 124 | 27.6 | 199 | 24.0 | 185 | 26.1 | 175 | 27.9 | 162 | 29.7 | 149 | 31.2 |
| 15° | 193 | 23.1 | 180 | 24.9 | 168 | 26.4 | 155 | 28.2 | 141 | 29.7 | 224 | 26.1 | 211 | 27.9 | 199 | 30.3 | 182 | 31.8 | 170 | 33.6 |
| 20° | 219 | 24.9 | 203 | 26.7 | 188 | 28.5 | 175 | 30.3 | 160 | 32.1 | 254 | 27.6 | 240 | 29.7 | 224 | 32.1 | 209 | 34.5 | 193 | 35.7 |
| 25° | 247 | 26.4 | 232 | 28.5 | 213 | 30.3 | 199 | 32.1 | 180 | 34.2 | 285 | 29.1 | 271 | 31.5 | 252 | 33.9 | 234 | 35.7 | 216 | 37.8 |
| 30° | 278 | 27.9 | 263 | 30.0 | 244 | 32.1 | 224 | 33.9 | 203 | 36.3 | 322 | 30.6 | 304 | 32.7 | 283 | 35.1 | 263 | 37.5 | 242 | 39.6 |
| 35° | 314 | 29.4 | 296 | 31.5 | 275 | 33.9 | 250 | 35.7 | 230 | 38.1 | 361 | 31.5 | 343 | 33.9 | 319 | 36.9 | 296 | 39.0 | 273 | 41.1 |
| 40° | 350 | 30.6 | 330 | 33.0 | 309 | 35.1 | 283 | 37.5 | 263 | 39.9 | 405 | 32.4 | 381 | 34.8 | 355 | 37.8 | 330 | 40.5 | 306 | 42.3 |
| 45° | 391 | 31.5 | 368 | 33.9 | 343 | 36.3 | 315 | 38.7 | 291 | 41.4 | 450 | 33.0 | 425 | 35.4 | 397 | 38.4 | 369 | 40.8 | 340 | 43.5 |
| 50° | 433 | 32.1 | 405 | 34.8 | 379 | 37.5 | 350 | 39.9 | 324 | 42.3 | 502 | 33.3 | 469 | 35.7 | 438 | 38.7 | 407 | 41.1 | 376 | 43.8 |
| 55° | 474 | 32.7 | 446 | 35.1 | 417 | 38.1 | 386 | 40.8 | 357 | 43.8 | 549 | 33.3 | 515 | 35.7 | 481 | 38.7 | 448 | 41.4 | 412 | 44.1 |

**R-12 COMMERCIAL TEMPERATURE**

| | 157DCN | | | | | | | | | | 208DCN | | | | | | | | | |
|---|---|---|---|---|---|---|---|---|---|---|---|---|---|---|---|---|---|---|---|---|
| | SDT = Saturated Discharge Temperature °F | | | | | | | | | | SDT = Saturated Discharge Temperature °F | | | | | | | | | |
| SST | 95° | | 105° | | 115° | | 125° | | 135° | | 95° | | 105° | | 115° | | 125° | | 135° | |
| | MBH | HP | MBH | HP | MBH | HP | MBH | HP | MBH | HP | MBH | HP | MBH | HP | MBH | HP | MBH | HP | MBH | HP |
| −5° | 93 | 12.3 | 85 | 13.2 | 76 | 13.8 | 70 | 15.0 | 62 | 15.9 | 103 | 15.3 | 96 | 15.9 | 89 | 16.5 | 79 | 17.4 | 69 | 18.6 |
| 0° | 105 | 14.1 | 97 | 14.7 | 88 | 15.9 | 79 | 16.5 | 72 | 17.7 | 118 | 16.2 | 110 | 17.4 | 100 | 18.3 | 90 | 19.5 | 82 | 20.4 |
| 5° | 118 | 15.6 | 110 | 16.5 | 100 | 17.4 | 93 | 18.3 | 82 | 19.5 | 137 | 18.3 | 124 | 19.2 | 116 | 20.1 | 106 | 21.3 | 96 | 22.5 |
| 10° | 134 | 17.1 | 124 | 18.0 | 113 | 19.2 | 106 | 20.1 | 96 | 21.3 | 151 | 19.5 | 141 | 20.7 | 131 | 21.9 | 121 | 23.1 | 110 | 24.6 |
| 15° | 149 | 18.6 | 139 | 19.5 | 129 | 20.7 | 118 | 21.3 | 108 | 23.1 | 172 | 21.0 | 160 | 21.6 | 149 | 23.7 | 137 | 24.9 | 127 | 26.4 |
| 20° | 170 | 19.5 | 158 | 21.0 | 147 | 22.2 | 134 | 23.4 | 124 | 24.6 | 196 | 22.2 | 183 | 23.7 | 170 | 25.2 | 158 | 26.7 | 144 | 28.5 |
| 25° | 191 | 21.3 | 178 | 22.2 | 165 | 23.7 | 151 | 24.9 | 139 | 26.1 | 219 | 23.4 | 206 | 25.2 | 193 | 26.7 | 180 | 28.5 | 165 | 30.3 |
| 30° | 216 | 22.5 | 203 | 23.7 | 188 | 25.2 | 172 | 26.4 | 158 | 27.9 | 247 | 24.6 | 232 | 26.4 | 219 | 27.9 | 206 | 30.0 | 191 | 31.8 |

**TABLE 5.1** Continued

| SST | 259DCN | | | | | | | | | | 311DCN | | | | | | | | | |
|---|---|---|---|---|---|---|---|---|---|---|---|---|---|---|---|---|---|---|---|---|
| | SDT = Saturated Discharge Temperature °F | | | | | | | | | | SDT = Saturated Discharge Temperature °F | | | | | | | | | |
| | 95° | | 105° | | 115° | | 125° | | 135° | | 95° | | 105° | | 115° | | 125° | | 135° | |
| | MBH | HP | MBH | HP | MBH | HP | MBH | HP | MBH | HP | MBH | HP | MBH | HP | MBH | HP | MBH | HP | MBH | HP |
| −5° | 118 | 15.0 | 108 | 16.5 | 98 | 17.7 | 90 | 19.5 | 80 | 20.4 | 134 | 18.0 | 124 | 19.5 | 113 | 20.7 | 103 | 21.9 | 90 | 23.1 |
| 0° | 134 | 17.1 | 124 | 18.6 | 113 | 20.1 | 103 | 21.6 | 93 | 22.8 | 155 | 20.1 | 144 | 21.6 | 134 | 23.4 | 121 | 24.6 | 110 | 26.1 |
| 5° | 151 | 19.2 | 141 | 20.7 | 129 | 21.3 | 118 | 23.7 | 108 | 25.2 | 178 | 22.2 | 165 | 24.0 | 155 | 25.8 | 147 | 27.0 | 129 | 28.5 |
| 10° | 172 | 21.0 | 160 | 22.8 | 147 | 24.3 | 137 | 26.1 | 124 | 27.6 | 199 | 24.0 | 185 | 26.1 | 175 | 27.9 | 152 | 29.7 | 149 | 31.2 |
| 15° | 193 | 23.1 | 180 | 24.9 | 168 | 26.4 | 155 | 28.2 | 141 | 29.7 | 224 | 26.1 | 211 | 27.9 | 199 | 30.3 | 182 | 31.8 | 170 | 33.6 |
| 20° | 219 | 24.9 | 203 | 26.7 | 188 | 28.5 | 175 | 30.3 | 160 | 32.1 | 254 | 27.6 | 240 | 29.7 | 223 | 32.1 | 209 | 34.5 | 192 | 35.7 |
| 25° | 247 | 26.4 | 232 | 28.5 | 213 | 30.3 | 199 | 32.1 | 180 | 34.2 | 285 | 29.1 | 271 | 31.5 | 252 | 33.9 | 234 | 35.7 | 216 | 37.8 |
| 30° | 278 | 27.9 | 263 | 30.0 | 244 | 32.1 | 224 | 33.9 | 203 | 36.3 | 322 | 30.6 | 304 | 32.7 | 283 | 35.1 | 263 | 37.5 | 242 | 39.6 |

SST = SATURATED SUCTION TEMPERATURE, °F
Courtesy Dunham–Bush, Inc.

3. Discharge pressure.

4. Type of refrigerant.

5. Suction temperature.

Other indirect factors influence the system performance and therefore the compressor performance, as noted in Chapter 4.

Changing these factors can have two important effects: capacity may be affected for a given size compressor; and energy consumption may be affected.

**TABLE 5.2** Compressor Capacity Correction Factors for Return (Suction) Gas Temperatures, for R-12

| Return Gas Temperature °F | Multiplier | Return Gas Temperature °F | Multiplier |
|---|---|---|---|
| 0 | .94 | 45 | .9815 |
| 5 | .9445 | 50 | .986 |
| 10 | .9490 | 55 | .9905 |
| 15 | .9435 | 60 | .995 |
| 20 | .958 | 65* | 1.0 |
| 25 | .9625 | 70 | 1.005 |
| 30 | .967 | 75 | 1.0095 |
| 35 | .972 | 80 | 1.014 |
| 40 | .977 | | |

Courtesy Dunham–Bush, Inc.

***Compressor Speed.*** The capacity of a compressor increases with an increase in speed. This is why modern compressors are designed for and operated at high speeds, so that smaller compressors can be used. The required horsepower also increases with speed, at a slightly more rapid rate than capacity. That is, there is a slight loss in energy efficiency at high speeds.

***Suction Pressure.*** Compressor capacity decreases as suction pressure decreases. There are two reasons for this. First the specific volume of the gas increases with a decrease in pressure. The compressor displacement is

**TABLE 5.3** Compressor Capacity Correction Factors for Subcooling Liquid, for R-12

| °F Subcooling | Multiplier |
|---|---|
| 0 | 1.000 |
| 1 | 1.006 |
| 5 | 1.030 |
| 10 | 1.050 |
| 15 | 1.070 |
| 20 | 1.090 |
| 25 | 1.110 |
| 30 | 1.130 |

Courtesy Dunham–Bush, Inc.

constant; that is, it handles a fixed volume flow rate of gas. The result is that the compressor handles less mass flow rate of refrigerant with a lower specific volume, and the refrigeration capacity decreases.

The second effect that changing suction pressure has on capacity is a result of the high pressure gas remaining in the clearance volume. At lower suction pressures this gas must expand further on the intake suction stroke, shortening the time available for drawing in new gas. This was illustrated in Figure 5.17, which shows a decrease in volumetric efficiency with an increase in compression ratio.

The power required decreases with a decrease in suction pressure, because less mass of refrigerant is compressed. However, the brake horsepower per ton, which expresses efficiency of energy use, increases. This is because the compression ratio has increased; more work is required to compress a given amount of gas.

Since suction pressure changes directly with suction temperature, the effect on performance is more conveniently plotted as suction temperature versus performance. The effect of suction temperature on performance is shown in Figure 5.18 for a typical set of conditions.

***Discharge Pressure.*** Compressor capacity decreases as discharge pressure increases, due mainly to two factors. First, the refrigerating effect decreases with an increase in condensing pressure (see Figure 4.9). Second, the volumetric efficiency is reduced because of the greater expansion of the higher pressure gas remaining in the cylinder. This is illustrated in Figure 5.17, which shows a decrease in volumetric efficiency with an increase in compression ratio.

The compressor power and the power per unit of capacity both increase with an increase in discharge pressure, due to the greater compression ratio. Since discharge pressure

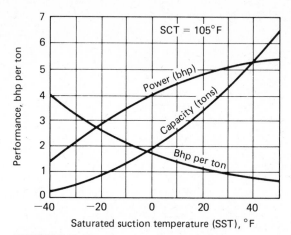

**FIGURE 5.18** The effect of changing suction temperature on performance of a small compressor (typical).

changes directly with condensing temperature, the effect on performance is more conveniently plotted as condensing temperature versus performance. The effect of condensing temperature on performance is shown in Figure 5.19 for a typical set of conditions.

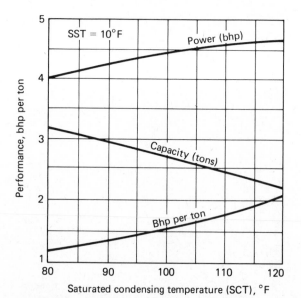

**FIGURE 5.19** The effect of changing condensing temperature on performance of a small compressor (typical).

**TABLE 5.4** Comparative Compressor Performance with Different Refrigerants

| Refrigerant | Capacity,[a] Btu/hr | Percent of R-12 Capacity |
|---|---|---|
| R-12 | 24,000 | 100 |
| R-22 | 38,400 | 160 |
| R-502 | 42,000 | 175 |

[a]Performance at 40°F SST and 105 SCT.

*Type of Refrigerant.* Refrigerants differ in physical properties that affect compressor performance; for example, they differ in their latent heat and specific volume. Comparisons are shown in Table 5.4 for a specific set of conditions. For example, referring to the table, if refrigerant R-502 were substituted for R-12 in a given compressor, the capacity would increase by 75 percent. That is, if the compressor capacity were 20 tons with R-12, it would increase to 35 tons if R-502 were used. Therefore, a smaller compressor could be used to produce the same capacity. The power would increase proportionally, however, so no improvement in energy conservation would result.

*Suction Temperature.* An increase in suction gas temperature superheating results in an increase in compressor capacity. (This effect is separate from capacity change accompanying a change in evaporating temperature) and it is accounted for in the compressor rating table corrections. An increase in suction gas temperature reduces the amount of refrigerant absorbed in the oil. This refrigerant occupies space otherwise available for new suction gas.

# ROTARY COMPRESSORS

## 5.17 Operation and Construction

Rotary compressors are positive displacement machines, the same as reciprocating compressors. The motion of the compressor, however, is rotary (circular), rather than reciprocating (linear). There are two types of construction of rotary compressors, the *rolling piston* (Figure 5.20) and the *rotating vane* (Figure 5.22).

The *rolling piston* type has a roller mounted on a shaft that is eccentric to the cylinder housing. A stationary blade or vane mounted in the cylinder housing is held against the roller by a spring. This effectively seals the suction from the discharge side of the compressor. Because the roller is not in the center of the housing, when it rotates the volume on the suction and discharge sides change (Figure 5.21). This compresses the gas, in a manner similar to the way a reciprocating compressor does. In Figure 5.21(*a*) the cylinder is full of gas at the suction pressure. As the rotor turns (clockwise) the volume decreases in the discharge side, Figure 5.21(*b*), and the gas pressure increases. (At the same time the volume increases on the suction side, drawing in new gas). When the compressed gas pressure rises above the discharge line

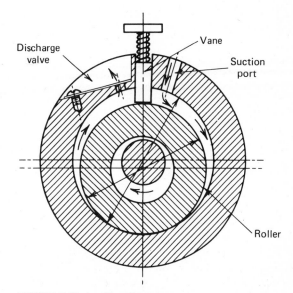

**FIGURE 5.20** A rolling piston type rotary compressor (sectional sketch). (Reprinted with permission from the 1979 Equipment ASHRAE Handbook and Product Director)

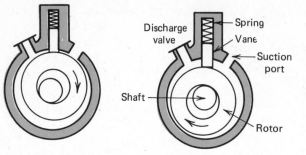

FIGURE 5.21 The operation of a rotary compressor. (a) Full volume of cylinder filled with gas on discharge side. (b) Gas compressing on discharge side. New suction gas being drawn in. (c) Pressure forces discharge valve open. Suction side filled with new gas.

pressure, the discharge valve opens, Figure 5.21(c).

The *rotating vane* type (Figure 5.22) has vanes in the rotor. When the rotor turns, the vanes are held against the cylinder by centrifugal force, separating the high side pressure from the low side pressure. The eccentric rotor functions in the same way as the rolling piston type.

Suction valves are not required with rotary compressors because flow is continuous and the vane separates high- and low-side pressures. However a check valve is used in the suction inlet line to prevent refrigerant migration to the evaporator during shutdown. A flapper (reed) discharge valve opens when compressor discharge pressure is reached.

Small hermetic rotary compressors are available up to about 5 hp (Figure 5.23). The compressed gas discharges into the compressor shell where it is used to cool the motor. Despite its relatively high temperature the discharge gas is below the motor operating temperature, and it removes sufficient heat from the motor because its density is much greater than that of the suction gas.

Lubricating oil is stored in a sump at the bottom of the compressor shell. Since the oil is at the pressure of the discharge gas in the shell, it flows naturally to wearing surfaces. A suction line accumulator is provided that collects any liquid refrigerant and oil.

Aside from its high volumetric efficiency, the small hermetic rotary compressor has other advantages over the hermetic reciprocating compressors. It is about one half the weight and the physical size of a comparable reciprocating compressor, and it has three

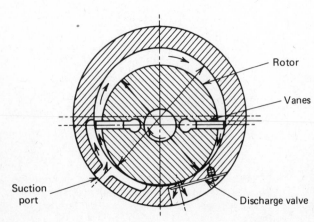

FIGURE 5.22 A rotating vane type rotary compressor (sectional sketch). (Reprinted with permission from the 1979 Equipment ASHRAE Handbook and Product Director)

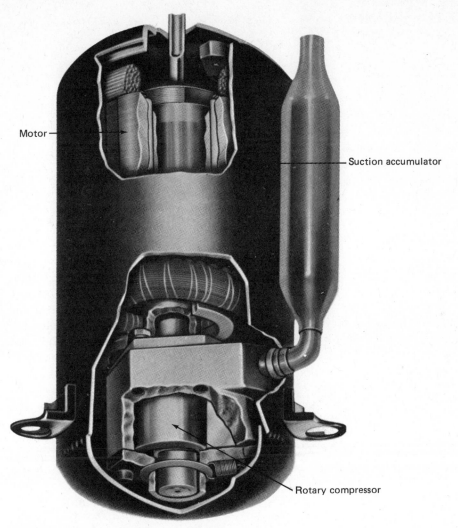

Motor

Suction accumulator

Rotary compressor

**FIGURE 5.23** Cut-away view of hermetic rotary compressor. (Fedders Compressor Company)

moving parts rather than eleven or so. The hermetic rotary is popular in household refrigerators and small package air conditioners.

Large rotary compressors are frequently used as the low pressure stage (booster stage) compressor in two-stage compression systems for very low temperatures (see Chapter 12), where the discharge from the lower stage feeds the suction of the high-stage compressor. The rotary compressor is especially suitable for the low pressure stage because of its small clearance volume. The reexpansion of trapped gas, which has a serious effect on efficiency at very low pressures, is less than with a reciprocating compressor. Capacity control of large rotary compressors can be achieved with hot gas bypass.

# HELICAL ROTARY (SCREW) COMPRESSORS

## 5.18 Operation and Construction

This compressor is also a positive displacement type, increasing pressure by decreasing the volume of the gas. The compressor has two meshing *rotors* shaped somewhat like common screws (Figure 5.24). The male rotor has protruding lobes, and is driven by the motor. The female rotor has grooves that the male lobes mesh with and drive. The rotors are housed in a casing.

Refrigerant gas is drawn axially into the rotors from the suction opening at one end of the housing. As the rotors turn, gas is trapped in the cavity between the two rotors. The male lobe gradually reduces the space between it and the bottom of the female cavity, increasing the gas pressure. At the same time the gas is carried toward the discharge end and out through the discharge opening.

Volumetric efficiency is high because clearance between the rotors and housing is very small, and there is no clearance requirement for suction and discharge valves. There is virtually no wear of the rotors, since they do not touch but contact only an oil film.

Figure 5.25 is a cut-away sketch of the slide valve operation. The slide valve position is

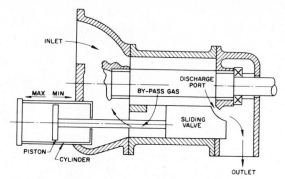

**FIGURE 5.25** Operation of screw compressor slide valve for capacity control. (Reprinted with permission from the 1979 Equipment ASHRAE Handbook and Product Directory)

controlled by a pilot piston. The piston is hydraulically actuated from a thermostat or other automatic control (not shown). At full load the slide valve is at its extreme left position and all suction gas is compressed and delivered to the wide open discharge port. On a call for capacity reduction, the piston moves the slide valve to the right, opening a bypass port. Some suction gas now bypasses the rotors and recirculates back to the inlet, reducing the compressor capacity.

Since practically no work is done on the bypassed suction gas, and the capacity control is modulating with the slide valve position, part load power reduction is linear with re-

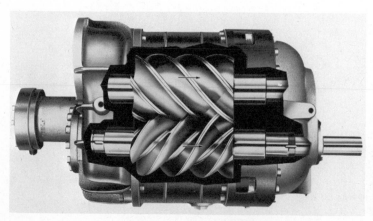

**FIGURE 5.24** Cut-away view of helical rotary (screw) compressor, showing male and female rotors and gas motion. (Courtesy Dunham-Bush, Inc.)

spect to capacity reduction. That is, for example, at 50 percent load the power required is 50 percent. This compares well with centrifugal compressor part load efficiency and is superior to reciprocating compressor performance with unloaders. Capacity modulation to about 10 percent is possible with the slide valve.

Oil is injected into the cylinder of screw compressors to lubricate the rotors and to create a tight film seal between the high and low side pressure. Use of oil injection results in a number of benefits, among which are:

1. Alleviation of the effect of a possible liquid slug because of dilution with the oil.

2. Some cooling effect, reducing hot gas discharge temperatures and the work of compression.

3. Helping maintain high compression ratios due to the oil film (and close tolerance between rotors).

4. Use of the oil mist for cooling the motor in hermetic screw compressors.

5. The injection oil provides a sound absorbing effect.

The lubrication system requires an oil pump, oil separator, oil filter, and oil cooler, with associated piping and valves. The oil separator is needed to remove the oil from the hot gas. Reliable and efficient oil filters are required since the quality of oil injected into the rotors is critical. The oil cooler removes the heat gained in the compression process.

Both accessible hermetic and open-type screw compressors are available. Capacities range up to about 1500 hp. Their reliability of service, small number of moving parts, minimum maintenance, and low vibration make them worthwhile competitors in their size range. They are offered in package water-chiller arrangements for air conditioning use, the same as reciprocating and centrifugal machines.

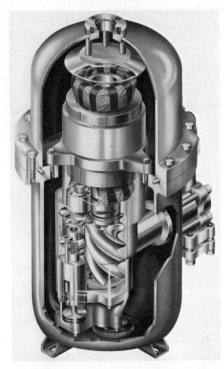

**FIGURE 5.26** Small (50 to 120 tons) hermetic screw compressor. (Courtesy Dunham–Bush, Inc.)

Significant improvement on performance can be gained by using an *economizer* arrangement, where some refrigerant flash gas at an intermediate pressure is taken into the compressor through a secondary suction and discharge. This can increase refrigeration capacity from 10 to 40 percent, depending on temperature conditions. Since this arrangement is similar to that used in centrifugal compressor systems, it will be explained in Chapter 10.

Small hermetic screw compressors (Figure 5.26) are now available that have many of the desirable features of reciprocating hermetics. There is no oil pump or external oil separator, and the motor is refrigerant cooled. Their capacity ranges from about 50 to 120 tons for water chilling.

## 5.19 Energy Conservation and Compressors

Some of the energy conserving factors discussed in this chapter can be summarized as follows.

1. Compressor capacity increases with higher suction pressure and lower discharge pressure.

2. Compressor power requirement decreases with decreasing compression ratio.

3. Compressor power increases with greater clearance volume.

4. Speed control results in excellent reduction of power with capacity decrease.

5. Cylinder unloading provides good power reduction with capacity decrease.

6. Screw compressors have excellent full load (and part load with slide valve control) power requirements.

7. An economizer arrangement (Chapter 10) with screw compressors reduces energy requirements considerably.

Using multiple compressors in a system can also save energy, since at partial loads some of the compressors can be operated at full load (generally the most efficient operating condition), while others are shut down. Of course this also results in the extra benefit of stand-by capacity in case of failure of a compressor.

## REVIEW QUESTIONS

1. List the main function and some secondary functions of a refrigeration compressor.

2. How does a positive displacement compressor increase the gas pressure?

3. What types of positive displacement compressors are there?

4. Describe the operation of and sketch a simple reciprocating compressor.

5. Explain what is meant by open and hermetic compressors. What is a semihermetic compressor?

6. Discuss some advantages of hermetic compressors.

7. Why are compressor seals required?

8. What are the two basic ways of compressor sealing? Describe a rotary seal.

9. Name and describe the two types of compressor suction and discharge valves.

10. What are the two ways of lubricating compressors?

11. Explain the function of the oil port and check valve in a compressor suction.

12. Under what conditions is there a problem with refrigerant entering a reciprocating compressor? Why?

13. What effect may mixing of oil and refrigerant have on the compressor?

14. Explain liquid floodback and liquid slugging, and their possible causes.

15. Describe some means of preventing floodbacks, and of preventing slugging.

16. Explain what refrigeration migration is, and its cause.

17. What are the possible effects of refrigerant migration?

18. Describe some means of preventing refrigerant migration.

19. Why is compressor capacity control desirable?

20. What undesirable effects may occur at part loads?

21. Name and describe the methods of compressor capacity control. List advantages and disadvantages of each.

22. Explain the use of a desuperheating expansion valve.

23. Explain what is meant by compressor displacement, compressor capacity, and volumetric efficiency.

24. What is clearance volume? What is its effect?

25. List the factors that affect compressor performance and explain how they affect it.

26. What are the two types of rotary compressors? What are the desirable features of rotary compressors?

27. What are the desirable features of screw compressors?

28. List some ways of reducing energy used to drive refrigeration compressors.

## PROBLEMS

5.1 A refrigeration system using R-717 operates at evaporating and condensing temperatures of 20°F and 110°F, respectively. What is the compression ratio of the compressor?

5.2 A compressor has a displacement of 85.7 CFM. It has a capacity of 216,000 Btu/hr when handling R-12 at saturated suction and discharge conditions of 40°F and 110°F, respectively. What is the compressor volumetric efficiency?

5.3 A refrigeration system using R-12 operates at an evaporating temperature of 10°F and a condensing temperature of 100°F. The required system capacity is 18 tons. Assuming a compressor of the type whose volumetric efficiency is shown in Figure 5.17 is used, determine the required compressor displacement. Assume ideal conditions, except that suction gas is superheated to 65°F.

5.4 Determine the displacement of a two-cylinder compressor with a 2.5-in. bore and 2.5-in. stroke, operating at 3500 rpm.

5.5 Select a compressor of the type whose ratings are shown in Table 5.1 for a capacity of 220,000 Btu/hr using R-12. Saturated suction and discharge temperatures are 25°F and 105°F, respectively. Actual suction gas temperature is 50°F. Liquid subcooling is 10°F.

5.6 Select a compressor of the type whose ratings are shown in Table 5.1 for a capacity of 21.0 tons of refrigeration, using R-12. Saturated suction and discharge temperatures are 35°F and 125°F, respectively. Actual suction gas temperature is 65°F. Liquid subcooling is 20°F.

5.7 A refrigeration system using R-22 operates at an evaporating temperature of 24°F and a condensing temperature of 104°F. The required system capacity is 45 tons. The compressor has a volumetric efficiency at 78 percent. Determine the required compressor displacement. Assume ideal conditions, except that suction gas is heated to 60°F.

5.8 An R-717 compressor with a displacement of 173 CFM operates in a system at evaporating and condensing temperatures of 20°F and 110°F. The volumetric efficiency of the compressor is 72 percent. Suction gas enters the compressor with 30°F superheat. Determine the refrigeration capacity in tons and kW and the compressor power in kW.

# Chapter 6

## HEAT TRANSFER IN REFRIGERATION. EVAPORATORS

The evaporator is the component of the refrigeration system where the end goal is accomplished: heat removal from the medium to be cooled. In this chapter we discuss types of evaporators, their construction, and factors affecting their performance. There is an overwhelming variety of shapes and arrangements of evaporators for special purposes, a subject that we will discuss only to a limited extent. The emphasis is on basic features and some of the more important design and operating questions. We also present some elements of the subject of heat transfer, essential for understanding both evaporators and condenser performance, and for making proper decisions concerning energy utilization.

## OBJECTIVES

A study of this chapter will enable you to:
1. Identify the three methods of heat transfer.
2. Explain the terms *resistance, conductance,* and *fouling factor.*
3. Explain the significance of the METD and the different flow arrangements.
4. Describe the basic difference between dry expansion and flooded evaporators.
5. Identify the major construction features and uses of different types of evaporators.
6. Select a liquid chiller.
7. Suggest some energy conservation measures in the selection and operation of evaporators.

### 6.1 Heat Transfer in Refrigeration

The transfer of heat is an essential process in refrigeration. The purpose of the evaporator is to transfer heat from the medium to be cooled. The purpose of the condenser is to transfer (reject) heat gained in the system to some convenient cooling medium. We will review a few basic principles of the subject of heat transfer. You will need to know this to determine equipment performance, to calculate refrigeration loads, to understand how to efficiently operate systems, and to minimize energy consumption.

### 6.2 Forms of Heat Transfer

Heat has been previously defined as that form of energy that flows or transfers from one body to another as a result of a temperature difference between them. There are three separate ways that heat transfer can occur: conduction, convention, and radiation.

> *Conduction is the form of heat transfer through a body that occurs without any movement of the body; it is a result of molecular or electron action.*

Conduction is most familiar in heat transfer through solids—for example, when the metal body of a pot is heated on a stove the heat flows through the handle and then to your hand. Conduction heat transfer can also occur through liquids and gases; however an additional form of heat transfer can occur in fluids, called convection.

*Convection is the form of heat transfer that results from gross movement of liquids or gases.*

A familiar example of convection is the air in a room heated by a unit such as a hot water convector. Heat is transferred to the air adjacent to the metal surface, increasing its temperature. This air then moves vertically upward because it is now less dense (lighter) than the surrounding cooler air. So air continually moves throughout the space. This form of convection is called *natural convection* because the fluid moves by natural gravity forces created by density differences. The less dense part of the fluid rises and the more dense (heavier) fluid drops. The rate of fluid motion created by natural convection effects is generally quite low, and therefore the resulting rate of heat transfer is small. The rate of fluid motion and therefore the rate of heat transfer can be increased by using a fan for gases or a pump for liquids. This is called *forced convection.*

*Thermal **radiation** is the form of heat transfer that occurs between two separated bodies as a result of a means called electromagnetic radiation, sometimes called wave motion.*

As with all forms of heat transfer, one body must be at a higher temperature than the other. Heat transfers between the two bodies even if there is a vacuum (an absence of all matter) between them. When there is a gas between the bodies heat still transfers but usually at a lesser rate. However the presence of an opaque solid object between the bodies will block radiation. Familiar examples of radiation are the heat our body receives when standing in front of a fire, and the heat received from the sun.

## 6.3 Thermal Resistance

The rate of heat transfer by conduction through a body is determined by the following equation.

$$Q = \frac{1}{R} \times A \times TD \tag{6.1}$$

where

$Q$ = rate of heat transfer, Btu/hr

$R$ = thermal resistance of the body, hr-ft²-°F/Btu

$A$ = surface area of body across which heat flows, ft²

$TD$ = temperature difference through body, °F

The meaning of this equation is of considerable significance in understanding the factors that affect the performance of a refrigeration system, especially with respect to energy use.

The *thermal resistance R* is a property of a substance that affects how much heat is transferred through it. Materials with a high resistance will transfer heat at a low rate—they are good insulators. Materials with a low $R$ value are good conductors of heat. We might include in the walls of a refrigerator a material such as urethane, which has a high thermal resistance, because this will reduce heat gains, thus reducing the energy use required in the refrigeration system. On the other hand, we might use copper tubing, which has a very low resistance, in an evaporator. This will result in good heat transfer from the medium to be cooled. Thermal resistances per inch of thickness for some substances are shown in Table 6.1.

Equation 6.1 shows that high $R$ values mean a low heat transfer rate, since $R$ appears in the denominator. It also shows that the heat transfer is directly proportional to the surface area $A$. If we wish to increase the refrigeration capacity of an evaporator, more tubes should be used. The heat transfer is also directly proportional to the temperature difference—the more the temperature difference is, the

**TABLE 6.1** Thermal Resistance (R), hr-ft²-°F/Btu, Per Inch of Thickness

| Substance | R, Per Inch |
|---|---|
| Aluminum | 0.0007 |
| Concrete (sand and gravel) | 0.08 |
| Copper | 0.004 |
| Glass fiber blanket | 3.1 |
| Steel | 0.003 |
| Urethane, expanded | 5.9 |
| Wood (oak) | 0.90 |

greater will be the heat transfer rate. We will have more to say about this shortly.

## 6.4 Conductance and Conductivity

The *conductance C* of a body is defined as the inverse of the resistance

$$C = \frac{1}{R} \qquad (6.2)$$

with $C$ in units of Btu/hr-ft²-°F. The thermal conductance of a material can be considered to be its ability to conduct heat, having the opposite meaning as thermal resistance.

It is convenient to define still another related term. The *thermal conductivity k* of a body is its conductance per unit of thickness, usually expressed in the units Btu/hr-ft²-°F per inch. Tables often report the conductivity of materials; the user can find the conductance as follows:

$$C = \frac{k}{L} \qquad (6.3)$$

where

$C$ = conductance, Btu/hr-ft²-°F

$k$ = conductivity, Btu/hr-ft²-°F per in. of thickness

$L$ = thickness of material, in.

***Example 6.1*** Four inches of insulation with a thermal conductivity $k = 0.26$ Btu/hr-ft²-°F

per in. is applied to the walls of a walk-in refrigerator. What is the conductance and resistance of the insulation?

*Solution*  From Equations 6.2 and 6.3,

$$C = \frac{k}{L} = \frac{0.25 \text{ Btu/hr-ft}^2\text{-°F per in.}}{4 \text{ in.}}$$

$$= 0.06 \text{ Btu/hr-ft}^2\text{-°F}$$

$$R = \frac{1}{C} = \frac{1}{0.06} = 16.7 \text{ hr-ft}^2\text{-°F/Btu}$$

## 6.5 Conductance of a Liquid or Gas Film

When heat transfer takes place between the surface of a solid and a fluid (liquid or gas), a thin film of the fluid adjacent to the surface has a thermal resistance and conductance, just as a solid does. The conductance of fluids is often called the *film coefficient;* sometimes the symbols $h$ or $f$ are used instead of $C$. The heat transfer that takes place between a solid and a surrounding fluid is usually a combination of conduction and convection occurring together, and sometimes it includes even radiation. When the conductance of a film is measured in actual test, these effects are lumped together and combined into one conductance or resistance value, to simplify calculations.

With a solid, the only factor that affects the thermal resistance is the composition of the material itself, except that there are a few changes that could occur in the field that might affect the resistance. For example, if glass fiber insulation is compressed, its resistance decreases.

The resistance of a fluid film, however, depends on many things besides its composition. Impurities in the fluid usually increase the resistance. The condition of the surface also affects it. Coating on the heat transfer surface, such as scale or oil, usually increase the resistance. This is why it is vital both to keep tube surfaces clean and to provide good oil return through systems.

A major factor affecting the fluid film resistance is the velocity of the fluid across the surface. The thermal resistance decreases as velocity increases. This is why forced convection improves heat transfer over that of natural convection. Another fact of importance concerning fluid films is that the thermal resistance of liquids is much less than that of gases. This is why a flooded evaporator is superior to a dry expansion type.

All of these points concerning fluid film resistance are related to the question of energy utilization. Decreasing thermal resistance increases the heat transfer in the evaporator (and other heat exchangers) resulting in more efficient energy use.

## 6.6 Overall Resistance and Conductance

The heat transfer that occurs in refrigeration applications is generally from one fluid to another, through fluid films and solids, such as the wall of a metal tube or the wall of a building. The *overall* or total thermal resistance in such cases is simply the sum of the individual resistances in series, as expressed by the following equation:

$$R_O = R_1 + R_2 + R_3 + \dots \qquad (6.4)$$

where

$$R_O = \text{overall thermal resistance}$$

$$R_1, R_2, R_3, \dots = \text{individual thermal resistances}$$

For example, if there were a building wall composed of two materials in series (one behind the other) there would be four individual resistances, including the air films on both sides, as shown in Figure 6.1.

The **overall thermal conductance** U, *also*

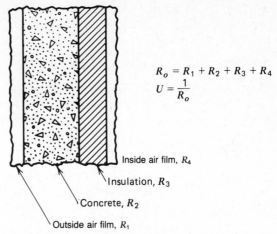

$$R_o = R_1 + R_2 + R_3 + R_4$$
$$U = \frac{1}{R_o}$$

Inside air film, $R_4$

Insulation, $R_3$

Concrete, $R_2$

Outside air film, $R_1$

**FIGURE 6.1** Overall thermal resistance of a number of resistances in series (a building wall).

called the **overall heat transfer** *coefficient, is defined as*

$$U = \frac{1}{R_O}$$

where

$U$ = overall thermal conductance, Btu/hr-ft$^2$-°F

$R_O$ = overall thermal resistance, hr-ft$^2$-°F/Btu

*The Fouling Factor* The condition of the water in a heat exchanger has a considerable effect on the thermal resistance of the water film. Mineral deposits from the water may coat the tube surface, increasing the thermal resistance. Other forms of contamination may occur. The standard procedure for accounting for these effects is to allow an appropriate thermal resistance, called the *fouling factor* or *fouling resistance.* For clean fresh water used in a closed circuit, as in a water chiller, the fouling factor is $R = 0.0005$ Btu/hr-ft$^2$-°F. For fresh water used in a condenser with a cooling tower, with good water treatment, a typical fouling factor is $R = 0.001$. In each application the fouling factor to be applied should be determined before selecting the heat exchangers.

## 6.7 The Heat Transfer Equation

The following equation is used to calculate heat transfer in liquid chiller evaporators and water cooled condensers.

$$Q = U \times A \times \text{METD} \qquad (6.5)$$

where

$Q$ = heat transfer rate, Btu/hr

$U$ = overall heat transfer coefficient, Btu/hr-ft$^2$-°F

$A$ = heat transfer surface of tubing, ft$^2$

METD = mean effective temperature difference between fluids, °F

The meaning of terms in this equation requires explanation. The overall heat transfer coefficient $U_0$, is found as follows, if the refrigerant is outside the tubes (a flooded chiller):

$$U = \frac{1}{R_O} = \frac{1}{R_r \times r + R_w + R_f + R_l} \qquad (6.6)$$

where

$R_O$ = overall thermal resistance, hr-ft$^2$-°F/Btu

$R_r$ = refrigerant film resistance

$R_w$ = tube wall resistance

$R_f$ = fouling factor resistance on liquid side

$R_l$ = liquid film resistance

$r$ = ratio of outside to inside tube surface area

Unlike the case of a flat wall, the area of tubing differs on the inside and outside surface. It is standard practice to use the inside tube surface with Equation 6.6. For this reason the resistance of the outside film is corrected by multiplying it by the ratio of the outside to the inside surface, $r$. For a flat wall, of course, $r = 1$.

## 6.8 The Mean Effective Temperature Difference

The temperature of one fluid is constantly changing in an evaporator or condenser, and therefore the temperature difference between the two fluids is not constant, as seen in Figure 6.2. A mean temperature difference must be determined for use in Equation 6.5. At first thought it might seem that the arithmetic average temperature difference should be used. This is not so, however, because the fluid temperature changes more rapidly at first, and then more gradually, as shown. It has been found that the *mean effective temperature difference* (METD) for heat transfer, also called the *log mean temperature difference* (LMTD), is

$$\text{METD} = \frac{\text{TD}_A - \text{TD}_B}{\ln \dfrac{\text{TD}_A}{\text{TD}_B}} \qquad (6.7)$$

where

METD = mean effective temperature difference for heat transfer, °F

$\text{TD}_A$ = temperature difference at one end of heat exchanger, °F

$\text{TD}_B$ = temperature difference at other end of heat exchanger, °F

***Example 6.2*** A water chiller cools water from 65 to 50°F with refrigerant at an evaporating temperature of 40°F. Find the METD and compare it to the arithmetic average TD.

*Solution* A sketch of the arrangement is shown in Figure 6.3. Equation 6.7 is used.

$$\text{TD}_A = 64 - 40 = 24°F$$

$$\text{TD}_B = 50 - 40 = 10°F$$

$$\text{METD} = \frac{\text{TD}_A - \text{TD}_B}{\ln \dfrac{\text{TD}_A}{\text{TD}_B}}$$

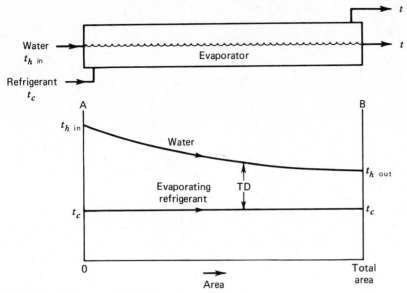

**FIGURE 6.2** Temperature profile in a refrigerant evaporator.

$$= \frac{24 - 10}{\ln \dfrac{24}{10}} = \frac{14}{0.875} = 16°F$$

The arithmetic average temperature is

$$\text{av. TD} = \frac{24 + 10}{2} = 17°F$$

Note that the METD is less than the average TD. If the average TD were used, the calculated heat transfer would be greater than the actual amount.

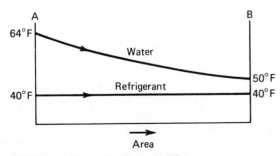

**FIGURE 6.3** Sketch for Example 6.2.

For convenience, Table 6.2 lists METD values for a number of combinations of temperature differences.

## 6.9 Counterflow and Parallel Flow

When the two fluids flow in the same direction in a heat exchanger the arrangement is called *parallel flow*. When the two fluids flow in opposite directions the arrangement is called *counterflow*. The two arrangements are shown in Figure 6.4 for a shell-and-tube heat exchanger with both fluids changing temperature. For parallel flow, the fluids enter and leave at the same end of the heat exchanger; for counterflow, the fluids enter and leave at opposite ends.

In heat exchangers where both fluids are changing temperature, such as chilled water coils for cooling air, and in cooling towers, the choice of counterflow or parallel flow arrangement has an important bearing on both the size of the equipment required and on energy consumption.

**TABLE 6.2** Mean Effective Temperature Difference (METD)

|   | Smaller Temperature Difference, °F | | | | | | | | | | | | | | | | | |
|---|---|---|---|---|---|---|---|---|---|---|---|---|---|---|---|---|---|---|
|   | 3 | 4 | 5 | 6 | 7 | 8 | 9 | 10 | 11 | 12 | 13 | 14 | 15 | 16 | 17 | 18 | 19 | 20 |
| 8 | 5.10 | 5.77 | 6.38 | 7.01 | 7.63 | 8.00 | 8.49 | 8.96 | 9.42 | 9.86 | 10.30 | 10.72 | 11.13 | 11.54 | 11.94 | 12.33 | 12.72 | 13.10 |
| 9 | 540 | 6.17 | 6.81 | 7.40 | 7.86 | 8.49 | 9.00 | 9.58 | 10.06 | 10.52 | 10.97 | 11.24 | 11.70 | 12.14 | 12.57 | 12.99 | 13.39 | 13.92 |
| 10 | 5.82 | 6.55 | 7.21 | 7.85 | 8.39 | 8.96 | 9.58 | 10.00 | 10.49 | 10.97 | 11.43 | 11.89 | 12.33 | 12.77 | 13.19 | 13.61 | 14.02 | 14.43 |
| 11 | 6.17 | 6.92 | 7.61 | 8.27 | 8.87 | 9.42 | 10.06 | 10.49 | 11.00 | 11.49 | 11.96 | 12.42 | 12.94 | 13.33 | 13.79 | 14.22 | 14.65 | 15.06 |
| 12 | 6.49 | 7.28 | 8.00 | 8.70 | 9.32 | 9.86 | 10.52 | 10.97 | 11.49 | 12.00 | 12.50 | 12.99 | 13.45 | 13.90 | 14.45 | 14.80 | 15.23 | 15.66 |
| 13 | 6.82 | 7.64 | 8.37 | 9.08 | 9.67 | 10.30 | 10.97 | 11.43 | 11.96 | 12.50 | 13.00 | 13.48 | 13.91 | 14.44 | 14.90 | 15.35 | 15.80 | 16.26 |
| 14 | 7.15 | 8.00 | 8.74 | 9.47 | 10.10 | 10.72 | 11.24 | 11.89 | 12.42 | 12.99 | 13.48 | 14.00 | 14.58 | 14.93 | 15.46 | 15.90 | 16.38 | 16.81 |
| 15 | 7.46 | 8.32 | 9.10 | 9.98 | 10.52 | 11.13 | 11.70 | 12.33 | 12.94 | 13.45 | 13.91 | 14.58 | 15.00 | 15.87 | 16.00 | 16.46 | 16.90 | 17.39 |
| 16 | 7.77 | 8.66 | 9.46 | 10.22 | 10.86 | 11.54 | 12.14 | 12.77 | 13.33 | 13.90 | 14.44 | 14.93 | 15.87 | 16.00 | 16.29 | 16.98 | 17.31 | 17.93 |
| 17 | 8.08 | 8.98 | 9.81 | 10.61 | 11.26 | 11.94 | 12.57 | 13.19 | 13.79 | 14.45 | 14.90 | 15.46 | 16.00 | 16.29 | 17.00 | 17.51 | 18.07 | 18.51 |
| 18 | 8.37 | 9.31 | 10.15 | 10.96 | 11.65 | 12.33 | 12.99 | 13.61 | 14.22 | 14.80 | 15.35 | 15.90 | 16.46 | 16.98 | 17.51 | 18.00 | 18.35 | 18.99 |
| 19 | 8.67 | 9.63 | 10.49 | 11.30 | 12.04 | 12.72 | 13.39 | 14.02 | 14.65 | 15.23 | 15.80 | 16.38 | 16.90 | 17.31 | 18.07 | 18.35 | 19.00 | 19.23 |
| 20 | 8.95 | 9.94 | 10.82 | 11.67 | 12.37 | 13.10 | 13.92 | 14.43 | 15.06 | 15.66 | 16.26 | 16.81 | 17.39 | 17.93 | 18.51 | 18.99 | 19.23 | 20.00 |
| 21 | 9.25 | 10.25 | 11.15 | 12.00 | 12.74 | 13.47 | 14.19 | 14.83 | 15.47 | 16.08 | 16.69 | 17.26 | 17.83 | 18.35 | 18.96 | 19.43 | 20.24 | 20.49 |
| 22 | 9.54 | 10.56 | 11.47 | 12.35 | 13.11 | 13.84 | 14.57 | 15.22 | 15.87 | 16.50 | 17.11 | 17.71 | 18.28 | 18.84 | 19.40 | 19.96 | 20.45 | 20.99 |
| 23 | 9.82 | 10.86 | 11.79 | 12.68 | 13.44 | 14.20 | 14.89 | 15.61 | 16.27 | 16.92 | 17.53 | 18.12 | 18.72 | 19.27 | 19.90 | 20.38 | 20.90 | 21.46 |
| 24 | 10.01 | 11.16 | 12.11 | 13.02 | 13.79 | 14.56 | 15.27 | 15.99 | 16.64 | 17.31 | 17.95 | 18.55 | 19.15 | 19.73 | 20.33 | 20.86 | 21.48 | 21.94 |
| 25 | 10.38 | 11.46 | 12.43 | 13.34 | 14.14 | 14.92 | 15.65 | 16.37 | 17.05 | 17.74 | 18.35 | 18.95 | 19.58 | 20.14 | 20.76 | 21.30 | 21.86 | 22.41 |
| 26 | 10.65 | 11.75 | 12.74 | 13.67 | 14.46 | 15.26 | 16.02 | 16.75 | 17.43 | 18.11 | 18.76 | 19.38 | 20.01 | 20.60 | 21.20 | 21.77 | 22.34 | 22.87 |
| 27 | 10.92 | 12.05 | 13.05 | 13.99 | 14.81 | 15.62 | 16.38 | 17.11 | 17.82 | 18.50 | 19.20 | 19.79 | 20.42 | 21.01 | 21.63 | 22.19 | 22.76 | 23.33 |
| 28 | 11.19 | 12.33 | 13.35 | 14.31 | 15.15 | 15.96 | 16.75 | 17.48 | 18.20 | 18.89 | 19.55 | 20.20 | 20.83 | 21.44 | 22.04 | 22.62 | 23.20 | 23.77 |
| 29 | 11.46 | 12.62 | 13.65 | 14.63 | 15.49 | 16.31 | 17.10 | 17.85 | 18.57 | 19.27 | 19.94 | 20.60 | 21.24 | 21.85 | 22.49 | 23.07 | 23.66 | 24.22 |
| 30 | 11.73 | 12.90 | 13.95 | 14.94 | 15.79 | 16.64 | 17.46 | 18.20 | 18.94 | 19.64 | 20.33 | 20.99 | 21.64 | 22.27 | 22.90 | 23.48 | 20.08 | 24.66 |
| 31 | 11.98 | 13.19 | 14.25 | 15.25 | 16.12 | 16.98 | 17.81 | 18.56 | 19.31 | 20.02 | 20.71 | 21.27 | 22.09 | 22.67 | 23.31 | 23.92 | 24.50 | 25.10 |
| 32 | 12.26 | 13.47 | 14.55 | 15.57 | 16.45 | 17.31 | 18.11 | 18.91 | 19.66 | 20.39 | 21.09 | 21.77 | 22.45 | 23.08 | 23.72 | 24.33 | 24.94 | 25.53 |
| 33 | 12.51 | 13.74 | 14.84 | 15.87 | 16.75 | 17.64 | 18.46 | 19.26 | 20.03 | 20.76 | 21.47 | 22.18 | 22.83 | 23.47 | 24.13 | 24.75 | 25.35 | 25.96 |
| 34 | 12.76 | 14.02 | 15.13 | 16.17 | 17.08 | 17.97 | 18.80 | 19.61 | 20.37 | 21.12 | 21.85 | 22.53 | 23.22 | 23.88 | 24.53 | 25.15 | 25.79 | 26.39 |
| 35 | 13.03 | 14.29 | 15.47 | 16.48 | 17.40 | 18.29 | 19.14 | 19.96 | 20.72 | 21.48 | 22.22 | 22.92 | 23.60 | 24.27 | 24.94 | 25.58 | 26.19 | 26.80 |
| 36 | 13.28 | 14.56 | 15.70 | 16.77 | 17.71 | 18.62 | 19.48 | 20.30 | 21.08 | 21.85 | 22.58 | 23.30 | 23.90 | 24.66 | 25.33 | 25.97 | 26.62 | 27.22 |
| 37 | 13.53 | 14.83 | 15.99 | 17.07 | 18.01 | 18.94 | 19.81 | 20.64 | 21.43 | 22.20 | 22.95 | 23.66 | 24.37 | 25.04 | 25.72 | 26.36 | 27.01 | 27.63 |
| 38 | 13.78 | 15.10 | 16.27 | 17.36 | 18.32 | 19.25 | 20.14 | 20.97 | 21.78 | 22.55 | 23.30 | 24.05 | 24.73 | 25.43 | 26.11 | 26.77 | 27.41 | 28.04 |
| 39 | 14.04 | 15.37 | 16.55 | 17.67 | 18.63 | 19.57 | 20.47 | 21.31 | 22.13 | 22.91 | 23.67 | 24.41 | 25.12 | 25.81 | 26.50 | 27.16 | 27.80 | 28.45 |
| 40 | 14.29 | 15.63 | 16.83 | 17.95 | 18.92 | 19.88 | 20.80 | 21.64 | 22.46 | 23.26 | 24.02 | 24.77 | 25.49 | 26.19 | 26.89 | 27.56 | 28.21 | 28.86 |

*(Row labels at left margin: Larger Temperature Difference, °F)*

For a given set of required conditions, counterflow will result in a greater METD than parallel flow. This means that less surface area (a smaller heat exchanger) will be required. The following example illustrates this.

**Example 6.3** A chilled water cooling coil with water entering at 40°F and exiting at 52°F is to be used to cool air from 85 to 55°F. Determine the METD for both the counterflow arrangement and the parallel flow arrangement.

*Solution* A sketch of the flow arrangements is shown in Figure 6.5.
For counterflow,

$$TD_A = 85 - 52 = 33°F$$

$$TD_B = 55 - 40 = 15°F$$

$$METD = \frac{33 - 15}{\ln\dfrac{33}{15}} = 22.8°F$$

For parallel flow,

$$TD_A = 85 - 40 = 45°F$$

$$TD_B = 55 - 52 = 3°F$$

$$METD = \frac{45 - 3}{\ln\dfrac{45}{3}} = 15.5°F$$

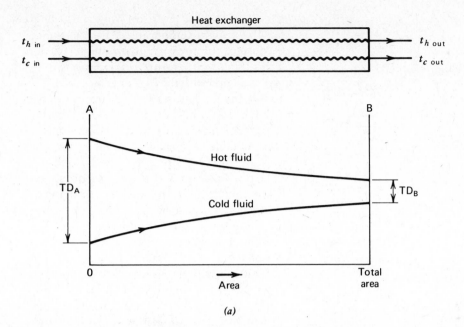

(a)

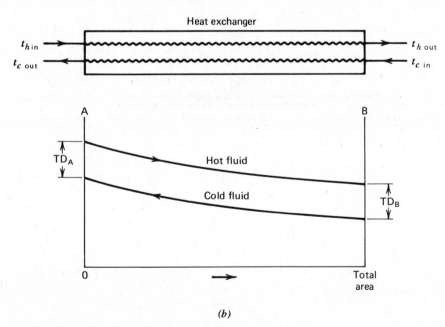

(b)

**FIGURE 6.4** Temperature profiles for parallel flow and counterflow in a heat exchanger (both fluids changing temperature). (a) Parallel flow. (b) Counterflow.

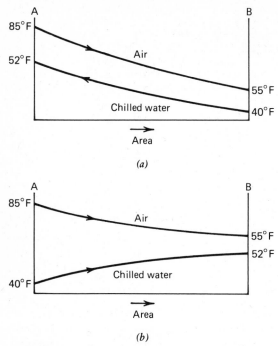

FIGURE 6.5 Sketch for Example 6.3. (a) Counterflow. (b) Parallel flow.

The counterflow arrangement also can allow a reduction in energy consumption in some situations. This point can be illustrated using the conditions shown in Figure 6.5. Notice that with the counterflow arrangement the minimum possible temperature to which the air could be cooled is 40°F, because the cold water and cold air are on the same end of the heat exchanger. In the parallel flow arrangement the air could only be cooled to 52°F. If it were necessary to cool the air below 52°F it might be necessary to reduce the chilled water supply temperature below 40°F. To achieve this it might be necessary to reduce the evaporating temperature in the water chiller, resulting in an increased compressor power.

For evaporators and condensers, the counterflow arrangement is not an advantage, since the refrigerant is at (approximately) constant temperature. For direct expansion coils

parallel flow may even be preferred. There may be a slight temperature drop in the coil because of the pressure drop due to friction. The higher temperature refrigerant is therefore matched with the higher temperature air, at the inlet. Counterflow is achieved thermally, even though the physical arrangement is parallel flow. This arrangement may be objectionable because it does not aid as much in superheating the refrigerant, however, since the leaving refrigerant does not receive heat from the air at the warmer temperature.

It is general practice to connect chilled water cooling coils for cooling air in a counterflow arrangement, for the reasons given. Actually the flow is not purely counterflow, because in each tube row the water and air are flowing at right angles to each other. This is called *crossflow*. The overall direction is still approximately counterflow, however. Crossflow is a common arrangement in some cooling towers, a subject discussed later.

The heat transfer equation (6.5) is used only in special applications for determining the required size of a heat exchanger in refrigeration work. It is not a simple matter to determine the overall conductance U. A further study of the subject of fluid mechanics is necessary to solve the problem this way. This is beyond the scope of our presentation, and fortunately is not needed. For most applications manufacturers present the rating and performance of their equipment in a tabular or graphical form.

The reason we did present the heat transfer equation and its meaning is twofold. First, you need this information to understand manufacturers' data adequately. Secondly, it is needed to make intelligent choices concerning energy conservation. We have already presented some examples of this, and will be referring to it again.

It is also necessary to point out that heat transfer in air conditioning cooling coils is even more complex than it is in liquid chillers, since dehumidification (condensation of the water vapor in the air) usually occurs. This subject is more appropriately covered in air conditioning texts. Manufacturers have simplified procedures for rating air cooling coils for refrigeration applications, however (see Chapter 14).

## 6.10 Function of the Evaporator

The evaporator (and the condenser) is an example of equipment called heat exchangers. Its purpose is to provide a continual and efficient transfer of heat from the medium to be cooled to the refrigerant fluid. The medium to be cooled may be a gas, liquid, or solid. Air and water are the most common substances cooled by evaporators. In the most familiar evaporator refrigerant flows through tubes while air to be cooled flows across the outside of the tubes. The tubes, often constructed in a coil configuration, are called the heat transfer surface. The following explanation of evaporator function will refer to this particular arrangement, for simplicity. However it should be understood that many other arrangements and constructions of evaporators exist, and that the method of heat transfer is the same in all of them.

Refrigerant enters the evaporator tubing at a low temperature and pressure as a result of its expansion through the flow control device (Figure 6.6). A small portion of the refrigerant has evaporated due to the sudden pressure drop, cooling the remaining liquid as well as the flash gas itself. The temperature of the refrigerant is controlled at a desired value, below that to which the air is to be cooled, by proper equipment selection and use of control devices. Since the air is at a higher temperature than the refrigerant, heat will flow from it through the evaporator heat transfer surface to the refrigerant.

The liquid refrigerant entering the evaporator is at its saturation (boiling) temperature. Therefore it will gradually boil as it receives heat from the air while flowing through the evaporator. In most types of evaporators all of the refrigerant has boiled by the time it has reached the evaporator exit, and in many cases it may even be a superheated vapor, depending on how much heat it receives and how much refrigerant is flowing.

## 6.11 Dry Expansion Evaporators and Flooded Evaporators

One way of classifying evaporators is according to the relative quantity of liquid and vapor refrigerant that flows through the evaporator.

In the *dry expansion* type of evaporator, the amount of refrigerant fed by the flow control device is just enough so that it all evaporates before it leaves the evaporator. Figure 6.6 shows an example of this type of evaporator, using a tubular coil through which the refrigerant flows. When a coil is used this way it is called a *direct expansion* (DX) *coil*. An important feature of this type is that the tube wall is not completely covered with liquid refrigerant. There is already some flash gas even when the refrigerant enters, and the proportion of vapor increases as the refrigerant moves downstream. Because the quantity of vapor is large and the amount of liquid is small, only part of the tube surface is wetted by liquid, the rest having contact only with the vapor. If the refrigerant is superheated part of the evaporator tube is not wetted at all.

The importance of this is that heat transfer from the tube surface to the liquid is much greater than it is to the gas. Much less effective use is made of the unwetted surface. To express this in a different way, more surface is required than would be the case if more of the tube surface, or better yet, if all of it were wetted.

This disadvantage can be remedied by using a *flooded evaporator,* as in Figure 6.7. The essential feature of this type is that most or all of the heat transfer surface is wetted by liquid refrigerant. In the particular arrangement shown, the liquid refrigerant is outside the tubing, in

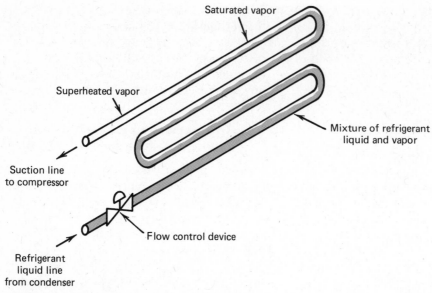

**FIGURE 6.6** Refrigerant conditions and flow in a dry expansion coil evaporator.

the shell. Enough refrigerant is used so that the tubes are always submerged in liquid refrigerant, assuring complete wetting of the tube surface. Liquid from the condenser enters through the flow control device, usually a float valve. The medium to be cooled, a liquid, flows inside the tubes. The vapor bubbles of boiling refrigerant disengage themselves from the liquid in the space at the top of the shell and flow to the suction line. This type of flooded evaporator is called a *flooded shell-and-*

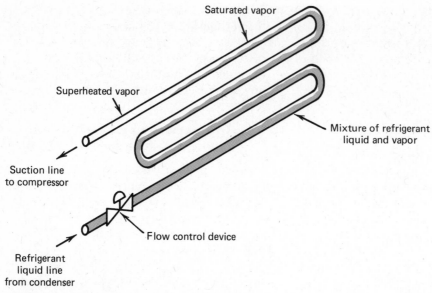

**FIGURE 6.7** Shell-and-tube flooded evaporator. (Reprinted with permission from the 1979 Equipment ASHRAE Handbook and Product Directory)

*tube* evaporator. It is often used in large system liquid chilling applications.

***Flooded Coil Evaporator.*** A flooded evaporator arrangement is also available in which the refrigerant flows inside the tubes, rather than outside. This is called a *flooded coil* evaporator (Figure 6.8).

The liquid refrigerant is delivered from the receiver or condenser through a low-side float valve, which serves as the flow control device, to a storage tank called a *suction trap, accumulator,* or *surge drum.* The flash gas that is formed when the refrigerant drops in pressure as it enters the accumulator is drawn off at the top and flows directly to the compressor suction line. Only liquid refrigerant enters the evaporator coil. The amount of refrigerant circulated through the coil is much more than that needed for the required refrigeration load, so that the tube wall is completely wetted with liquid. Vapor bubbles formed as the refrigerant boils are not sufficient in quantity to appreciably contact

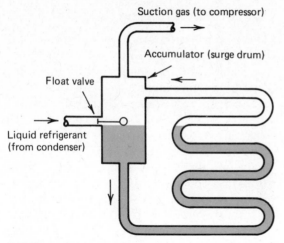

FIGURE 6.8 Flooded coil evaporator.

The flooded coil system can also be more energy efficient. A smaller temperature differential between the cooled fluid and evaporating refrigerant is possible; a higher evaporating temperature means less compressor power.

In the arrangement shown in Figure 6.8 the force needed to circulate the refrigerant through the flooded coil comes from the static head of liquid in the accumulator. Sometimes a refrigerant pump is used to obtain an even greater rate of circulation, improving the flooding of the coil still further. This variation on the flooded coil is called a *liquid overfeed* system.

## 6.12 Evaporator Surface Types

Although there are probably hundreds of variations of the shape and arrangement of the evaporator heat transfer surface, they can almost always be classified into two types: *tubular* or *plate* shaped.

Tubular heat transfer surfaces can be subclassified into either *bare pipe* or *finned tube* types (Figure 6.9). Fins are used on pipe or tubing to increase the surface area, thereby increasing the rate of heat transfer per unit length of tube. The finned surface is called *secondary* or *extended* surface and the unfinned (tube) surface is called the *primary* surface.

When used for cooling air below 32°F, the water vapor condensed from the air will freeze and collect on the tube and between fins. To prevent rapid blocking of the air flow between fins, the number of fins per inch is limited to about four or less for these applications. The ice formed will also increase the thermal resistance to heat transfer. Periodic defrosting is

the tube wall, considering the large amount of refrigerant. The liquid refrigerant that does not evaporate is recirculated back through the accumulator, while the vapor separates in the upper part of the accumulator and flows to the suction line.

The flooded coil evaporator will generally be more expensive than the direct expansion coil type. A large quantity of refrigerant is necessary to ensure flooding, resulting in the need for an accumulator and related piping, which are not needed with direct expansion coils. However, flooded coil evaporators have definite operating advantages in lower temperature systems. Because of the large vapor space in the accumulator, it is difficult for a liquid slug to get into the suction line. Control of oil return to the compressor is more positive—it can be returned directly from the accumulator, rather than having it pass through the evaporator.

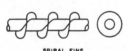

SPIRAL FINS

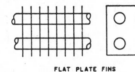

FLAT PLATE FINS

FIGURE 6.9 Some types of finned tube evaporator surface.

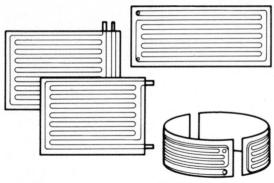

**FIGURE 6.10** Plate-type evaporators. (Dean Products, Inc.)

therefore necessary for both bare pipe and finned tube construction below 32°F, to maintain sufficient refrigeration. The intervals between defrosting can be much longer with bare pipe, since there is no significant blockage of air flow. Bare pipe is often used in cold storage warehouses. Even in this application, however, finned tube is now often used because of the much smaller space needed for the evaporator and the generally lesser cost.

Fins are useful only when there is a large difference in the heat transfer film coefficient between the two fluids. Fins are always put on the side with the high thermal resistance, since the extra surface area compensates for the larger resistance.

The plate-type evaporator (Figure 6.10) is constructed with hollowed out passages in a flat plate, through which the refrigerant flows. The plate construction offers some secondary heat transfer surface, but is also useful for cooling flat packaged products that contact the surface. This type of evaporator has the additional advantage of serving as a structural component, such as the walls of a household refrigerator or reach-in cooler, when constructed in a boxlike shape. A number of construction arrangements of evaporators, such as the direct expansion coil, double pipe, shell and tube, shell and coil, and Baudelot cooler, will now be described.

## 6.13 Direct Expansion (DX) Coil

This type of evaporator (Figure 6.11) is used for cooling air, both in the air conditioning range and for lower temperatures. It is a dry expansion type evaporator—a mixture of liquid and vapor is fed through the tubes and no liquid is recirculated. The flow control device is generally either a thermostatic expansion valve or capillary tube. The most common shape is in the form of a flat coil with straight tubes and return bends, provided in the required number of rows. This arrangement is used in forced convection air handling units with a fan. Special shapes such as a boxlike arrangement are also used to suit convenient refrigeration applications.

The length of tubing in a single-circuit arrangement is limited because pressure drop increases with length of tube and refrigerant flow rate. Reduced suction pressure results in increased compressor power. To keep the pressure drop within reasonable limits, parallel multiple circuit arrangements (Figure 6.12) are used in all but the smallest units.

With multicircuit coils, provisions must be

**FIGURE 6.11** Direct expansion (DX) coil. (Courtesy Halstead & Mitchell, A Division of Halstead Industries, Inc.)

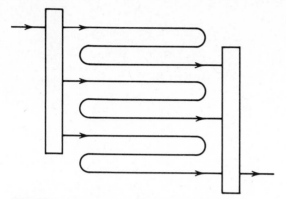

**FIGURE 6.12** Example of multicircuit (parallel) coil design.

made to ensure that an equal amount of refrigerant goes to each circuit, and with the same proportion of liquid and flash gas in each. There will be a greater pressure drop in the lines feeding circuits further from the expansion valve, resulting in more flash gas and an inadequate amount of liquid and some circuits will be starved. Another problem is that more liquid refrigerant will flow to circuits on the bottom of the coil because of the greater density, and more flash gas will feed circuits on top, also causing uneven distribution. Unequal feeding of circuits results in reduction of capacity since some tubes are not fully utilized.

Refrigerant *distributors* (Figure 6.13) are used to provide equal flow of refrigerant liquid and vapor from the expansion valve to each coil circuit. The refrigerant liquid and vapor are caused to mix thoroughly in the body of the distributor, and the length of each distributor is the same, so that every circuit is fed equally.

Direct expansion coils are generally constructed of copper tube with aluminum fins, although aluminum tubing is also used, especially in small units.

## 6.14 Forced Air Evaporators

The group of evaporators that are used for cooling air, with fans to circulate the air across the refrigerant coils, are called *forced air* evaporators. Variations in this group include *unit coolers, product coolers, air conditioning units, blower coils,* and *cold diffusers.* These names are not standardized; different names are often used for the same unit. Construction of forced air evaporators varies according to the use. Some examples are shown in Figure 6.14. Either direct expansion coils or flooded coils may be used.

Low air velocities are used (below 300 FPM) when prevention of dehydration is of concern, or very low noise levels are desired. Medium

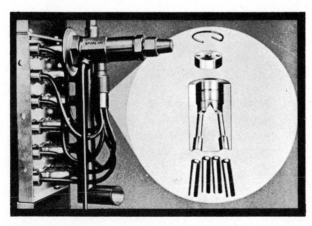

**FIGURE 6.13** A refrigerant distributor for a DX coil.

*(a)*

*(b)*

**FIGURE 6.14** Examples of forced air evaporators.
(Courtesy Halstead & Mitchell, A Division of Halstead
Industries, Inc.)

velocities (300 to 700 fpm) are used for general cold storage application where excess dehydration will not occur and in air conditioning work. For air conditioning, velocities above this would result in condensed water blowing into the air stream. However, baffle-type eliminators can be used to trap water drops. Very high velocities (up to 2000 FPM) are used when it is desired to achieve a very

high heat transfer rate, such as in blast freezers, where high velocity low temperature air is blown over food products that need to be frozen very quickly.

Instead of using dry coils, some forced air units are arranged for sprayed coils. A pump, piping, and a spray header are part of the unit (Figure 6.15). Spraying the coil with a liquid increases the heat transfer rate. Water is used

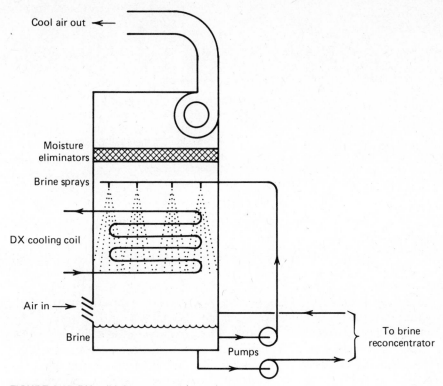

Cool air out

Moisture
eliminators

Brine sprays

DX cooling coil

Air in

Brine

Pumps

To brine
reconcentrator

**FIGURE 6.15** DX coil brine spray cooler.

above freezing temperatures; if the air contacting the coil is expected to be below 32°F brine or a glycol solution is used.

## 6.15 Liquid Coolers

This type of evaporator, also called a *liquid chiller,* is used for cooling water or other liquids. They may be either of the dry expansion or flooded type. Included among them are *shell-and-tube, shell-and-coil, double-pipe,* and *Baudelot* coolers. Their differences are primarily in construction, to suit the application. Each is now briefly discussed.

## 6.16 Shell-and-Tube Chillers

This type consists of a bundle of straight tubes in a cylindrical shell. It may be of the dry expansion type (Figure 6.16) or flooded type

(Figure 6.17). The single tubes are supported by tube sheets on both ends and sometimes intermediately. The ends of the shell, called heads, may be one integral piece with the shell or they may be separate and removable, through a flanged and bolted construction. Tubes are made of nonferrous materials when used with fluorocarbon refrigerants; copper tubing is used with water; copper–nickel and other materials are used with brine. The shell is usually steel.

The *dry expansion chiller* (Figure 6.16) has the evaporating refrigerant flowing inside the tubes, fed from a thermostatic expansion valve. The liquid to be cooled is in the shell. *Baffles* are provided that extend part way across the shell, alternately. This forces the circulating liquid to flow transversely across all the tubes, preventing it from missing some of them, and also increases the liquid velocity,

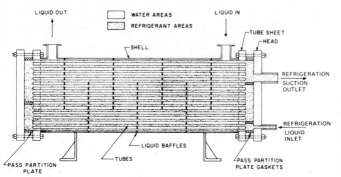

**FIGURE 6.16** Dry expansion shell-and-tube chiller with straight tubes. (Reprinted with permission from the 1979 Equipment ASHRAE Handbook and Product Directory)

since the flow area is made smaller. These effects increase the heat transfer rate.

The refrigerant (tubes) side may be constructed with a *one pass* (once through) or *a multiple pass* arrangement, by providing partitions in the heads. Increasing the number of passes for a given refrigerant flow rate causes a higher velocity and therefore an improved refrigerant side heat transfer coefficient. However this must be balanced against the increased pressure drop when considering costs and energy use. Sometimes the tubes are furnished with inner fins to increase the refrigerant side heat transfer area.

A shell-and-tube dry expansion cooler using U-tubes is also available (Figure 6.18). The tubes are fastened to a tube sheet on one end only, which permits them to expand and contract, thus making this type especially suitable for low temperature brine cooling systems. If straight tube coolers were used, unacceptably large stresses might occur as the tube at-

tempted to expand and contract over the large temperature range.

Dry expansion chillers are widely applied for water chilling for air conditioning, used with either reciprocating or screw compressors. The compressor, evaporator, and controls can be assembled and tested in the factory. The combination is called a *package liquid chiller* (Figure 6.19). Most units used for water chilling are offered now as package units, to reduce costs and ensure better reliability. The package chiller may also include a water cooled condenser.

The *flooded shell-and-tube* chiller (Figure 6.17) has the liquid to be cooled flowing through the tubes, with liquid refrigerant in the shell. The amount of refrigerant is enough to completely submerge the tubes, so that the tube surface is completely wetted. The bubbles of evaporated refrigerant gas rise to the surface and break away from the liquid. A large volume must be allowed above the tubes

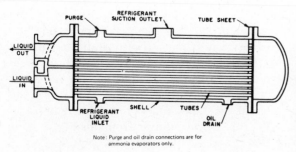

**FIGURE 6.17** Flooded shell-and-tube chiller. Note that purge and oil drain connections are for ammonia evaporators only. (Reprinted with permission from the 1979 Equipment ASHRAE Handbook and Product Directory)

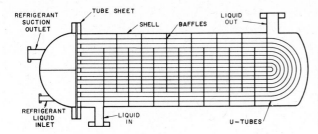

**FIGURE 6.18** Dry expansion shell-and-tube chiller with U-tubes. (Reprinted with permission from the 1979 Equipment ASHRAE Handbook and Product Directory)

to collect the refrigerant vapor and to prevent liquid carryover to the suction line. In addition, *eliminators* are often provided to catch liquid droplets. These are either overlapping Z-shaped blades or a mesh extending across the shell.

The liquid refrigerant flow control devices used are high or low pressure float valves or an orifice. To ensure distribution of refrigerant equally throughout the length of the chiller, a header trough may be provided along the bottom of the shell.

Some flooded chillers have a pump and liquid spray header that provides complete wetting of the tubes; then there is no need for submerged tubes. This arrangement is sometimes used at low temperatures.

Tubes are usually manufactured with integral external fins when the chiller is used with fluorocarbon refrigerants, to increase the surface area. The water (tube) side is generally available with a number of choices of multiple pass arrangements, with all the water flowing through only a group of tubes, and passing back and forth through the evaporator (Figure 6.7). The number of passes is created by separating groups of tubes with partitions in the heads. Depending on the water flow rate, the number of passes is chosen to give high velocity (and thus high heat transfer), limited

**FIGURE 6.19** Package liquid chiller. (Courtesy of Dunham–Bush, Inc.)

by the increase of pressure drop with the number of passes. The heads, called *water boxes* with flooded shell-and-tube chillers, are often removable so that tubes may be mechanically cleaned, or even replaced. This is of more concern with flooded shell-and-tube chillers than with dry expansion chillers, because if the water freezes inside a tube it is more likely to break it than if the water were in the shell. Furthermore there is more likelihood of contaminants fouling the water circuit than the refrigerant circuit; the ability to clean the inside of the tubes is therefore important.

The maximum size and capacity is limited in dry expansion shell-and-tube chillers because the liquid–vapor mixture flows through relatively small tube areas. This restriction is not as limiting with flooded chillers where only a liquid, at a much greater average density, flows through the tube. Thus flooded shell-and-tube chillers are applied to large capacity systems, and are especially combined with centrifugal compressors. A more detailed description of this type of chiller is in Chapter 10.

About 90 percent of the liquid coolers used with reciprocating compressors are of the dry expansion type, due both to lower cost and because oil return problems are more difficult to handle with flooded coolers.

## 6.17 Shell-and-Coil, Double-Pipe, Baudelot, and Tank Chillers

The *shell-and-coil* chiller (Figure 6.20) has a helical-shaped direct expansion coil in a shell containing the liquid to be cooled. Relatively low in cost compared to a shell-and-tube construction, it is used to cool drinking water and other beverages, as well as in industrial applications.

The *double-pipe* chiller consists of a pipe within another pipe. One fluid is circulated in the inner pipe and another is circulated in the outer annulus between the two pipe walls. It is usually constructed in a flat arrangement with return bends. The relatively high cost and

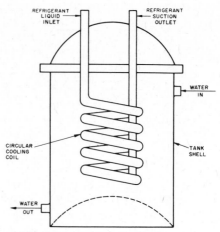

**FIGURE 6.20** Shell-and-coil chiller.

difficulty of access to the tube walls limit it to special applications.

The *Baudelot cooler* (Figure 6.21) consists of a direct expansion pipe coil, with the pipes run horizontally one above the other. The liquid to be cooled is distributed over the top pipe, contacting each pipe row as it falls by gravity. A trough at the bottom collects the cooled liquid. This type of evaporator is convenient for cooling liquids near their freezing point, since a freeze-up will generally not damage equipment. Being open, it also provides aera-

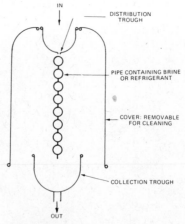

**FIGURE 6.21** Baudelot cooler (sectional view).

tion where this is desirable. It is used for cooling milk and similar applications in the food industry.

A *tank-type* chiller is simply a rectangular tank with a submerged refrigerant coil. It can be used to cool a liquid where sanitation or contamination is not of concern. One use is to cool brine in the tank; the brine is circulated through the tank, which contains sealed cans of a product such as ice cream.

## 6.18 Rating and Selection of Liquid Chillers

Although capacity ratings of evaporators as individual items are available from manufacturers, the ratings are also available for package liquid chiller combinations, including the compressor, chiller, and either water cooled or air cooled condenser. Most applications permit use of package equipment. Because of the lower overall cost and ease of installation, it is advisable to use package units when possible. This section presents rating data of a group of small package liquid chillers with air cooled condensers (Table 6.3).

**Example 6.4**  Select a package compressor–chiller for cooling 20 GPM of water from 55 to 45°F. The ambient air temperature is 100°F.

*Solution*  Using Equation 2.4, the required capacity is

$$\text{Tons} = \frac{\text{GPM} \times \text{TC}}{24} = \frac{20 \times 10}{24} = 8.3 \text{ tons}$$

From Table 6.3, a Model ARPC–010SS unit has a capacity of 8.4 tons for the conditions listed. The required power input is 9.5 kW.

**TABLE 6.3** Air Cooled Package Chiller Ratings (60 Hz)[ab]

| | | Based on 6° to 14° Cooling Range | | | | | | | | | | | | EER @ ARI Base Rating Condition |
| | Outlet Water Temperature °F | Ambient Temperature °F | | | | | | | | | | | | |
| | | 90°F | | 95°F | | 100°F | | 105°F | | 110°F | | 115°F | | |
| Model | | Tons | K.W. | Tons | K.W. | Tons | K.W. | Tons | K.W. | Tons | K.W. | Tons | K.W. | |
| ARPC-008S | 42 | 6.3 | 7.6 | 6.1 | 7.8 | 5.8 | 8.0 | 5.6 | 8.1 | 5.3 | 8.2 | 5.2 | 8.3 | 9.5 |
| | 44 | 6.5 | 7.8 | 6.3[d] | 8.0[d] | 6.1 | 8.1 | 5.8 | 8.2 | 5.6 | 8.4 | 5.4 | 8.5 | |
| | 45 | 6.7 | 7.9 | 6.4 | 8.0 | 6.2 | 8.1 | 5.9 | 8.3 | 5.7 | 8.5 | 5.5 | 8.6 | |
| | 46 | 6.8 | 7.9 | 6.6 | 8.1 | 6.4 | 8.3 | 6.2 | 8.4 | 5.8 | 8.6 | 5.6 | 8.8 | |
| | 48 | 7.0 | 8.0 | 6.8 | 8.2 | 6.6 | 8.4 | 6.4 | 8.6 | 6.1 | 8.8 | 5.8 | 9.0 | |
| | 50 | 7.4 | 8.1 | 7.0 | 8.4 | 6.8 | 8.6 | 6.6 | 8.8 | 6.4 | 9.0 | 6.1 | 9.2 | |
| ARPC-008SS[c] | 42 | 6.6 | 7.2 | 6.5 | 7.4 | 6.3 | 7.5 | 6.1 | 7.7 | 5.9 | 7.8 | 5.7 | 8.0 | 10.7 |
| | 44 | 6.9 | 7.3 | 6.7[d] | 7.5[d] | 6.5 | 7.6 | 6.3 | 7.8 | 6.1 | 8.0 | 5.8 | 8.2 | |
| | 45 | 7.0 | 7.4 | 6.8 | 7.6 | 6.6 | 7.7 | 6.4 | 8.0 | 6.2 | 8.1 | 5.9 | 8.3 | |
| | 46 | 7.2 | 7.4 | 6.9 | 7.6 | 6.7 | 7.9 | 6.5 | 8.0 | 6.3 | 8.1 | 6.1 | 8.4 | |
| | 48 | 7.4 | 7.5 | 7.2 | 7.8 | 7.0 | 8.0 | 6.7 | 8.2 | 6.5 | 8.3 | 6.3 | 8.5 | |
| | 50 | 7.6 | 7.7 | 7.4 | 7.9 | 7.2 | 8.1 | 6.9 | 8.3 | 6.7 | 8.5 | 6.5 | 8.8 | |
| ARPC-010SS[c] | 42 | 8.4 | 8.8 | 8.1 | 8.9 | 7.9 | 9.2 | 7.7 | 9.4 | 7.4 | 9.6 | 7.3 | 9.8 | 11.2 |
| | 44 | 8.6 | 8.9 | 8.5[d] | 9.1[d] | 8.1 | 9.4 | 8.0 | 9.6 | 7.7 | 9.8 | 7.5 | 10.0 | |
| | 45 | 8.7 | 9.0 | 8.6 | 9.2 | 8.4 | 9.5 | 8.1 | 9.7 | 7.9 | 10.0 | 7.6 | 10.1 | |
| | 46 | 8.9 | 9.1 | 8.7 | 9.3 | 8.5 | 9.6 | 8.3 | 9.8 | 8.0 | 10.1 | 7.8 | 10.3 | |
| | 48 | 9.1 | 9.2 | 9.0 | 9.5 | 8.7 | 9.7 | 8.6 | 10.0 | 8.3 | 10.2 | 8.0 | 10.5 | |
| | 50 | 9.5 | 9.4 | 9.2 | 9.7 | 9.0 | 10.1 | 8.9 | 10.1 | 8.6 | 10.4 | 8.4 | 10.7 | |

(continued)

**TABLE 6.3** Continued

| Model | Outlet Water Temperature °F | Based on 6° to 14° Cooling Range | | | | | | | | | | | | EER @ ARI Base Rating Condition |
|---|---|---|---|---|---|---|---|---|---|---|---|---|---|---|
| | | Ambient Temperature °F | | | | | | | | | | | | |
| | | 90°F | | 95°F | | 100°F | | 105°F | | 110°F | | 115°F | | |
| | | Tons | K.W. | Tons | K.W. | Tons | K.W. | Tons | K.W. | Tons | K.W. | Tons | K.W. | |
| ARPC-010T | 42 | 9.8 | 12.3 | 9.5 | 12.6 | 9.1 | 12.9 | 8.9 | 13.0 | 8.6 | 13.1 | 8.3 | 13.2 | |
| | 44 | 10.2 | 12.6 | 9.8[d] | 12.9[d] | 9.6 | 13.2 | 9.1 | 13.3 | 8.9 | 13.4 | 8.6 | 13.6 | |
| | 45 | 10.3 | 12.7 | 10.1 | 13.0 | 9.7 | 13.3 | 9.4 | 13.5 | 9.0 | 13.6 | 8.7 | 13.7 | 9.1 |
| | 46 | 10.6 | 12.8 | 10.2 | 13.1 | 9.8 | 13.4 | 9.6 | 13.6 | 9.1 | 13.7 | 8.9 | 13.9 | |
| | 48 | 10.8 | 13.1 | 10.6 | 13.4 | 10.2 | 13.7 | 9.8 | 13.9 | 9.5 | 14.1 | 9.1 | 14.4 | |
| | 50 | 11.2 | 13.6 | 10.9 | 13.8 | 10.6 | 14.1 | 10.2 | 14.3 | 9.8 | 14.5 | 9.5 | 14.7 | |
| ARPC-015SS[c] | 42 | 11.9 | 13.2 | 11.7 | 13.5 | 11.3 | 13.9 | 11.1 | 14.2 | 10.8 | 14.6 | 10.5 | 14.8 | |
| | 44 | 12.4 | 13.4 | 12.1[d] | 13.8[d] | 11.8 | 14.2 | 11.4 | 14.4 | 11.1 | 14.8 | 10.8 | 15.1 | |
| | 45 | 12.7 | 13.6 | 12.3 | 14.0 | 11.9 | 14.3 | 11.7 | 14.6 | 11.3 | 15.0 | 11.1 | 15.3 | 10.5 |
| | 46 | 12.9 | 13.9 | 12.4 | 14.2 | 12.2 | 14.4 | 11.9 | 14.9 | 11.4 | 15.1 | 11.3 | 15.4 | |
| | 48 | 13.3 | 14.1 | 13.0 | 14.5 | 12.5 | 14.7 | 12.3 | 15.1 | 11.9 | 15.4. | 11.7 | 15.6 | |
| | 50 | 13.8 | 14.4 | 13.4 | 14.7 | 13.0 | 15.1 | 12.7 | 15.4 | 12.3 | 15.6 | 12.0 | 15.8 | |
| ARPC-015T | 42 | 12.1 | 15.4 | 11.8 | 15.8 | 11.3 | 16.1 | 10.8 | 16.4 | 10.4 | 16.8 | 10.1 | 17.3 | |
| | 44 | 12.8 | 16.0 | 12.3[d] | 16.4[d] | 11.8 | 16.6 | 11.3 | 16.8 | 11.0 | 17.2 | 10.5 | 17.7 | |
| | 45 | 13.0 | 16.1 | 12.4 | 16.6 | 12.0 | 16.7 | 11.6 | 17.0 | 11.2 | 17.4 | 10.8 | 17.9 | 9.0 |
| | 46 | 13.2 | 16.3 | 12.9 | 16.7 | 12.3 | 17.1 | 11.9 | 17.2 | 11.3 | 17.6 | 11.0 | 18.1 | |
| | 48 | 13.8 | 16.6 | 13.2 | 17.0 | 12.8 | 17.6 | 12.3 | 17.8 | 11.9 | 18.2 | 11.4 | 18.5 | |
| | 50 | 14.3 | 17.1 | 13.8 | 17.4 | 13.2 | 18.0 | 12.9 | 18.2 | 12.3 | 18.6 | 11.9 | 19.0 | |
| ARPC-020T | 42 | 15.6 | 17.6 | 15.2 | 17.8 | 14.6 | 18.2 | 14.2 | 18.9 | 13.8 | 19.1 | 13.4 | 19.4 | |
| | 44 | 16.2 | 17.8 | 15.7[d] | 18.2[d] | 15.2 | 18.7 | 14.6 | 19.2 | 14.3 | 19.4 | 13.9 | 19.8 | |
| | 45 | 16.4 | 18.0 | 16.0 | 18.4 | 15.4 | 19.0 | 15.1 | 19.3 | 14.5 | 19.6 | 14.1 | 20.1 | 10.4 |
| | 46 | 16.7 | 18.1 | 16.3 | 18.6 | 15.6 | 19.2 | 15.2 | 19.5 | 14.9 | 19.8 | 14.3 | 20.3 | |
| | 48 | 17.3 | 18.4 | 16.7 | 19.0 | 16.3 | 19.4 | 15.7 | 20.0 | 15.3 | 20.3 | 14.9 | 20.7 | |
| | 50 | 17.8 | 18.8 | 17.4 | 19.2 | 16.7 | 19.8. | 16.3 | 20.2 | 15.7 | 20.8 | 15.4 | 21.2 | |
| ARPC-020SS[c] | 42 | 17.1 | 19.7 | 16.7 | 20.2 | 16.2 | 20.8 | 15.7 | 21.3 | 15.3 | 21.7 | 14.9 | 22.4 | |
| | 44 | 17.6 | 20.4 | 17.2[d] | 20.6[d] | 16.7 | 21.2 | 16.2 | 21.8 | 15.7 | 22.4 | 15.3 | 22.8 | |
| | 45 | 17.9 | 20.5 | 17.4 | 20.8 | 17.1 | 21.4 | 16.5 | 21.9 | 16.2 | 22.6 | 15.6 | 23.1 | 10.0 |
| | 46 | 18.3 | 20.7 | 17.8 | 21.0 | 17.3 | 21.6 | 16.8 | 22.1 | 16.4 | 22.8 | 15.7 | 23.4 | |
| | 48 | 18.8 | 21.2 | 18.4 | 21.7 | 17.8 | 22.0 | 17.4 | 22.6 | 17.1 | 23.2 | 16.4 | 23.8 | |
| | 50 | 19.5 | 21.6 | 19.1 | 22.1 | 18.5 | 22.6 | 17.9 | 23.0 | 17.7 | 23.6 | 16.8 | 24.2 | |

[a]For capacity ratings at 85°F ambient temperature multiply the ratings of 90°F ambient by 1.03 × tons and .97 × kW.
[b]For 50 hertz capacity ratings, derate above table by .85 multiplier.
[c]All models with suffix 'SS' denote single D/B-metric accessible hermetic compressors.
[d]ARI Base rating conditions 95° ambient, 44° leaving water.
Courtesy Dunham-Bush, Inc.

## 6.19 Energy Utilization and Evaporators

In our discussion of evaporators, two general factors that enhance efficient energy utilization have been stressed. One is the promotion of increased heat transfer; the other is the maintaining of the highest reasonable evaporating temperature. It should be noted that under one circumstance these two factors are opposing. That is, one way of increasing evaporator heat transfer is to increase the temperature difference between the medium to be cooled and the evaporating refrigerant. A lower evaporating temperature, however, increases compressor power. With this in mind, we can still list specific factors that increase heat transfer without decreasing evaporating temperature. Effectively this means that for a given heat transfer (refrigeration) capacity, the evaporating temperature is higher, and less power is used.

1. Counterflow arrangement increases heat transfer over parallel flow, since the METD is greater.

2. A flooded (wetted) evaporator surface is more effective than a dry expansion surface, which is only partially wetted.

3. Refrigerant sprays may increase surface wetting.

4. Equal flow of refrigerant to each circuit in a direct expansion coil should be provided, through use of distributors.

5. Maintenance of clean surfaces prevents reduction of the heat transfer coefficient.

6. Increased surface area, through use of fins or simply more tubing, increases heat transfer.

7. Having higher fluid velocities increases the heat transfer coefficient, on both the refrigerant and air or water side. In liquid chillers this is achieved by increasing the number of passes.

## REVIEW QUESTIONS

1. Name the three ways heat can be transferred, and describe an example of each.

2. What is the difference between forced and natural convection?

3. Explain the thermal terms *resistance, conductance, film coefficient, conductivity,* and *fouling factor.*

4. Describe and sketch parallel flow, counterflow, and crossflow of two fluids.

5. What are the potential advantages of counterflow? When are these advantages not realized?

6. What is the purpose of an evaporator?

7. Explain the difference between dry expansion and flooded-type evaporators. What are their relative advantages?

8. What is the purpose of a suction trap (accumulator)?

9. What is a liquid overfeed system?

10. Explain what is meant by primary and secondary heat transfer surface.

11. What are the three types of heat transfer surfaces? Discuss their relative advantages.

12. What is a DX coil and how is it constructed?

13. What is the purpose of multicircuiting? What problems may occur with it, and how are they solved?

14. Discuss the relative advantages of low and high air velocities across cooling coils.

15. Discuss the basic construction differences and relative advantages of dry expansion versus flooded shell-and-tube chillers.

16. Explain what baffles, water boxes, and eliminators are, and their function.

17. Why are some dry expansion chillers made with U-tubes?

18. Discuss the features of and applications of shell-and-coil, double-pipe, and Baudelot coolers.

19. Discuss some means of reducing energy use through evaporator design, operation, or maintenance.

## PROBLEMS

6.1 Insulation with a resistance value of R-20 is required for the walls of a cold storage room. Insulation material with a thermal conductivity of 0.30 Btu/hr-ft$^2$-°F per in. is available. How many inches of insulation thickness are required?

6.2  A DX water chiller cools water from 58 to 42°F with refrigerant evaporating at 30°F. Find the METD and compare it to the arithmetic average TD.

6.3  A chilled water coil with water entering at 44°F and leaving at 52°F cools air from 78 to 56°F. Find the METD for both a counterflow and parallel flow arrangement.

6.4  Select a package compressor–chiller from Table 6.3 for cooling 25 GPM of water from 56 to 42°F. The ambient air temperature is 95°F. What is the coefficient of performance (COP) and EER at these conditions?

6.5  If the ambient air temperature for the unit in Problem 6.4 is 105°F, what would be the increased cost of operation after 2000 full load hours, if electricity costs $0.10 per kilowatt hour? What is the COP and EER at the new condition?

6.6  A brine chiller has 118 ft$^2$ of heat transfer surface area and an overall heat transfer coefficient of 208 Btu/hr-ft$^2$-°F when cooling brine from 24 to 6°F with refrigerant at −10°F. What is the cooling capacity in tons of refrigeration?

6.7  Find the overall thermal resistance and overall heat transfer coefficient for a flooded chiller with the following conditions:

Refrigerant film conductance $C_r = 310$ Btu/hr-ft$^2$-°F

Tube wall resistance $R_w = 0.00035$ hr-ft$^2$-°F/Btu

Water fouling factor $R_f = 0.001$ hr-ft$^2$-°F/Btu

Water film conductance $C_l = 1300$ Btu/hr-ft$^2$-°F

The ratio of outside to inside tube surface area is 3.6 to 1.0.

# Chapter 7

# CONDENSERS AND COOLING TOWERS

In this chapter we discuss the types, construction, features, and performance of refrigerant condensers and cooling towers. Water treatment as it relates to this equipment is also covered.

## OBJECTIVES

A study of this chapter will enable you to:
1. Describe the major construction features and relative advantages of different types of condensers.
2. Explain why head-pressure control is needed and describe different control methods.
3. Discuss problems and solutions for winter operation of condensers and cooling towers.
4. Select a water cooled condenser, air cooled condenser, condensing unit, and cooling tower.
5. Identify the different types of cooling towers and their features.
6. Discuss needs and solutions for cooling tower water treatment.
7. Suggest some energy conservation measures in the selection and operation of condensers and cooling towers.

## 7.1 Function and Operation of the Condenser

The purpose of the condenser in the refrigeration system is to remove heat from the refrigerant vapor leaving the compressor (or generator in an absorption system), so that the refrigerant will condense to its liquid state. It will then be able to achieve a refrigeration effect by evaporation.

The condenser is a heat exchanger, like the evaporator; in the condenser, heat is transferred from the refrigerant to a cooling medium, either air or water. As with any heat transfer, the cooling medium must be at a lower temperature than the refrigerant.

Refrigerant always leaves the compressor at a temperature well above its saturation (condensing) temperature; that is, it is superheated. In the first part of the condenser, sensible heat removal takes place—the vapor is cooled to its saturation temperature. After this, further heat removal gradually condenses the refrigerant—the latent heat is removed. The condenser size may be just large enough so that the refrigerant leaves the condenser as a saturated liquid at the condensing temperature. In most cases however, the condenser heat transfer surface area is great enough so that the liquid refrigerant is subcooled below its saturation temperature before it leaves the condenser. Figure 7.1 illustrates this sequence of events.

The condenser must remove all of the heat gained by the refrigerant in the refrigeration system. This consists of the heat gained in the evaporator (from the refrigeration load) plus the heat gained from compressing the refrigerant gas. The heat removed is called the *heat of rejection.*

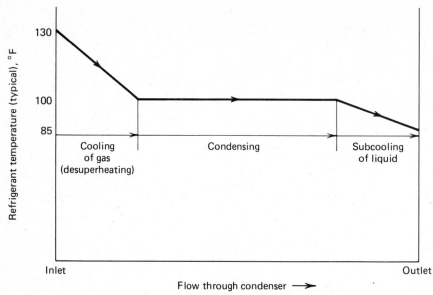

**FIGURE 7.1** Heat removed from the refrigerant in a condenser.

## 7.2 Types of Condensers

Refrigerant condensers can be classified into three groups, according to the cooling medium used and how the heat is transferred to it. These are *water cooled, air cooled,* and *evaporative* condensers. The water and air cooled condensers utilize the sensible heat capacity of the cooling fluids. That is, the water or air increases in temperature. The evaporative condenser makes use primarily of the latent heat of vaporization of water. Water droplets are evaporated into the surrounding air. The heat gained is taken from the refrigerant.

In all three types, water or air are used because they are readily available in sufficient quantity, at no cost or at reasonable cost, and they generally have desirable physical properties. We will discuss in more detail each type of condenser in the following sections.

## 7.3 Water Cooled Condensers

Types of water cooled condensers can be classified according to their construction: *double-pipe, shell-and-coil, vertical shell-and-tube,* and

*horizontal shell-and-tube.* Each has features that make it suitable for certain applications.

Steel pipe or tube is the material used for ammonia condensers since copper and ammonia react chemically. Copper tube is used with halocarbons when fresh water is the cooling medium. Other nonferrous materials that are more corrosion resistant are used with salt water. Integral finned tubing with small fins is frequently used with halocarbon refrigerants to increase the refrigerant-side surface area.

The water supply for water cooled condensers can be either a once-through or recirculated arrangement. In once-through use the water comes from a permanent supply in sufficient quantity and is wasted after passing through the condenser. The supply may be from the city, a river, a lake, or wells. In the case of city water there are usually restrictions that limit use to very small quantities.

In most situations an adequate water supply for once-through use is not available, and the water must be recirculated. In order to do this, the water must be recooled after leaving the condenser. This is accomplished by utilizing the cooling effect obtained from evaporating a

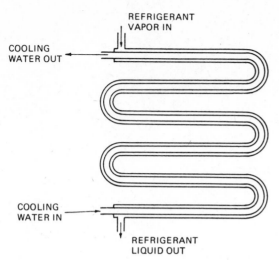

**FIGURE 7.2** Sectional view of a double-pipe condenser.

small quantity of the water. Cooling towers are generally used for this, although occasionally a cooling pond is used.

## 7.4 Double-Pipe Condenser

This condenser consists of two pipes or tubes, one within the other (Figure 7.2). The cooling water is circulated through the inner pipe and the refrigerant is circulated through the outer pipe. In this way some additional heat is transferred from the refrigerant to the ambient air surrounding the condenser, reducing the required size.

A compact construction is a double tube circular coil arrangement (Figure 7.3). The cost is inexpensive, but the pipe cannot be mechanically cleaned. Chemical cleaning is required.

Another type of double-pipe condenser is constructed of straight lengths of pipe with headers and removable end plates (Figure 7.4). This makes it possible to clean the inner pipe with mechanical cleaning tools.

A counterflow arrangement should always be used in the double-pipe condenser to increase the heat transfer. This type of condenser is available up to about 20 tons of capacity.

## 7.5 Shell-and-Coil Condenser

This type of water cooled condenser consists of one or more continuous spiral-shaped tubular coils in a cylindrical shell (Figure 7.5). Hot refrigerant gas enters the top of the shell

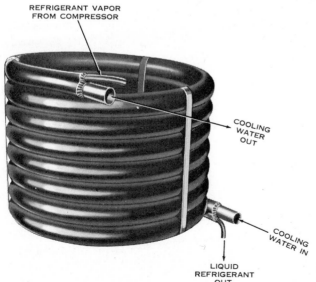

**FIGURE 7.3** Double-tube coil condenser.

**FIGURE 7.4** Double-pipe condenser with removable endplates for mechanical cleaning.

and the condensed liquid leaves the bottom. The coiled tubing cannot be cleaned mechanically. The shell-and-coil construction is simpler and less costly than the shell-and-tube type. It is available up to about 15 tons of capacity. Both vertical and horizontal types are available. The vertical arrangement is convenient when floor space is limited.

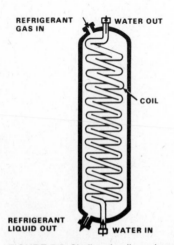

**FIGURE 7.5** Shell-and-coil condenser (vertical type).

## 7.6 Horizontal Shell-and-Tube Condenser

The construction of this type is similar to that of the shell-and-tube evaporator. It consists of bundles of straight tubes within a shell. The cooling water flows through the tubes. The refrigerant gas enters the top of the shell. As it condenses it falls by gravity to the bottom where it leaves (Figure 7.6).

The tubes are supported by tube sheets. The ends or heads of the shell, called water boxes, are available with partitions so that different numbers of water-pass arrangements are possible. This allows high water velocities for a given flow, to increase the heat transfer.

The water box heads are removable so that the tubes may be mechanically cleaned. This is an important desirable feature of the shell-and-tube condenser. It is available in sizes from about 5 tons to thousands of tons of capacity.

The close arrangement of tubes results in large capacities for a physically compact piece of equipment. The bottom of the shell serves

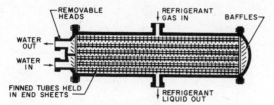

**FIGURE 7.6** Horizontal shell-and-tube condenser.

as a liquid refrigerant storage, so that a separate receiver is not required, unless needed for other purposes.

## 7.7 Vertical Shell-and-Tube Condenser

This type is used in some ammonia plants. The water inlet is open at the entrance on top of the condenser. Cooling water is pumped to the top and then it flows by gravity through the vertical tubes to a collecting sump. Refrigerant gas enters the side of the shell in the middle and the condensed liquid is drained from the bottom (Figure 7.7).

The open construction of the vertical condenser allows the tubes to be cleaned without shutting down the system. Another desirable feature is that the capacity can be increased by pumping more water, yet the increased fric-

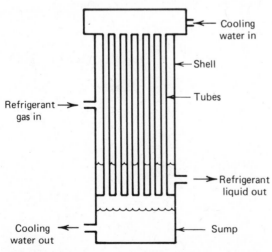

**FIGURE 7.7** Vertical shell-and-tube condenser.

tion head loss through the tubing does not become a penalty on the pump power requirement.

## 7.8 Purging

An important concern in refrigeration systems, especially in those with shell-and-tube water cooled condensers, is the effect on performance and the possibility of corrosion caused by the presence of gases other than the refrigerant vapor. The primary source of these gases is air, which may leak into the system when shut down, or may leak into parts of the system when operating, if any parts are below atmospheric pressure. Unwanted gases in the system may be classified into the *noncondensables*, those that cannot be condensed by cooling them with available means, and the *condensables*. The oxygen and nitrogen in air are examples of noncondensables. The water vapor in atmospheric air is an example of a condensable gas.

Noncondensable gases will migrate and collect in the top of the condenser shell. As with any gases, they exert a pressure. This raises the condenser pressure, resulting in increased compressor power requirement. The gases may also reduce the heat transfer film coefficient on the tubes. Some gases may even corrode parts of the system.

Both noncondensable and condensable gases must be removed by *purging*. This may be done manually or automatically through a connection to the upper part of shell-and-tube condensers. Refrigerant vapor will also unavoidably be removed in the purging, so provisions are generally made for recovering it by condensing it, and then separating it from the noncondensables. This is accomplished with a device called a purge unit (see Chapter 10). For large systems that operate below atmospheric pressure, periodic purging is necessary. For small units operating at high pressures, periodic purging is not normally required. Any air that enters the system when

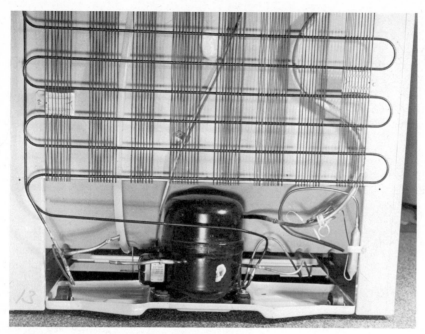

**FIGURE 7.8** Air cooled condenser used with household refrigerators (natural draft type with wire fins). (Frigidaire Co.)

the system is first charged or after repairs can be manually vented.

## 7.9 Air Cooled Condensers

The air cooled condenser is generally constructed of finned tubing arranged in rows of coils. Refrigerant flows through the tubes and the air flows across the tubes. Fins are used because of the low heat transfer coefficient on the air side.

Small air cooled condensers that do not have fans rely on the natural convection of the warmed air to cause air flow. An example is the condenser often used on household refrigerators (Figure 7.8). Its tubing is usually made of steel, with steel wire fins, which costs less than copper. Steel is permissible because this condenser is located indoors and is not subject to corrosion.

Most air cooled condensers have fans

(forced convection) to increase the air flow rate and thus keep the size of the condenser small. They may be constructed for either vertical air flow or horizontal air flow (Figure 7.9). The vertical air-flow unit is independent

**FIGURE 7.9** Typical forced draft air cooled condenser arrangement.

of wind effects. Horizontal air-flow units should be oriented with summer prevailing winds. In any case, having deflecting baffles is desirable, to prevent any opposing wind effects.

Copper tubing with aluminum fins is usually used with halocarbons. The structural casing is made of galvanized steel or aluminum. Fans may be of either the propeller or the centrifugal type, depending on the air resistance. These units are usually located outdoors, often on a roof. Fan noise can be a serious problem when the condenser is located close to occupied spaces.

Forced convection air cooled condensers are available in capacities from about 5 to 200 tons. They are popular because they are simple to operate, they require no water or cooling tower, they have little corrosion problem, and they can be operated in winter (with head-pressure control), without concern of water freezing. Initial costs are usually lower than for other types. However, they are energy inefficient. Water is generally available in summer at a temperature considerably below that of the ambient air. An air cooled refrigeration unit will therefore usually have a much higher condensing temperature than a water cooled or evaporative unit, and it will require considerably more compressor power. Against this must be balanced the absence of pump power requirements.

## 7.10 Evaporative Condensers

The evaporative condenser transfers heat primarily by the cooling effect obtained when water evaporates. A schematic diagram is shown in Figure 7.10.

*Operation.* Water is pumped to a header and through spray nozzles over the refrigerant coil. Heat from the refrigerant evaporates the water into the surrounding air. Air from the surroundings is moved through the condenser by a fan. The water vapor content (humid-

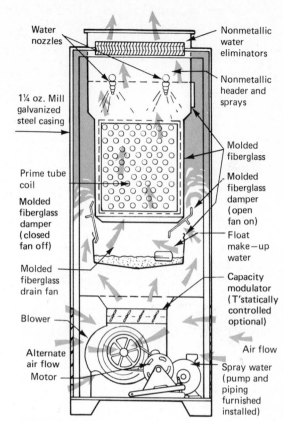

**FIGURE 7.10** Evaporative condenser arrangement. (Courtesy Dunham–Bush, Inc.)

ity) of the air increases as it picks up the evaporated spray water. The humid air is discharged into the atmosphere. The unevaporated spray water collects in a pan or sump at the bottom of the condenser, and is recirculated. The air flows at a fairly high velocity, and picks up water droplets. In order to minimize the water loss, called *drift*, eliminator baffles are provided across the air outlet. They are constructed of offset-shaped plates that the water hits and falls back from by gravity.

Most of the heat transfer takes place by evaporation of water into the surrounding air stream; a small amount comes from sensible heating. The heat transfer rate per unit of surface area is much higher than with air cooled condensers because the film coefficient of the liquid is higher than that of gas. The result is that evaporative condensers require less tubing. This, along with their use of centrifugal fans, allows them to be physically smaller than air cooled condensers.

*Construction.* The condensing coil tubing is usually made of steel or copper. Finned tubing is not used because the heat transfer rate is very high. Furthermore scale would be harder to remove from finned tubing. Casings are often made of galvanized steel. Centrifugal fans are used because the pressure drop through the unit is significant. Fans may be located for either a blow-through or draw-through arrangement. If located at the air outlet (fan draw-through) the fans must be constructed of materials able to withstand the corrosive effects of the moisture laden air.

Evaporative condensers are available in sizes up to about 200 tons. They are usually located outdoors but can be located indoors, using connecting ductwork. A typical unit is shown in Figure 7.11.

*Water Loss and Make-up.* Water is lost from an evaporative condenser in three ways. First, water is evaporated from the cooling effect. Second, some water drops are also swept out in the exiting air stream. This is called the *drift* loss. Finally an additional quantity of water is intentionally removed from the sump at a steady rate. This is called *bleed-off.* Water is bled off to prevent an excess buildup of mineral content that would increase scale formation on heat transfer surfaces. Only pure water is lost by evaporation, but the replacement water contains minerals. The mineral content therefore increases in time. The additional bleed-off removes mineral laden water, thus keeping the mineral concentration at a reasonable level. This does not replace possible need for water treatment, however.

*Make-up water* to replace these losses is sup-

**FIGURE 7.11** View of an evaporative condenser. (Courtesy Dunham–Bush, Inc.)

plied automatically to the sump through a float valve that opens as the water level falls. Since the combined total of the three effects is about 4 percent of the water rate circulated and the water rate is about 1.5 GPM per ton to achieve good wetting of the tubes, about 0.06 GPM of water per ton is required for makeup. This is about half the amount required for systems with a water cooled condenser and cooling tower.

*Comparison of Evaporative and Water Cooled Condensers.* The evaporative condenser is more compact and generally less expensive than the water cooled condenser–cooling tower combination. Compressor power requirements are about the same for both. Pumping power requirements are less for the evaporative condenser for two reasons: the water flow rate is lower, and the pump head is less, due to the shorter length of piping. Evaporative condensers are more subject to scale and corrosion, however, and good maintenance to reduce these problems is more critical. In a cooling tower, water is contacting and evaporating only in free air, but in an evaporative condenser the water and air contacts the heat transfer tubing, resulting in possible corrosion and scale formation.

***Comparison of Evaporative and Air Cooled Condensers.*** The lowest temperature to which water can be cooled by evaporation is the ambient wet bulb temperature (WB). The wet bulb is the temperature to which air is cooled when water is evaporated into it until the air reaches a condition at which it is completely saturated with water vapor.

The water is cooled to within a few degrees of the WB in an evaporative condenser. This temperature is considerably lower than that of the ambient air in summer. The result is that condensing temperatures for evaporative condensers (and water cooled condensers with cooling towers) are usually 15 to 20°F below those for air cooled condensers. Consequently, significantly less compressor power is required. Table 7.1 compares typical energy requirements for the three types of condensers.

Corrosion, scale, and possible water freeze-up are problems that require careful maintenance with evaporative condensers, but do not exist with air cooled condensers.

***Winter Operation.*** If the system is to be operated in below-freezing weather, special provisions must be made if the evaporative condenser is outdoors. One solution is to provide a heating source in the sump. Another is to locate an auxiliary tank in a heated space indoors, below a roof mounted condenser. The water continually drains from the sump to the indoor tank.

Another solution is to operate the evaporative condenser with a dry coil in winter. That is, the water is drained from the system, and it operates as an air cooled condenser. Since the capacity of the unit is much less with dry coil operation it must be checked to see if it is adequate for the expected refrigeration load in winter.

***Subcooling.*** Subcooling of the refrigerant, generally desired, can be accomplished in a few ways. The coil can be made large enough to handle the additional heat transfer. Or a separate subcooling coil can be provided. The coil can be located on the air inlet side so that it is contacted by the colder air or water. The coil could also be immersed in the drain pan water. When using a subcooling coil, it should be located downstream from the receiver (Figure 7.12). If the subcooled liquid were piped into the receiver from the condenser, it might be reheated in the warm receiver, resulting in flashing in the liquid line.

## 7.11 Condenser Pressure Control

The condenser or head pressure will change with the refrigeration load and with the tem-

**TABLE 7.1** Comparative Performance of Condensers (Typical)

| Condenser Type | Inlet Temperature, °F | Outlet Temperature, °F | Condensing Temperature, °F | Compressor Power, kW/ton at 40°F SST |
|---|---|---|---|---|
| Water cooled | 85 | 95 | 105 | 0.93 |
| Evaporative | — | — | 105 | 0.93 |
| Air cooled | 95 | 108 | 120 | 1.14 |
| | 110 | 123 | 135 | 1.42 |

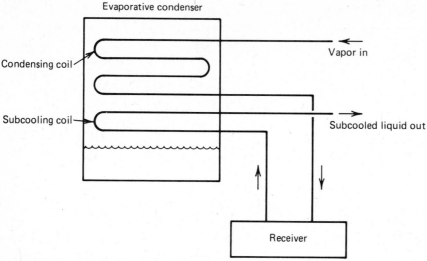

**FIGURE 7.12** Arrangement of condenser subcooling coil—on discharge side of receiver.

perature and flow rate of the cooling medium. If the refrigeration load increases, the amount of refrigerant flowing through the condenser increases. This raises the condensing (head) pressure, and therefore the condensing temperature. A high condensing temperature will result in a reduction in system capacity, increased compressor power, and possible overloading of the compressor motor; damage may occur to both compressor and motor. Safety controls on the unit protect against high head pressure.

A decrease in refrigeration load results in the opposite pressure effect. The flow control device throttles flow through the system. Less refrigerant enters the condenser, and the condensing pressure and temperature drop. A decrease in the temperature of the cooling water or air will have the same effect. Within limits this is desirable, since it reduces compressor power. For systems with expansion valves, however, the expansion valve capacity is a function of the pressure drop across it. If the high-side pressure is too low, the valve capacity will decrease too much and starve the evaporator. This may result in insufficient

refrigeration capacity, frost formation on the coil, insufficient velocity to return oil, and safety control cutout of the compressor. In order to prevent these problems, controls are necessary to maintain adequate condensing pressure.

All head-pressure controls operate by controlling condenser capacity. If the condenser capacity is reduced it cannot condense refrigerant at the same rate, and the head pressure builds up.

Controls may be activated directly from condenser pressure, or from the cooling medium temperature.

## 7.12 Head-Pressure Control of Air Cooled Condensers

Air cooled condensers are especially subject to low head pressure when operating in climates with low winter air temperatures. The two general means of head-pressure control used in air cooled condensers are those that use air-side control and those that use refrigerant-side control.

Air-side control operates by reducing the

air flow rate through the condenser, thereby decreasing its capacity and resulting in a rise in head pressure. Three methods can be used: fan cycling, damper modulation, and fan speed control.

*Fan cycling.* Fans are cycled off and on in response to the signal. A direct head-pressure control signal is not used, because it results in too rapid a cycling. This would cause the expansion valve to hunt and also may cause the fan motor to burn out. Instead control is from the ambient air temperature.

Fan cycling is not suitable with a single fan because the head pressure would rise above the high pressure cut-out setting. When used with a multiple fan unit, fans may be dropped in sequence in response to air temperature, but one fan is always left operating.

*Damper Modulation.* In this method dampers in the air stream throttle to reduce air flow across the condenser coil, reducing capacity and therefore raising head pressure. Control may be arranged from either condenser pressure or ambient air temperature.

Fan power requirements for some types of fans increase as the air flow is throttled and air resistance increases. Care must be taken that the fan motor size is adequate in this situation.

*Fan Speed Control.* Solid-state speed control devices are used to reduce fan motor speed and thus air flow. The motor used is a type whose speed reduces as voltage drops. The solid-state device reduces voltage to the motor, in response to a signal from the condensing pressure or air temperature.

An additional off-cycle problem associated with low condenser pressure exists with air cooled condensers. In winter, with the condenser located outdoors, pressure in the condenser will be lower than in other parts of the system (unless it is a low temperature system), and refrigerant will migrate from higher pressure components, including the evap-

orator, lowering the evaporator pressure. When the system controls call for cycling on, the evaporator low pressure safety control will prevent the compressor from starting. One way of solving this potential problem is to use a time delay that bypasses the low pressure control on start-up.

*Refrigerant-side Control.* In this type of air cooled condenser control, the amount of active heat transfer surface is reduced by flooding the coil with liquid refrigerant. One method of doing this is shown in Figure 7.13. A bypass valve from the compressor opens when condenser pressure falls. The hot gas bypasses into the liquid line from the condenser to the receiver. This blocks liquid flow from the condenser, and condenser capacity falls. The hot gas pressure pressurizes the receiver, so that sufficient pressure exists to operate the expansion valve. A throttling valve to the condenser operates in conjunction with the bypass valve to throttle flow to the condenser as the bypass valve opens. In addition, on shutdown this valve and a check valve in the condenser outlet close, isolating the condenser, thus preventing migration of refrigerant to it.

Note that a refrigerant receiver is required with this method of control. A larger charge of

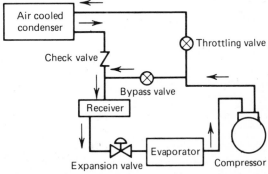

**FIGURE 7.13** Head-pressure control arrangement of an air cooled condenser, using refrigerant bypass (other arrangements are possible).

refrigerant is also required to flood the coil as well as to operate the system.

Air-side control provides good head-pressure control only to about 40°F outside temperature. Refrigerant-side control will operate well below that temperature.

## 7.13 Head-Pressure Control of Evaporative Condensers

At low refrigeration loads or at low outdoor wet bulb temperatures, the condensing pressure in evaporative condensers will fall below acceptable levels. Methods for maintaining adequate head pressure include fan cycling, damper modulation, and dry coil operation.

*Fan Cycling.* The fan is cycled off and on by a condensing pressure control signal. Unacceptably rapid cycling can occur under certain load conditions. Multispeed fan motor operation is a preferable alternative. The pump is not cycled off, because this leaves a film of scale on the tubes each time the pump stops.

*Damper Modulation.* Modulating dampers can be used to throttle air flow through the unit, in response to a condensing pressure controller. A variation is to use a set of dampers and a recirculation duct to mix discharge air with fresh incoming air. The mixed air has a higher humidity content and thereby less evaporative cooling capacity.

*Dry Coil Operation.* The circulating water spray system is not operated, and the unit operates as an air cooled condenser. The capacity decreases, thereby increasing head pressure. This method is usually combined with one of the others, so that greater flexibility and range can be obtained. The water must be drained if the system is to be operated below freezing weather.

## 7.14 Head-Pressure Control of Water Cooled Condensers

Head pressure is maintained in water cooled condensers by throttling water flow. With condensers that use once-through water, head-pressure control is obtained with a water regulating valve (Figure 7.14). This valve throttles water flow if condensing pressure drops. Capacity is reduced, and the pressure rises to its controlled value. The water regulating valve has an additional function of conserving water. This is especially important when city water is used because there is a charge for it.

The valve should always be installed in the discharge line leaving the condenser, so that the condenser is always filled with water. This reduces alternate wetting and drying of the tubes which would increase scale formation.

When recirculated water from a cooling tower is used, condensing pressure is maintained by controlling water temperature. This can be done with a valving arrangement in the condenser–tower piping. One method is with a bypass valve between the condenser discharge and inlet (Figure 7.15). The valve may be controlled from condensing water temper-

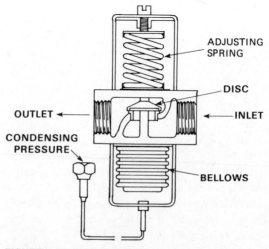

**FIGURE 7.14** Water regulating valve used to control head pressure in a water cooled condenser.

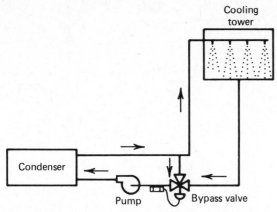

**FIGURE 7.15** Head-pressure control arrangement of a water cooled condenser, using bypass around the cooling tower (other arrangements are possible).

ature or directly from condensing pressure. When the head pressure drops the bypass opens more. This increases condenser inlet water temperature, reducing capacity and raising head pressure.

Alternate methods of controlling head pressure when cooling towers are used are to throttle air flow through the tower by use of air dampers or by tower fan-speed control. The tower cooling capacity is reduced and warmer water returns to the condenser.

## 7.15 Condenser Performance

The condenser must remove both the heat gained in the evaporator from the refrigeration load and the heat of compression resulting from the power required to compress the gas. The rate of heat removed in the condenser is called the (total) *heat of rejection*. It was expressed in Equation 4.11

$$Q_c = Q_e + P$$

where

$Q_c$ = total heat of rejection in condenser

$Q_e$ = heat gained in evaporator (refrigeration load)

$P$ = heat equivalent of power to compress gas

The required size of a condenser, that is, its required heat transfer surface area $A$ to remove the heat of rejection is determined from the heat transfer equation 6.5.

$$Q = U \times A \times \text{METD}$$

In order to use the heat transfer equation to find the required condenser size the heat transfer coefficient $U$ must be determined. This is somewhat difficult, since the value of $U$ depends on many variables, such as fluid velocity, turbulence, viscosity, temperature, and the like. For this reason manufacturers often present rating data for their condensers in a simplified manner. In the following sections we examine various forms in which rating data are presented.

## 7.16 Rating and Selection of Water Cooled Condensers

A manufacturer's ratings for a group of water cooled condensers are shown in Table 7.2 and Figures 7.16 and 7.17. Table 7.2 lists the basic physical data of each condenser. Figure 7.16 lists the heat transfer coefficients, and Figure 7.17 lists the water pressure drops. To select a condenser for a given application, the following data are required.

1. Total heat of rejection, $Q_c$.

2. Condensing temperature.

3. Condensing water entering temperature.

4. Condensing water GPM or temperature rise.

5. Water fouling resistance.

6. Dimensional limitations of condenser and water pressure drop limitations, if any.

An approximate rule of thumb used at air conditioning temperature ranges is that the total heat of rejection is about 20 to 25 percent more than the refrigeration load. The proportion increases as the evaporating temperature decreases. Typical condenser water supply rates used are in the range of 2.5 to 3 GPM per

**TABLE 7.2** Shell-and-Tube Water Cooled Condenser Ratings

| | | | | | | | | |
|---|---|---|---|---|---|---|---|---|
| | Performance and Physical Data[a] | | | | | | | |
| | Capacity & Water P.D.[b] | | | | Physical Data | | | |
| | EWT 85°F; C.T. 105°F | | | | | Effective | Pumpdown | Approximate Minimum |
| Model | Tons[c] | GPM | Number of Passes | P.D. PSI | Number of Tubes | Surface Ft.² | Capacity (lb) | Operating Charge |
| GTR 804B[b] | 20.0 | 60 | 4 | 7.2 | 40 | 92 | 58 | 13 |
| GTR 806B | 29.6 | 100 | 2 | 3.6 | 40 | 140 | 87 | 21 |
| GTR1004A[b] | 26.0 | 81 | 4 | 7.7 | 52 | 119 | 95 | 19 |
| GTR1004B[b] | 32.0 | 96 | 4 | 7.2 | 64 | 147 | 89 | 23 |
| GTR1006B | 41.5 | 128 | 2 | 2.5 | 64 | 224 | 133 | 35 |
| GTR 808B | 40.3 | 120 | 2 | 5.9 | 40 | 191 | 118 | 35 |
| GTR1008A | 54.4 | 162 | 2 | 5.9 | 52 | 249 | 194 | 46 |
| GTR1008B | 64.5 | 192 | 2 | 5.9 | 64 | 306 | 181 | 47 |
| GTR1206B | 64.8 | 200 | 2 | 2.5 | 100 | 358 | 185 | 47 |
| GTR1208A | 84.7 | 252 | 2 | 5.9 | 84 | 401 | 267 | 66 |
| GTR1208B | 100.8 | 300 | 2 | 5.9 | 100 | 477 | 246 | 67 |
| GTR1406A | 84.2 | 260 | 2 | 2.5 | 130 | 465 | 205 | 66 |
| GTR1408A | 131.1 | 390 | 2 | 5.9 | 130 | 621 | 273 | 81 |
| GTR1408B | 151.0 | 468 | 2 | 5.9 | 154 | 735 | 243 | 70 |

[a]Data for R-22.
[b]New models.
[c]Capacity ratings are based on scale factor of 0.0005.
Courtesy of Acme Division, Gulf & Western Manufacturing Co., Jackson, Michigan.

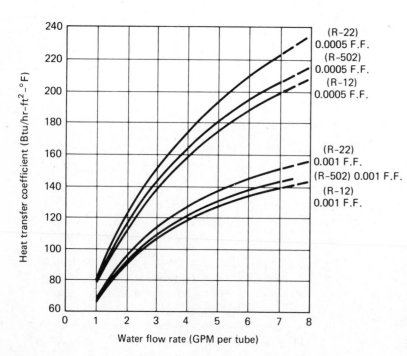

**FIGURE 7.16** Heat transfer coefficients for water cooled condensers listed in Table 7.2. (Courtesy of Acme Division, Gulf & Western Manufacturing Co., Jackson, Michigan)

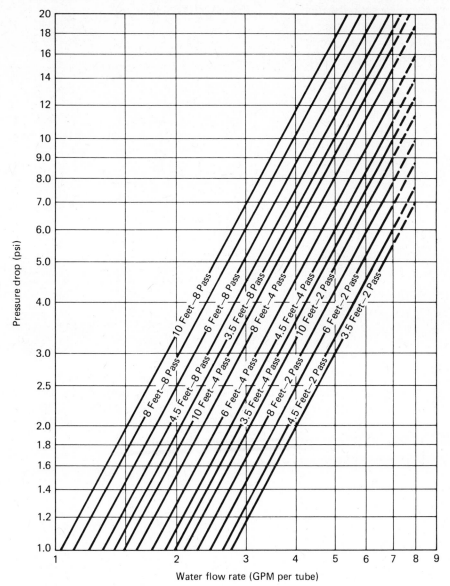

**FIGURE 7.17** Water pressure drop for water cooled condensers listed in Table 7.2. (Courtesy of Acme Division, Gulf & Western Manufacturing Co., Jackson, Michigan)

ton of refrigeration when recirculated water is used. When once-through wasted water is used, a smaller water quantity is generally used, in the range of 1 to 2 GPM per ton, to conserve water use.

Use of the rating tables is illustrated in the following example.

***Example 7.1*** Select the smallest required size condenser for the following conditions, with a system using R-22.

1. Refrigeration load = 100 tons. Compressor BHP = 140.

2. Condensing temperature = 105°F.

3. Condensing water supply temperature = 85°F.

4. Condensing water temperature rise = 10°F.

5. Fouling resistance (fouling factor) = 0.001.

*Solution*

1. The total heat rejection, using Equation 4.11, is

$$Q_c = Q_e + P$$

$$= 100 \text{ tons} \times \frac{12{,}000 \text{ Btu/hr}}{1 \text{ ton}}$$

$$+ 140 \text{ hp} \times \frac{2545 \text{ Btu/hr}}{1 \text{ hp}}$$

$$= 1{,}200{,}000 + 356{,}300$$

$$= 1{,}556{,}000 \text{ Btu/hr}$$

$$= 129.7 \text{ tons}$$

2. Using Equation 2.4, the water flow rate is

$$\text{GPM} = \frac{24 \times \text{tons}}{\text{TC}}$$

$$= \frac{24 \times 129.7}{(95 - 85)} = 311 \text{ GPM}$$

3. The METD is now found.

$$\text{GTD} = 110 - 85 = 25°F$$

$$\text{LTD} = 110 - 95 = 15°F$$

Using Table 6.2, the METD = 19.6°F.

4. Select a trial condenser size. Table 7.2 lists the capacity in tons for the conditions listed. From Table 7.2, Model No. 1408A has a capacity of 131.1 tons of heat rejection, and has 130 tubes, 2 passes, and 621 ft$^2$ of surface.

5. Find the flow rate per tube for this condenser.

$$\text{GPM/tube} = \frac{\text{GPM} \times \text{number of passes}}{\text{number of tubes}}$$

$$= \frac{311 \times 2}{130} = 4.8 \text{ GPM/tube}$$

6. The condenser size can now be checked at the actual conditions to see if it is satisfactory.

From Figure 7.16 the *U*-factor is 135.

Using the heat transfer equation (6.5), the required surface area is

$$A = \frac{Q}{U \times \text{METD}}$$

$$= \frac{1{,}556{,}000}{135 \times 19.6} = 588 \text{ ft}^2$$

Model No. 1408A is satisfactory.

7. The water pressure drop is found from Figure 7.17. The last number in the model number indicates the length in feet (8 ft).

From Figure 7.17 the pressure drop through a two pass, 8-ft-long condenser is 3.8 psi.

## 7.17 Rating and Selection of Air Cooled Condensers

Manufacturers generally present rating data for air cooled condensers (and often for water cooled condensers) in a simplified manner, so that it is not necessary to use the heat transfer equation. The air flow rates are fixed for each size condenser, so the $U$-value is approximately constant. The only variable is therefore the temperature difference between the ambient air and the condensing refrigerant. Table 7.3 is an example of air cooled condenser ratings.

*Example 7.2* Select an air cooled condenser for a system using R-12, in New York City, with a total heat rejection of 190,00 Btu/hr. The ambient air temperature is 95°F and the condensing temperature is 115°F.

**TABLE 7.3** Air Cooled Condenser Ratings/Direct Drive Models (60 Hz)

| | Refrigerant R22 | | | | |
|---|---|---|---|---|---|
| | Total Heat Rejection, MBH[a] | | | | |
| Model | Temperature Difference (TD), °F | | | | |
| LSBC | 30 | 25 | 20 | 15 | 1 |
| 061D | 83 | 69 | 55 | 41 | 2.75 |
| 141D | 122 | 100 | 81 | 61 | 4.05 |
| 142D | 160 | 132 | 107 | 80 | 5.35 |
| 183D | 250 | 208 | 166 | 125 | 8.30 |
| 202D | 277 | 230 | 185 | 138 | 9.25 |
| 222D | 315 | 263 | 210 | 160 | 10.50 |
| 261D | 387 | 323 | 285 | 193 | 14.25 |
| 181D | 475 | 395 | 316 | 238 | 15.8 |
| 241D | 562 | 468 | 374 | 281 | 18.7 |
| 182D | 616 | 512 | 410 | 308 | 20.5 |
| 242D | 656 | 545 | 436 | 328 | 21.8 |
| 161D | 830 | 690 | 552 | 415 | 27.6 |
| 201[b] | — | — | — | — | — |
| 221D | 984 | 820 | 666 | 492 | 32.8 |
| 281D | 1105 | 920 | 736 | 552 | 36.8 |
| 282D | 1306 | 1098 | 870 | 653 | 43.5 |

**TABLE 7.3** Continued

| | Refrigerant R502 | | | | |
|---|---|---|---|---|---|
| | Total Heat Rejection, MBH[a] | | | | |
| Model | Temperature Difference (TD), °F | | | | |
| LSBC | 30 | 25 | 20 | 15 | 1 |
| 061D | 80 | 67 | 54 | 40 | 2.70 |
| 141D | 118 | 98 | 79 | 59 | 3.95 |
| 142D | 154 | 128 | 102 | 77 | 5.10 |
| 183D | 240 | 201 | 161 | 120 | 8.05 |
| 202D | 270 | 224 | 180 | 135 | 9.00 |
| 222D | 306 | 255 | 203 | 153 | 10.15 |
| 261D | 375 | 313 | 250 | 187 | 12.50 |
| 181D | 460 | 383 | 306 | 230 | 15.3 |
| 241D | 546 | 455 | 364 | 273 | 18.2 |
| 182D | 598 | 498 | 398 | 299 | 19.9 |
| 242D | 636 | 530 | 424 | 318 | 21.2 |
| 161D | 804 | 670 | 536 | 402 | 26.8 |
| 201[b] | — | — | — | — | — |
| 221D | 958 | 798 | 633 | 479 | 31.9 |
| 281D | 1072 | 892 | 714 | 536 | 35.7 |
| 282D | 1280 | 1060 | 844 | 653 | 42.7 |

| | Refrigerant R12 | | | | |
|---|---|---|---|---|---|
| | Total Heat Rejection, MBH[a] | | | | |
| Model | Temperature Difference (TD), °F | | | | |
| LSBC | 30 | 25 | 20 | 15 | 1 |
| 061D | 78 | 65 | 52 | 39 | 2.60 |
| 141D | 115 | 96 | 76 | 57 | 3.80 |
| 142D | 150 | 125 | 100 | 75 | 5.00 |
| 183D | 235 | 195 | 156 | 118 | 7.80 |
| 202D | 260 | 217 | 173 | 130 | 8.65 |
| 222D | 296 | 248 | 198 | 149 | 9.90 |
| 261D | 363 | 303 | 242 | 182 | 12.10 |
| 181D | 446 | 370 | 296 | 223 | 14.8 |
| 241D | 529 | 440 | 352 | 264 | 17.6 |
| 182D | 580 | 482 | 386 | 289 | 19.3 |
| 242D | 616 | 512 | 410 | 308 | 20.5 |
| 161D | 777 | 647 | 518 | 388 | 25.9 |
| 201[b] | — | — | — | — | — |
| 221D | 924 | 770 | 616 | 462 | 30.8 |
| 281D | 1038 | 865 | 692 | 519 | 34.6 |
| 282D | 1226 | 1020 | 816 | 613 | 40.8 |

[a]MBH = thousands of Btu/hr
[b]Not available in direct drive
Courtesy Dunham–Bush, Inc.

*Solution* The temperature difference is $115 - 95 = 20°F$. From Table 7.3 a model No. LSBC 222 D condenser is adequate, with a capacity of 198,00 Btu/hr.

Air cooled condenser ratings are generally based on air mass flow rates delivered at sea level. At higher altitudes the fan will deliver a smaller mass flow rate, since the air density decreases. This will reduce the heat transfer rate. To correct for this effect, the required total heat rejection should be increased, by 5 percent for each additional 2000 feet of elevation.

**Example 7.3** Using the previous example, select a condenser if the unit is located in Salt Lake City, Utah (approximate elevation is 4000 ft).

*Solution* The heat rejection is increased by 10 percent.

$$190,000 \times 1.10 = 209,000 \text{ Btu/hr}$$

The next size condenser, a Model 261 D, is now required, with a listed capacity of 242,000 Btu/hr. Another possible solution might be to increase the design temperature difference by increasing the condensing temperature, using the smaller unit. However this increases the compressor power.

## 7.18 Condensing Units

The great majority of refrigeration equipment used today is manufactured and supplied in various packaged forms, rather than as individual components. One of the most popular is the *condensing unit,* in which the compressor, condenser, and controls are all assembled and tested in the factory. This reduces installation costs, ensures proper matching of components for size, and lessens the likelihood of installation errors occurring.

When components are selected separately, their capacities seldom exactly match, and it may be necessary to determine the resulting capacity of the combination, called the *balance point.* When package units are used this is not necessary, as the capacity is determined by the manufacturer. The subject of determining the balance point is taken up in Chapter 14.

## 7.19 Rating and Selection of Air Cooled Condensing Units

Typical ratings of a group of air cooled condensing units are shown in Table 7.4. In order to select a unit, the following information is required.

1. Refrigeration load.

**TABLE 7.4** Air Cooled Condensing Unit Ratings[ab]

| Model | Suction Temperature °F | Condenser Entering Air Temperature, °F | | | | | | | | | |
| | | 85°F | | 95°F | | 100°F | | 105°F | | 115°F | |
| | | Tons | kW[c] | Tons | kW | Tons | kW | Tons | kW | Tons | kW |
|---|---|---|---|---|---|---|---|---|---|---|---|
| ACU 025 | 30 | 21.8 | 25.5 | 19.2 | 27.0 | 18.5 | 27.2 | 17.7 | 27.5 | 16.1 | 29.0 |
| | 35 | 23.5 | 27.5 | 21.8 | 28.5 | 21.0 | 29.2 | 20.2 | 29.5 | 18.3 | 31.0 |
| | 40 | 26.2 | 29.0 | 24.4 | 30.0 | 23.6 | 31.0 | 22.7 | 31.5 | 21.0 | 33.0 |
| | 45 | 29.1 | 30.5 | 27.3 | 32.0 | 26.4 | 32.7 | 25.5 | 33.5 | 24.6[d] | 34.7 |
| | 50 | 32.2 | 31.5 | 30.2 | 33.5 | 29.3 | 34.5 | 28.4 | 35.5 | 27.7[d] | 36.0 |
| ACU 030 | 30 | 24.5 | 29.5 | 22.7 | 30.5 | 21.8 | 31.5 | 20.6 | 32.0 | 18.5 | 33.0 |
| | 35 | 27.5 | 31.0 | 25.2 | 32.5 | 24.3 | 33.5 | 23.4 | 34.0 | 21.3 | 35.0 |
| | 40 | 31.1 | 32.5 | 28.6 | 34.5 | 27.5 | 35.0 | 26.6 | 36.0 | 24.5 | 37.5 |
| | 45 | 34.4 | 34.0 | 32.0 | 36.0 | 30.9 | 37.0 | 29.8 | 38.0 | 27.7 | 39.5 |
| | 50 | 38.0 | 35.5 | 35.5 | 37.5 | 34.4 | 38.5 | 33.5 | 39.5 | 32.3[d] | 40.5 |

TABLE 7.4 Continued

| Model | Suction Temperature °F | Condenser Entering Air Temperature, °F | | | | | | | | | |
|---|---|---|---|---|---|---|---|---|---|---|---|
| | | 85°F | | 95°F | | 100°F | | 105°F | | 115°F | |
| | | Tons | kW[c] | Tons | kW | Tons | kW | Tons | kW | Tons | kW |
| ACU 040 | 30 | 31.5 | 38.0 | 28.9 | 39.5 | 27.5 | 40.5 | 26.0 | 41.5 | 23.8 | 43.0 |
| | 35 | 35.2 | 40.0 | 32.6 | 42.0 | 31.2 | 43.0 | 29.7 | 44.0 | 27.1 | 46.0 |
| | 40 | 39.6 | 42.5 | 36.7 | 44.5 | 35.4 | 45.5 | 34.1 | 46.5 | 31.2 | 48.5 |
| | 45 | 44.0 | 45.0 | 41.4 | 47.0 | 40.0 | 48.0 | 38.5 | 49.5 | 35.6 | 51.5 |
| | 50 | 49.1 | 47.0 | 46.2 | 49.5 | 44.7 | 50.5 | 43.3 | 51.5 | 41.8[d] | 52.5 |
| ACU 050 | 30 | 42.4 | 51.0 | 39.0 | 54.0 | 37.0 | 55.0 | 35.2 | 56.0 | 31.9 | 59.0 |
| | 35 | 47.3 | 54.0 | 44.0 | 57.0 | 42.2 | 58.5 | 40.3 | 60.0 | 36.7 | 62.5 |
| | 40 | 52.8 | 57.0 | 49.5 | 60.0 | 48.2 | 61.5 | 45.8 | 63.0 | 42.2 | 66.0 |
| | 45 | 58.7 | 60.0 | 55.4 | 63.5 | 53.5 | 65.0 | 51.7 | 67.0 | 48.0 | 69.0 |
| | 50 | 64.9 | 63.0 | 61.2 | 66.5 | 59.4 | 68.5 | 57.8 | 70.0 | 55.4[d] | 72.0 |
| ACU 060 | 30 | 49.0 | 58.5 | 44.9 | 61.0 | 43.1 | 62.0 | 41.2 | 63.0 | 37.1 | 66.0 |
| | 35 | 55.0 | 62.0 | 50.9 | 65.0 | 48.6 | 66.5 | 46.7 | 68.0 | 42.6 | 70.5 |
| | 40 | 61.0 | 66.0 | 57.3 | 69.0 | 55.0 | 70.5 | 52.7 | 72.0 | 48.6 | 75.0 |
| | 45 | 67.8 | 69.0 | 63.7 | 72.5 | 61.4 | 74.0 | 59.6 | 76.0 | 55.0 | 79.5 |
| | 50 | 75.2 | 72.5 | 71.0 | 76.0 | 68.8 | 78.0 | 66.4 | 80.0 | 64.6[d] | 82.0 |
| ACU 075 | 30 | 60.0 | 71.0 | 55.2 | 75.0 | 52.6 | 76.0 | 50.2 | 78.5 | 41.8 | 81.5 |
| | 35 | 67.5 | 75.5 | 62.5 | 79.5 | 59.8 | 81.5 | 57.6 | 83.5 | 52.8 | 87.0 |
| | 40 | 75.3 | 80.0 | 70.4 | 85.0 | 67.6 | 87.0 | 65.3 | 88.0 | 60.3 | 92.0 |
| | 45 | 84.2 | 84.5 | 79.0 | 89.5 | 76.4 | 91.5 | 73.5 | 93.5 | 68.6 | 97.0 |
| | 50 | 93.5 | 88.5 | 88.0 | 94.0 | 85.1 | 96.0 | 82.5 | 98.0 | 79.4 | 100.0 |
| ACU 090 | 30 | 71.9 | 89.0 | 66.4 | 93.0 | 62.9 | 94.5 | 60.0 | 96.0 | 54.1 | 100.0 |
| | 35 | 80.2 | 95.0 | 74.7 | 99.0 | 71.5 | 101.0 | 68.3 | 103.0 | 61.9 | 107.0 |
| | 40 | 89.8 | 100.0 | 83.9 | 105.0 | 80.7 | 107.0 | 77.5 | 109.0 | 71.5 | 113.5 |
| | 45 | 100.4 | 106.0 | 93.5 | 110.5 | 90.3 | 113.0 | 87.0 | 115.5 | 84.3[d] | 117.5 |
| | 50 | 111.3 | 110.0 | 104.3 | 116.0 | 100.8 | 119.0 | 97.6 | 122.0 | 93.9[d] | 124.0 |
| ACU 100 | 30 | 82.5 | 103.0 | 76.5 | 107.5 | 73.8 | 109.5 | 70.6 | 112.0 | 64.6 | 116.0 |
| | 35 | 93.0 | 109.5 | 86.6 | 115.0 | 83.9 | 117.5 | 80.2 | 120.0 | 73.3 | 125.0 |
| | 40 | 104.0 | 116.0 | 97.2 | 122.0 | 93.9 | 124.5 | 90.3 | 127.0 | 83.4 | 133.0 |
| | 45 | 115.9 | 122.0 | 108.6 | 128.5 | 105.1 | 131.0 | 102.7 | 134.0 | 98.0[d] | 137.5 |
| | 50 | 128.8 | 128.0 | 121.0 | 135.0 | 118.0 | 138.0 | 113.7 | 141.0 | — | — |
| ACU 120 | 30 | 91.7 | 115.0 | 84.3 | 120.0 | 80.7 | 122.5 | 77.0 | 125.0 | 69.7 | 131.0 |
| | 35 | 102.7 | 123.0 | 94.4 | 129.0 | 90.7 | 132.0 | 87.0 | 135.0 | 78.8 | 140.0 |
| | 40 | 114.6 | 130.5 | 107.2 | 137.0 | 102.7 | 140.0 | 98.0 | 143.0 | 91.7 | 148.5 |
| | 45 | 128.3 | 138.0 | 121.0 | 144.0 | 115.5 | 147.0 | 111.8 | 151.0 | 106.3[d] | 154.0 |
| | 50 | 143.0 | 145.0 | 134.7 | 152.0 | 129.7 | 156.0 | 124.6 | 159.0 | — | — |

Notes: [a]Direct interpolation for conditions between ratings is permissible but not extrapolation.
    [b]Altitude correction

| Elevation, ft | 2000 | 4000 | 6000 |
|---|---|---|---|
| Capacity Factor | 0.99 | 0.98 | 0.97 |

[c]kW input shown is for compressor only (see electrical data for fan hp).
[d]100°F Condenser Entering Air Temperature.
Courtesy Dunham–Bush, Inc.

2. Saturated suction temperature (SST).

3. Air temperature entering condenser.

4. Altitude.

**Example 7.4**  Select an air cooled condensing unit at sea level for a refrigeration load of 25 tons. SST = 30°F, air entering temperature = 100°F.

*Solution*  From Table 7.4 a Model ACU 40 has a refrigeration capacity of 27.5 tons at the conditions given. The compressor power input is 40.5 kW at 27.5 tons. The energy efficiency ratio (EER) can also be found:

$$\text{Capacity} = 27.5 \text{ tons} \times 12,000 \ \frac{\text{Btu/hr}}{\text{ton}}$$

$$= 330,000 \text{ Btu/hr}$$

$$\text{EER} = \frac{\text{Capacity (Btu/hr)}}{\text{Power input (W)}}$$

$$= \frac{330,000}{40.5 \times 1000} = 8.1$$

# COOLING TOWERS

## 7.20 Water Cooling by Evaporation

When recirculated water is used in condensers, it is then cooled by evaporation of some of the water into the surrounding ambient air. The latent heat required to evaporate the water is drawn from the unevaporated water, reducing the temperature of both the liquid water and water vapor. The surrounding air is also cooled by this effect.

Because of the high latent heat of vaporization of water (about 1000 Btu/lb) only a small portion of the water used needs to be evaporated. Although the *cooling tower* is the most common device used for cooling water by evaporation, occasionally ponds are used.

## 7.21 Cooling Ponds and Spray Ponds

Occasionally a natural or artificial pond of water is used to cool condenser water. The natural evaporation from the surface cools the body of water in the pond. The condenser water is pumped from the cooling pond and then emptied back into it. Sometimes the pond water is sprayed into the air (a spray pond). This increases the evaporation and heat transfer rate considerably for a given area of pond, because the surface area of water is greatly increased by breaking it into small droplets.

Cooling ponds and spray ponds are undesirable for a number of reasons. Their capacity varies considerably with the wind velocity, and is very difficult to predict. With very low wind velocities the size of the pond required may be unacceptably large. At high wind velocities a considerable amount of spray water may be carried off (this is called drift loss). This increases the water cost if it is purchased, and the drift may be annoying or even harmful to the environment.

## 7.22 Cooling Tower Types

A cooling tower is an enclosed structure designed to cool water by evaporation in a controlled and efficient manner. Tower designs are oriented toward breaking the water up into drops, thus increasing the surface area for evaporation, in as small a structure as is feasible. Towers may be classified in a number of ways, which will be discussed in the following sections.

## 7.23 Nonmechanical and Mechanical Draft Towers

The word *draft* refers to the pressure difference necessary to cause air to flow through a device such as a cooling tower. *Nonmechanical* draft towers do not have fans to develop the pressure to move air through the tower. Air motion is achieved by other means. Two types

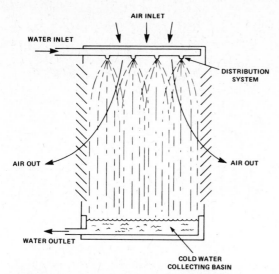

**FIGURE 7.18** Atmospheric spray cooling tower. (Reprinted with permission from 1979 Equipment ASHRAE Handbook and Product Directory)

of nonmechanical draft towers are discussed here: the *atmospheric spray* tower and the *ejector* tower.

One of the first tower types used was the *atmospheric spray* tower (Figure 7.18). The warm water is pumped to the top of the tower and sprayed through nozzles downward into the empty volume in the tower. The effect of the spray motion is to draw or induce air downward through the open air inlet on top. The air flows out through louvers on the sides of the tower. Wind effects may also cause additional air flow horizontally through the tower. The cooled water is collected in the basin or pan at the bottom and returned to the condenser.

The atmospheric spray tower is not very efficient, because the rate of air flow created by the induction effect is small. As a result, a larger structure is needed than for other types. Furthermore, the variation of wind effects changes and makes it difficult to predict the cooling capacity.

A modern type of nonmechanical draft tower is the *ejector* tower (Figure 7.19). A high velocity horizontally directed water spray induces inlet air and carries it through the tower. The performance of this type of tower is predictable and also comparable in capacity to mechanical draft towers.

A *mechanical draft* tower uses fans to create the pressure (draft) to move the ambient air through the tower. This enables movement of large volumes of air through a relatively small space, decreasing the overall size of the tower for a given required capacity. Since the air flow rate is controlled at a known quantity not dependent on wind, it also means that the capacity of the tower can be accurately determined.

There are two types of mechanical draft towers, *forced draft* and *induced draft*. (Figure 7.20). The forced draft tower has the fan located at the air inlet, and thus forces the air through. The induced draft type has the fan at the air outlet, and thus draws the air through.

Fans may be of either the centrifugal or the propeller type. Centrifugal fans create a higher pressure and are therefore more suitable when there is considerable resistance to

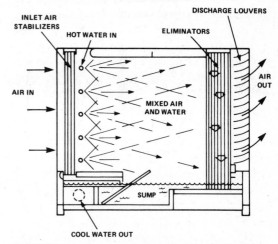

**FIGURE 7.19** Ejector cooling tower. (Reprinted with permission from 1979 Equipment ASHRAE Handbook and Product Directory)

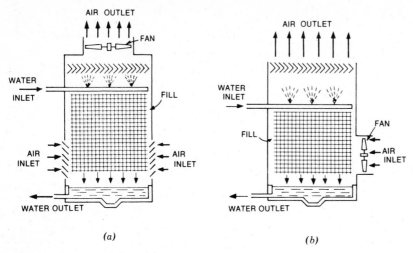

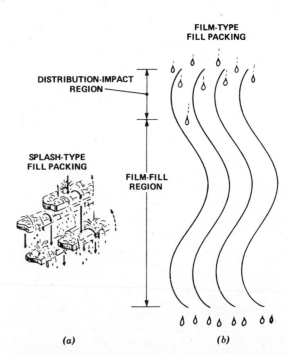

**FIGURE 7.20** Induced draft and forced draft cooling towers (counterflow arrangement). (a) Induced draft, counterflow. (b) Forced draft, counterflow.

air flow through the tower. Propeller fans tend to be noisier. Centrifugal fans are not generally used in the induced draft arrangement. The moist air is corrosive and because of their construction it is difficult to prevent corrosion of centrifugal fans. In both mechanical draft and ejector towers eliminators are generally installed in the leaving air stream, to catch the water that would be entrained and carried out with the discharge air.

In mechanical draft towers the warm water is pumped to the top of the tower and then either sprayed downward through nozzles or delivered to a trough with holes in the bottom through which the water falls. The space inside the tower is packed with material called the *fill*. The fill serves two purposes, to increase the water heat transfer surface area, and to slow down the velocity of the falling water. This keeps the water in the tower for a longer time, thereby increasing the cooling effect.

There are two types of fill, the *splash* type and the *film* type (Figure 7.21). The splash type consists of loosely arranged slats that the water splashes over while descending, break-

**FIGURE 7.21** Types of cooling tower fill. (a) Splash-type fill. (b) Film-type fill. (Reprinted with permission from the 1979 Equipment ASHRAE Handbook and Product Directory)

ing into drops. This type of fill is used in larger towers. The film-type fill is much more densely packed, and is designed to create a thin film of water on the fill surface. Film-type fill is used in smaller towers.

## 7.24 Flow Arrangement of Air and Water

Cooling towers can be classified into three types according to the relative directions of flow of air and water with respect to each other: *parallel flow, counterflow,* and *crossflow.* Parallel flow means that the air and water flow in the same direction. The ejector type, shown in Figure 7.19, is an example of a tower using parallel flow. In the counterflow arrangement (Figure 7.20) the air and water move in opposite directions. In the crossflow type (Figure 7.22) the air and water move at right angles to each other. Although the explanation given in Chapter 6 concerning the advantages of counterflow in a heat exchanger holds true for cooling towers, there are many other factors in cooling tower design that affect heat transfer. Apparently all three types are competitive in actual towers available.

## 7.25 Materials of Construction

Smaller factory assembled towers are generally constructed of either metal or plastic casing and fill. Galvanized steel is the most

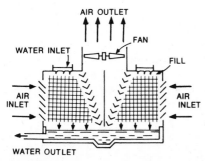

**FIGURE 7.22** Induced draft cooling tower (crossflow arrangement).

common metal. Stainless steel is sometimes used when very corrosive conditions are encountered. Larger field erected towers are usually basically of wood construction, either redwood or fir. The wood is treated with preservatives. When fire codes require it, however, the structure may be metal. Mineral composition boards are often used for the casing and louvers.

## 7.26 Capacity Control

Capacity control of cooling towers is desirable both to conserve energy and to maintain condenser head pressure when expansion valves are used. Fan cycling or fan speed control with two-speed motors are both used to vary the capacity of cooling towers. Many systems have multiple tower units, so that the towers can be started or stopped one at a time. Modulating damper control is another effective method often used on centrifugal fan units. The use of condenser water bypass to control condenser–cooling tower capacity has been discussed previously in this chapter.

## 7.27 Winter Operation

The operation of cooling towers in below-freezing temperatures requires special precautions. Capacity control should be designed to keep the circulating water temperature above freezing. To prevent water in the basin from freezing a heating coil may be submerged in the water. One can use an indoor storage tank in the winter, then the tower basin operates dry, draining to the tank. Another concern with some types of towers is the formation of ice on the louvers, which would block air flow. In some cases the airflow direction can be reversed to warm and deice the louvers.

## 7.28 Water Loss

There are three causes of loss of some of the water circulating through a cooling tower.

First is the evaporation required to produce cooling. In a typical operating condition a cooling tower–condenser circulates about 3 GPM per ton of refrigeration. Under these circumstances about 1 percent of the water is evaporated to produce the required cooling, that is, about 0.03 GPM per ton. The second cause of water loss is the drift of water drops carried out with the discharge air. This quantity is a small fraction of the evaporation loss.

Water supplied to the cooling tower contains dissolved solids. Dirt from the surroundings will also continually enter the tower. The evaporation loss results in an increase in concentration of solids in the system, since only the water evaporates. If only that quantity lost by evaporation and drift were replaced, the concentration of solids would reach a level at which they would precipitate out of the water on surfaces as a coating, or *scale*. This would reduce the heat transfer effectiveness of the condenser. This problem is handled by regularly removing water from the tower basin, called *blowdown* or *bleed-off*. This is the third cause of water loss. Typically, about the same quantity of water is removed by blowdown as is lost by evaporation. In any case, you should obtain recommendations from a water treatment specialist about the quantity to be removed if you are in doubt. Additional procedures may be required to prevent scale; this subject will be covered in the next section. Water makeup to replace losses is usually provided through a water supply connection to the tower basin, controlled by a float valve in the basin.

The humid air leaving the cooling tower is close to its saturated condition. Under certain atmospheric conditions it may be cooled to a temperature at which fog will occur. Usually the only objection to fog is the annoyance caused by its presence. It is sometimes possible to eliminate it by changing operating conditions.

## 7.29 Water Treatment

Proper water treatment is an essential aspect of the cooling tower–condenser system to prevent loss of capacity, deterioration of the components, excess maintenance, and waste of energy. Four separate effects may require water treatment: *scale, corrosion, organic growths,* and *silt*.

*Scale* is the coating that results from the precipitation of dissolved solids out of water. It adds a thermal resistance (fouling resistance) to the condenser tubing and reduces the system refrigeration capacity. Some types of scale can also cause deterioration of materials. As mentioned previously, blowdown is the main way of preventing scale. Chemical additives may also be required, however.

*Corrosion* is the deterioration of metals caused by chemical reaction. Cooling tower components are subject to corrosion because of the presence of air, water, and substances in the water. Corrosion control can be handled by a number of methods, one or more of which may be required.

Corrosion is enhanced when the water is in an acid condition. The acidity is measured by a unit called the pH. Water having a pH of 7 is in a neutral condition. Values below 7 indicate an acidic condition; values above 7 indicate an alkaline condition. Water is often in an acidic condition in cooling towers because dissolved carbon dioxide forms carbonic acid. There are other acid-forming gases, particularly in industrialized polluted areas—sulfur dioxide, for example.

Corrosion control can be treated by adding chemicals that raise the pH of the water. The problem with this, however, is that it is often necessary to raise the pH to a highly alkaline level to stop corrosion completely. An alkaline hastens scale formation.

One solution to this dilemma is to add an alkaline chemical to increase the pH to a slightly acid condition, and then to add an *inhibitor*. This is a chemical that forms a protective film coating on the metal surfaces. Some inhibitors that protect against corrosion or scale are chromates, polyphosphates, and nitrates.

*Organic growths* include *algae, slime,* and *fungi*. They may cause deterioration, particularly of wood, and may coat heat transfer surfaces, reducing system capacity. Also of concern are possible health problems. The microorganisms that cause "legionnaires' disease" have been found in cooling tower water. Organic growth is generally destroyed by periodic dosing of the system with a biocide such as chlorine.

Dirt from the surroundings will gradually build up in the cooling tower basin in the form of a silt. This can be removed mechanically by periodic cleaning.

It must be stressed that the services of a water treatment specialist should always be used.

## 7.30 Wet Bulb Temperature

The minimum temperature to which the air and water can be cooled is called the air *wet bulb* (WB) temperature. The wet bulb temperature is defined as the temperature to which air is cooled when water is evaporated into the air to a saturated condition, with no heat being added to or removed from the mixture. The term *saturated condition* means that the air has absorbed all the water vapor it can hold. The wet bulb temperature of air can be measured by wrapping the sensing stem of a thermometer with a wet cloth and then moving the air past the sensing stem. The amount of water vapor that the air contains, called the humidity, can be stated in various ways, such as *relative humidity* and *humidity ratio*. The greater the initial humidity of the air, the less water vapor it can absorb. As a result, its wet bulb temperature is higher, that is, the temperature to which the water can be cooled is higher.

A further discussion of this subject can be found in air conditioning texts.

Design wet bulb and dry bulb (actual) temperatures are shown in Table 14.4.

## 7.31 Cooling Tower Rating and Selection

It is desirable to cool the condenser water to as low a temperature as practical, since lower temperatures mean less compressor power. (Temperature must not be so low as to result in inadequate head pressure, of course). In reality, the water is cooled to within about 5 to 10°F of the entering air WB temperature. The difference between the entering air WB and leaving water temperature is called the *approach*. The number of degrees the water is cooled is called the tower *range*. The tower capacity, called the *loading*, is the condenser heat rejection, of course, if the tower is used with a vapor compression refrigeration plant. For air conditioning applications ranges of around 10°F are common in humid climates under design conditions. Circulation rates of 3 GPM per ton and a heat rejection of 1.25 times the refrigeration load are corresponding approximate figures. These values are listed only to give you a sense of the numbers used. In an actual application, calculations must be made under varying assumptions, in order to arrive at the optimum size of tower and other components to result in the best initial and operating costs.

It should be noted that the load and resulting temperature range on cooling towers used in absorption refrigeration systems is considerably greater than with a vapor compression system (see Chapter 3).

Ratings for a group of cooling towers are shown in Table 7.5. The ratings are listed in GPM, a common way used by manufacturers.

***Example 7.5*** A cooling tower is to be selected for a vapor compression plant with a conden-

**TABLE 7.5** Cooling Tower Ratings (Capacity is in GPM of water)

| Hot water on °F | 90 | 90 | 95 | 90 | 95 | 95 | 95 | 97 | 100 | 102 | 103 | 105 | 95 | 100 | 102 | 103 | 105 | 95 | 97 | 100 | 102 | 103 | 105 | 95 | 103 | 105 |
|---|---|---|---|---|---|---|---|---|---|---|---|---|---|---|---|---|---|---|---|---|---|---|---|---|---|---|
| Cold water off °F | 80 | 80 | 85 | 80 | 85 | 85 | 85 | 87 | 85 | 85 | 85 | 85 | 85 | 85 | 85 | 85 | 85 | 85 | 87 | 85 | 85 | 85 | 85 | 85 | 85 | 85 |
| Wet bulb °F | 65 | 70 | 70 | 72 | 72 | 75 | 75 | 75 | 75 | 75 | 75 | 75 | 76 | 76 | 76 | 76 | 76 | 78 | 78 | 78 | 78 | 78 | 78 | 80 | 80 | 80 |
| F-115-A | 101 | 87 | 120 | 79 | 113 | 118 | 101 | 97 | 95 | 91 | 88 | 82 | 102 | 67 | 63 | 60 | 55 | 78 | 78 | 76 | 63 | 73 | 67 | 80 | 55 | 51 |
| F-115-B | 123 | 105 | 147 | 97 | 139 | 145 | 123 | 117 | 108 | 104 | 100 | 94 | 116 | 81 | 78 | 73 | 68 | 98 | 94 | 85 | 81 | 78 | 73 | 84 | 68 | 63 |
| F-115-C | 140 | 121 | 168 | 110 | 158 | 166 | 140 | 134 | 121 | 118 | 114 | 105 | 130 | 91 | 88 | 84 | 82 | 111 | 107 | 98 | 92 | 89 | 84 | 95 | 76 | 72 |
| F-115-D | 159 | 136 | 187 | 124 | 176 | 185 | 159 | 150 | 127 | 121 | 117 | 110 | 135 | 100 | 104 | 100 | 94 | 124 | 110 | 104 | 104 | 100 | 94 | 107 | 87 | 81 |
| F-120-A | 163 | 140 | 196 | 129 | 185 | 193 | 163 | 156 | 162 | 158 | 148 | 140 | 173 | 114 | 117 | 114 | 105 | 131 | 125 | 114 | 108 | 104 | 98 | 111 | 91 | 85 |
| F-120-B | 212 | 181 | 250 | 166 | 235 | 247 | 212 | 200 | 181 | 173 | 166 | 156 | 200 | 160 | 154 | 146 | 140 | 165 | 160 | 146 | 138 | 133 | 125 | 142 | 115 | 108 |
| F-125-A | 234 | 202 | 280 | 183 | 263 | 277 | 234 | 224 | 203 | 198 | 186 | 176 | 224 | 178 | 173 | 164 | 156 | 186 | 178 | 164 | 154 | 149 | 140 | 159 | 128 | 120 |
| F-125-B | 265 | 227 | 314 | 207 | 294 | 309 | 265 | 251 | 211 | 203 | 194 | 185 | 251 | 200 | 198 | 183 | 176 | 207 | 200 | 183 | 173 | 166 | 157 | 178 | 144 | 136 |
| F-130-A | 274 | 237 | 327 | 217 | 307 | 324 | 274 | 263 | 249 | 238 | 223 | 211 | 263 | 208 | 203 | 191 | 185 | 217 | 208 | 191 | 179 | 174 | 162 | 189 | 150 | 140 |
| F-130-B | 319 | 262 | 377 | 249 | 353 | 371 | 319 | 301 | 281 | 270 | 258 | 247 | 301 | 240 | 232 | 220 | 211 | 249 | 240 | 220 | 208 | 201 | 188 | 214 | 174 | 162 |
| F-140-A | 366 | 316 | 436 | 289 | 409 | 432 | 366 | 351 | 324 | 316 | 297 | 281 | 351 | 277 | 270 | 254 | 247 | 289 | 277 | 254 | 239 | 231 | 216 | 250 | 200 | 185 |
| F-140-B | 424 | 362 | 501 | 337 | 470 | 494 | 424 | 401 | 362 | 347 | 333 | 314 | 401 | 320 | 308 | 293 | 281 | 337 | 320 | 293 | 277 | 266 | 250 | 285 | 231 | 216 |
| F-150-A | 468 | 405 | 560 | 367 | 526 | 555 | 468 | 449 | 405 | 396 | 372 | 352 | 449 | 357 | 348 | 328 | 314 | 372 | 357 | 328 | 309 | 299 | 280 | 318 | 256 | 241 |
| F-150-B | 531 | 454 | 628 | 415 | 589 | 618 | 531 | 502 | 423 | 406 | 388 | 377 | 502 | 401 | 386 | 367 | 352 | 415 | 401 | 367 | 347 | 333 | 314 | 357 | 289 | 270 |
| F-160-A | 551 | 475 | 655 | 435 | 614 | 649 | 551 | 527 | 487 | 475 | 446 | 423 | 527 | 417 | 406 | 382 | 377 | 435 | 417 | 382 | 359 | 348 | 324 | 377 | 301 | 278 |
| F-160-B | 638 | 545 | 754 | 498 | 707 | 742 | 638 | 603 | 543 | 522 | 500 | 471 | 603 | 481 | 464 | 440 | 423 | 498 | 481 | 440 | 417 | 400 | 377 | 429 | 348 | 324 |
| F-175-A | 703 | 609 | 841 | 551 | 790 | 833 | 703 | 674 | 609 | 594 | 558 | 529 | 674 | 536 | 522 | 493 | 471 | 551 | 536 | 493 | 464 | 449 | 420 | 478 | 384 | 362 |
| F-175-B | 797 | 681 | 942 | 623 | 884 | 928 | 797 | 754 | 652 | 626 | 600 | 565 | 754 | 601 | 580 | 551 | 529 | 623 | 601 | 551 | 522 | 500 | 471 | 536 | 435 | 406 |
| F-190-A | 843 | 730 | 1009 | 661 | 948 | 1000 | 843 | 809 | 730 | 713 | 669 | 635 | 809 | 643 | 626 | 591 | 565 | 661 | 643 | 591 | 556 | 539 | 504 | 574 | 461 | 435 |
| F-190-B | 957 | 817 | 1131 | 748 | 1061 | 1113 | 957 | 904 | 818 | 799 | 669 | 635 | 783 | 722 | 696 | 661 | 635 | 748 | 722 | 661 | 626 | 600 | 565 | 643 | 522 | 487 |

| | | | | | | | | | | | | | | | | | | | | | | | | | |
|---|---|---|---|---|---|---|---|---|---|---|---|---|---|---|---|---|---|---|---|---|---|---|---|---|---|
| F-1100-A / F-2100-A | 970 | 840 | 1160 | 760 | 1090 | 970 | 1150 | 770 | 740 | 720 | 680 | 930 | 750 | 720 | 690 | 650 | 800 | 930 | 680 | 640 | 620 | 580 | 660 | 530 | 500 |
| F-1100-B / F-2100-B | 1100 | 940 | 1300 | 860 | 1220 | 1100 | 1280 | 860 | 830 | 800 | 760 | 1040 | 840 | 810 | 770 | 730 | 900 | 1040 | 760 | 710 | 690 | 640 | 740 | 600 | 560 |
| F-1120-A / F-2120-A | 1102 | 951 | 1310 | 870 | 1229 | 1102 | 1299 | 870 | 835 | 812 | 765 | 1055 | 846 | 812 | 777 | 754 | 904 | 1055 | 765 | 719 | 696 | 649 | 754 | 603 | 566 |
| F-1120B / F-2120-B | 1276 | 1090 | 1508 | 997 | 1415 | 1276 | 1484 | 997 | 962 | 928 | 881 | 1206 | 974 | 951 | 893 | 846 | 1050 | 1206 | 881 | 835 | 800 | 754 | 858 | 696 | 649 |
| F-2140-A | 1406 | 1218 | 1682 | 1102 | 1580 | 1406 | 1667 | 1116 | 1073 | 1044 | 986 | 1348 | 1087 | 1044 | 1000 | 942 | 1160 | 1348 | 986 | 928 | 898 | 841 | 957 | 768 | 725 |
| F-2140-B | 1595 | 1363 | 1885 | 1247 | 1769 | 1595 | 1856 | 1247 | 1203 | 1160 | 1102 | 1508 | 1218 | 1189 | 1116 | 1058 | 1305 | 1508 | 1102 | 1044 | 1000 | 942 | 1073 | 870 | 812 |
| F-2175-A | 1687 | 1461 | 2018 | 1322 | 1896 | 1687 | 2001 | 1339 | 1287 | 1252 | 1183 | 1618 | 1305 | 1252 | 1200 | 1031 | 1392 | 1618 | 1183 | 1113 | 1078 | 1009 | 1148 | 922 | 870 |
| F-2175-B | 1914 | 1635 | 2262 | 1496 | 2122 | 1914 | 2227 | 1496 | 1444 | 1392 | 1322 | 1809 | 1461 | 1426 | 1339 | 1270 | 1566 | 1809 | 1322 | 1252 | 1200 | 1131 | 1287 | 1044 | 974 |
| F-2220-A | 1940 | 1680 | 2320 | 1520 | 2180 | 1940 | 2300 | 1540 | 1480 | 1440 | 1360 | 1860 | 1500 | 1440 | 1380 | 1300 | 1600 | 1860 | 1360 | 1280 | 1240 | 1160 | 1320 | 1060 | 1000 |
| F-2220-B | 2200 | 1880 | 2600 | 1720 | 2440 | 2200 | 2560 | 1720 | 1660 | 1600 | 1520 | 2080 | 1680 | 1620 | 1540 | 1460 | 1800 | 2080 | 1520 | 1420 | 1380 | 1280 | 1480 | 1200 | 1120 |
| F-2230-A | 2204 | 1902 | 2621 | 1740 | 2459 | 2204 | 2598 | 1740 | 1670 | 1624 | 1531 | 2111 | 1693 | 1624 | 1554 | 1508 | 1808 | 2111 | 1531 | 1438 | 1392 | 1299 | 1508 | 1206 | 1132 |
| F-2230-B | 2552 | 2180 | 3016 | 1995 | 2830 | 2552 | 2969 | 1995 | 1925 | 1856 | 1763 | 2412 | 1948 | 1902 | 1786 | 1693 | 2110 | 2412 | 1763 | 1670 | 1600 | 1508 | 1716 | 1392 | 1299 |
| F-2300-A | 2813 | 2436 | 3364 | 2204 | 3161 | 2813 | 3335 | 2234 | 2146 | 2088 | 1972 | 2697 | 2175 | 2088 | 2001 | 1885 | 2320 | 2697 | 1972 | 1856 | 1798 | 1682 | 1914 | 1531 | 1450 |
| F-2300-B | 3190 | 2726 | 3770 | 2494 | 3538 | 3190 | 3712 | 2494 | 2407 | 2320 | 2204 | 3016 | 2436 | 2378 | 2232 | 2117 | 2610 | 3016 | 2204 | 2088 | 2001 | 1885 | 2146 | 1740 | 1624 |
| F-2350-A | 3375 | 2923 | 4036 | 2644 | 3793 | 3375 | 4002 | 2679 | 2575 | 2505 | 2366 | 3236 | 2610 | 2505 | 2401 | 2262 | 2784 | 3236 | 2366 | 2227 | 2157 | 2018 | 2296 | 1844 | 1740 |
| F-2350-B | 3828 | 3271 | 4524 | 2992 | 4245 | 3828 | 4454 | 2992 | 2888 | 2784 | 2644 | 3619 | 2923 | 2853 | 2679 | 2540 | 3132 | 3619 | 2644 | 2505 | 2401 | 2262 | 2575 | 2088 | 1948 |

Courtesy Binks Manufacturing Co.

ser heat rejection of 950,000 Btu/hr. The ambient air design WB is 76°F. The cooling range is 10°F and the approach is 9°F.

*Solution* In order to use Table 7.5, the required GPM that corresponds to the condenser heat rejection load must be determined.

$$\text{GPM} = \frac{Q_c}{500 \times \text{TC}} = \frac{950,000}{500 \times 10}$$
$$= 190 \text{ GPM}$$

The approach is 9°F. The cold water off (leaving the tower) is therefore 76 + 9 = 85°F. The range is 10°F, therefore the hot water on is 85 + 10 = 95°F. From Table 7.5 it is seen that a Model F-120-B has an adequate capacity, 200 GPM.

## 7.32 Energy Utilization in Condensers and Cooling Towers

Many of the specific ways of minimizing energy consumption related to condensers and cooling towers are based on keeping condensing pressure as low as practical, without causing operating problems. Some of the following suggestions depend on this.

1. Maintain clean heat transfer surfaces, through proper water treatment and maintenance.
2. Compare the required power for air cooled condensers with that of either evaporative or water cooled.
3. Use capacity control methods on cooling towers that reduce fan power requirements.
4. Select condensers and towers with a large heat transfer surface area. Design the system for subcooling of liquid.
5. Prevent collection or purge noncondensable gases in the condenser.

## 7.33 Condenser Heat Recovery

Frequently a refrigeration system is in an installation where heat energy is also needed. In these situations the available heat rejected from the condenser should be considered, since it replaces the use of costly and depletable fuels.

Two needs that are commonly encountered are the heating of air for heating and air conditioning purposes and the heating of service (domestic) hot water. In some cases the quantity of heat or the temperature available from the refrigerant condenser may have to be supplemented, but the partial use may still prove to be an overall economy.

There are many varied methods and types of equipment for using the condenser heat, and each installation has its own unique solution. Special arrangements or devices such as double bundle condensers, run-around coils, heat wheels, and heat pipes are used to recover heat from condensers or other sources. The utilization of this heat is appropriately a subject for air conditioning or water heating. However, we will discuss a few common uses in which the focus is on the refrigeration system aspects, without attempting to catalog the great variety of ingenious heat recovery arrangements available.

With water cooled condensers, a simple solution is to send the heated condenser water directly to a heat recovery exchanger (to heat air or water, as required for the building). When the heat is not needed, some or all of the condenser water is sent to the cooling tower in the usual manner. This arrangement has a serious disadvantage because the condenser water, at times exposed to the atmosphere through the cooling tower circuit, may become contaminated enough to seriously foul the heat recovery heat exchanger surface.

One means of preventing condenser water contamination is to use extremely fine water filters in the condenser–cooling tower circuit.

These can become clogged quickly, however, and then require backflushing to clean them.

Another solution to the contamination problem is to use a *double bundle* condenser (Figure 7.23). This condenser contains two sets of condensing water tubes, each with enough surface to handle the total heat rejected. One set is connected to the cooling tower circuit, the other to the heat exchanger. When heat recovery is required, the circuit to the heat exchanger is used. Since this water circuit is closed, contamination is avoided. Of course the same result can be achieved using two separate condensers.

A natural and convenient use of condenser heat exists in frozen food storage warehouses. The ground underneath these buildings must be kept heated to prevent it from freezing due to the low temperatures in the warehouse. If the ground water were to freeze, it would expand and heave (break) the concrete floor and columns. The refrigeration plant rejected condenser heat can be used to heat the ground. Warm condenser water is used to heat glycol or another low freezing point liq-uid in a heat exchanger. The glycol is then circulated through piping installed under the floor.

Condenser heat recovery can significantly reduce energy use in supermarket refrigeration and air conditioning operations. It is often combined with other energy saving techniques. Supermarkets generally use centrally located refrigeration equipment to serve the store's food-display cases. Since the refrigeration must be provided all year, the condenser heat can be used to heat air for the store heating and air conditioning system. One simple arrangement is shown in Figure 7.24. When heating is required, the hot gas diverts from the air cooled condenser to a heating coil in the air handling unit.

The condenser heat can also be used in a heating coil to reheat the cooled supply air to the store in the summer. Reheat is used to provide humidity control of air in spaces. (It is desirable to keep the humidity low in a supermarket to minimize the latent heat load and frost accumulation in the open refrigerated display cases.) The air is cooled to a low tem-

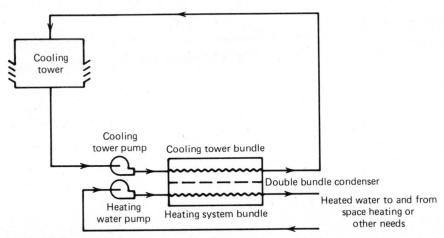

**FIGURE 7.23** Double bundle condenser arrangement for heat recovery from a water cooled condenser. Condenses water circulated through heating system bundle when needed. Control valves, bypasses, and the like not shown.

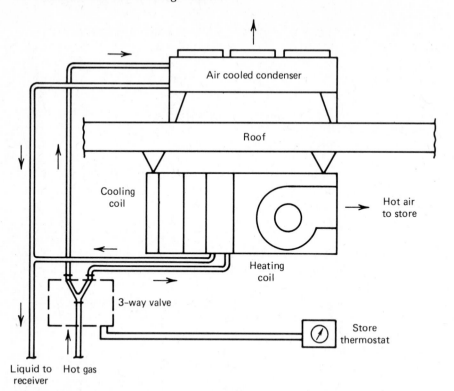

**FIGURE 7.24** An arrangement for using hot gas from supermarket refrigeration units in heating (or reheat) coils of the store air conditioning units. Thermostat controls three-way valve position to divert hot gas from condenser to heating coil in store air conditioning unit, when required.

perature in the air conditioning equipment to dehumidify it, and then reheated to provide a comfortable supply air temperature.

Another common energy saving practice in supermarkets is to draw the return air from the store at the floor level in front of the display cases, through the ducts that carry the refrigerant piping to the cases (Figure 7.25). Since the air near the cases is lower than the general air temperature in the store, energy is saved when the cooler air is returned to the air conditioning cooling coil. A secondary benefit of this arrangement is that by drawing the cold air away, conditions near the display cases are a little more comfortable for customers.

It might also be noted, although it also is not a condenser heat recovery use, that when calculating the supermarket air conditioning load the cooling effect of the cold display case is subtracted from the expected load, to arrive at the true air conditioning load. This of course results in reduced equipment size selected, and usually in more efficient operations.

Another possible energy saving use of condenser heat that should be considered is in defrosting evaporator coils that operate with a surface temperature below freezing. There are various methods of using the refrigerant hot gas heat for defrosting, discussed in Chapter 12.

## REVIEW QUESTIONS

1. What is the purpose of a refrigerant condenser?

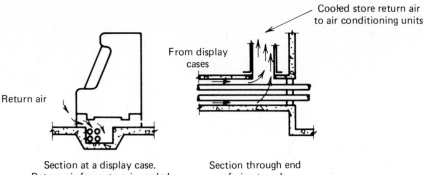

Section at a display case. Return air from store is cooled as it passes near case; this also draws uncomfortably cold air away from customer.

Section through end of pipe trench

**FIGURE 7.25** Returning store air around display cases and through refrigerant piping trenches to save energy and improve comfort. (Reprinted with permission from the 1982 Applications ASHRAE Handbook and Product Directory)

2. Name and describe the three types of condensers, classified according to the cooling mediums, and how the medium is used.

3. Name and describe the types of water cooled condensers, classified according to construction.

4. List the relative advantages and disadvantages of the different types of water cooled condensers.

5. Explain the meaning of purging.

6. What are noncondensables? What effect can they have?

7. List the relative advantages and disadvantages of water cooled, air cooled, and evaporative condensers.

8. Describe three methods for operating an evaporative condenser in winter.

9. Why is high condenser pressure control needed? How is it accomplished?

10. Why is low head-pressure control required? How is it accomplished?

11. List and describe four methods of low head-pressure control used for air cooled condensers. Discuss their relative advantages.

12. Sketch a refrigerant-side low head-pressure control arrangement for an air cooled condenser.

13. List and describe three methods of low head-pressure control for an evaporative condenser.

14. Describe a low head-pressure control arrangement for once-through water cooled condensers.

15. Describe three methods of low head-pressure control for water cooled condensers using cooling tower recirculated water.

16. What is a condensing unit? What are its advantages?

17. How is water cooled in a cooling tower?

18. Other than a cooling tower, what other means are used sometimes to cool water? What are their disadvantages?

19. What is meant by draft?

20. Name two types of nonmechanical draft towers and explain their operation. How

is the air motion achieved? What are their advantages and disadvantages as compared to mechanical draft towers?

21. What is meant by forced and induced draft?

22. Discuss the relative advantages and disadvantages of centrifugal versus propeller fans for cooling towers.

23. What is the purpose of the fill? What are the two types?

24. Discuss procedures for operating cooling towers in winter.

25. What are three causes of water loss from tower operation? What would occur if there were no blowdown?

26 List and describe the possible physical and chemical effects that may require water treatment in cooling towers.

27. What is pH? Which values represent acid, neutral, and alkaline conditons?

28. What is an inhibitor? How are they used in cooling tower water treatment?

29. What types of organic growths are of concern in cooling towers? What are their possible effects?

30. Explain the terms *approach, range,* and *wet bulb.*

31. What is a double bundle condenser and what is its purpose?

32. List some methods of reducing energy use in condenser and cooling tower design, operation, and maintenance.

## PROBLEMS

7.1 Select the smallest required water cooled condenser for the following conditions: refrigeration load is 35.0 tons; compressor kW is 42; refrigerant is R-12; condensing temperature is 105°F; condensing water supply temperature is 80°F; condensing water temperature rise is 12°F; fouling resistance is 0.0005.

7.2 Select the smallest required water cooled condenser for the following conditions: condenser heat rejection is 730,000 Btu/hr; refrigerant is R-22; condensing temperature is 105°F; condensing water enters condenser at 85°F and leaves at 95°F; fouling resistance is 0.001.

7.3 Select an air cooled condenser for a system using R-502, in Dallas, Texas, with a total heat rejection of 340,000 Btu/hr. The temperature difference is 18°F.

7.4 Select an air cooled condenser for a system using R-22 with a total heat rejection of 180,000 Btu/hr, in Denver, Colorado (approximate elevation 5000 ft). The temperature difference is 20°F.

7.5 Select a cooling tower for a loading (capacity) of 1.76 million Btu/hr, in Chicago, Illinois. The cooling range is 15°F and the approach is 10°F. WB is 78°F.

7.6 What is the heat rejection capacity of a Model F-175-A cooling tower with an ambient air design WB of 78°F, approach of 7°F, and a range of 10°F?

# Chapter 8

# REFRIGERANT FLOW CONTROL (EXPANSION) DEVICES

We have already discussed three of the major components of the vapor compression system: the compressor, condenser, and evaporator. The final major component, covered in this chapter, is the *flow control* device, also called the *expansion* or *metering* device. There are various types of flow control devices. We will discuss their means of functioning, their construction, and applications.

## OBJECTIVES

A study of this chapter will enable you to:
1. Describe the functions of refrigerant flow control devices.
2. List and describe each type of flow control device.
3. Know the applications and limitations of each type of flow control device.
4. Explain how a thermostatic expansion valve controls superheat.
5. Know the factors to consider when choosing between each type of TEV.

### 8.1 Purpose of the Flow Control Device

The flow control device should accomplish two functions in the vapor compressor system.

1. It should regulate the flow rate of liquid refrigerant to the evaporator, according to the demand.
2. It should create a pressure drop from the high side to the low side of the system. This results in the expansion of the flowing refrigerant, causing a small amount of it to evaporate, so that it cools down to the evaporating temperature.

In most situations the flow control device should feed the liquid refrigerant to the evaporator at the same rate that it is being pumped from the evaporator by the compressor. That is, the evaporator should neither be overfed nor starved. The flow control device should respond to a change in conditions that require a change in flow rate. When the heat load on the evaporator increases, the flow control device should respond to feed more refrigerant, and when the load decreases, it should reduce flow. We will see that each device carries out this function in a different manner, and indeed that some do not do it satisfactorily under certain circumstances. This is one of the reasons why different types of flow control devices are available, and why each has a different application.

Another point that requires clarification is that the flow control device is not a pressure control device. In some applications it is desirable to control evaporator or suction pressure at a certain value, or to limit it to a high or low value, or both. In most cases the flow control not only does not control low-side pressure, but may create problems because it lets pressure vary. Where pressure control is required, additional devices may be required (see Chapter 11), or a modification to the flow control device is needed, or both. The effect of the flow control device on pressure will be discussed later in this chapter.

## 8.2 Types of Flow Control Devices

All flow control devices have a restricted passage or opening, which creates the pressure difference for them to carry out their expansion functions. Most types are constructed as valves—that is, the restricted passage can be open or closed, and in some cases it can be modulated between full open and full closed. Among these types are the *hand expansion valve, thermostatic expansion valve, high side* and *low side float valves* and *automatic expansion valve.*

Other flow control or expansion devices have a fixed size restricted opening. These types include the *capillary tube* and the *orifice.* Some flow control devices are more suitable for direct expansion evaporators; others are suitable for flooded evaporators, as will be seen.

## 8.3 Hand Expansion Valve

This is a valve that is manually adjusted to feed more or less refrigerant as required. A needle valve is used because it is possible to get fine control increments with this type. A hand expansion valve is satisfactory only when an operator is regularly available and even then only when the load changes slowly. This valve was used before automatic-type flow control devices were developed. It is not generally suitable for the conditions encountered in modern systems.

## THE THERMOSTATIC EXPANSION VALVE

The most widely used of all flow control devices is the *thermostatic expansion valve* (TEV). It can be used with all sizes of systems with either direct expansion coils or dry expansion liquid chillers.

It does an excellent job of automatically controlling refrigerant flow to the evaporator at the rate it is required, over a wide range of loads, while keeping most of the evaporator heat transfer surface working to evaporate refrigerant despite the varied conditions. This aids in keeping compressor power requirements low.

## 8.4 Construction

Figure 8.1 is a schematic diagram of the principal operating parts of the thermostatic expansion valve. Figure 8.2 is a cut-away view of what a valve and its parts actually look like. Understanding the construction will help you more clearly understand how it functions.

Referring to Figure 8.1, liquid refrigerant

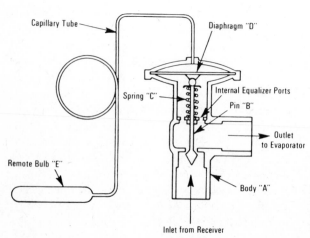

**FIGURE 8.1** Schematic section through a thermal expansion valve (TEV), internal equalizer type.

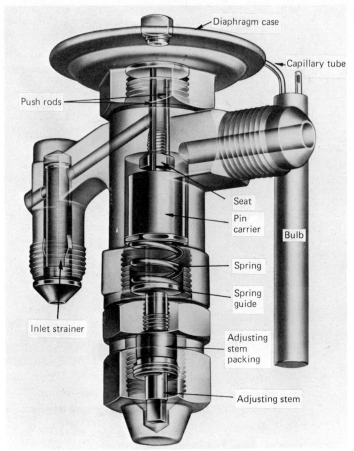

Push rods

Inlet strainer

Diaphragm case

Capillary tube

Seat

Pin carrier

Bulb

Spring

Spring guide

Adjusting stem packing

Adjusting stem

**FIGURE 8.2** Cut-away view of a thermal expansion valve, internal equalizer type. (Sporlan Valve Co.)

flows through the opening in the valve seat and past the valve pin. The restricted opening causes the required pressure drop for refrigerant expansion.

The spring pushes against the pin and thus tends to hold the valve closed. A spring guide holds the spring in place and keeps it aligned. The adjustment stem can be turned to increase or decrease the spring pressure. A flexible diaphragm is connected to the push rods which in turn are connected to the pin. Movement of the diaphragm downward will move the pin away from the seat and open the valve port.

The top of the diaphragm is connected to a

small-diameter long tube called the capillary tube and then to a hollow bulb. The bulb, tube, and chamber on top of the diaphragm all form one closed space, which contains a fluid that exerts pressure on the diaphragm. The bulb is attached to the suction line, close to the evaporator, making good contact with the suction line along the whole length of the bulb.

In Figure 8.2 the same parts are seen assembled in the valve body. The top part of the body and the diaphragm are called the power head. The adjusting stem is covered with a removable nut for protection. Note that an internal port connects the valve outlet to the space underneath the diaphragm. This is called the *internal equalizer*. We will discuss this type of TEV now and another type, which does not have an internal equalizer port, later.

## 8.5 How the Thermostatic Expansion Valve Functions

The ideal flow control device should regulate the flow rate of liquid refrigerant to the evaporator as needed, under varying load requirements. It should also result in utilization of all of the evaporator heat transfer surface for evaporation of refrigerant, regardless of changing conditions. In the explanation that follows, of how the thermostatic expansion valve functions, we will examine how well it fits these needs.

*The Operating Pressures.* Three pressures act to move the valve toward an open or closed position (Figure 8.3).

The bulb pressure ($p_b$) resulting from the pressure exerted by the fluid in the bulb, stem, and valve head, acts on the top of the dia-

phragm to open the valve. The spring pressure $p_s$ acts on the pin to close the valve. The evaporator pressure $p_e$ acts on the bottom of the diaphragm to close the valve. When the opening and closing pressures balance each other, the valve pin is in a stable fixed position. That is, when the valve is not opening or closing, the following balance of pressures exists

$$p_b = p_s + p_e \qquad (8.1)$$

If the bulb (opening) pressure is greater than the total closing pressure (the spring pressure plus the evaporator pressure) the valve will move to a position more open than it was previously, and more refrigerant will flow. On the other hand, the valve will move toward a more closed position if the closing pressures are greater than the opening pressure.

*The Bulb Charge.* The fluid that fills the bulb is called the valve charge. Different types of charges are available. That is, both the kind of fluid and its quantity can be varied. The type of charge affects the operation of the valve under certain conditions. We will discuss the operation of a thermostatic expansion valve with a *conventional liquid charge* (or sometimes called just a *liquid charge*). Later we will discuss how a valve operates when it has a *gas charge* or a *cross charge*.

The same substance is used for the (conventional) liquid charge and the refrigeration system. That is, if the system uses R-12, the bulb charge is R-12. Furthermore, the quantity of charge with which the bulb is filled is great enough so that there is always a mixture of liquid and gas in the bulb at any temperatures and pressures encountered.

At this point it is essential to recall that since there is a mixture of liquid and gas, the charge is always in a saturated condition. Therefore, whatever its temperature, the liquid charge exerts only one possible pressure, its saturated pressure. These values can be found in the saturated property tables, of course.

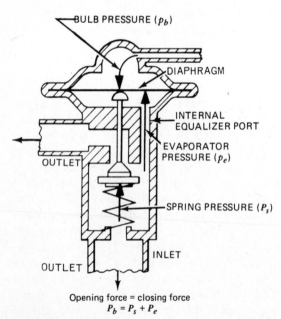

**FIGURE 8.3** Illustration of pressures acting on a thermal expansion valve.

***Superheat Control.*** It has been pointed out that in order to ensure against refrigerant liquid entering the compressor, it is common practice to have the refrigerant leave the evaporator slightly superheated. Recall that superheat is defined as the difference between the actual temperature of the superheated vapor and its saturation temperature, at the same pressure. About 6 to 10°F valve control superheat is usually satisfactory to protect the compressor, when additional suction line superheat occurs. It is not possible to control exactly at 0°F superheat, without the likelihood of some liquid entering the suction line. On the other hand, excess superheat means that the evaporator heat transfer surface is not being efficiently used.

*The thermostatic expansion valve operates by controlling at a constant superheat condition leaving the evaporator.* Let us see how this is done by taking an example at a specified set of conditions, in which it is desired to maintain 10°F of superheat leaving the evaporator. The conditions are shown in Figure 8.4.

The system uses R-12, with a conventional liquid charged expansion valve. The valve is in stable position—all forces are in balance. The evaporator temperature is 20°F. The evapora-

tor pressure is therefore 21.1 psig, the corresponding saturation pressure. The spring pressure has been set at 7.4 psi. The total closing force is the sum of these two pressures. If the valve is in a stable position, the opening (bulb) force must be equal to this. That is

$$p_b = p_s + p_e = 7.4 + 21.1 = 28.5 \text{ psig}$$

Since the bulb charge is also refrigerant R-12, and in a saturated state, we can determine its temperature at 28.5 psig from the saturated property tables, 30°F. This must also be the temperature of the refrigerant in the system at the evaporator exit, since the suction line and bulb are attached to each other and have good thermal contact. Therefore, the refrigerant is leaving the evaporator with $30 - 20 = 10°F$ of superheat.

If it were desired to change the superheat, all that would be necessary would be to adjust the spring pressure. For instance if more superheat were required, the spring pressure should be increased, because this increases the total closing force. This would cause the valve to move to a more closed position, reducing the refrigerant flow rate. Since the heat load is the same, the refrigerant would leave the evaporator at a higher superheat. This would

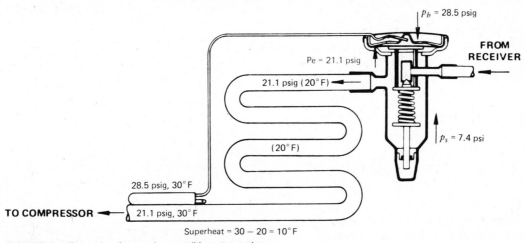

**FIGURE 8.4** Example of operating conditions to produce a 10°F superheat with a TEV.

raise the bulb temperature and therefore pressure, and the valve would stop closing. However, less efficient use would be made of the evaporator surface.

Let us see how the TEV responds if the refrigeration heat load changes. If the heat load increases, the refrigerant will leave the evaporator at a higher superheat. The bulb charge temperature increases and therefore its pressure rises, according to its saturation pressure–temperature characteristics. This increases the opening force in the diaphragm. The valve opens more, the refrigerant flow rate increases, and the superheat decreases back to its initial setting.

If the valve is feeding too much refrigerant for the load, as would occur if the load suddenly dropped, the superheat would decrease. This would decrease the bulb temperature and charge pressure, and the opening force would decrease. The closing force would be temporarily greater, moving the valve to a more closed position. Less refrigerant now flows, and the refrigerant becomes more superheated again leaving the evaporator, until it reaches the initial superheat.

The following example illustrates how superheat can be measured in the field.

**Example 8.1** The evaporating pressure of a system using R-12, with a liquid charged TEV, reads 37.0 psig. What should the bulb (suction) temperature at the evaporator outlet be if an 8°F superheat is wanted? What is the spring pressure at this condition?

*Solution* The evaporating temperature corresponding to 37.0 psig for R-12 is 40°F. Therefore the suction temperature should be

$$t_{bulb} = t_{evap.} + superheat$$

$$= 40 + 8 = 48°F$$

The bulb pressure at 48°F is 44.7 psig for R-12. The spring pressure therefore is

$$p_s = p_b - p_e = 44.7 - 37.0 = 7.7 \text{ psig}$$

The following example illustrates the effect that changing spring pressure has on superheat.

**Example 8.2** If the spring pressure is increased to 13.9 psi by turning the adjustment stem, for the unit in Example 8.1, what is the effect on the system performance?

*Solution* The bulb pressure is now

$$p_b = p_s + p_e = 13.9 + 37.0 = 50.9 \text{ psi}$$

At this pressure the temperature of the R-12 charge is 54°F, according to the saturation tables. The refrigerant superheat leaving the evaporator is therefore 54 − 40 = 14°F. This means that much of the evaporator surface is not being used for the useful refrigerating effect, and that it is being starved of refrigerant.

## 8.6 The Effect of Pressure Drop on the TEV Performance

When there is significant pressure drop between the valve outlet and the evaporator exit, the thermostatic expansion valve with an internal equalizer construction will not function properly. This is best understood by examining the conditions for a specific situation. Let us assume that the internal equalizer TEV used in Example 8.1 is installed in a unit with an evaporator coil pressure drop of 10 psi. The evaporator inlet temperature is still 40°F. The spring pressure setting is 7.7 psi, which would produce an 8°F superheat in the coil with no pressure drop, as was shown in the example. The same closing forces operate. The internal equalizer results in a pressure corresponding to 40°F, 37.0 psia. The bulb pressure (opening) will not open the valve until it rises to the closing forces, at

$$p_b = p_s + p_e = 7.7 + 37.0 = 44.7 \text{ psig}$$

The bulb charge will reach this pressure when its (saturation) temperature reaches 48°F; this must also be the temperature of the refriger-

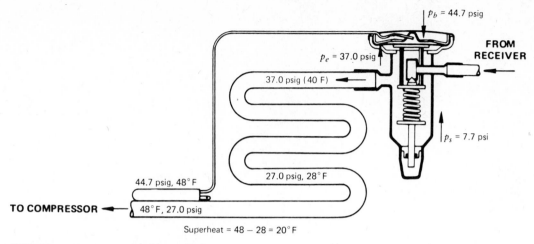

**FIGURE 8.5** Effect of evaporator pressure drop on performance with an internal equalizer TEV.

ant leaving the evaporator. This refrigerant temperature is the same as that at which the valve controls in the coil with no pressure drop.

The pressure of the refrigerant near the exit of the evaporator, however, has dropped by 10 psi, to 27.0 psig, as shown in Figure 8.5. The corresponding saturation (evaporating) temperature at the evaporator exit would be 28°F. Therefore the refrigerant leaves the evaporator with $48 - 28 = 20°F$ superheat, rather than 8°F superheat. That is, the valve will control at 20°F superheat. A considerable part of the heat transfer surface is not used for refrigeration because the evaporator is starved. The system will probably not produce the refrigeration capacity it was designed for.

## 8.7 The External Equalizer TEV

We have seen that use of the internal equalizer expansion valve in an evaporator with a large pressure drop will starve the coil, cause excess superheat, and reduce system capacity. The cause of this problem is that one of the closing forces, that from the internal equalizer connec-

tion, was sensing the evaporator inlet pressure, and not the pressure where control was wanted from, at the evaporator outlet.

The problem can be solved by using an *external equalizer* thermostatic expansion valve (Figure 8.6). This valve does not have an internal equalizer port. Instead there is an external opening in the body of the valve under the diaphragm. This opening should be connected with an external equalizer line to a point past where the significant pressure drop occurs. This is usually in the suction line at the exit of the evaporator. (It should be connected downstream of the bulb, for reasons to be explained later). The valve is then not affected by pressure drop in the evaporator.

*Example 8.3* An external equalizer liquid charged TEV is installed in an R-12 system with an evaporator coil pressure drop of 10 psi. The evaporator inlet temperature is 40°F. Spring pressure is 7.7 psi. At what superheat does the valve control?

*Solution* The conditions are shown in Figure 8.7. The evaporator inlet pressure is 37.0 psig, the saturation pressure corre-

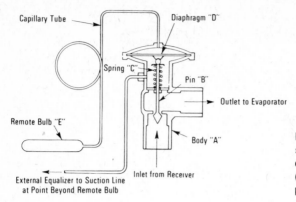

**FIGURE 8.6** Schematic section through an external-equalizer-type TEV (used with high evaporator pressure drop).

sponding to 40°F for R-12. But the closing force from the external equalizer is the evaporator outlet pressure, $37.0 - 10.0 = 27.0$ psig. The bulb pressure can now be determined:

$$p_b = p_s + p_e = 7.7 + 27.0 = 34.7 \text{ psig.}$$

The bulb temperature at 34.7 psig for saturated R-12 is about 38°F. This is the refrigerant temperature leaving the evaporator.

The saturation temperature of the refrigerant leaving the evaporator, corresponding to 27.0 psig, is 28°F. The refrigerant superheat leaving the evaporator is therefore $38 - 28 = 10$°F.

The results of Example 8.3 show that use of the external equalizer valve instead of the internal equalizer type reduced the superheat leaving the evaporator from 20 to 10°F, making more efficient use of the evaporator.

It is also noted that the superheat is 10°F as opposed to the 8°F obtained with the evaporator coil with no pressure drop. The reason for this is that the saturation pressure–temperature relationship for R-12 changes with the suction pressure.

General practice is to use an external equalizer type TEV on coils with a pressure drop greater than about 2.5 psi in the air conditioning temperature range (30 to 45°F), 1.5 psi in

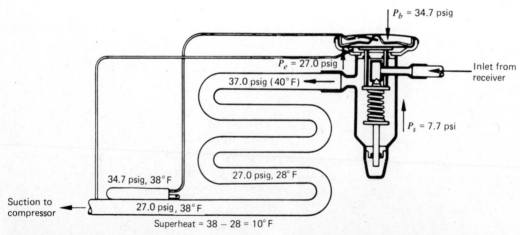

**FIGURE 8.7** Operating conditions for Example 8.3 with evaporator pressure drop, using an external equalizer TEV. Note results compared to those shown in Figure 8.5 with an internal equalizer TEV.

the medium temperature range (0 to 25°F), and 0.5 psi in the low temperature range (below 0°F). An external equalizer valve must also be used when a refrigerant distributor (see Chapter 6) is used at the evaporator inlet, since the distributor pressure drop will have the same effect as it would in the evaporator.

## 8.8 Pressure Limiting Valves

When the suction pressure to a refrigeration compressor increases, both the capacity and the motor current increase. Excessive suction pressures may result in an overload and damage to the motor. The thermostatic expansion valves discussed thus far do not control suction pressure. On the contrary, they permit suction pressure to rise as the load increases, by feeding more refrigerant to the evaporator.

*Pressure limiting* thermostatic valves are available that limit the maximum value of the suction pressure. This feature is sometimes called maximum operating pressure (MOP). This type of valve will control in the same way as a standard valve in the range of suction pressures that are permissible for the compressor. If the maximum operating pressure is reached, the valve will not feed an increased flow rate of refrigerant, and the suction pressure will no longer rise. High suction pressure could cause overloading of the compressor motor.

The pressure limiting valve also aids in preventing liquid floodback to the compressor on start-up. When the compressor starts, the bulb is often at a relatively high (ambient) temperature. The charge will be at a high pressure and will thus open the valve wide, causing a sudden surge of liquid refrigerant. If a pressure limiting valve is used, it will not open until the suction pressure drops below the MOP. During this time the compressor pumps the relatively small quantity of refrigerant remaining in the evaporator. The suction temperature drops and the opening force opens the valve in the normal control mode.

Another undesirable feature of the valve opening wide at start up, as exists with liquid charge valves, is that it delays pull-down time of the evaporating temperature.

There are two kinds of pressure limiting thermostatic expansion valves: the *limited charge* type and the *mechanical* type.

## 8.9 The Limited (Gas) Charge Thermostatic Expansion Valve

In the liquid charge valve the amount of fluid is great enough so that there is always some liquid present in the bulb regardless of temperature. In the limited charge valve, also called the *gas charge* valve, the quantity is smaller, enough so that above a certain evaporator temperature it all vaporizes. The pressure of a gas does not increase sharply with an increase in temperature, unlike the case with a saturated liquid–gas mixture. Therefore, as the evaporator temperature and pressure increases above a maximum point, the bulb pressure does not increase, and the valve does not open further. It thus acts as a pressure limiting valve.

The limited charge TEV is often used in air conditioning applications where high suction pressures are likely to occur. A limitation on the installation is that the valve head or capillary tube must not be in a location where they can become colder than the bulb. If this occurs the charge may condense in the head or tubing. Control from the bulb will be lost and the valve will close.

## 8.10 The Mechanical Pressure Limiting Valve

This type of valve has a conventional liquid charge so that control from the bulb functions in the usual manner below the maximum operating pressure. The valve has two diaphragms instead of one. The upper diaphragm is held down by a spring and does not function during normal operation (Figure 8.8). The lower diaphragm functions in the

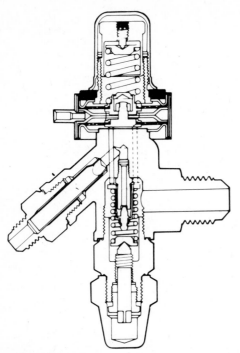

**FIGURE 8.8** Pressure limiting TEV, mechanical type with double diaphragm.

usual manner, with the bulb pressure acting on it from a connection between the diaphragms. When this pressure increases above a certain value, however, the diaphragms effectively become locked together as a rigid unit, and a change in the bulb pressure has no further effect. Any increase in evaporator pressure acts on the underside of the lower diaphragm, tending to close the valve against the upper spring pressure, thus limiting the suction pressure increase. Under these conditions the valve functions like a constant pressure expansion valve (to be discussed later in this chapter).

## 8.11 System and Valve Hunting

Under certain situations the thermostatic expansion valve may alternately open and close continually in an excessive manner. This occurrence is called *hunting*. When the valve opens too wide the superheat drops, suction pressure rises, and liquid floodbacks may occur. When the valve closes too much, the evaporator is starved, superheat is too high, and the suction pressure drops.

Hunting can result from any of a number of causes. There is an inherent time lag in the response to a signal of any mechanical system including the thermostatic expansion valve and evaporator. The signal originates from the conditions at the evaporator outlet. But the valve feeds to the evaporator inlet. For example, when the bulb pressure calls for more refrigerant and the valve opens, it may take a few minutes in a long circuit for the increased flow rate to reach the evaporator outlet. Before that time the refrigeration load might decrease and the increased flow rate might not be wanted, resulting in overfeeding of the evaporator. The lag may then result in the opposite direction as the valve starts to throttle and continues to do so until the effect is felt at the bulb.

Hunting can be reduced by designing the evaporator circuits with a reasonably short length (this reduces heat transfer, though). Hunting can also be caused by uneven air flow across the coil or uneven refrigerant flow in different circuits. Aside from providing proper system design, hunting can be reduced by using a cross-charge-type expansion valve, or by increasing the thermal lag of the bulb.

## 8.12 The Cross Charge Thermostatic Expansion Valve

This type of TEV has a liquid charge, but the fluid used has a pressure–temperature characteristic different than the refrigerant used in the system. Figure 8.9 illustrates this. The $p$–$t$ curve of the saturated fluid for the bulb charge is flatter than that of the refrigerant in the evaporator. This means that for a given change in temperature, the bulb charge pressure changes less than the evaporating refrigerant pressure. The bulb response is less

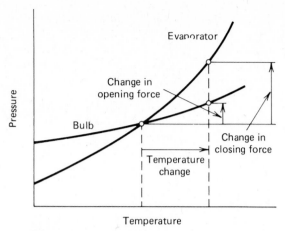

**FIGURE 8.9** Pressure–temperature curves for cross-charge-type TEV, illustrating its antihunting effect.

sensitive than that of the conventional liquid charge valve.

This difference dampens out hunting effects. For instance, if the evaporator pressure and temperature increase, indicating a need for more refrigerant, the bulb temperature rises. Because of the cross charge, however, the bulb opening pressure increases at a slower rate than if a conventional charge were used. This prevents a too sudden and excessive opening of the valve. The opposite dampening effect occurs when evaporator pressure drops.

The cross charge valve also helps to prevent floodback and overloading of the compressor motor on start-up. After shutdown the evaporator and bulb are both at the same relatively high temperature, of course. However the bulb fluid pressure is much less than the evaporator refrigerant pressure. The valve will therefore remain closed until the small amount of refrigerant in the evaporator is heated to a high superheat by the load; this increases the bulb temperature and pressure to a point where the valve begins to open. The delayed opening until high superheat occurs prevents liquid floodback and motor overloading.

## 8.13 Bulb Thermal Lag

Hunting can also be dampened by increasing the *thermal lag* time of the bulb. This may be done by increasing the mass of metal of the bulb, or by inserting an additional block of metal in the bulb. Then this metal has to be heated along with the bulb charge, causing a delay, and thus the response to an evaporator temperature increase is delayed.

## 8.14 Pressure Equalizing Features

When the compressor stops and the expansion valve closes, the high- and low-side pressure differential may remain for a period of time. When the compressor starts it must have a high starting torque to overcome this pressure increase. It is often desirable, however, to be able to use low starting torque, less expensive motors. This is possible when a pressure equalizing feature, also called off-cycle unloading, is included in the expansion valve. One way of accomplishing this is by having a small bleed hole through the valve seat. When the valve closes, refrigerant slowly bleeds from the high side to the evaporator and pressures equalize.

## 8.15 Pilot Operated Valves

Above a certain physical size it is not feasible to construct a thermostatic expansion valve that will perform satisfactorily. For large systems it is therefore common to use a pilot operated arrangement (Figure 8.10). A small pilot TEV is installed to sense suction line superheat. The outlet of this valve feeds the operating chamber of the main valve. When the suction line superheat increases, the pilot valve opens and the pressure on the main valve chamber causes it to open more.

## 81.6 TEV Location and Installation

An improper installation of the thermostatic expansion valve and related elements will af-

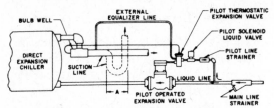

**FIGURE 8.10** Pilot operated TEV arrangement. (Reprinted with permission from the 1979 Equipment ASHRAE Handbook & Product Directory)

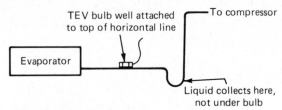

**FIGURE 8.11** Illustration of proper location and attachment of TEV bulb.

fect system performance. Some of these factors, concerning the piping installation, will be mentioned here; other factors will be discussed in Chapter 11.

The valve inlet must receive only liquid. This means that the liquid line size and components in the liquid line must not have a pressure drop enough to cause flashing. Subcooling in the condenser is helpful in preventing this.

The body and capillary tubing of gas charged valves should be located in a relatively warm location so that control from the bulb is not lost.

***Bulb Location.*** Proper bulb location is critical to providing good valve performance. The bulb should be located on a horizontal suction line at the evaporator outlet. It should also be mounted on the upper part of the line, since oil flowing on the bottom of the pipe could give a false temperature reading. Good thermal contact is necessary between the bulb and pipe—the bulb should maintain contact along its whole length.

Care must be taken to prevent liquid refrigerant and oil from collecting at the bulb location; this would cool the bulb and cause the valve to throttle. This is accomplished by the piping connection shown in Figure 8.11. A short trap is provided downstream of the bulb. Refrigerant and oil drains to the trap rather than collecting under the bulb. This arrangement is required whether the compressor is above or below the evaporator, with one ex-

ception. If the system is under pumpdown control and the compressor is below the evaporator, a trap is not required. During operation the refrigerant and oil drain by gravity away from the bulb. With pumpdown control any refrigerant in the evaporator is pumped out before the compressor stops.

An external equalizer should be connected downstream from the bulb. If it is located before the bulb, refrigerant leaking from the valve through the equalizer line may cool the bulb and cause the valve to throttle closed, starving the evaporator.

## 8.17 The Thermal Electric Expansion Valve

This type of valve can be used as a flow control valve, and it has other uses. It has a motor that opens and closes the valve in response to changes in an electric voltage input. A liquid sensor called a thermistor is installed at the point in the evaporator or suction line where complete evaporation is desired (Figure 8.12). The sensor is wired in series with the motor as shown. The electric resistance of the sensor increases with decreasing temperature. The presence of liquid refrigerant cools the thermistor, increasing its resistance. This decreases the voltage to the motor and the valve throttles, decreasing refrigerant flow. When the thermistor senses superheated gas, the reverse sequence occurs. Since such close control of superheat is possible, the thermal electric valve can make efficient use of evaporator surface, and aid in energy conservation.

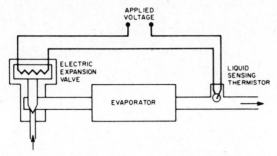

**FIGURE 8.12** Thermal electric expansion valve and sensor. (Reprinted with permission from the 1979 Equipment ASHRAE Handbook & Product Directory)

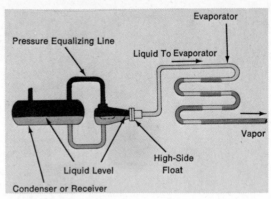

**FIGURE 8.14** Arrangement for connecting high-side float valve in the system.

## 8.18 Float Valves

Float valves are used as refrigerant flow control devices in some applications. They can be grouped into *high-side* and *low-side* float valves. A high-side float valve is shown in Figure 8.13. A valve pin and port separate the high and low sides of the system. A float ball connected to the pin rests on the surface of the liquid refrigerant. As the float rises the valve opens, and as it drops the valve closes.

The operation of the high-side float valve is shown in the schematic arrangement of Figure 8.14. The float valve is located on the high side of the system, between the condenser and evaporator. The level of refrigerant liquid is

the same in the valve and in the condenser, since they are freely connected. When the condenser refrigerant level rises the float rises and opens the valve, feeding more refrigerant to the evaporator. If the refrigerant flow rate to the condenser is reduced, the condenser level will drop and the valve will throttle flow to the evaporator.

The high-side float valve regulates flow rate by feeding refrigerant to the evaporator at the same rate that it leaves the condenser. This makes the quantity of refrigerant charge in a dry expansion system critical. If there is insufficient refrigerant the evaporator may be starved and if there is too much a DX evaporator may be overfed and floodback to the compressor may occur. High-side float valves are often used in centrifugal refrigeration systems with shell-and-tube condensers and flooded chillers (Chapter 10).

The low-side float valve regulates the refrigerant flow rate by controlling the liquid refrigerant level in the evaporator. It is used with flooded evaporators. A low-side float valve is shown in Figure 8.15. The float is installed in the low pressure side of the system; it may be located directly in the evaporator or in a surge drum or float chamber.

A schematic arrangement of a low-side float valve installation is shown in Figure 8.16. The

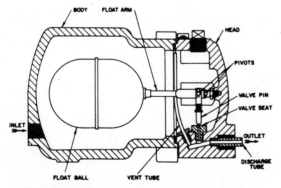

**FIGURE 8.13** High-side float valve. (Reprinted with permission from the 1979 Equipment ASHRAE Handbook & Product Directory)

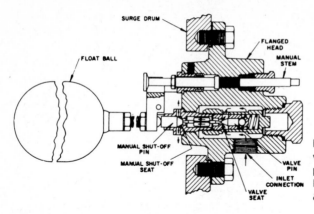

**FIGURE 8.15** Low-side float valve. (Reprinted with permission from the 1979 Equipment ASHRAE Handbook & Product Directory)

liquid line is connected to the valve inlet. If the liquid level is high enough in the chamber, the valve remains closed. When the liquid level drops, the float drops and opens the valve port, admitting more refrigrant from the liquid line. The refrigerant pressure drops as it flows from the high side through the valve to the float chamber. Low pressure liquid is fed to the evaporator through a connection from the chamber. There is also a connection directly to the suction line from the float chamber. This takes care of the flash gas formed when the refrigerant expands through the valve.

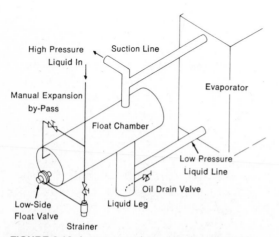

**FIGURE 8.16** Arrangement for connecting a low-side float valve in the system. (Reprinted with permission from the 1979 Equipment ASHRAE Handbook & Product Directory)

## 8.19 The Constant Pressure Expansion Valve

This type of valve, also called an *automatic expansion valve,* is used as a refrigerant expansion device in certain limited applications. A schematic cross section of the valve is shown in Figure 8.17. Two pressures operate on the valve. The constant spring pressure acts on the top of the diaphragm to open the valve, and the evaporator pressure acts on the bottom of the diaphragm, tending to close the valve. When the evaporator pressure increases the valve moves to a more closed position. This reduces the refrigerant flow rate entering the evaporator and the evaporator pressure drops. If the evaporator pressure decreases the opposite effect occurs. The spring pressure now exceeds the evaporator pressure and the valve moves to a more open position. Refrigerant flow rate increases and the evaporator pressure increases again.

This explanation shows that the constant pressure expansion valve regulates the refrigerant flow so as to maintain a constant evaporator pressure. This method of controlling flow rate, however, is undesirable unless the refrigeration load is relatively constant. If there is a decrease in refrigeration load, compressor operation will cause suction pressure to drop. The constant pressure valve will then open to increase pressure. But this increases refrigerant flow, which is exactly opposite to

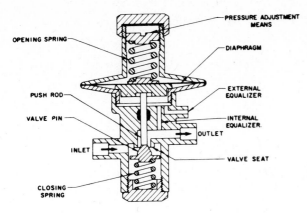

**FIGURE 8.17** Constant pressure expansion valve (schematic).

what is wanted if the load decreases. On the other hand, when the refrigeration load increases the valve will react to starve the evaporator. The constant pressure expansion valve will alternately overfeed and starve the evaporator if there is appreciable load variation. This results in inefficient use of evaporator surface, excess energy use, and in the case of overfeeding, possible liquid floodback.

The constant pressure expansion valve has limited use when it is desirable to maintain constant evaporator conditions and when the nature of the system is such that the load does not vary much. This type of valve is used in self-contained soft drink and water coolers, where the product is kept at the same temperature at all times.

## 8.20 The Capillary Tube

This flow control device is a very small diameter length of tubing. The typical inside diameter ranges from 0.02 to 0.10 in., and lengths range from 2 to 12 ft or more. The device is used in small hermetic units with direct expansion coils. The name *capillary tube* is misleading. Capillary action (the tendency for a liquid to adhere to a tube wall) has nothing to do with the way the flow control functions.

The capillary tube will not perform satisfactorily if the quantity of refrigerant charge in the system varies from the proper amount.

Furthermore, any foreign material may block or otherwise affect the flow through the small tube. For these reasons capillary tubes are suitable only for hermetic units. Because of its very low cost and freedom from need of maintenance it is very widely used in household refrigerators, room air conditioners, and small package air conditioning units.

*Operating Characteristics.* Because of the narrow opening and long length, the capillary tube has a large pressure drop through it. It thus acts as a suitable expansion device. It also does a reasonably good job of controlling flow rate under varied conditions, despite the fact that it is not adjustable.

The size of a capillary tube is selected so that it delivers the proper flow rate at a specified design load and temperature. The quantity of charge in the system is just enough to fill the evaporator. If the refrigeration load drops, the suction pressure falls, the tube momentarily delivers more refrigerant than the compressor can handle, and the evaporator fills with liquid. This starves the condenser of liquid and some gas enters the capillary from the condenser. But the gas has a much greater specific volume than the liquid and therefore the mass flow rate through the tube decreases. The desired flow rate control has occurred—in response to the reduced load the flow rate to the evaporator has decreased.

The reverse action occurs if the refrigerant load increases. The suction pressure increases and the compressor pumps a greater mass flow rate of refrigerant. This starves the evaporator and fills the condenser with liquid. The capillary tube now delivers more refrigerant since it is fed all liquid, and a balanced condition is restored.

Although the capillary tube performs satisfactorily over a reasonable range of conditions, it is not equally efficient at all conditions. As seen from the preceding, except at design conditions the heat transfer surface is not fully used, as it is with the thermostatic expansion valve. It would be expected that more power would be required in systems using a capillary tube rather than a TEV.

*System Practices.* It has been pointed out that the quantity of refrigerant charge in capillary tube systems is critical. The refrigerant charge should be the minimum necessary for the task—enough to fill the evaporator. For this reason a refrigerant receiver is not used. An excess charge will cause high discharge pressure and perhaps result in liquid floodback to the compressor. Too little will permit vapor to enter the capillary tube and result in a loss in refrigeration capacity.

The capillary tube, of course, cannot be closed when the compressor stops. The refrigerant will therefore equalize throughout the system, and some will migrate to the evaporator. This creates the possibility of liquid entering the compressor on start-up. A suction line liquid accumulator tank is often included in the system to prevent liquid entering the compressor on start-up and when running.

On the other hand, the equalization of pressure throughout the system on shut-down is also a benefit. The compressor does not have to operate against a pressure differential on start-up, and low starting torque inexpensive motors can be used.

## 8.21 The Orifice

An orifice is simply a restricted opening in a pipe through which a fluid is flowing. It may be a sharp hole or group of holes in a plate inserted in the pipe, or a gradual restriction, called a *well-rounded orifice* or *Venturi*. Orifices can be used as a refrigerant flow control and expansion device. One propietary orifice arrangement, used as a flow control device with flooded chillers in centrifugal refrigeration systems, is shown in Figure 8.18.

This orifice arrangement consists of a plate with holes followed by a well-rounded orifice, inserted in the liquid line. The restricted openings create the desired pressure drop. Regardless of the liquid head exerted, a well-rounded orifice meters a constant volume of fluid. At full load the column of liquid is high enough so that its head prevents flashing of liquid before it enters the rounded orifice, and all the flashing takes place through it. As the load decreases, however, the supply of liquid decreases and the liquid level column falls. This decreases the pressure enough so that the liquid now partially flashes when it passes

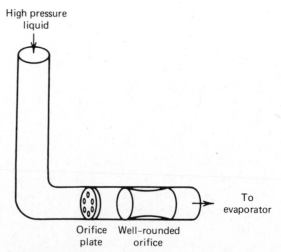

**FIGURE 8.18** Arrangement of orifices as a flow control device.

through the first orifice. The rounded orifice is now supplied with a mixture of liquid and vapor whose specific volume is greater. Since it delivers a constant volume, the mass flow rate is less. The orifice has carried out its function of varying flow rate with load.

## 8.22 Energy Utilization and Flow Control Devices

Following is a summary of some of the points discussed in this chapter relating to energy utilization and conservation as affected by flow control devices.

1. The thermostatic expansion valve provides efficient use of the evaporator surface over a wide range of loads.

2. If there is a significant pressure drop in either the evaporator or the refrigerant distributor, an external equalizer type TEV must be used. The internal equalizer valve will result in inefficient use of the evaporator.

3. Hunting in a system will result in inefficient use of evaporator surface. If the system is subject to hunting a cross charge or other antihunting type TEV must be used.

4. The capillary tube is a less-energy-efficient flow control device than the TEV.

5. The constant pressure expansion valve is a very inefficient flow control device if there is significant load variation.

## REVIEW QUESTIONS

1. What are the purposes of the flow control device?

2. How is pressure drop accomplished in any flow control device?

3. Name the types of flow control devices.

4. Name the major parts of a thermostatic expansion valve. Explain its operation, using a sketch.

5. What are the three operating forces in a TEV?

6. Explain how a TEV controls refrigerant flow rate in response to load changes.

7. What is superheat? Why could a TEV also be called a superheat control valve?

8. What effect would pressure drop in an evaporator coil have with an internally equalized TEV?

9. Explain the difference in construction of an internally equalized and external equalizer TEV.

10. Explain the application and operation of an external equalizer TEV.

11. Explain the use of a pressure limiting TEV. What two types are there?

12. Explain the operation of a limited charge TEV.

13. Explain hunting and its possible causes.

14. Explain the operation of a cross charge TEV.

15. What is thermal lag in a TEV and how is it used?

16. Explain a pressure equalizing feature of a TEV and its purpose.

17. What is a pilot operated valve and when is it used?

18. List the proper practices concerning the location and installation of a TEV.

19. Describe the construction and operation of a thermal electric expansion valve.

20. Describe the operation of a refrigerant float valve.

21. What is an important concern in the application of a high-side float valve?

22. Sketch and describe the operation of a constant pressure expansion valve.

23. Explain the possible difficulties created by the action of a constant pressure expansion valve. What results might occur?

What application is this type of valve suitable for?

24. Explain how a capillary tube controls refrigerant flow rate in response to load changes.

25. Compare the advantages and disadvantages of a capillary tube and a TEV.

26. What is of concern because of the fact that a capillary tube cannot provide tight shut-off?

27. What is a positive feature of the fact that a capillary tube cannot provide tight shut-off?

28. Describe some means of conserving energy by proper selection, application, and operation of flow control devices.

## PROBLEMS

8.1 A system using R-22 and a liquid charged TEV is operating at an evaporating temperature of 26°F. The spring pressure is 13 psi. What is the refrigerant superheat leaving the evaporator?

8.2 If the spring pressure for the unit in Problem 8.1 is descreased to 3 psi, what is the refrigerant superheat? What might occur as a result?

8.3 If the spring pressure for the unit in Problem 8.1 is increased to 24 psi, what is the refrigerant superheat? What might occur as a result?

8.4 A system using R-502 has an evaporator with a pressure drop of 8 psi. The evaporating temperature is 6°F. A liquid charged internal equalized TEV is used, with the spring pressure set to provide 10°F superheat. What is the actual superheat? What might occur as a result?

8.5 A system using R-12 has an evaporator coil with an 8 psi pressure drop. The evaporator inlet temperature is 22°F. An external equalizer liquid charged TEV is installed, with a spring pressure setting of 6 psi. What is the refrigerant superheat?

# Chapter 9

## REFRIGERANTS, BRINES, OILS, AND CONTAMINANTS

In this chapter we discuss refrigerants, brines, and oils that are used in refrigeration systems. Included are their properties and characteristics that concern performance and safety. Undesirable contaminants that may be in the system are also discussed.

## OBJECTIVES

A study of this chapter will enable you to:
1. Determine how properties of refrigerants affect refrigeration system performance.
2. Identify refrigerant characteristics that relate to safety or operation.
3. Identify the major refrigerants and their application.
4. Identify brines and their desirable properties.
5. Identify and describe characteristics of refrigerant lubricating oils.
6. Identify refrigeration system contaminants, their effects, and means of dealing with them.

## 9.1 Choice of Refrigerants

In both the vapor compression and absorption refrigeration system, the cooling is achieved by the evaporation of a liquid. Therefore, any fluid that can be made to change state from a liquid to a gas could serve as a refrigerant. Many factors make some substances more suitable than others, however, depending on the application: Equipment size, energy consumption, safety, and maintenance are some

of the concerns that are affected by choice of refrigerant.

## 9.2 Properties That Affect Performance

Some physical properties of a refrigerant may have an effect on equipment capacity or power required. These include:

Temperature–pressure characteristics.

Latent heat of vaporization.

Specific volume and density of vapor.

Specific heat of liquid.

*Temperature and Pressure Characteristics.*
The boiling temperature (saturation point) of a fluid changes with its pressure. Furthermore, temperature–pressure values are different for each substance. Six ideas should be kept in mind when choosing a refrigerant.

1. It is desirable for the pressure at evaporating conditions to be above atmospheric, to avoid inward leakage of air.
2. The compressor discharge pressure should not be excessive, so that extra strength high-side equipment is not required.
3. A low compression ratio is desirable, since compressor power increases directly with the compression ratio.
4. The compressor discharge temperature should not be excessive, to avoid such

problems as breakdown or dilution of the lubricating oil, decomposition of the refrigerant, or formation of contaminants such as sludge or acids. All of these can lead to compressor damage.

5. The compressor discharge pressure must not be above the critical pressure of the refrigerant. This is the pressure above which there is no separate liquid or vapor state. The refrigerant could not be condensed at constant pressure under this circumstance.

6. The evaporating temperature must not be below the freezing temperature of the refrigerant. This is one disadvantage of using water as a refrigerant.

*Latent Heat of Vaporization.*  A high latent heat of vaporization is desirable because it means there is a high refrigeration effect. (The refrigeration effect is the amount of cooling achieved for each pound of refrigerant evaporated. It is less than the latent heat of vaporization, but it is proportional to it.) This means that with a greater refrigeration effect a smaller mass flow rate of refrigerant is required for a given required cooling capacity. This tends to result in a need for smaller equipment and pipe sizes.

*Specific Volume of Vapor.*  A low specific volume of refrigerant is desirable because this reduces the required compressor displacement and piping size.

*Specific Heat of Liquid.*  A low specific heat of the liquid refrigerant is desirable. The refrigerant passing through the expansion device is cooled by a portion of it flashing into a gas. Since the heat required to cool the liquid decreases as its specific heat decreases, it follows that less flash gas is required. This reduces the total flow rate of refrigerant required to produce a given cooling capacity.

## 9.3 Comparative Performance of Refrigerants

The saturation pressure–temperature characteristics for some refrigerants have been shown in Figure 2.6 and in the property tables. These can be used to compare refrigerants for desirable evaporating and condensing temperatures.

Performance factors such as the refrigeration effect, theoretical displacement, and coefficient of performance can be calculated from the equations developed in Chapter 4. Some of this information is summarized in Table 9.1. Although the results are based on an ideal cycle, they are useful for comparative purposes.

The volume flow rate (CFM/ton) and coefficient of performance (COP) are especially important measures of performance. The CFM/ton is an indication of compressor size (displacement) and the COP is a measure of energy consumption. Note, for instance, that the volume flow rates for R-22 and R-502 are considerably less than for R-12; this is an important advantage of R-22 and R-502 over R-12: compressor size for the same capacity is significantly smaller. Note that the COP for all of the refrigerants listed is about the same value. That is, there is no greatly significant advantage of one refrigerant over another in terms of energy efficiency.

## 9.4 Safety Characteristics

There are a number of possible harmful characteristics of refrigerants.

*Toxicity.*  This refers to the degree to which a substance is a toxin or poison. Many refrigerants are nontoxic, including all the halocarbons. However, this should not be confused with the fact that any refrigerant is an asphyxiant, even when nontoxic. That is, the individual may suffocate because the refrigerant replaces oxygen. For this reason good ventila-

**TABLE 9.1** Comparative Physical and Performance Data of Refrigerants

| Name | 12 Dichlorodifluoromethane | 22 Monochlorodifluoromethane | 114 Dichlorotetrafluoromethane | 290 Propane | 500 Azeotrope R-12/152a 73.8% CCl₂F₂ + 26.2% CH₃CHF₂ | 502 Azeotrope R-22/15 48.8% CCl₂F₂ + 51.2% CClF₂CF₃ | 717 Ammonia | 1270 Propylene |
|---|---|---|---|---|---|---|---|---|
| Chemical formula | $CCl_2F_2$ | $CHClF_2$ | $C_2Cl_2F_2$ | $C_3H_8$ | | | $NH_3$ | $C_3H_6$ |
| Molecular weight | 120.93 | 86.48 | 170.93 | 44.10 | 99.29 | 111.64 | 17.03 | 42.09 |
| Boiling Temperature at 1 atm (°F) | −21.6 | −41.4 | 38.4 | −43.7 | −28.0 | −50.1 | −28 | −53.9 |
| Freezing Temperature at 1 atm (°F) | −252 | −256 | −137 | −305.8 | −254 | a | −107.9 | −301 |
| Critical Temperature (°F) | 233.6 | 204.8 | 294.3 | 206.3 | 221.1 | 194.1 | 271.4 | 197.2 |
| Critical pressure (psia) | 597 | 716 | 474 | 617.4 | 631 | 618.7 | 1657 | 670.3 |
| Density liquid at 100 °F | 78.79 | 71.24 | 88.4 | 29.58 | 69.28 | 71.97 | 36.4 | 30.3 |
| Specific volume vapor at 0°F | 1.61 | 1.37 | 4.75 | 2.68 | 1.66 | 0.88 | 9.12 | 2.26 |
| Specific heat liquid at 100°F | 0.240 | 0.313 | 0.249 | 0.6727 | 0.306 | 0.308 | 1.158 | 0.609 |
| Liquid head ft/psi at 100°F | 1.84 | 2.04 | 1.65 | 4.89 | 2.10 | 1.98 | 3.96 | 4.74 |
| Saturation Pressure (psia) At: −40°F | 9.31 | 15.22 | 1.91 | 16.09 | 10.95 | 18.8 | 10.41 | 20.59 |
| 0°F | 23.85 | 38.66 | 5.95 | 38.34 | 27.98 | 45.78 | 30.42 | 47.95 |
| 20°F | 35.74 | 57.73 | 9.69 | 55.76 | 41.96 | 67.16 | 48.21 | 69.16 |
| 100°F | 131.86 | 210.60 | 45.85 | 188.25 | 155.90 | 230.89 | 211.90 | 227.58 |
| 125°F | 183.77 | 292.64 | 67.55 | 257.18 | 217.7 | 316.06 | 307.8 | 308.97 |
| Thermal conductivity (k) Saturated liquid, 0 °F | 0.0490 | 0.0630 | 0.0437 | 0.0680 | 0.0530 | 0.0469 | 0.3350 | 0.0780 |
| Saturated vapor, 100°F | 0.0060 | 0.0068 | a | 0.0126 | a | 0.0071 | 0.0180 | 0.0116 |
| Viscosity—centipoise Saturated liquid, 0°F | 0.3133 | 0.2670 | 0.5994 | 0.1575 | 0.2823 | 0.2728 | 0.2282 | 0.1253 |
| Saturated vapor, 100°F | 0.0132 | 0.0140 | 0.0121 | 0.0091 | 0.0130 | 0.0142 | 0.0117 | 0.0096 |
| Basic cycle: 0°F/100°F Refrigeration effect Btu/lb | 46.2 | 65.2 | 38.1 | 108.2 | 55.8 | 40.1 | 457 | 115.4 |
| Liquid circulated lb/min-ton | 4.33 | 3.07 | 5.25 | 1.85 | 3.58 | 4.98 | 0.438 | 1.73 |
| Volume flow CFM/Ton | 6.97 | 4.20 | 24.93 | 4.95 | 5.95 | 4.38 | 3.99 | 3.93 |
| C.O.P | 3.66 | 3.50 | 3.62 | 3.42 | 3.50 | 3.26 | 3.62 | 3.43 |
| Safety group – U.L. Class | 6 | 5a | 6 | 5b | 5a | 5a | 2 | 5a |
| Safety group –ANSI B9.1 | 1 | 1 | 1 | 3 | 1 | 1 | 2 | 3 |
| Explosive range (% by volume) | Nonflammable | Nonflammable | Nonflammable | 2.3–7.3 | Nonflammable | Nonflammable | 16–25 | 2.0–10 |

aNot available.
Carrier Corp., Syracuse, N.Y.

tion should be ensured in refrigeration equipment rooms even when using nontoxic refrigerants.

***Flammability and Explosiveness.*** Flammability refers to the extent to which a substance burns with a flame, and therefore whether it is a fire hazard or not. The halocarbons are nonflammable and nonexplosive. Ammonia is flammable in certain concentrations.

Refrigerants are classified into three groups by the Safety Code for Mechanical Refrigeration of the American National Standards Institute (ANSI) as to their safety in use. This rating includes both toxicity and flammability. Group 1 refrigerants, including the halocarbons are considered nontoxic and nonflammable and can be used in occupied buildings for air conditioning. Certain standards of ventilation and other features in equipment rooms are required, however. Group 2 refrigerants, including ammonia, cannot be used in air conditioning systems, and equipment must be installed outside a building or in special rooms. Group 3 refrigerants, including propane, are the most hazardous, and are permitted only for industrial use, with very special restrictions.

The Underwriters' Laboratories (UL) also rates safety of refrigerants, using a different grouping system, from 1 to 6, in which 6 is the safest type.

Other possible health effects of refrigerants should be considered. Some refrigerants may cause dryness or irritation of the skin. Refrigerants with boiling points below 32°F at atmospheric pressure may freeze on contact with the skin and cause frostbite. Excess inhalation, even of some nontoxic refrigerants, may cause heart or central nervous system disturbances.

## 9.5 Characteristics Related to Operation or Maintenance

Some refrigerant characteristics affect system operation or maintenance.

***Chemical Stability.*** A refrigerant must be chemically stable (that is, not decompose) in the temperature range it is exposed to in the system. Decomposition can result in the production of contaminants such as acids, sludges, or noncondensable gases.

***Chemical Inertness.*** A refrigerant should not react chemically with any materials it encounters in the system. For example, ammonia will react with copper and dissolve it. Since hydrocarbon refrigerants dissolve rubber, other materials must be used for seals and gaskets. Halocarbon refrigerants will cause deterioration of some plastics, but not others.

***Effect on Lubricants.*** A refrigerant should not reduce the lubricating quality of the refrigerant oil, either by chemical or physical action. Refrigerant-oil miscibility is desirable to the degree that oil is carried to wearing parts, but not to the extent that lubrication is ineffective.

***Leakage Tendency.*** A lower tendency to leak from the system is desirable, for cost and sometimes safety concerns. Higher pressures increase leakage, of course. Generally, refrigerants with lower molecular weights leak at a greater rate. Ammonia, which has one of the lowest refrigerant molecular weights, has a high leakage tendency.

***Ease of Leak Detection.*** It is desirable that refrigerant leaks be easily detected, so that loss of refrigerant is minimized. Methods used for leak detection depend on refrigerant properties, as will be discussed.

***Cost and Availability.*** Reasonable cost and adequate availability are obviously desirable refrigerant characteristics.

## 9.6 Leak Detection

Leak detection methods are discussed here primarily to the extent that they relate to refrigerants. Detailed description of leak detection procedures is more properly a subject for service manuals.

Leaks may be detected either by pressurizing the system and checking for leakage to the outside, or by drawing a partial vacuum in the system and then checking for a rise in pressure on a test gage. The vacuum method can indicate if there is a leak, but not where it is located. A vacuum leak test is normally performed after pressure testing and repair of leaks has been completed, as a final check.

When pressure testing a newly installed system, either the refrigerant or a mixture of refrigerant and an inert gas such as nitrogen is used. The latter method is more economical if there is considerable loss of refrigerant when testing.

Leak testing methods and the equipment used differ as to their sensitivity, cost, and refrigerants for which they are suitable. The electronic leak detector (Figure 9.1), used with halocarbon refrigerants, is a very sensitive device that can detect extremely small leaks (as little as 1 ounce per 100 years). The detector has an element in the probing tip that creates an electric emission in the presence of a halocarbon gas. The electric signal is converted in the device either to a visual or an audible signal.

The halide torch is also used for detecting halocarbon refrigerant leaks. This device consists of a small propane tank, a burner with a copper element, and a "sniffer" hose (Figure 9.2). The hose is used with a probe at the joint where a leak is suspected to be. Any gas is drawn into the hose and to the burner. The burner's flame will change to a blue–green color in the presence of both a halocarbon gas and copper, indicating a leak. The halide torch has a leak sensitivity of about 1 ounce per year.

A problem that can occur when using either the electronic or the halide torch detector is that if there is a large leak the device may be activated by refrigerant in the general area,

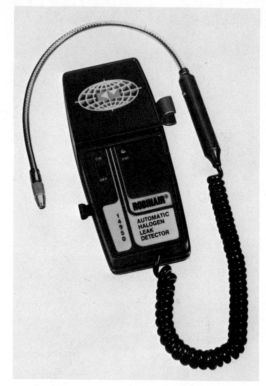

**FIGURE 9.1** Electronic leak detector. (Courtesy of Robinair Mfg. Div.)

making it difficult to locate the sources of leaks. Good ventilation may help to alleviate this problem.

The soap bubble test is a simple yet often effective method of discovering sources of leaks. The joint or connection is coated with a soap or detergent solution. Escaping gas forms bubbles at the leak. The soap bubble method can be used with any refrigerant. It is more effective when the pressure in the system is high.

Ammonia leaks can be detected by burning a sulfur candle near the suspected source. Reaction with the ammonia forms a visible white cloud. Another method is to use an indicator paper that changes color in the presence of ammonia.

The methods described apply primarily to

**FIGURE 9.2** Halide torch leak detector. (Courtesy of Robinair Mfg. Div.)

testing complete systems after installation, including the piping, fittings, valves, and accessories. Additional leak testing procedures, as well as these, may be used by manufacturers to test assembled package units. For example, a unit may be pressurized, submerged in water, and then observed to see if there are leaking gas bubbles.

Another factory leak test is the mass spectrometer method. The unit is placed in an enclosure that is evacuated and then surrounded by helium. Evacuation is taken through a device called a mass spectrometer.

The presence of helium in the evacuated gas (which indicates an inward leak) is indicated on the spectrometer readout scale. This method is extremly sensitive. It is used for the final leak test with absorption refrigeration machines.

## 9.7 Refrigerant Composition

The substances that are used as refrigerants in vapor compression systems include halocarbons, ammonia, and hydrocarbons. Ammonia and water are used in absorption systems. The chemical formulas and names of refrigerants are not important in our discussion, and will not be emphasized. All refrigerants are designated by a standard code numbering system, such as R-11, R-12, R-502, R-717. The halocarbons were formerly often called by the trade name of each manufacturer. For example, R-12 was called Freon 12, Genetron 12, Isotron 12, or Ucon 12.

***Halocarbons.*** These are the most widely used group of refrigerants. Their name indicates that they are derivatives of hydrocarbons (compounds of hydrogen and carbon), but also that they contain elements called halogens (such as chlorine and fluorine). The name *fluorocarbons* is also used, since those halocarbons that have been used as refrigerants all contain fluorine. Only a few of the halocarbons used as refrigerants will be mentioned here.

The halocarbons generally have very desirable characteristics. They have low toxicity, are nonflammable, and have good chemical stability. A wide choice is available with different pressure–temperature characteristics and boiling points, so that a particular halocarbon can be found for almost any application. However, although they are not toxic under ordinary circumstances, very high temperatures (as in open flames) can cause decomposition that produces toxic gases.

The halocarbon refrigerants R-12, R-22, and R-502 are widely used in reciprocating compressor systems for both air conditioning and commercial refrigeration applications. Their pressure–temperature characteristics at typical evaporating and condensing conditions and their low specific volume make them suitable to match the characteristics of reciprocating compressors, as discussed previously in this chapter.

R-22 has a lower specific volume and greater latent heat of vaporization than R-12, at the same evaporating temperature. Therefore, with R-22, a smaller compressor can sometimes be used than with R-12 to achieve the same refrigeration capacity. R-22 is not generally recommended at low commercial temperatures, however. Its characteristics are such that the discharge pressure and temperature will usually be excessive.

R-502 is an azeotropic mixture of two halocarbons (R-22 and R-115). An azeotrope is a mixture that behaves as if it were a homogeneous substance. R-502 has a low specific volume and therefore may result in a smaller compressor being needed if used to replace R-12. Its pressure–temperature characteristics are such that it can also be used in the low commercial temperature range, unlike R-22.

R-11, R-113, and R-114 are halocarbon refrigerants with a high specific volume. For this reason they are suitable in centrifugal refrigeration compressors, which are inherently high volume capacity devices. For very large centrifugal systems, however, lower specific volume refrigerants such as R-12 are used, to keep the compressor size reasonably small.

A problem involving fluorocarbons, not directly associated with the refrigeration system, is their potential effect on the earth's ozone layer. Ozone filters out excess ultraviolet solar radiation, which otherwise would be quite damaging to humans. There is a difference of opinion on the extent of this effect; research is attempting to resolve the problem.

*Ammonia (R-717).* This refrigerant is toxic and in certain concentrations explosive, which excludes its use for many applications. It is used, with proper restrictions, in refrigeration storage, ice making, and industrial applications, although halocarbons are also used. Ammonia has a low specific volume and high latent heat of vaporization relative to halocarbons, which may result in smaller equipment being used, compared to other refrigerants.

Vapor compression plants with ammonia will generally use about 1 to 2 percent less power than those with halocarbons at the same conditions. Ammonia is also a much less expensive chemical. These energy and cost factors can be significant in large systems. But, as noted elsewhere, the high discharge temperature of ammonia requires water cooling of the compressor, to prevent lubrication and contamination problems.

Ammonia is used as a refrigerant in the aqua–ammonia absorption refrigeration system. Water has a high affinity for absorbing ammonia, which makes the pair attractive, and pressures in the system are neither extremely low nor high.

*Hydrocarbons.* Some hydrocarbons, including propane, methane, and ethane are used as refrigerants. They are very flammable and explosive, however, which greatly limits their use. They are sometimes used in petrochemical plants and oil refineries, partially because of their availability.

*Water.* Water is used as a refrigerant in the lithium bromide–water absorption system (see Chapter 13). It is ideal in safety, cost, and availability characteristics. Its very low pressures at suitable evaporating temperatures results in extremely low system pressures, creating the problem of inward air leakage. The use of water as a refrigerant is limited to evaporating temperatures above its freezing point, 32°F (0°C), of course.

Water is not suitable as a refrigerant in

vapor compression systems. Its presence would make corrosion prevention extremely difficult. Furthermore, its very high specific volume as a vapor would result in a need for excessively large equipment.

## 9.8 Secondary Coolants (Brines)

The evaporating refrigerant in both the vapor compression system and absorption system is often used to cool a liquid which is then used to cool the final load. This is often the arrangement in large air conditioning systems. The evaporating refrigerant circulates through a water chiller. The chilled water then is distributed to air conditioning cooling coils in the spaces to be cooled. The liquid being chilled in this type of application is called a *secondary coolant* or *secondary refrigerant* to distinguish it from the primary refrigerant, the evaporating liquid.

A secondary liquid coolant can be distributed long distances without problems. If a primary refrigerant were used, flashing might occur as a result of excessive pressure drop, creating operating and control problems.

The secondary coolant also is useful when the primary refrigerant is toxic. For instance, an ammonia refrigerant plant can be installed in a remote location, with a safe secondary coolant distributed to the load.

Aside from water, solutions of water and another substance are often used as secondary coolants. These solutions are commonly referred to as "brines." The origin of this name is that a solution of sodium chloride and water (the same ingredients as sea water) was one of the first combinations used in ice making.

Brines are used instead of water as secondary coolants because their freezing points are generally much lower. This makes them suitable for many applications in low temperature refrigeration where a liquid coolant is desirable. The freezing point of brines changes with the concentration of the salt in the solu-

tion. The lowest freezing point is called the *eutectic* temperature.

Brines that are often used in modern refrigeration include solutions of sodium or calcium chloride and water, ethylene glycol and water, propylene glycol and water, and methanol and water. Some pure substances with low freezing points are also used, including methylene chloride, trichloroetheylene, and some of the halocarbon refrigerants.

***Physical Properties of Brines.*** The following physical properties of brines are of importance in performance and energy requirements.

1. *Specific heat.* A high specific heat is desirable because a lower flow rate of brine is required to remove a given amount of heat. This reduces pumping power and perhaps equipment size.
2. *Thermal conductivity.* A high thermal conductivity increases the heat transfer rate.
3. *Viscosity.* A low viscosity means there will be less friction and therefore a lower pumping power. Low viscosity also increases heat transfer rates.
4. *Specific gravity.* A high specific gravity increases the heat transfer rate. However, a high specific gravity also increases pumping power.

Further desirable brine characteristics are nontoxicity, noncorrosiveness, nonflammability, and reasonable cost.

Sodium chloride and calcium chloride (salt) solutions are low in cost, relatively nontoxic, and are nonflammable. They have been used widely in the food industry. Sodium chloride is used when open contact with food occurs. Its eutectic temperature is $-6°F$, which limits its use to product temperatures above $0°F$. Calcium chloride is suitable for applications down to about $-30°F$. Both these salts are quite corrosive to many metals, including copper and steel, which detracts from their desirability. *Corrosion inhibitors* can be added to the solution, but they must be carefully controlled and monitored to maintain their effectiveness.

Corrosiveness of glycols can be effectively controlled by adding inhibitors. Propylene glycol is relatively nontoxic but its viscosity is quite high, leading to high pumping power requirements. Ethylene glycol is more toxic but it has a lower viscosity. Glycols have good thermal properties and are widely used in industrial applications.

At very low temperatures (below −30°F) the viscosity of most brines is too high for practical use, although methyl chloride and R-11 have reasonably low viscosities at these temperatures.

# REFRIGERATION OILS

## 9.9 Purposes of Refrigeration Oils

Oils are used in refrigeration compressors to lubricate surfaces that contact and rub against each other. The oil forms a thin film between the surfaces. The lubrication serves two main purposes: to reduce wear of parts and to decrease frictional resistance. Reduction in wear prevents damage to equipment, lengthens its life, and lessens maintenance. Decreasing frictional resistance results in lower power requirements to drive the compressor.

For all types of compressors lubrication is required at shaft bearings. Reciprocating compressors also have a large contact area between the pistons and the cylinder walls. Rotary and screw compressors have similar contact areas but they are much smaller. Centrifugal compressors do not require lubrication between the impeller and casing, since there is no contact between them. Lubrication methods have been discussed in the chapters covering compressors.

The refrigeration oil accomplishes some additional functions besides that of lubrication. In positive displacement compressors it provides a liquid seal between the high and low pressure sides (discharge and suction) of the compressor. If this seal did not exist refrigerant gas would leak around the piston and adequate compression could not be achieved. The oil also serves as a cooling agent, carrying away heat generated by friction in the parts it lubricates.

## 9.10 Composition of Oils

Oils used as refrigeration lubricants are generally derived from petroleum, a mineral oil. Organic oils (vegetable or animal) are not suitable for refrigeration applications, primarily because they form acids during use.

Petroleum is a complex mixture composed primarily of hydrocarbons. For the purposes of our discussion, the composition can be grouped into three types of substances: naphthenes, paraffins, and aromatics. A small quantity of nonhydrocarbon substances such as sulfur also are present. The proportion of the three types of hydrocarbons varies, depending on the origin. Some paraffins precipitate out a hard wax at low temperatures, an undesirable characteristic for refrigeration use. This is not usually of concern, however, because the refining process for producing refrigeration oils includes dewaxing. The refining process also removes other undesirable components which might create acids during use.

Synthetic oils have been developed that are suitable for some refrigeration applications. For example, mineral oil and R-22 have limited miscibility. Some synthetic oils mix more completely with R-22. High miscibility improves oil return to the compressor.

Additives are sometimes put in refrigeration oils to improve desired properties, such as viscosity and chemical stability, and to inhibit corrosion.

## 9.11 Properties of Refrigeration Oils

The physical and chemical properties that are of importance in determining if a refrigeration oil will perform satisfactorily include viscosity, pour point, wax separation, dielectric strength, flash point, chemical stability, moisture content, foaming tendency, color, solubility of air, and oil–refrigerant miscibility. These characteristics and their effects will be discussed briefly.

*Viscosity.* This is a property of fluids that causes resistance to flow. It is sometimes called internal friction. A high viscosity (thick) oil increases resistance to motion of lubricated parts, thereby increasing power requirements. Furthermore, if the viscosity is too high the oil may not even penetrate between surfaces to be lubricated. On the other hand, if the viscosity is too low (thin) the oil film may be squeezed out from between the surfaces, and lubrication is inadequate. Also, the oil may not maintain an effective pressure seal between compressor discharge and suction.

Viscosity of oil decreases with high temperature and increases with low temperature. At high temperatures the concern is that it may be too thin to lubricate adequately, and at low temperatures the concern is that frictional resistance is too high. In low temperature applications it is possible that with the improper oil, viscosity could be so high that oil remains in the evaporator and does not return to the compressor. Generally speaking, an oil should be selected with the lowest viscosity possible throughout its temperature range that will still permit it to adequately lubricate the compressor and act as a pressure seal. This minimizes energy requirements.

With most halocarbon refrigerants, often a mixture of oil and refrigerant lubricates, so the viscosity of this mixture is of importance. This subject will be discussed shortly.

*Pour Point.* The pour point of an oil is defined as the lowest temperature at which it will flow. Refrigerant oil should be selected with a suitably low pour point so that fluidity is ensured at the low-side conditions. The pour point is of importance in systems where the refrigerant and oil do not mix. For those halocarbon refrigerants in which there is a mixture of oil and refrigerant on the low side, the pour point temperature of the pure oil would have no relevance.

*Wax Separation.* Wax that naturally exists in petroleum is removed as part of the refining process, but very small amounts still remain in the refrigeration oil. When the temperature of the oil is reduced, the wax may separate out as a solid. It may clog capillary tubes or expansion valves, affecting performance. Naphthene-based oils generally form a softer wax than paraffin-based oils, which is not as harmful, but is still undesirable.

The wax forming tendency of an oil is determined by the *floc test*. The oil is cooled until lumps (flocs) of wax appear. This temperature is called the *floc point*. A refrigeration oil should be chosen that does not form wax at the lowest temperatures encountered in the application.

*Dielectric Strength.* Oils are generally good electrical insulators—they have high electrical resistance. The *dielectric strength* of an oil is a measure of its electrical resistance. It is defined as the voltage at which its resistance will break down and it will become a good electric conductor. A refrigeration oil normally has a dielectric strength rating of 25 kilovolts or more.

The dielectric rating serves two purposes as a measure of desirable refrigeration oil characteristics. Contaminants in the oil, such as water, reduce its electrical resistance. Therefore a high dielectric rating indicates that the oil is relatively free of contaminants. In hermetic units, a high dielectric rating indicates that the oil will not contribute to a possible electric short circuit in the motor.

*Flash Point.* The *flash point* of an oil is the temperature at which the oil vapor will ignite if exposed to a flame. The flash point is not used to measure the combustibility of refrigeration oils, since there generally is no danger of this occurring under the conditions of use. The flash point, however, is an indication of the stability of the oil to resist decomposition at higher temperatures. A refrigeration oil should have a flash point well over 300°F.

*Chemical Stability.* A good refrigeration oil should be chemically stable—that is, it should not decompose or form harmful products under the conditions encountered. High temperatures may cause a breakdown of the refrigerant, leaving carbon deposits (carbonization) that can be harmful. Oils may react with refrigerants or contaminants in the system, producing acids or sludge products. Chemical stability is measured both by laboratory testing and by testing the oil in actual systems.

The resistance of oil to oxidation (called oxidation stability) is used as one measure of chemical stability. The oil is heated in the presence of oxygen and the amount of sludge formation is noted. Oxidation itself is not a problem under the sealed conditions encountered in refrigeration systems, but this test is a measure of general chemical stability.

*Moisture Content.* A good refrigeration oil should have a very low moisture content, since water can form corrosive products and may freeze if present. The refining process generally reduces the moisture level to an acceptable value. Care should be taken that the moisture content does not increase during handling.

*Foaming Tendency.* Oils vary in their tendency to foam, depending on their composition. Generally an excessive foaming tendency is undesirable, since this reduces the lubrication effectiveness of the oil.

*Color.* The color of a refrigeration oil is not of significance in itself, but is an indication of its quality. A dark oil indicates that some undesirable components have not been removed in the refining process. A pale yellow color is an indication of good quality. It is possible to overrefine the oil so that constituents that contribute to good lubrication are removed. This is indicated by a water clear color, called "white oils." At one time this was thought to be the proper color for a good refrigeration oil. Recently developed refining methods have produced a good refrigeration oil that is also colorless but this should be distinguished from the unsatisfactory white oils.

*Solubility of Air.* Oil can dissolve air, and may initially contain air in solution. This air is removed during the refining process, but care should be taken that excessive air is not dissolved during handling. The effect of air on system performance is discussed in Chapter 7.

## 9.12 Oil–Refrigerant Miscibility

Most of the halocarbon refrigerant gases are very soluble in oil; that is, they have a high *miscibility*. R-11 and R-12 are completely miscible with oil at all temperatures encountered in refrigeration applications. R-22 is completely miscible at higher temperatures but only partially miscible at lower temperatures. That is, the proportion of R-22 that can be dissolved in oil is reduced at lower temperatures.

In the refrigeration system the refrigerant and oil unavoidably mix. For instance, during shutdown the refrigerant gas may migrate to the oil crankcase due to its pressure, mixing with the oil there. The mixture contacts and lubricates wearing surfaces. The viscosity of the mixture decreases as the proportion of refrigerant increases. This complicates the problem of ensuring adequate lubrication, especially as the mixture proportions may change with conditions.

The oil–refrigerant mixture that lubricates the piston and cylinder walls is swept along through the system. This means that continual oil return to the crankcase must be ensured, or else it may be starved of adequate oil.

With refrigerants whose solubility in oil decreases with lower temperatures, such as R-22, some of the oil may separate out when the mixture reaches the evaporator. This aggravates the oil return problem since it is easier to move the mixture than the more viscous and denser oil. The oil may also coat heat transfer surfaces, reducing the cooling capacity.

Ammonia and oil are not miscible to any significant degree, and therefore the viscosity of the oil is not reduced from dilution. Oil can still be swept through part of the system and then collect in equipment, however, so oil separation and return is still a problem. Detailed discussions of the oil return problem and methods for resolving it are covered in Chapters 5 and 11.

# CONTAMINANTS

Substances that may be present in the refrigeration system and that can cause physical damage or affect performance include air, water (moisture), wax, foreign particles, acids, and sludge. We will discuss the possible sources of these contaminants, their effect, and treatment.

## 9.13 Air

Air may be present in the refrigeration system because it was not evacuated completely before being charged with refrigerant, or because there are leaks in a part of the system

that is below atmospheric pressure (if any). Other possible sources of air, such as in solution in oil, are generally negligible.

Air will collect in the condenser where it will adversely affect system performance by increasing the discharge pressure, which reduces cooling capacity or increases power consumption, or both. The higher discharge pressure caused by the presence of air in the condenser results in higher discharge temperatures. This can cause more rapid deterioration of motor insulation in hermetic units. The oxygen in the air is one of the substances required for some chemical reactions that may harm the system. Some of these reactions will be discussed.

Air is initially removed from the system by proper evacuation techniques, as described in service manuals. During the operation of large subatmospheric systems, it can be removed by purging it and other noncondensable gases (see Chapter 10).

## 9.14 Water (Moisture)

Water may be present in a refrigeration system from the following sources:

1. Inadequate dehydration of equipment when manufactured or during field service.

2. Water in the oil or refrigerant.

3. Leaks in part of the system below atmospheric pressure, resulting in the inward leakage of air containing water vapor.

4. Leaks from a water cooled condenser to the refrigerant side of the unit.

Moisture in the system can result in the following harmful effects:

1. *Freezing of the water.* Ice formation in the expansion device may block flow of refrigerant, and ice formation in the evaporator may reduce heat transfer.

2. *Corrosion of metals.* This may occur in the form of acid, sludge, or copper plating, all

of which require water and oxygen. These contaminants will be described.

3. *Damage to the motor insulation in hermetic compressors.* This may cause insulation breakdown, leading to motor failure.

Moisture is removed from refrigeration equipment by dehydration in the factory. Heat, hot dry air, or vacuum methods are used. In the field, proper evacuation techniques will remove moisture as well as air. Care must be taken that water is not present in the refrigerant or oil added to the system.

To maintain dryness during operation, driers are installed permanently in the liquid line piping. These devices contain a dessicant, a substance that absorbs water. Driers are described in Chapter 11.

## 9.15 Foreign Particles

Many types of undesirable materials may enter the system during manufacture or installation. This includes iron and copper oxides from soldering or welding, solder flux, dirt, cleaning agents, and metal particles. Such foreign matter may plug up passages, interfering with cooling or with lubrication. Some substances may react to form acids or sludge. Abrasive particles may wear out motor insulation. Metal particles may cause an electrical short.

Any foreign matter should be removed during manufacture and installation. During operation, combination filter–driers and suction line strainers are used to trap foreign particles.

## 9.16 Wax, Sludge, and Acids

Some wax will remain in the refrigerant oil even after refining. Oils used in manufacturing and left in the system may also contain wax. If the wax precipitates out of oil it can plug expansion device openings and seriously affect performance. A refrigeration oil should be chosen that does not precipitate wax at the temperatures encountered.

Sludge is a sticky substance formed due to decomposition of the oil from heat. The decomposition of the oil, called *carbonization* or *coking*, forms carbon. The carbon may form into sludge in the presence of contaminants. Sludge can block flow and thus affect performance, and it can be corrosive. Its formation is best prevented by using the proper oil, keeping the system clean, and avoiding overheating. Filter–driers may serve to trap sludge.

Acids may be present in the oil, or they may be formed by reactions of foreign substances with water or oxygen, or by reactions of oil and refrigerant under certain conditions. Acids may corrode metal parts or may cause deterioration of motor insulation. The best preventative is to keep the system clean. Some desiccants used in driers may also remove acids.

## 9.17 Copper Plating

A type of contamination that warrants specific mention is called *copper plating*. This is the formation of a thin layer of copper on compressor parts, especially bearings and valves. It usually occurs by the dissolving of copper in the presence of an oil–refrigerant mixture, followed by plating out of the copper on metal surface due to reactions with impurities, water, and oxygen. If the copper plating becomes too thick it can interfere with performance or damage equipment. The best prevention is to use high quality oil and refrigerant and to keep up with proper cleaning, as already described.

## REVIEW QUESTIONS

1. What effect can the choice of refrigerant have on the refrigeration system?
2. What physical properties of a refrigerant may affect the system performance? Describe how each effect occurs.

3. What is a disadvantage of using R-12 rather than R-22 and R-502?

4. What are the major safety characteristics to be considered when selecting a refrigerant?

5. What should be considered, when choosing a refrigerant, that may affect system operation and maintenance?

6. Describe two ways of testing the refrigeration system for leaks.

7. What two indications of sensing leaks can be used with any refrigerant?

8. Describe two ways of sensing leaks used only with halocarbon refrigerants.

9. Describe two ways of sensing leaks used only with ammonia.

10. Describe how a leak test is performed with lithium bromide absorption refrigeration machines.

11. What is the general chemical composition of halocarbon refrigerants?

12. Why are halocarbon refrigerants desirable? What is a potential undesirable characteristic?

13. What advantage and disadvantage does R-22 have as compared to R-12?

14. What is an azeotrope? What popular halocarbon refrigerant is an azeotrope? For what reasons is it often used instead of R-22?

15. Describe a desirable and an undesirable feature of ammonia for use as a refrigerant.

16. What hydrocarbons are used as refrigerants? What undesirable feature do they have?

17. Where is water used as a primary refrigerant? What problem exists with its use? What limitation is there on its use?

18. Explain the meaning of the terms *primary refrigerant* and *secondary refrigerant* (coolant).

19. What is a brine? Why is it used as a secondary coolant?

20. What properties of brines are important in refrigeration? Describe how they affect performance.

21. List three types of brines and their applications.

22. What are the two main purposes of lubrication oils?

23. What benefits to the refrigeration system occur from lubrication?

24. What two secondary functions does the lubrication oil serve?

25. What are the substances that a refrigeration lubrication oil may be composed of?

26. List and describe the properties that are of importance for a refrigeration oil.

27. What should be the viscosity of a refrigerant oil?

28. What should be the pour point of a refrigerant oil? When is the pour point meaningless?

29. Why may wax in the oil be a problem? What is the floc point? What type of oil has less potential wax formation problems?

30. For what two reasons should the dielectric strength of the oil be known?

31. Why is it important to know the flash point of the oil?

32. What is carbonization? What causes it?

33. What is miscibility?

34. Using the behavior of R-22 and oil, explain the problems that may be caused by the degree of miscibility.

35. List the possible contaminants in a refrigeration system. Describe their effects.

36. What is copper plating? What is its effect?

# Chapter 10

## CENTRIFUGAL COMPRESSORS AND SYSTEMS

In addition to the reciprocating, rotary, and screw (helical rotary) compressors, centrifugal compressors are used in refrigeration systems.

In this chapter we discuss the principles, construction, performance, and design features of these compressors. The centrifugal compressor is widely used in large air conditioning systems; it is essential for any refrigeration practitioner involved with large systems to have a sound knowledge of this type of compressor. The total amount of energy consumed by all centrifugal systems annually is extremely large, and energy use and conservation is therefore an important consideration. Since most centrifugal compressors are used in liquid chiller systems the arrangement, ratings, and selection of these units are discussed.

## OBJECTIVES

A study of this chapter will enable you to:
1. Identify the major parts and describe the operation of a centrifugal compressor.
2. Sketch and explain surging.
3. Identify and compare the methods of centrifugal compressor capacity control.
4. Describe the basic construction of centrifugal refrigeration machines.
5. Identify the controls used on centrifugal machines.
6. Select a centrifugal water chiller.
7. Suggest energy conservation measures in selection and operation of centrifugal machines.

## 10.1 Centrifugal Compressor Construction and Principles

The centrifugal compressor consists of one or more *impellers* with a number of curved vanes, mounted on a shaft, and housed in a spiral shaped casing, called a *volute* casing (Figure 10.1). The construction is similar to that of a centrifugal pump.

The centrifugal compressor differs from the other types of refrigeration compressors in the way that it increases the gas pressure. We saw that the reciprocating compressor, called a positive displacement machine, simply decreased the volume of gas, thereby increasing its pressure. The centrifugal compressor is called a dynamic machine, which means that its moving parts exert a continual force on the constantly flowing gas, increasing its energy.

When the impeller rotates, refrigerant gas is drawn into the suction of the compressor, axially through an opening in the center of the

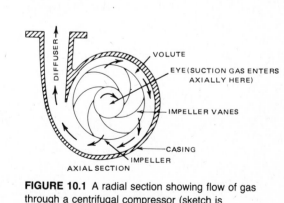

**FIGURE 10.1** A radial section showing flow of gas through a centrifugal compressor (sketch is conceptual—actual construction is more complex).

impeller, called the *eye*. The vanes on the spinning impeller exert a centrifugal force on the gas, forcing it to the periphery of the casing, and around the casing circumference to the discharge opening. Both the pressure and the velocity of the gas are increased by the centrifugal force. To express this in another way, two forms of the energy of the gas have been increased: static pressure and kinetic (velocity) energy. The velocity energy is sometimes called velocity pressure. The increased velocity energy is converted into a further increase in pressure by slowing down the gas. This is done by gradually increasing the size of the volute-shaped discharge opening, called the *diffuser*. About one half the total pressure increase is from the conversion of kinetic energy to pressure.

Because there is a small clearance between the impeller and casing, friction is of concern only with bearings, and high rotating speeds are possible; the centrifugal compressor is thus inherently a large volume, large tonnage machine. Capacities range from 100 to 10,000 tons of refrigeration (at temperatures suitable for air conditioning). In the smaller capacities (up to 2000 tons) hermetic centrifugal compressors are generally used, and open compressors are used for larger systems.

It is not practical to manufacture centrifugal compressors below about 100 tons capacity. The wheels (impellers) become so small in diameter that the frictional losses in the compressor would require a large part of the power requirements, making the efficiency unacceptably low. The maximum capacity is limited by the largest diameter impellers that are practical to build, considering structural strength requirements.

## 10.2 Impeller Staging

The pressure (commonly called *head*) that can be achieved with a single impeller (called single staging) is limited by a number of factors. The pressure increase is a function of the gas velocity, which in turn depends on the impeller tip speed. Higher tip speeds require greater strength impellers, and a practical limit is reached. Another factor is the effect of approaching sonic velocity. As the gas velocity approaches the velocity of sound, shock waves and the separation of the gas from the impeller blades may occur (this is similar to what happens as an aircraft approaches sonic velocity). This causes very large turbulence and frictional losses, increasing power requirements unacceptably.

When conditions require a greater pressure increase than is practical with a single impeller, two or more impellers can be arranged so that the discharge from the first stage impeller is fed to the suction of the second stage impeller, achieving a greater overall pressure increase. Up to 10 stages are used in compressors for very low temperature refrigeration. Figure 10.2 shows some possible arrangements of the impellers for a two-stage compressor. As will be explained in the next section, two impeller stages are often used even when not required for the pressure needed, to decrease energy consumption.

## 10.3 Thermodynamic Cycle and System

The centrifugal compressor system operates on the same vapor compression refrigeration system and cycle as described as Chapter 4. The system consists of compressor, condenser, flow control device, and evaporator (Figure 10.3). The evaporator is the flooded liquid chiller type and the condenser is water cooled. The flow control device is either a float valve or orifice.

The cycle for a single stage compressor is as shown in the $p–h$ diagram of Figure 10.4. The refrigerant leaves the evaporator as a saturated vapor (3), not superheated as it generally is with direct expansion evaporators and reciprocating compressors. The refrigerant

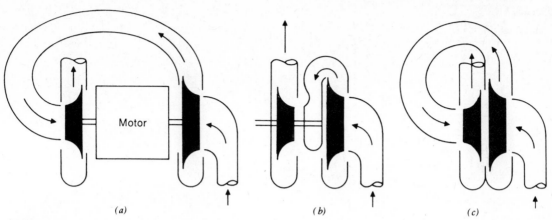

(a)  (b)  (c)

**FIGURE 10.2** Different possible arrangement of impellers for a two-stage compressor. Opposing forces tend to balance each other with arrangements (a) and (c), reducing thrust on bearings.

liquid is sometimes subcooled in the condenser (1 and 1′).

***The Economizer Cycle.*** When two or more stages of compression are used, the system performance can be improved significantly over that with a single stage compressor. Re-

call that in the vapor compression system the liquid refrigerant is cooled as it expands through the flow control device, by the evaporation of a small part of the refrigerant (the flash gas). This flash gas flows through the evaporator and is compressed along with the evaporated refrigerant.

With a two stage compressor it is possible to carry out the expansion process in two steps. The system is shown in Figure 10.5. An economizer chamber is located between the condenser and evaporator. Liquid refrigerant from the condenser enters the first section of the chamber. The liquid expands through a

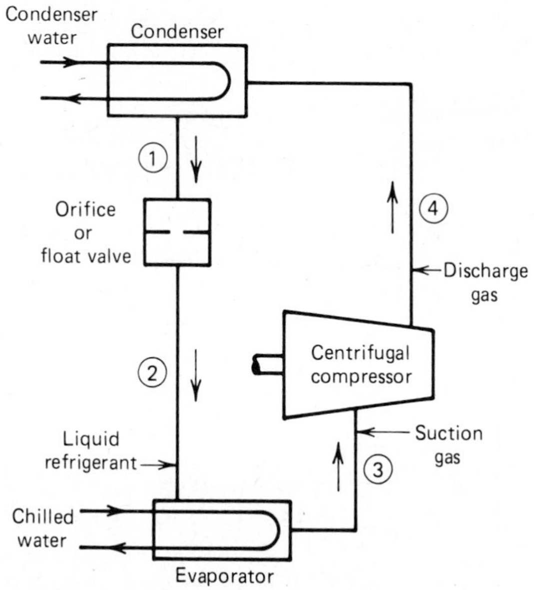

**FIGURE 10.3** Centrifugal compression system—basic components and arrangement.

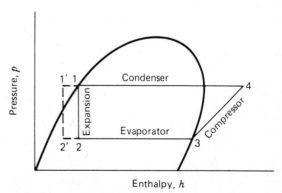

**FIGURE 10.4** *P–h* diagram of basic vapor compression cycle with centrifugal compression system.

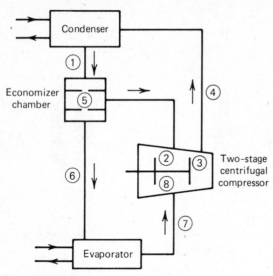

**FIGURE 10.5** Economy cycle arrangement using two-stage centrifugal compressor and economizer chamber.

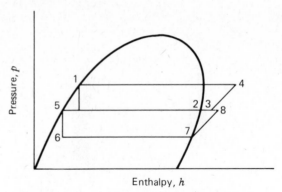

**FIGURE 10.6** $P$–$h$ diagram for economizer cycle.

flow control device to the second section of the chamber. This section is maintained at an intermediate pressure—the suction pressure to the second stage compressor—because it is connected by a pipe to that part of the system. The portion of the refrigerant that has flashed to a gas at this pressure goes to the suction of the high stage compressor where it is compressed to the condensing pressure. The liquid in the second section, now at an intermediate pressure and temperature, expands through a low-side flow control device to the evaporator pressure and temperature, and then through the evaporator to the low stage compressor.

The thermodynamic cycle, called the *economizer* cycle, is shown in the $p$–$h$ diagram of Figure 10.6. Cycle 1–2–3–4 is the high stage compression and 5–6–7–8 the low stage compression. There are different mass flow rates in each part of the system, so if a cycle analysis is carried out, this must be accounted for. However, it is clear that not all of the refrigerant is compressed from the evaporating pressure to the condensing pressure, as it

would be in a single stage machine. The intermediate stage flash gas is compressed only from the intermediate pressure to the condensing pressure. This reduces the total compressor power requirement by as much as 10 percent in the air conditioning range, and more at lower temperatures. More than one stage of economizer arrangement can be used if there are more than two stages of compression.

## 10.4 Centrifugal Compressor Performance Characteristics–Choking and Surging

The capacity (flow rate) of a centrifugal compressor varies greatly with the pressure (head) that it produces. That is, it is a variable displacement machine. This is quite different from the performance of a reciprocating compressor, which is essentially a constant displacement machine. Aside from the relatively minor effect of the clearance volume, the reciprocating compressor (at a given speed) delivers a constant volume flow rate, regardless of pressure.

This variable displacement characteristic of centrifugal compressors makes them ideal for operating at varied part-load conditions, and for conserving energy, a subject discussed later.

The performance characteristic curve,

which shows how the volume flow rate delivered varies with head, can be used to explain some features of behavior that are of importance in operating and selecting centrifugal compressors. Fig. 10.7 is a typical performance curve, for a given speed.

It would seem at first that a compressor should be selected to operate near its maximum flow capacity, such as at point A, so that a smaller compressor could be used for a required flow rate. This is not desirable, however. At high flows the velocity approaches sonic velocity, increasing the internal head losses and resulting in the steep curve of sharply dropping head produced, as shown. This is called *choking* flow. Compressor efficiency drops seriously at this condition; selection should be avoided in this range, called the "stonewall."

Point B is a typical desirable operating condition. Let us say that the compressor head produced (B), just equals the head required, which is a result of the head losses from friction in the system. Suppose, however the system head required decreases slightly, to B'. The compressor increases its flow to B'. This increased flow causes greater friction head loss in the system and the compressor performance returns to its equilibrium condition B. The compressor operation is stable for reasonable changes in head or flow around B.

A different situation occurs, however, if the compressor operation is at point C, to the left of the peak of the performance curve. Suppose there is a slight decrease in the required system head. the compressor will now operate at C', delivering less flow. At the reduced flow the system friction and required head decrease still further until momentarily the compressor is starved of gas, and delivers no flow, point D. The high pressure gas in the condenser then flows in reverse through the compressor. The compressor has enough gas to pump and will now suddenly begin to discharge the gas at a high flow rate, say point B'. But this causes the system head loss to increase, say to C, and the compressor operation drops back to C. The operation now alternately shifts or

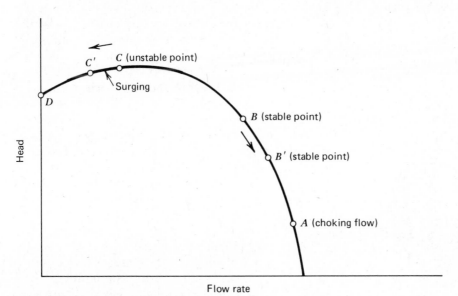

**FIGURE 10.7** Performance characteristic curve for a centrifugal compressor, showing stable operating condition, surging, and choking flow.

hunts between B′ and C, and the refrigerant alternately surges back and forth through the compressor. This phenomenon is called *surging*. It is accompanied by a pulsating noise. It is usually more annoying than dangerous. However, if let to continue, overheating of the refrigerant could occur, which might lead to overheating of bearings.

## 10.5 Capacity Control

Normally the compressor would not be selected at design conditions for a capacity to the left of the peak of its curve, so that surging would not occur. However in most applications the compressor capacity must be reduced to handle reduced cooling loads. There are three methods of capacity control: *suction damper, speed control,* and *variable inlet guide vanes.*

The suction damper is a simple one-piece butterfly damper in the suction line, that rotates to throttle flow (Figure 10.8). When it throttles flow back along the compressor performance curve, operation will eventually reach the unstable surge region. This is at

**FIGURE 10.8** Butterfly-type suction damper for controlling centrifugal comrpessor capacity (flow rate).

about 40 to 50 percent of full load. For this reason and because the reduction in power requirements is not as much as with other capacity control methods, suction damper control is undesirable. It does, however, have low initial cost.

Speed control is another method of varying centrifugal compressor capacity. If the compressor is driven by a steam turbine, speed control is easily accomplished by throttling steam flow to the turbine. Energy saving characteristics are excellent. About 40 percent of full load power requirements is needed at 50 percent capacity. Minimum load is limited to 40 to 50 percent however, to ensure stable operation above the surge point. If the compressor drive is an electric motor, a variable speed type called a wound rotor motor can be used. These are not used often, however, because of their high cost.

The development of solid state controls has led to a relatively simple and inexpensive motor speed control device that is available with a hermetic centrifugal compressor.

For both suction damper and speed control methods, hot gas bypass is required to reduce capacity below about 50 percent. No further reduction in power occurs below this point. Typical power versus capacity curves are shown in Figure 10.9.

An excellent method of varying compressor capacity uses adjustable *inlet guide vanes,* also called *prerotation vanes* (Figure 10.10). A damper constructed of wedge-shaped vanes arranged like sections of a pie is installed in the compressor suction inlet.

The sections rotate around the center, closing or opening the available inlet area to vary the refrigerant gas flow rate.

In addition to throttling flow, the guide vanes change the direction of the gas, according to their position. This is a very desirable characteristic. There is an optimum direction at which the gas should enter the compressor impeller vanes to minimize power requirements. This required direction changes as

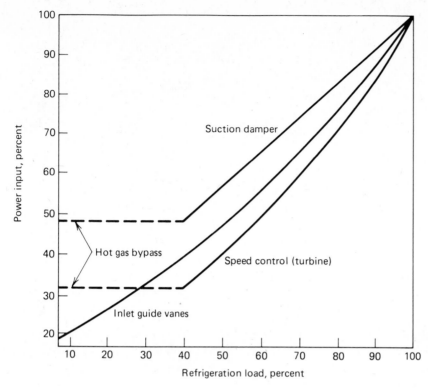

FIGURE 10.9 Power versus capacity of centrifugal compressors—comparison of control methods.

FIGURE 10.10 Inlet guide vanes for controlling centrifugal compressor capacity. (The Trane Co., La Crosse, WI)

flow rate changes. When the inlet guide vanes rotate toward closure, they also change the direction of the gas so that it enters the impeller at the most efficient angle. Called prerotation or preswirl, this feature results in continual reduction of power with load, as seen in Figure 10.9.

The prerotation guide vane method of capacity control has other desirable energy and cost saving features. It results in a change of the shape of the compressor head-flow performance curve, so that capacity can be reduced to about 10 percent of full load before surging would occur. Power requirements thus decrease continually, unlike with hot gas bypass.

When starting, the guide vanes are normally kept closed, so that the compressor has no gas to compress and starts unloaded. This reduces the power requirements at start-up. The main value of this is not in the energy consumed (the time period is short) but in other effects. If the compressor starts loaded, the motor will draw a great inrush current (four to five times normal). This could overheat the windings and damage the motor. There is also a very expensive charge by utility companies for the maximum current demand, even for a short period of time.

## 10.6 Centrifugal Refrigeration Machines

Practically all centrifugal refrigeration systems are used for chilling liquids, and the great majority of these are used in water chillers for air conditioning. The term *centrifugal water chiller* is used to refer to the complete machine, consisting of compressor, evaporator for chilling water, condenser, interconnecting piping, controls, and accessories.

Centrifugal water chillers are made in both hermetic and open compressor arrangements. In sizes ranging from about 100 to 2000 tons, hermetic machines have completely replaced open machines on the market, because of their cost, ease of installation, and compactness. Figure 10.11 shows a hermetic compressor, and Figure 10.12 shows an

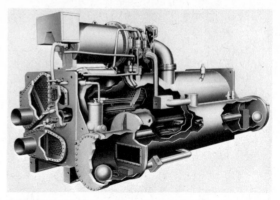

**FIGURE 10.12** A hermetic centrifugal water chiller—note that compressor, condenser, evaporator, connections, and controls are all assembled. (Courtesy of Carrier Corp., a subsidiary of United Technologies Corp.)

assembled hermetic chiller. Our discussion will focus on hermetic machines.

In some hermetic machines the compressor is directly driven from a two-pole motor, at about 3550 rpm for 60 Hz current. Some machines have speed-increasing gears to run the compressor at higher rpm, to keep the impeller size small. Variable inlet guide vanes are generally used for capacity control with hermetic machines.

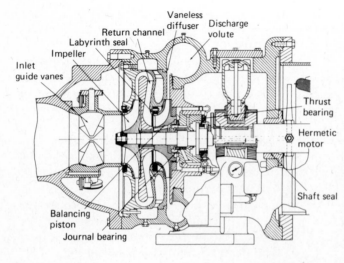

**FIGURE 10.11** Sectional view (taken axially) through a single-stage hermetic centrifugal refrigeration compressor. (Reprinted with permission from the 1979 Equipment ASHRAE Handbook & Product Directory)

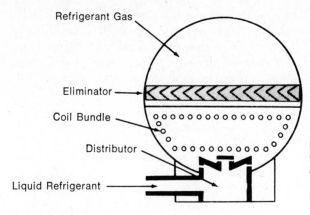

Refrigerant Gas

Eliminator

Coil Bundle

Distributor

Liquid Refrigerant

**FIGURE 10.13** Section through flooded chiller used with a centrifugal refrigeration system. (The Trane Co., La Crosse, WI)

Evaporators are of the flooded chiller type, with the refrigerant flowing through the shell and water to be chilled flowing through the tubes (Figure 10.13). Liquid refrigerant enters at the bottom and the vapor leaves at the top. To prevent any liquid droplets from entering the compressor, *eliminators* are used. These are multiple bend baffles or wire mesh installed above the tube bundle, that catch any liquid entrained in the vapor. Sometimes a perforated plate is also installed across the space to ensure uniform boiling in all places.

On the water side, arrangements are available with a different number of passes, usually from one to four pass, using partitioning baffles in the water box. Increasing the number of passes improves the heat transfer, but it also increases the water pressure drop. The water boxes on the ends are bolted for removal. This permits access to the tubes, which then may be cleaned internally. The shell, water boxes, and tube sheets that hold the tubes are made of ferrous materials (steel or cast iron) and the tubes are copper.

Condensers are usually of the water cooled type, with a shell and tube construction similar to that of the evaporator. The hot gas enters at the top and the condensed liquid leaves at the bottom. In materials, removable water box construction, and number of water passes available, the condenser is similar to the

evaporator, unless the condensing water is corrosive.

For smaller hermetic chillers, some manufacturers combine the evaporator and condenser into a single shell to reduce manufacturing costs and make the unit more compact. Some manufacturers use two-stage impellers for all sizes, with direct drive at 3550 rpm. Other manufacturers use speed increasing gears and one stage of compresion for smaller size chillers, and two stages for larger machines.

When the refrigerant enters the compressor suction, it exerts a considerable force axially on the impellers. This may require the use of special thrust bearings on the end of the shaft to absorb the force. With two-stage compressors, it is possible to arrange the impellers and piping so that gas flows in opposite directions into the suction of each impeller, thereby balancing out the two thrust forces, as in Figure 10.2 (a) and (c). With this arrangement a special (and expensive) thrust bearing is not needed.

The flow control device is usually either a float valve or simply an orifice. The hermetic motor is refrigerant cooled in some models, water cooled in others. Controls and gauges are furnished in a panel, assembled and wired as required. The complete machine may be assembled as one package in smaller sizes or with the compressor separate in larger sizes. The unit is mounted on rubber vibration isolation pads.

The construction of the open centrifugal chiller is similar to the hermetic chiller described. The compressor is generally driven at higher speeds than 3600 rpm through either speed increasing gears if a motor is used, or directly by a steam turbine.

## 10.7 Lubrication

The only parts that require lubrication on centrifugal machines are the bearings, and gears if they are used. The impeller does not touch the casing, so lubrication is not required there. In addition to the conventional shaft journal bearings to support the weight, thrust bearings are used. These are end bearings that take the force exerted by the refrigerant gas as it travels axially.

The lubrication system consists of an oil pump, piping system, oil filter, and a water cooled oil cooler to keep the oil at its proper temperature (Figure 10.14). An electric oil heater is furnished to reduce the amount of refrigerant dissolved in the oil on shutdown. This refrigerant would otherwise come out of solution on start-up, producing a refrigerant–oil foam, which could interfere with oil pump flow.

An oil pressure relief valve relieves excess pump pressure. An oil pressure safety control will not permit the compressor to start until adequate pressure is developed, and will also shut down the compressor on low oil pressure.

## 10.8 Refrigerants

A number of refrigerants are used in centrifugal systems. In smaller sizes R-11 or R-113, refrigerants with a high specific volume, are used. Then reasonable size impellers (not too large or small a diameter) can be used. Furthermore, since the saturation pressure–temperature characteristics of R-11 and R-113 are such that pressures will be below 15 psig, and the ASME code requires higher strength vessels above this pressure, construction costs are kept down. In addition, operating engineers with a high pressure license, often required in many localities for systems operating above 15 psig, are not called for.

In larger capacity machines low specific volume refrigerants such as R-12, R-22, and R-114 are used, since this results in a need for a smaller compressor, and smaller gas piping. This reduces initial and installation costs. The lower weight reduces structural support costs. Internal pressures, however, are higher.

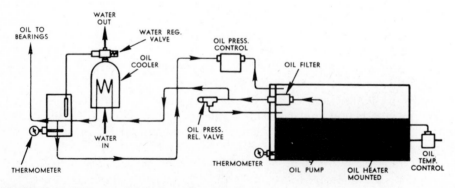

**FIGURE 10.14** Compressor lubrication system used with a centrifugal chiller. (The Trane Co., La Crosse, WI)

## 10.9 Purging

When R-11 and other low specific volume refrigerants are used the gas pressures on the low side are well below atmospheric. As a result air and water vapor will unavoidably leak into the system through joints. The gas will collect in the condenser, raising condensing pressure and reducing the capacity of the machine. The water vapor may combine with the refrigerant to form acids and corrode parts of the equipment. When refrigerants such as R-11 are used, the machine is furnished with a purge system to remove the air (the noncondensables) and water vapor. Figure 10.15 shows one type of purge system. Air and water vapor that have collected in the system are extracted from a connection near the top of the condenser. A small amount of refrigerant is also unavoidably removed. The gases pass to the purge compressor, which raises the pressure to a value at which the refrigerant can be condensed. The gases then flow to a water cooled condenser that condenses the water vapor and refrigerant vapor. The water vapor is lighter, and settles on top where it may be drained and discarded. The

refrigerant is drained back to the evaporator and the air is vented through a purge valve.

## 10.10 Controls

The compressor capacity control usually is operated from a temperature sensor located in the leaving chilled water line. The signal from the sensor modulates the inlet guide vanes to close or open in response to falling or rising chilled water temperature.

The operating and safety controls are designed and furnished to operate as an interconnected control system. A *guide vane switch* prevents the compressor from starting unless the inlet guide vanes are closed, so that the compressor starts under minimum load, drawing less electric current and reducing utility company demand charges.

The current drawn by the motor during operation is also limited to a pre set controlled value. A current limiting device (called a *demand limit control*) senses the current being drawn, and if it exceeds the set value, it overrides the chilled water temperature signal, closing the inlet guide vanes. This prevents

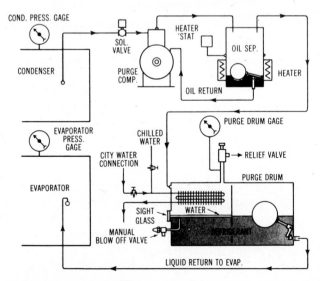

**FIGURE 10.15** Purge system used with a centrifugal chiller. (The Trane Co., La Crosse, WI)

any overload of the motor, and reduces demand charges. It may be reset at different times of the year. For example, in winter it might be reset so that the maximum current demand is 60 percent of that used in the summer, based on expected maximum loads.

Safety controls and interlocks are also furnished. A condenser *high pressure cutout* will stop the compressor on excessive condenser pressure.

A refrigerant *low temperature cutout* stops the compressor if the evaporator refrigerant temperature falls below a safe set point.

A *low oil pressure cutout* prevents the compressor from starting until the oil pump pressure reaches the required set point, and stops the compressor if the oil pressure falls below the set point.

An *oil pressure time delay relay* prevents the compressor from starting until a few seconds after oil pressure has been established.

An *antirecycle timer* prevents the compressor from being restarted for a set number of minutes after shutdown.

A *chilled water low temperature switch* prevents the compressor from starting if the chilled water temperature is below a set point.

Interlocks are usually provided so that the compressor cannot start before other components such as the chilled water and condensing water pump, and the cooling tower fan.

Most, if not all of the above controls are prewired and assembled in a control panel, and the whole system operates automatically once it is started. The panel usually contains numerous warning lights and perhaps alarms, as well as pressure and temperature gauges.

## 10.11 Rating and Selection

The capacity ratings for centrifugal refrigeration machines are usually presented by manufacturers in tabular form. Efficient combinations of compressor, evaporator, and con-

denser are offered as a package from which the designer chooses that which meets the needs of the project. Initial and operating costs should be considered when alternate choices are available.

Table 10.1 presents rating data for a group of hermetic centrifugal water chillers, listed in order of size from smaller to larger. The following data are needed in order to select the proper unit:

1. Refrigeration load.
2. Chilled water leaving temperature and flow rate.
3. Condensing water leaving temperature and flow rate.
4. Evaporator and condenser fouling factors.
5. Number of passes in evaporator and condenser.

The performances shown in Table 10.1 are for a two-pass evaporator and condenser, 2.4 GPM/ton chilled water flow rate (10°F TD), 3 GPM/ton condenser water flow rate (10°F TD), and a fouling factor of 0.0005 hr-ft$^2$-°F/Btu for both evaporator and condenser. To use the table for other fouling factors, adjustments are made as follows: If the condenser fouling factor is 0.001, add 2.5°F to the condenser water leaving temperature. If the evaporator fouling factor is 0.001, subtract 2°F from the chilled water leaving temperature.

It should be understood that the "adjusted" temperatures as found from these procedures, to be used in Table 10.1, are for selection purposes only. The actual design temperatures remain as chosen by the engineer.

The performance changes if evaporators and condensers other than two-pass are used, and if water flow rates are different than specified. For brevity, corrections to performance for these situations are not shown here.

The water pressure drop through the evaporator and condenser increases as the

**TABLE 10.1** Performance Ratings for a Group of Hermetic Centrifugal Water Chillers[a]

| Compressor 020 Evaporator 2D Condenser 2D | Leaving Condenser Water Temperature, °F | | | | Compressor 032 Evaporator 2D Condenser 2D | Leaving Condenser Water Temperature, °F | | | |
|---|---|---|---|---|---|---|---|---|---|
| Leaving Evaporator Water Temperature, °F | 90 | 95 | 100 | | | 90 | 95 | 100 | |
| 40 | 198 | 186 | 174 | Tons | 40 | 309 | 292 | 274 | Tons |
|  | 140 | 140 | 140 | kW |  | 196 | 196 | 196 | kW |
| 42 | 205 | 193 | 180 | Tons | 42 | 320 | 302 | 284 | Tons |
|  | 140 | 140 | 140 | kW |  | 196 | 196 | 196 | kW |
| 44 | 213 | 200 | 187 | Tons | 44 | 332 | 315 | 294 | Tons |
|  | 140 | 140 | 140 | kW |  | 196 | 196 | 196 | kW |
| 46 | 221 | 210 | 193 | Tons | 46 | 344 | 326 | 304 | Tons |
|  | 140 | 140 | 140 | kW |  | 196 | 196 | 196 | kW |
| 48 | 229 | 217 | 200 | Tons | 48 | 352 | 338 | 314 | Tons |
|  | 140 | 140 | 140 | kW |  | 196 | 196 | 196 | kW |
| 50 | 233 | 225 | 210 | Tons | 50 | 359 | 343 | 326 | Tons |
|  | 140 | 140 | 140 | kW |  | 196 | 196 | 196 | kW |

| Compressor 050 Evaporator 2D Condenser 2D | Leaving Condenser Water Temperature, °F | | | | Compressor 080 Evaporator 2D Condenser 2D | Leaving Condenser Water Temperature, °F | | | |
|---|---|---|---|---|---|---|---|---|---|
| Leaving Evaporator Water Temperature, °F | 90 | 95 | 100 | | | 90 | 95 | 100 | |
| 40 | 493 | 466 | 437 | Tons | 40 | 782 | 747 | 704 | Tons |
|  | 308 | 308 | 308 | kW |  | 498 | 498 | 498 | kW |
| 42 | 511 | 482 | 452 | Tons | 42 | 803 | 773 | 729 | Tons |
|  | 308 | 308 | 308 | kW |  | 498 | 498 | 498 | kW |
| 44 | 530 | 500 | 468 | Tons | 44 | 831 | 800 | 755 | Tons |
|  | 308 | 308 | 308 | kW |  | 498 | 498 | 498 | kW |
| 46 | 548 | 520 | 484 | Tons | 46 | 861 | 828 | 782 | Tons |
|  | 308 | 308 | 308 | kW |  | 498 | 498 | 498 | kW |
| 48 | 562 | 539 | 502 | Tons | 48 | 890 | 857 | 809 | Tons |
|  | 308 | 308 | 308 | kW |  | 498 | 498 | 498 | kW |
| 50 | 574 | 553 | 520 | Tons | 50 | 913 | 883 | 838 | Tons |
|  | 308 | 308 | 308 | kW |  | 498 | 498 | 498 | kW |

| Compressor 125 Evaporator 2D Condenser 2D | Leaving Condenser Water Temperature, °F | | | | Compressor 155 Evaporator S1 Condenser S1L | Leaving Condenser Water Temperature, °F | | | |
|---|---|---|---|---|---|---|---|---|---|
| Leaving Evaporator Water Temperature, °F | 90 | 95 | 100 | | | 90 | 95 | 100 | |
| 40 | 1,180 | 1,123 | 1,072 | Tons | 40 | 1,532 | 1,513 | 1,480 | Tons |
|  | 813 | 813 | 813 | kW |  | 1,180 | 1,180 | 1,180 | kW |
| 42 | 1,220 | 1,161 | 1,108 | Tons | 42 | 1,618 | 1,567 | 1,520 | Tons |
|  | 813 | 813 | 813 | kW |  | 1,180 | 1,180 | 1,180 | kW |
| 44 | 1,260 | 1,200 | 1,145 | Tons | 44 | 1,638 | 1,618 | 1,581 | Tons |
|  | 813 | 813 | 813 | kW |  | 1,180 | 1,180 | 1,180 | kW |
| 46 | 1,292 | 1,235 | 1,184 | Tons | 46 | 1,698 | 1,682 | 1,641 | Tons |
|  | 813 | 813 | 813 | kW |  | 1,180 | 1,180 | 1,180 | kW |
| 48 | 1,335 | 1,277 | 1,222 | Tons | 48 | 1,751 | 1,740 | 1,692 | Tons |
|  | 813 | 813 | 813 | kW |  | 1,180 | 1,180 | 1,180 | kW |
| 50 | 1,379 | 1,320 | 1,263 | Tons | 50 | 1,845 | 1,817 | 1,760 | Tons |
|  | 813 | 813 | 813 | kW |  | 1,180 | 1,180 | 1,180 | kW |

[a]For illustrative purposes only; not to be used for actual selection.
The Trane Company, La Crosse, WI.

number of passes increases. This also plays a role in the selection, as the pump power will increase. However, the refrigeration capacity increases with number of evaporator passes, thereby increasing the COP and reducing compressor power required. The relative effects of these opposing factors should be considered to determine the best energy conserving selection.

Today, because of the large number of choices, actual selections for best results are often made through computer programs. This is another reason a limited amount of manual selection data has been presented here.

Only a small selection of the hermetic centrifugal capacity sizes available have been shown. When using Table 10.1, values should be interpolated.

An example illustrates the selection procedure.

**Example 10.1**  Select a hermetic centrifugal water chiller to produce 450 tons of refrigeration. The chilled water is cooled from 54 to 44°F. Condensing water temperature rise is from 85 to 95°F. Fouling factors are 0.0005 for evaporator and 0.001 for condenser.

*Solution*  Searching through Table 10.1, at the leaving chilled water and condenser water temperatures specified, the smallest satisfactory chiller combination listed is Compressor 055, Evaporator 2D, Condenser 2D (500 tons). The capacity must be corrected for the condenser fouling factor of 0.001, however, as described previously.

"Adjusted" leaving condenser water temperature is 95 + 2.5 = 97.5°F.

The capacity is now interpolated:

$$\text{capacity} = 500 - (500 - 468) \times \frac{97.5 - 95}{100 - 95}$$

$$= 484 \text{ tons}$$

The corrected capacity is still adequate.

The COP of the chiller can also be determined

$$\text{COP} = \frac{484 \text{ tons}}{308 \text{ kW}} \times \frac{3.52 \text{ kW}}{1 \text{ ton}} = 5.5$$

For a possible more energy efficient selection by changing flow rates, temperatures or passes, an optimizing computer selection might be considered.

## 10.12  Energy Conservation

Energy conservation methods applied to centrifugal chillers have become an especially important consideration because of the vast quantity of power used. In summary:

1. Multistage compression with the economizer cycle decreases power requirements over single stage compression.

2. Variable inlet guide vane capacity control will result in good reduction of power with capacity reduction.

3. Increasing the number of water passes in the heat exchangers (evaporator and condenser) will reduce compressor power requirements. However increased pumping costs must be balanced against this.

4. Demand limiting devices that limit the current that the motor will draw will reduce utility company demand charges.

5. Noncondensable gases collecting in the condenser should be purged often.

6. Good reduction of power with capacity reduction can be achieved with speed control. For open machines, consider using steam turbine or even engine drive. For hermetic units consider using variable speed motor drive through a solid state electronic inverter.

## 10.13  Free Cooling

Chilled water for cooling is often required in large air conditioned buildings even at low

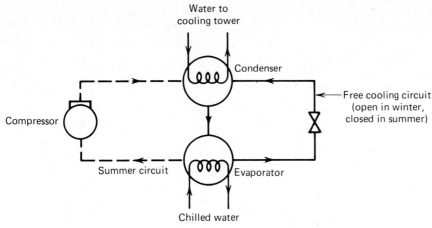

Water to
cooling tower

Condenser

Free cooling circuit
(open in winter,
closed in summer)

Compressor

Summer circuit   Evaporator

Chilled water

**FIGURE 10.16** "Free" cooling circuit arrangement for
chilling water in winter without operating compressor.

outside temperatures. This may result from
high solar radiation and high lighting loads.
When centrifugal or reciprocating water chillers are used, "free cooling" may be available
(Figure 10.16). At low outside temperatures
the condenser water can be cooled to a low
temperature in the cooling tower. The condenser refrigerant is therefore also cooled to a
low temperature. This refrigerant can then be
pumped or drained to the evaporator, where
it will chill the water for air conditioning. The
evaporated refrigerant then flows back to the
condenser, completing the cycle.

The free cooling operation produces from
about 10 to 30 percent of the full design
capacity of a centrifugal chiller. This is usually
adequate to handle the cooling load on a cold
day. It should be noted that although the
energy to drive the compressor is saved, the
system does not provide completely free cooling. The cooling tower fans must be operated,
and a refrigerant pump may be necessary to
move the liquid refrigerant from the condenser to the evaporator.

## REVIEW QUESTIONS

1. Describe and sketch the basic parts of a
   centrifugal compressor.
2. Explain how a centrifugal compressor increases the pressure of a gas.
3. Why are centrifugal compressors used in
   large capacity refrigeration systems?
4. What does impeller staging mean and
   why is it often necessary?
5. Explain an economizer cycle arrangement; sketch the equipment arrangement
   and $p$–$h$ diagram.
6. Explain choking flow and surging in a
   centrifugal compressor, with the aid of a
   performance characteristic curve.
7. Name and describe three methods of
   changing centrifugal compressor capacity. Discuss their relative advantages and
   disadvantages.
8. Name and describe the typical controls
   used with a centrifugal water chiller.

9. List some methods of conserving energy use in selection, operation, or maintenance of a centrifugal water chiller.

10. Describe and sketch a "free cooling" arrangement with a water chiller.

## PROBLEMS

10.1 Select a hermetic centrifugal water chiller to produce 420 tons of refrigeration. Chilled water is cooled from 52°F to 42°F. Condensing water enters at 85°F, leaves at 95°F. Fouling factors are 0.0005 for evaporator and condenser. Find the COP.

10.2 Find the effect on the performance of the chiller selected in Problem 10.1 if the condenser fouling factor is 0.001. Find the COP.

10.3 Select a hermetic centrifugal water chiller to produce 700 tons of refrigeration. Chilled water is cooled from 60°F to 50°F. Condenser water enters at 83°F, leaves at 93°F. Fouling factors are 0.0005 for evaporator and condenser. Find the COP.

10.4 Find the effect on the performance of the chiller selected in Problem 10.3 if the evaporator fouling factor is 0.001. Find the COP.

# Chapter **11**

# THE REFRIGERANT PIPING SYSTEM

In this chapter the piping system that conveys the refrigerant between equipment in the vapor compression system is discussed. The design, arrangement, and sizing of the piping, and accessory devices that are used in the piping system will be covered.

The design and installation of the piping system in packaged equipment is, of course, taken care of by the manufacturers. When the refrigeration system is only partly packaged, or when it is a completely field erected system, the engineer and contractor must know how to properly design and install the piping.

The piping practices discussed here generally apply to the halocarbon refrigerants such as R-12, R-22, and R-502. Some of the practices apply to ammonia systems but others do not, so the reader should not generalize from the information presented. We will point out some of the features that are different in ammonia systems.

## OBJECTIVES

A study of this chapter will enable you to:
1. Identify the functions of refrigerant piping systems.
2. Explain how oil is moved through the system.
3. Specify the applications for oil separators and how they should be installed.
4. Lay out and size the refrigerant piping.
5. Identify refrigeration system accessories and their functions.

## 11.1 Functions of the Piping System

It might seem that any piping that conveys the refrigerant through the system at a proper rate is adequate, but this is far from the complete truth. In addition to carrying the refrigerant, the piping must serve other functions. If it does not, the system will not perform satisfactorily, and damage to equipment may occur. The functions that the piping system should accomplish are to:

1. Provide the correct refrigerant flow rate.
2. Not have excess pressure drop.
3. Prevent liquid refrigerant or oil slugs from entering the compressor.
4. Provide for lubricating oil return to the crankcase.

The size (diameter) of the piping must be adequate so as not to restrict the refrigerant flow rate. Neither should there be unnecessary length, changes in direction, or restrictions which also might restrict the flow rate.

The pipe size, length, and fittings should not result in excessive pressure drop. Pressure drop represents a loss of energy. Both suction line and hot gas line pressure drops result in need for increased compressor power, as shown in Chapter 4, and should be kept to a reasonable minimum. Excess pressure drop in the liquid line may result in flash gas forming before the expansion valve. This will reduce system capacity and also cause erratic performance.

The piping system arrangement and its accessories should prevent either liquid refrigerant or slugs of oil from entering the compressor, from both the suction and hot gas lines. Liquids can directly damage compressor parts. Liquid refrigerant may also thin out the oil so that lubrication is inadequate.

*Oil Return.*   Oil is continually carried into the piping system when it is swept off the cylinder walls by the refrigerant gas leaving the compressor. The piping system arrangement and its accessories should ensure that oil circulating through the system is returned to the compressor crankcase. If not, the crankcase may become starved of an adequate supply of oil for compressor lubrication.

Oil and halocarbon refrigerants often mix to form a homogeneous fluid, rather than remaining separate. The degree of miscibility depends on temperature, pressure, and whether the refrigerant is in the liquid or gaseous state.

The oil carried by the refrigerant gas through the hot gas discharge line is in the form of a mist of droplets, largely separated from the refrigerant. In the condenser the oil dissolves in the liquid refrigerant to form a homogeneous liquid, which then flows through the liquid line. In the evaporator the refrigerant boils off as a gas, separating from the oil.

The return of oil through the liquid line is not a special problem, since the liquid flowing is homogeneous. Movement of the oil through the suction and discharge lines requires special piping design considerations, however. Both velocity and gravity effects may be relied on to carry the oil back to the compressor.

Under certain conditions with halocarbon systems oil return cannot be achieved by good piping practice alone. This is also true with all ammonia systems; since oil and ammonia do not mix, the ammonia will not entrain the oil adequately. In these cases an oil separator and additional return arrangements are required. We will discuss this later on in the chapter.

Other information related to the question of refrigerant–oil mixtures and oil return is discussed in Chapters 5 and 9.

The procedures for proper sizing of piping to ensure that it serves the requirements described will be discussed later in the chapter. First we will discuss the correct practices for the piping layout for each line.

## 11.2 Hot Gas Lines

The hot gas or discharge line carries refrigerant vapor and droplets of oil. It should be designed and installed so that

1.  Pressure drop is not excessive (to be discussed later).

2.  The compressor is protected against liquid entering from the discharge line.

3.  Oil is carried to the condenser.

*Condenser Below Compressor.*   Figure 11.1 shows the recommended hot gas piping arrangement if the condenser is at an elevation lower than the compressor. The piping is direct, without any unnecessary turns. The horizontal line should be pitched down in the direction of flow to prevent oil from draining back into the compressor when not operating.

The pitch should be at least ½ inch for each 10 feet of length. This recommended pitch holds for all horizontal hot gas and suction lines, to ensure good drainage in the direction of flow.

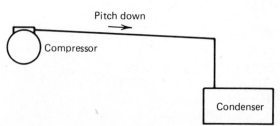

**FIGURE 11.1** Hot gas piping (condenser below evaporator).

**Condenser and Compressor on Same Level.** Figure 11.2 shows the recommended hot gas piping arrangement if the condenser is on the same level as the compressor. The line may be on a horizontal level, with the proper pitch, or it may loop overhead to avoid crossing the floor. In this case a short horizontal section extends from the compressor to trap the small amount of oil that might drain from the short riser during shutdown. The loop should not be over eight feet in height.

**Condenser above Compressor.** Installations with the condenser located above the compressor present a more difficult problem, with solutions depending on a number of conditions.

Since a vertical riser will always be a necessary part of the piping, oil will drain back down this section during the off period. Provisions must be made to prevent this oil from flowing back into the compressor. During operation the vertical riser must be sized to have a gas velocity high enough to lift the oil along with it.

Horizontal lines must also have velocities adequate to move the oil. The minimum velocities required are less for horizontal lines, since the oil does not have to be lifted against gravity. Recommended velocities for all lines

will be discussed with pipe sizing. All horizontal lines should be pitched in the direction of flow as recommended previously.

If the condenser is located where it may be at a higher temperature than the compressor during shutdown, the higher pressure of the refrigerant in the condenser will cause it to migrate to the hot gas line and then condense in the compressor head. On start-up this could damage the compressor. A check valve in the hot gas line at the condenser inlet will solve this problem.

When the vertical height of the hot gas riser is eight feet or less, a horizontal section at the compressor will be adequate to trap the small quantity of oil that drains from the riser during shutdown (Figure 11.3).

If the vertical section of the hot gas riser is greater than eight feet, a trap must be installed at the bottom of the riser (Figure 11.4). The trap collects oil that drains from the riser during shutdown. The shape of the trap also aids in lifting the oil collected when the system starts up. The hot gas tends to be broken into droplets and swept along as the gas strikes it. The trap should be small so that it does not collect too much oil and starve the compressor.

A second trap is required at the midpoint if the vertical section is between 25 and 50 feet

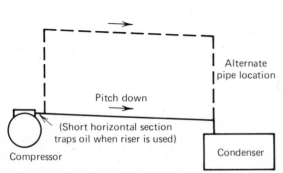

**FIGURE 11.2** Hot gas piping (condenser on same level as compressor).

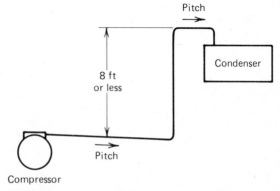

**FIGURE 11.3** Hot gas piping (condenser above compressor, 8 ft. or less).

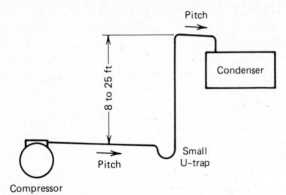

**FIGURE 11.4** Hot gas piping (condenser 8 to 25 ft. above compressor).

(Figure 11.5). For each additional 25 feet or part thereafter, another trap is required.

*Compressors with Unloader Capacity Control.* The previous recommendations for vertical risers apply when the compressor operates in an on–off mode. In this situation the flow rate and therefore velocity of the hot gas are approximately constant when the compressor runs. The hot gas line is sized for a gas velocity adequate to lift the oil. When the compressor has unloading features, the reduced hot gas flow rate and velocity at part load may not be great enough to lift the oil in the vertical section.

This condition is determined when the piping is sized. An example will be given later. If gas velocity is inadequate under low load conditions, two solutions are possible–use double risers or an oil separator.

*Double Risers.* The double hot gas riser arrangement is shown in Figure 11.6. The smaller diameter riser (closest to the compressor) is sized to handle the low gas flow rate at minimum load and the larger riser is sized to handle the remainder of the gas at full load, both with sufficient gas velocities.

At full load the gas is flowing through each riser at sufficient velocity to move the oil. When the compressor capacity drops, the reduced velocity is insufficient to lift the oil and it drains back through both risers and fills the trap at the bottom of the larger riser. This blocks that riser, and all gas flow is diverted to the small riser, which is sized for adequate gas velocity at the minimum capacity flow rate.

When capacity increases, the higher velocity from the greater flow rate of gas forces the oil out of the trap and both risers operate again at sufficient velocity.

Note that the larger riser is connected to the horizontal section of pipe leading to the condenser by an inverted loop, rather than being connected directly to the bottom of the hori-

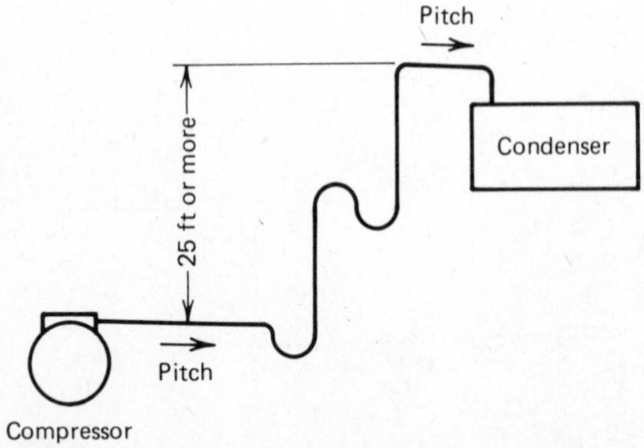

**FIGURE 11.5** Hot gas piping (condenser above compressor, over 25 ft.; additional trap required for each 25 ft.).

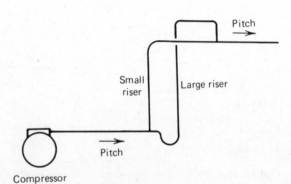

**FIGURE 11.6** Double hot gas riser.

zontal line. This prevents oil from draining back down the large riser when only the small riser is active. The continual accumulation of oil at part load in the large riser could starve the compressor crankcase and lubrication failure could occur.

*Oil Separator.* Another solution if adequate gas velocity cannot be maintained in the single hot gas riser is to install an *oil separator* in the discharge line (Figure 11.7). The oil separator traps and separates oil carried with the hot gas from the compressor. The oil separator should be located at the base of the single riser so that on shutdown it catches the small quantity of oil that is not trapped.

The oil is returned from a connection that is made from the separator to the compressor suction. If the separator is exposed to a temperature colder than the condenser, refrigerant may migrate to the separator during shutdown, and dilute the lubricating oil. In this situation a solenoid valve at the condenser may be required to isolate it from the separator.

Generally the double hot gas riser is used more often than the oil separator to control oil movement in halocarbon systems. Oil separators are discussed later.

## 11.3 Suction Lines

Liquid refrigerant and oil are mixed as they enter the evaporator, but when the refriger-

ant boils, the vapor and the oil separate, and the oil must be carried along to the compressor either by the gas velocity or by gravity. The design of the suction line is similar to that of hot gas lines. That is, the piping should ensure oil return to the compressor crankcase, it should prevent liquid refrigerant or oil slugs from entering the compressor suction, and it should be sized so that pressure drop is not excessive. Design of the suction line is more critical than that of the hot gas line, because oil return is more difficult. At low evaporating temperatures compressor capacity decreases, therefore the flow rate of refrigerant vapor decreases. The density of the refrigerant also decreases as the suction pressure decreases. This reduces the ability of the vapor to sweep the oil droplets along, and oil can hang up in the evaporator. On the other hand, the problem of liquid slugging into the compressor suction may occur (see Chapter 5).

*General Recommendations.* Horizontal lines should be pitched in the direction of flow, to assist in oil return. A vertical riser and trap should be provided at the evaporator outlet to collect oil drained from the vertical riser. The trap also serves to collect liquid downstream from the expansion valve bulb (see Chapter 8).

*Evaporator and Compressor on Same Level.* Figure 11.8 shows the recommended arrangement if the evaporator and compressor are at the same elevation. A vertical riser and loop are provided to prevent liquid from draining into the compressor. The trap at the

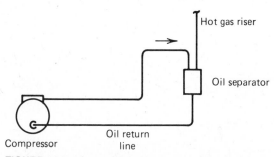

**FIGURE 11.7** Arrangement of oil separator in hot gas riser.

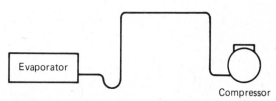

**FIGURE 11.8** Suction piping (evaporator and compressor on same level).

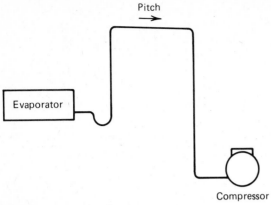

**FIGURE 11.9** Suction piping (evaporator above compressor).

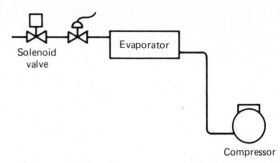

**FIGURE 11.11** Suction piping with pump down control.

evaporator outlet collects any liquid drainage during shutdown.

***Evaporator above Compressor.*** If the evaporator is above the compressor a vertical riser and loop with a trap at the evaporator are provided (Figure 11.9).

***Evaporator below Compressor.*** The trap and vertical riser are shown in Figure 11.10. An additional trap should be provided for each 25 feet of riser, the same as for the hot gas riser.

***Pumpdown Control.*** If the system is provided with pumpdown control, the loop and trap to prevent collected liquid from draining to the compressor is not required when the

evaporator is above the compressor. With pumpdown control a solenoid-operated valve is located at the evaporator inlet (Figure 11.11). The control thermostat is connected to close the valve instead of stopping the compressor. The compressor continues to operate long enough to remove any refrigerant in the evaporator and suction line, and then stops on low suction pressure, through action of a low pressure controller.

***Double Riser.*** When the compressor is provided with steps of capacity control, or multiple compressors are operated in sequence, a double riser is used to maintain refrigerant gas velocity to ensure oil lift, in the same way as with a hot gas riser. The arrangement is shown in Figure 11.12.

Using the double riser, for both suction and hot gas lines, can sometimes be avoided, particularly in air conditioning applications, even when the compressor has unloading features. By sizing the riser for a high gas velocity at full

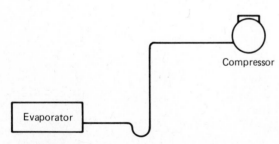

**FIGURE 11.10** Suction piping (evaporator below compressor).

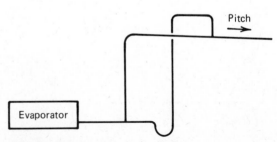

**FIGURE 11.12** Double suction riser.

load, the velocity at minimum load may still be adequate to lift the oil. This results in a high piping pressure drop, which causes a decrease in refrigeration capacity or increase in the compressor's need for power (Chapter 5). The energy penalty is not as great at higher suction temperatures, however, and may be acceptable to the user. At commercial refrigeration temperatures the penalty is greater and usually not acceptable.

Multiple evaporators are often used with one compressor. Some combinations, with recommended suction piping arrangements to ensure oil return and protect the compressor, are shown in Figure 11.13. The same principles determine the arrangement—to prevent liquid drainage to the compressor on shutdown, and to collect oil from vertical risers. Figure 11.13(a) shows a split coil evaporator suction piping. For separate evaporators on different levels the piping is as shown in Figure 11.13(b). Figure 11.13(c) shows the arrangement for evaporators both above and below the suction line.

## 11.4 Liquid Lines

The oil and liquid halocarbon refrigerant mix before entering the liquid line, so oil return is not a problem in designing the liquid line. The primary consideration is the prevention of the formation of flash gas in the liquid line. Flash gas will increase the volume of refrigerant reaching the expansion valve; this reduces the mass flow rate through the valve, and refrigeration capacity decreases. The high velocity gas through the valve port may also erode the seat and pin.

Flashing will occur in the liquid line if the pressure falls below the saturation pressure corresponding to the temperature of the liquid refrigerant. The pressure drop in the

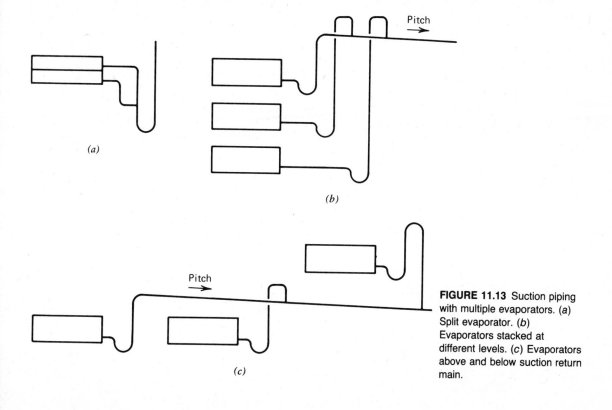

**FIGURE 11.13** Suction piping with multiple evaporators. (a) Split evaporator. (b) Evaporators stacked at different levels. (c) Evaporators above and below suction return main.

liquid line is therefore critical. Pressure drop will result from friction in the piping and its accessories. Additional pressure drop will occur if the evaporator is above the receiver (or condenser, if there is no receiver). This is called static head. The pressure at the top of the liquid (at the evaporator) will be less than that at the bottom because of the weight of the column of liquid. For R-12, R-22, R-502, and ammonia a one-foot-high column of liquid exerts a pressure of approximately 0.5 psi.

***Example 11.1*** Refrigerant R-12 leaves a condenser at 110 psig and 94°F. The evaporator is 10 feet above the condenser. Friction loss in the liquid line and its accessories is 2 psi. Will flashing occur before the expansion valve?

*Solution* The arrangement is shown in Figure 11.14. The total pressure drop from the static head and friction is:

$$\text{head} = 10 \text{ ft} \times 0.5 \text{ psi/ft} = 5 \text{ psi}$$

$$\text{friction} = \underline{2 \text{ psi}}$$

$$\text{total pressure drop} = 7 \text{ psi}$$

The pressure at the expansion valve is therefore $110 - 7 = 103$ psig.

Referring to the saturated property tables for R-12, the saturation pressure of the refrigerant at 94°F is 106.5 psig. The refrigerant is slightly subcooled leaving the condenser, by 2°F, since at 110 psig the saturation temperature is 96°F.

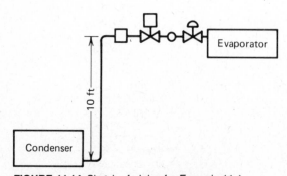

**FIGURE 11.14** Sketch of piping for Example 11.1.

At the expansion valve the pressure (103 psig) has dropped below the saturation pressure (106.5 psig) and therefore flashing will occur.

To allow for a reasonable pressure drop in the liquid line and yet avoid flashing, condensers are generally designed and selected for considerable subcooling of the liquid refrigerant, from 12 to 20°F (see Chapter 7). Additional measures can also be taken, such as using a liquid-suction heat exchanger.

If the evaporator is located below the receiver–condenser, then the static head aids in preventing flashing, since the column of liquid increases the pressure at the evaporator.

When the evaporator is located below the receiver, refrigerant could siphon to the evaporator during shutdown. On start-up liquid floodback to the compressor could occur. If the system has a solenoid valve in the liquid line for pump down control then this problem cannot occur. If there is no solenoid valve then the liquid line should have an inverted loop (Figure 11.15).

***Multiple Compressors.*** When two or more compressors are connected to operate in parallel, the piping connections are made with the same basic principle as with a single compressor—proper oil return to each compressor and prevention of liquid to the compressors. To accomplish this, some special features are needed when interconnecting the compressors.

Figure 11.16 shows the suction and hot gas connections for compressors operating in parallel. The suction arrangement ensures that each compressor runs at the same suction pressure and receives oil equally. A common header is used, run full size and above the compressor. Branches are taken from the side, full size. No reduction is made until the vertical drop.

The hot gas lines are also connected to a common header, run below the compressor

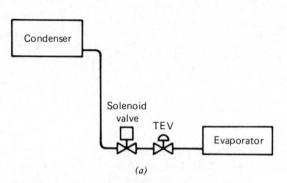

**FIGURE 11.15** Liquid line piping. (*a*) Liquid line with solenoid valve for pump down control. (*b*) Liquid line with inverted loop—no solenoid valve.

discharge connections. This serves as a loop, preventing liquid from draining back to the compressors, and oil from draining into an idle compressor.

Equalizing connections are also required when compressors are in parallel (Figure 11.17). An oil equalizer line, connected between crankcases, run at the level of or below the oil equalizer tappings provided, ensures uniform oil levels. A crankcase gas equalizer line connected between the crankcases prevents unequal crankcase gas pressures, thereby preventing oil from blowing out of a compressor. When condensing units are con-

nected in parallel, a condensing pressure equalizer is also required between condensers to prevent hot gas from blowing through one condenser to the liquid line.

## REFRIGERANT PIPE SIZING

### 11.5 Design Conditions for Refrigerant Piping

Experience has led to there being recommended design pressure drops and velocities in refrigerant piping. These recommended

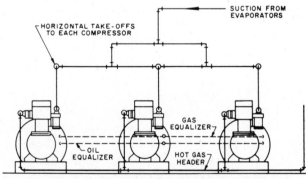

FIGURE 11.16 Suction and hot gas connections for compressors operating in parallel. Gas equalizer must be large enough to approximate the same crankcase pressure in all compressors with any combination of idle and operating compressors (any pressure difference is reflected by a difference in all levels). (Reprinted with permission from the 1980 Systems ASHRAE Handbook & Product Directory)

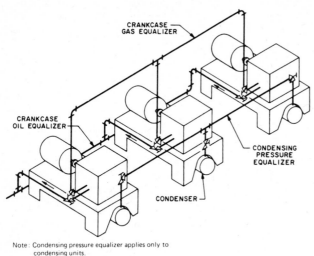

CRANKCASE GAS EQUALIZER

CRANKCASE OIL EQUALIZER

CONDENSING PRESSURE EQUALIZER

CONDENSER

Note: Condensing pressure equalizer applies only to condensing units.

**FIGURE 11.17** Equalizing connections for compressors and condensing units operating in parallel. Condensing pressure equalizer applies only to condensing units. (Reprinted with permission from the 1980 Systems ASHRAE Handbook & Product Directory)

values compromise cost of the piping and energy cost increases as a result of excessive pressure drop, since smaller diameter piping causes an increase in friction loss. This applies particularly in the case of the suction and hot gas lines. In the case of liquid lines, sizes are based on keeping pressure drop below values that would result in the liquid flashing.

In addition to these factors, pipe sizes should be such that fluid velocities are within certain minimum and maximum limits. For a given flow rate, velocity increases with decreasing pipe size. Velocities should be high enough to ensure good oil return in the suction and hot gas lines. On the other hand, velocities that are too high lead to excessive pressure drop, noise, and vibration. In liquid lines high velocities can lead to liquid hammer when valves close.

## 11.6 Pressure Drop

It is common practice in the refrigeration industry to express the recommended design pressure drops in refrigerant lines as an equivalent temperature change.

The **equivalent temperature change** is *defined as the corresponding change in satura-*

*tion temperature that would occur for the pressure drop specified.*

The equivalent temperature change is a useful way of expressing pressure drop because the ratings of compressors are based on saturated suction and discharge temperatures (Chapter 5).

**Example 11.2** The evaporating temperature in a refrigeration unit using R-12 is 38°F. The suction line pressure drop is equivalent to 3°F. What is the suction line pressure drop in psi?

*Solution* From the saturated property table for R-12 the pressure drop is

$$P_{sat} \text{ at } 38°F = 35.2 \text{ psig}$$

$$P_{sat} \text{ at } 35°F = \underline{32.6}$$

$$\text{pressure drop} = 2.6 \text{ psi}$$

As explained in Chapter 4, the temperature of the refrigerant in the suction line does not actually decrease by the equivalent temperature change. It is simply a convenient means of expression, because for one value of equivalent temperature change the actual pressure drop in psi varies with the evaporating temperature. Instead of recommending different pressure drops for every condition, only one value is needed.

It is typical design practice for halocarbons to use 2°F as an equivalent pressure drop in sizing all three lines—suction, hot gas, and liquid piping, regardless of evaporating or condensing conditions. Experience has shown that these values lead to a good compromise on cost of pipe as opposed to the power required. The recommended values are approximate, and must be used with flexibility, depending on conditions.

The penalty of increased power consumption per ton of refrigeration for a given pressure drop in psi increases as the suction temperature decreases. Therefore a smaller pressure drop is recommended as the evaporating temperature decreases. It can be seen from the saturated property tables that for a given change in temperature the pressure change decreases at lower temperatures. This is why a fixed equivalent temperature change is a useful way of specifying pressure drop—regardless of evaporating temperature, the energy penalty is about the same. The same holds true for the discharge conditions.

The actual pressure drop in psi for a given equivalent temperature change is greater at discharge conditions than at evaporating conditions, but for each psi change the energy penalty is much less at discharge temperatures.

The following table shows some actual pressure drops for a 2°F equivalent saturation temperature change. The reader may confirm this from the refrigerant tables.

## 11.7 Pipe Sizing Charts

Pressure drop of fluids through piping is determined from equations developed in the subject of fluid mechanics. For convenience in sizing refrigerant piping, the results of these equations are arranged in tables or charts. Figures 11.18 to 11.20 show pressure drop data for refrigerants R-12, R-22, and R-502, for the suction, hot gas, and liquid lines.

The use of the charts for pipe sizing is illustrated by the follow example.

***Example 11.3*** An R-12 system has a design refrigeration load of 40 tons. Evaporating and condensing temperatures are 20°F and 100°F. Piping is type L copper tubing. Find the required suction line size, if the design pressure drop is equivalent to 2°F. The length of the suction line is 70 feet.

*Solution* The procedure is as follows:

1. From the R-12 property tables (or Table 11.1) the pressure drop corresponding to 2°F is found to be 1.4 psi.

2. Since Figure 11.18 is based on a pressure drop per 100 feet of pipe, the design pressure drop is corrected to this length:

$$\text{Pressure drop} = 1.4 \text{ psi} \times \frac{100 \text{ ft}}{70 \text{ ft}}$$

$$= 2.0 \text{ psi per 100 ft}$$

3. Entering Figure 11.18 on the pressure drop scale on the bottom at 2.0 psi and 100°F condensing temperature, a vertical construction line is drawn upward. (Note: the pressure drop scale has a slant, varying with condensing temperature.)

TABLE 11.1 Pressure Drop Equivalent for a 2°F Change in Saturation Temperature

| Saturation Temperature, °F | Pressure Drop, psi | |
|---|---|---|
| | R-12 | R-22 |
| −10 | 0.8 | 1.4 |
| 0 | 1.0 | 1.6 |
| 10 | 1.2 | 1.9 |
| 20 | 1.4 | 2.2 |
| 30 | 1.6 | 2.5 |
| 40 | 1.8 | 2.8 |
| 80 | 3.0 | 4.7 |
| 100 | 3.7 | 5.8 |
| 120 | 4.5 | 7.1 |

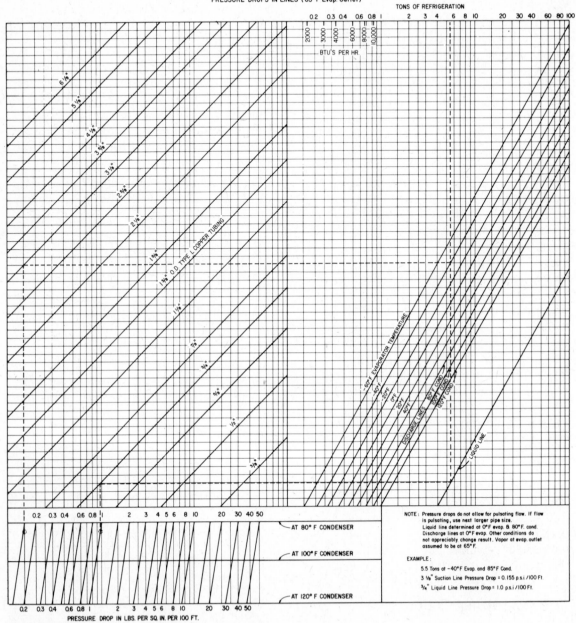

**FIGURE 11.18** R-12 pipe sizing charts. (Copyright 1968 by E.I. duPont de Nemours & Co. "Freon" Products Division. Reprinted by permission)

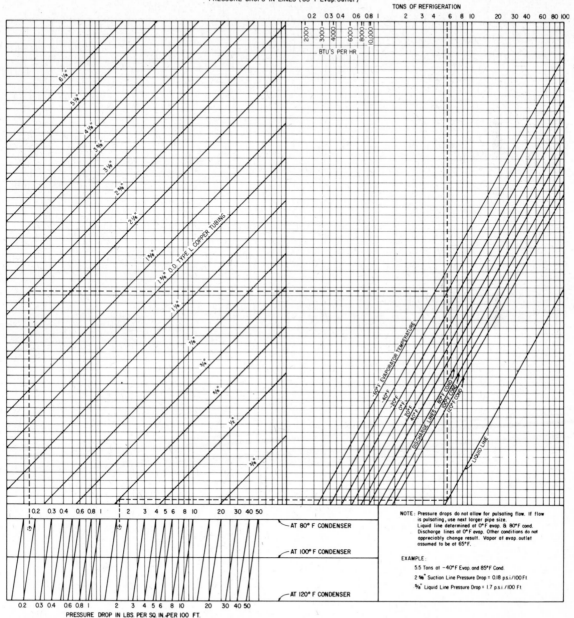

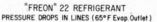

**FIGURE 11.19** R-22 pipe sizing charts (Copyright 1968 by E.I. duPont de Nemours & Co. "Freon" Products Division. Reprinted by permission)

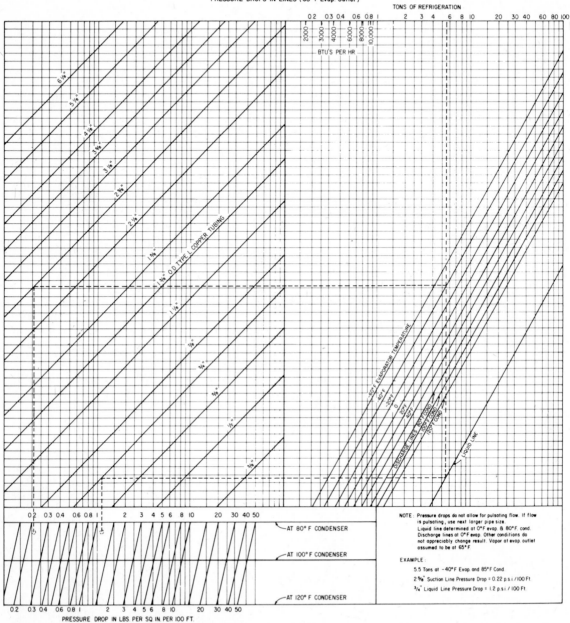

**FIGURE 11.20** R-502 pipe sizing charts. (Copyright 1968 by E.I. duPont de Nemours & Co. "Freon" Products Division. Reprinted by permission)

4. Entering the capacity scale (upper right) at 40 tons, a vertical construction line is drawn down to the intersection with a 40°F evaporator temperature (diagonal lines).

5. A horizontal construction line is then drawn from this intersection, to the left. Where this line intersects the vertical pressure drop line, find the required pipe size. This falls between 2⅝ and 3⅛ in. O.D.

6. A 3⅛ in. O.D. is selected, since the smaller diameter choice would increase the pressure drop considerably.

   Figure 11.21 illustrates the construction for the solution.

In this example, with the graphical solution falling between two pipe sizes, the larger was chosen, assuming a greater pressure drop than that equivalent to 2°F was unacceptable. The actual pressure drop will be less than 2°F, as illustrated in the following example.

***Examples 11.4*** Find the pressure drop and equivalent temperature drop for the conditions in Example 11.3 if the load is 40 tons and a 3⅛ in. O.D. suction line is used.

*Solution*

1. Proceed horizontally on the same horizontal construction line used for the 40 ton load until it intersects the 3⅛ in. O.D. size line.

2. Project a vertical construction line from this point to the pressure drop scale at 100°F condensing temperature.

3. The intersection reads the new pressure drop, which is 1.4 psi per 100 feet. The pressure drop for the 70 foot suction line is therefore:

$$\text{Pressure drop} = 1.4 \text{ psi} \times \frac{70}{100} = 1.0 \text{ psi}$$

4. From the R-12 property tables, it was found that a pressure drop of 1.4 psi corresponded to 2°F at 20°F. By taking a ratio of the new pressure drop to the old one, the equivalent temperature drop is:

$$\text{Equivalent temperature drop} = \frac{1.0}{1.4} \times 2°F$$

$$= 1.4°F$$

One significance of the results in Example 11.4 is that the loss in energy resulting from friction is less than was originally allowed, because of the larger pipe size. Another way of looking at this is that a greater refrigeration capacity in tons could be handled by the 3⅛ in. O.D. line, if a 2°F equivalent temperature drop is taken. Figure 11.18 can be used in a similar manner to find this result, which is about 45 tons. (The student should verify this by working out the solution.)

Whether the system produces a greater tonnage (45) or whether it produces 40 tons at less energy loss cannot be determined from this procedure. This depends on the size and balance between components, as well as on the capacity controls. These subjects are discussed in Chapters 5 and 14.

## 11.8 Equivalent Length of Piping

Pressure drop occurs not only in a straight pipe but also through fittings and valves in the pipe line. It is convenient to express the pressure drop through a fitting or valve as the *equivalent length* (E.L.) of straight pipe that would have the same pressure drop. The length of actual piping is then added to the equivalent length of fittings and valves to find a total equivalent length of piping. Table 11.2 lists equivalent lengths of fittings and valves.

Note that the equivalent lengths depend on the pipe size, and therefore they cannot be precisely determined until a pipe size is chosen. To resolve this problem a trial value of the

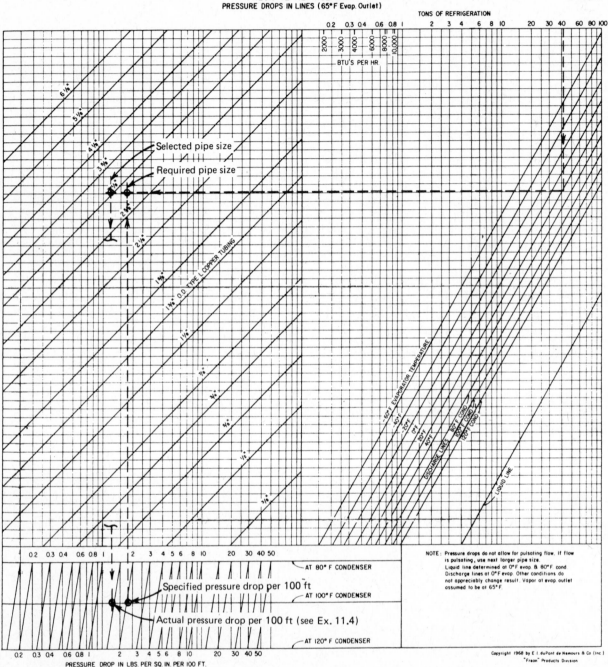

**FIGURE 11.21** Sketch showing solution to Example 11.3.

TABLE 11.2 Equivalent Lengths in Feet of Fittings and Valves, Type L Copper Tubing

| Line Size, Inches O.D. | Globe Valve and Solenoid Valve | Angle Valve | Short Radius Ell | Long Radius Ell | Tee Line Flow and Sight Glasses | Tee, Branch Flow |
|---|---|---|---|---|---|---|
| ½ | 70 | 24 | 4.7 | 3.2 | 1.7 | 6.6 |
| ⅝ | 72 | 25 | 5.7 | 3.9 | 2.3 | 8.2 |
| ¾ | 75 | 25 | 6.5 | 4.5 | 2.9 | 9.7 |
| ⅞ | 78 | 28 | 7.8 | 5.3 | 3.7 | 12 |
| 1⅛ | 87 | 29 | 2.7 | 1.9 | 2.5 | 8 |
| 1⅜ | 102 | 33 | 3.2 | 2.2 | 2.7 | 10 |
| 1⅝ | 115 | 34 | 3.8 | 2.6 | 3.0 | 12 |
| 2⅛ | 141 | 39 | 5.2 | 3.4 | 3.8 | 16 |
| 2⅝ | 159 | 44 | 6.5 | 4.2 | 4.6 | 20 |
| 3⅛ | 185 | 53 | 8.0 | 5.1 | 5.4 | 25 |
| 3⅝ | 216 | 66 | 10 | 6.3 | 6.6 | 30 |
| 4⅛ | 248 | 76 | 12 | 7.3 | 7.3 | 35 |
| 5⅛ | 292 | 96 | 14 | 8.8 | 7.9 | 42 |
| 6⅛ | 346 | 119 | 17 | 10 | 9.3 | 50 |

equivalent lengths of fittings is chosen, and later corrected, if necessary. Common estimates are to add between 50 and 100 percent to the length of straight pipe as a trial for pressure drop through fittings. The following example illustrates this procedure.

**Example 11.5**  A suction line consists of 22 feet of straight pipe and three 90° short radius ells, type L copper tubing. The system uses R-12, with a design capacity of 30 tons. Saturated suction and discharge temperatures are 40°F and 105°F. The design pressure drop is equivalent to 2°F. Find the required suction line size.

*Solution*

1. Since the pipe size is not yet known, the equivalent lengths of fittings cannot yet be found. Assume they add 50 percent to the piping length. Therefore,

   Estimated total E.L. = 1.5 × 22 = 33 ft.

2. Figure 11.18 is now used to find the required pipe size for 33 feet, as done in

Example 11.3. The result is 2⅛ in. O.D. (The student should carry out this selection.)

3. The equivalent lengths of the fittings can now be determined from Table 11.2 for a 2⅛ in. O.D. line:

$$3 \text{ ells} \times 5.2 \text{ ft} = 15.6 \text{ ft}$$

This gives a total equivalent length (T.E.L.) of

$$\text{T.E.L.} = 22 + 15.6 = 37.6 \text{ ft}$$

4. Figure 11.18 is used again to find out if the 2⅛ in. O.D. size is adequate with this increased length. Allowed pressure drop (40°F) is

$$1.8 \text{ psi} \times \frac{100}{37.6} = 4.8 \text{ psi per 100 ft}$$

Finding the intersection for this condition, the 2⅛ in. O.D. size is still adequate.

## 11.9 Pipe Sizes for Oil Return in Risers

The pipe sizing procedure must be checked for suction and hot gas vertical risers to ensure that the refrigerant flow rate is adequate to move oil up the riser. Tables 11.3 and 11.4 show the minimum tonnage to ensure entrainment of oil up vertical suction and hot gas risers. Note the correction factors listed in the notes to the tables, depending on temperature.

The pipe size as determined by the procedures previously explained should be checked to determine if it is small enough to carry oil up vertical risers. This is especially important if the compressor and system have capacity reduction features, since the velocity will decrease as the capacity and flow rate decrease. The following example illustrates the use of Table 11.3 or 11.4.

**Example 11.6**  The refrigeration system described in Example 11.5 has compressor ca-

## TABLE 11.3 Minimum Tonnage for Oil Entrainment up Suction Risers Type L Copper Tubing

| | | | Pipe OD. In. | | | | | | | | | | | |
|---|---|---|---|---|---|---|---|---|---|---|---|---|---|---|
| | | | 0.500 | 0.625 | 0.750 | 0.875 | 1.123 | 1.375 | 1.625 | 2.125 | 2.625 | 3.125 | 3.625 | 4.125 |
| | | Suction | Area, In.² | | | | | | | | | | | |
| Refrig-erant | Sat. Temp., F | Gas Temp., F | 0.146 | 0.233 | 0.348 | 0.484 | 0.825 | 1.256 | 1.780 | 3.094 | 4.770 | 6.812 | 9.213 | 11.970 |
| 12 | −40.0 | −30.0 | 0.045 | 0.061 | 0.133 | 0.201 | 0.391 | 0.662 | 1.02 | 2.04 | 3.51 | 5.48 | 7.99 | 11.1 |
| | | −10.0 | 0.044 | 0.078 | 0.130 | 0.196 | 0.381 | 0.645 | 0.997 | 1.99 | 3.42 | 5.34 | 7.78 | 10.8 |
| | | 10.0 | 0.044 | 0.080 | 0.132 | 0.199 | 0.388 | 0.655 | 1.01 | 2.02 | 3.47 | 5.42 | 7.91 | 11.0 |
| | −20.0 | −10.0 | 0.059 | 0.106 | 0.175 | 0.264 | 0.513 | 0.868 | 1.34 | 2.68 | 4.60 | 7.19 | 10.5 | 14.5 |
| | | 10.0 | 0.058 | 0.103 | 0.171 | 0.258 | 0.503 | 0.850 | 1.31 | 2.62 | 4.51 | 7.04 | 10.3 | 14.2 |
| | | 30.0 | 0.059 | 0.105 | 0.173 | 0.262 | 0.510 | 0.863 | 1.33 | 2.66 | 4.57 | 7.14 | 10.4 | 14.4 |
| | 0.0 | 10.0 | 0.077 | 0.139 | 0.229 | 0.345 | 0.673 | 1.14 | 1.76 | 3.51 | 6.03 | 9.42 | 13.7 | 19.1 |
| | | 30.0 | 0.075 | 0.134 | 0.221 | 0.334 | 0.650 | 1.10 | 1.70 | 3.39 | 5.82 | 9.09 | 13.3 | 18.4 |
| | | 50.0 | 0.075 | 0.135 | 0.223 | 0.337 | 0.657 | 1.11 | 1.72 | 3.43 | 5.89 | 9.19 | 13.4 | 18.6 |
| | 20.0 | 30.0 | 0.094 | 0.169 | 0.279 | 0.421 | 0.820 | 1.39 | 2.14 | 4.28 | 7.35 | 11.5 | 16.7 | 23.2 |
| | | 50.0 | 0.095 | 0.170 | 0.280 | 0.423 | 0.825 | 1.39 | 2.16 | 4.30 | 7.39 | 11.5 | 16.8 | 23.4 |
| | | 70.0 | 0.095 | 0.170 | 0.281 | 0.425 | 0.828 | 1.40 | 2.17 | 4.32 | 7.42 | 11.6 | 16.9 | 23.4 |
| | 40.0 | 50.0 | 0.121 | 0.217 | 0.358 | 0.541 | 1.05 | 1.78 | 2.76 | 5.50 | 9.45 | 14.8 | 21.5 | 29.8 |
| | | 70.0 | 0.117 | 0.210 | 0.347 | 0.524 | 1.02 | 1.73 | 2.67 | 5.33 | 9.16 | 14.3 | 20.8 | 28.9 |
| | | 90.0 | 0.117 | 0.211 | 0.348 | 0.526 | 1.02 | 1.73 | 2.68 | 5.34 | 9.18 | 14.3 | 20.9 | 29.0 |
| 22 | −40.0 | −30.0 | 0.067 | 0.119 | 0.197 | 0.298 | 0.580 | 0.981 | 1.52 | 3.03 | 5.20 | 8.12 | 11.8 | 16.4 |
| | | −10.0 | 0.065 | 0.117 | 0.194 | 0.292 | 0.570 | 0.963 | 1.49 | 2.97 | 5.11 | 7.97 | 11.6 | 16.1 |
| | | 10.0 | 0.066 | 0.118 | 0.195 | 0.295 | 0.575 | 0.972 | 1.50 | 3.00 | 5.15 | 8.04 | 11.7 | 16.3 |
| | −20.0 | −10.0 | 0.087 | 0.156 | 0.258 | 0.389 | 0.758 | 1.28 | 1.98 | 3.96 | 6.80 | 10.6 | 15.5 | 21.5 |
| | | 10.0 | 0.085 | 0.153 | 0.253 | 0.362 | 0.744 | 1.26 | 1.95 | 3.88 | 6.67 | 10.4 | 15.2 | 21.1 |
| | | 30.0 | 0.086 | 0.154 | 0.254 | 0.383 | 0.747 | 1.26 | 1.95 | 3.90 | 6.69 | 10.4 | 15.2 | 21.1 |
| | 0.0 | 10.0 | 0.111 | 0.199 | 0.328 | 0.496 | 0.986 | 1.63 | 2.53 | 5.04 | 8.66 | 13.5 | 19.7 | 27.4 |
| | | 30.0 | 0.108 | 0.194 | 0.320 | 0.484 | 0.942 | 1.59 | 2.46 | 4.92 | 8.45 | 13.2 | 19.2 | 26.7 |
| | | 50.0 | 0.109 | 0.195 | 0.322 | 0.486 | 0.946 | 1.60 | 2.47 | 4.94 | 8.48 | 13.2 | 19.3 | 26.8 |
| | 20.0 | 30.0 | 0.136 | 0.244 | 0.403 | 0.608 | 1.18 | 2.00 | 3.10 | 6.18 | 10.6 | 16.6 | 24.2 | 33.5 |
| | | 50.0 | 0.135 | 0.242 | 0.399 | 0.603 | 1.17 | 1.99 | 3.07 | 6.13 | 10.5 | 16.4 | 24.0 | 33.3 |
| | | 70.0 | 0.135 | 0.242 | 0.400 | 0.605 | 1.18 | 1.99 | 3.08 | 6.15 | 10.6 | 16.5 | 24.0 | 33.3 |
| | 40.0 | 50.0 | 0.167 | 0.300 | 0.495 | 0.748 | 1.46 | 2.46 | 3.81 | 7.60 | 13.1 | 20.4 | 29.7 | 41.3 |
| | | 70.0 | 0.165 | 0.296 | 0.488 | 0.737 | 1.44 | 2.43 | 3.75 | 7.49 | 12.9 | 20.1 | 29.3 | 40.7 |
| | | 90.0 | 0.165 | 0.296 | 0.488 | 0.738 | 1.44 | 2.43 | 3.76 | 7.50 | 12.9 | 20.1 | 29.3 | 40.7 |

NOTE: The tonnage is based on 90°F liquid temperature and superheat as indicated by the listed temperature. For other liquid line temperatures, use correction factors in the table below.

| | Liquid Temperature, F | | | | | | | | |
|---|---|---|---|---|---|---|---|---|---|
| Refrigerant | 50 | 60 | 70 | 80 | 100 | 110 | 120 | 130 | 140 |
| 12 and 500 | 1.17 | 1.13 | 1.09 | 1.04 | 0.96 | 0.91 | 0.87 | 0.81 | 0.76 |
| 22 | 1.17 | 1.14 | 1.10 | 1.06 | 0.98 | 0.94 | 0.89 | 0.85 | 0.80 |
| 502 | 1.24 | 1.18 | 1.12 | 1.06 | 0.94 | 0.87 | 0.81 | 0.74 | 0.67 |

Reprinted with permission from 1981 Fundamentals ASHRAE Handbook & Product Directory.

**TABLE 11.4** Minimum Tonnage for Oil Entrainment up Hot Gas-Risers Type L Copper Tubing

| | | | Pipe OD. In. | | | | | | | | | | | |
|---|---|---|---|---|---|---|---|---|---|---|---|---|---|---|
| | | | 0.500 | 0.625 | 0.750 | 0.875 | 1.123 | 1.375 | 1.625 | 2.125 | 2.625 | 3.125 | 3.625 | 4.125 |
| | | Discharge | Area, In.$^2$ | | | | | | | | | | | |
| Refrigerant | Sat. Temp., F | Gas Temp., F | 0.146 | 0.233 | 0.348 | 0.484 | 0.825 | 1.256 | 1.780 | 3.094 | 4.770 | 6.812 | 9.213 | 11.970 |
| 12 | 80.0 | 110.0 | 0.161 | 0.289 | 0.478 | 0.721 | 1.41 | 2.38 | 3.67 | 7.33 | 12.6 | 19.7 | 28.7 | 39.8 |
| | | 140.0 | 0.150 | 0.270 | 0.443 | 0.672 | 1.31 | 2.21 | 3.42 | 6.83 | 11.7 | 16.3 | 26.7 | 37.1 |
| | | 170.0 | 0.143 | 0.256 | 0.423 | 0.638 | 1.24 | 2.10 | 3.25 | 6.49 | 11.1 | 17.4 | 25.4 | 35.2 |
| | 90.0 | 120.0 | 0.167 | 0.299 | 0.494 | 0.745 | 1.45 | 2.46 | 3.80 | 7.58 | 13.0 | 20.3 | 29.6 | 41.1 |
| | | 150.0 | 0.155 | 0.278 | 0.459 | 0.694 | 1.35 | 2.29 | 3.53 | 7.05 | 12.1 | 18.9 | 27.6 | 38.3 |
| | | 180.0 | 0.147 | 0.264 | 0.436 | 0.639 | 1.28 | 2.17 | 3.36 | 6.70 | 11.5 | 18.0 | 26.2 | 36.3 |
| | 100.0 | 130.0 | 0.171 | 0.307 | 0.506 | 0.765 | 1.49 | 2.52 | 3.89 | 7.77 | 13.4 | 20.8 | 30.4 | 42.2 |
| | | 160.0 | 0.159 | 0.285 | 0.470 | 0.710 | 1.38 | 2.34 | 3.62 | 7.22 | 12.4 | 19.4 | 28.2 | 39.2 |
| | | 190.0 | 0.151 | 0.271 | 0.448 | 0.677 | 1.32 | 2.23 | 3.43 | 6.88 | 11.8 | 18.4 | 28.9 | 37.3 |
| | 110.0 | 140.0 | 0.174 | 0.312 | 0.515 | 0.778 | 1.52 | 2.56 | 3.96 | 7.91 | 13.6 | 21.2 | 30.9 | 42.9 |
| | | 170.0 | 0.162 | 0.290 | 0.479 | 0.724 | 1.41 | 2.38 | 3.69 | 7.36 | 12.6 | 19.7 | 28.8 | 39.9 |
| | | 200.0 | 0.153 | 0.274 | 0.452 | 0.683 | 1.33 | 2.25 | 3.49 | 6.95 | 11.9 | 18.6 | 27.2 | 37.7 |
| | 120.0 | 150.0 | 0.175 | 0.314 | 0.518 | 0.782 | 1.52 | 2.58 | 3.96 | 7.95 | 13.7 | 21.3 | 31.1 | 43.2 |
| | | 180.0 | 0.162 | 0.291 | 0.480 | 0.725 | 1.41 | 2.39 | 3.69 | 7.37 | 12.7 | 19.8 | 28.8 | 40.0 |
| | | 210.0 | 0.153 | 0.274 | 0.452 | 0.682 | 1.33 | 2.25 | 3.47 | 6.93 | 11.9 | 18.6 | 27.1 | 37.6 |
| 22 | 80.0 | 110.0 | 0.235 | 0.421 | 0.695 | 1.05 | 2.03 | 3.46 | 5.35 | 10.7 | 18.3 | 28.6 | 41.8 | 57.9 |
| | | 140.0 | 0.223 | 0.399 | 0.659 | 0.996 | 1.94 | 3.28 | 5.07 | 10.1 | 17.4 | 27.1 | 39.6 | 54.9 |
| | | 170.0 | 0.215 | 0.385 | 0.635 | 0.960 | 1.87 | 3.16 | 4.89 | 9.76 | 16.8 | 26.2 | 38.2 | 52.9 |
| | 90.0 | 120.0 | 0.242 | 0.433 | 0.716 | 1.06 | 2.11 | 3.56 | 5.50 | 11.0 | 18.9 | 29.5 | 43.0 | 59.6 |
| | | 150.0 | 0.226 | 0.406 | 0.671 | 1.01 | 1.97 | 3.34 | 5.16 | 10.3 | 17.7 | 27.6 | 40.3 | 55.9 |
| | | 180.0 | 0.216 | 0.387 | 0.540 | 0.956 | 1.88 | 3.18 | 4.92 | 9.82 | 16.9 | 26.3 | 38.4 | 53.3 |
| | 100.0 | 130.0 | 0.247 | 0.442 | 0.730 | 1.10 | 2.15 | 3.83 | 5.62 | 11.2 | 19.3 | 30.1 | 43.9 | 60.8 |
| | | 160.0 | 0.231 | 0.414 | 0.884 | 1.03 | 2.01 | 3.40 | 5.26 | 10.5 | 18.0 | 28.2 | 41.1 | 57.0 |
| | | 190.0 | 0.220 | 0.394 | 0.650 | 0.982 | 1.91 | 3.24 | 3.00 | 9.96 | 17.2 | 26.8 | 39.1 | 54.2 |
| | 110.0 | 140.0 | 0.251 | 0.451 | 0.744 | 1.12 | 2.19 | 3.70 | 5.73 | 11.4 | 19.6 | 30.6 | 44.7 | 62.0 |
| | | 170.0 | 0.235 | 0.421 | 0.693 | 1.05 | 2.05 | 3.46 | 3.35 | 10.7 | 18.3 | 28.6 | 41.8 | 57.9 |
| | | 200.0 | 0.222 | 0.399 | 0.658 | 0.994 | 1.94 | 3.28 | 5.06 | 10.1 | 17.4 | 27.1 | 39.5 | 54.8 |
| | 120.0 | 150.0 | 0.257 | 0.460 | 0.760 | 1.15 | 2.24 | 3.78 | 5.85 | 11.7 | 20.0 | 31.3 | 45.7 | 63.3 |
| | | 180.0 | 0.239 | 0.428 | 0.707 | 1.07 | 2.08 | 3.51 | 5.44 | 10.8 | 18.6 | 29.1 | 42.4 | 58.9 |
| | | 210.0 | 0.225 | 0.404 | 0.666 | 1.01 | 1.96 | 3.31 | 5.12 | 10.2 | 17.6 | 27.4 | 40.0 | 55.5 |

NOTE: The tonnage is based on a saturated suction temperature of 20 F with 15 F superheat at the indicated saturated condensing temperature with 15 F subcooling. For other saturated suction temperatures with 15 F superheat, use the following correction factors:

| | | | | |
|---|---|---|---|---|
| Saturation suction temperature, F | −40 | −20 | 0 | 40 |
| Correction Factor | 0.88 | 0.95 | 0.96 | 1.04 |

Reprinted with permission from 1981 Fundamentals ASHRAE Handbook & Product Directory.

pacity modulation to 20 percent of full load. Check if the pipe size selected is small enough to return oil up a vertical riser at minimum load. Suction gas temperature is 50°F and subcooling is 15°F.

*Solution*   The minimum load is $0.2 \times 30 = 6$ tons. From Table 11.3, a $2\frac{1}{8}$ in. O.D. pipe will be satisfactory down to a load of 5.5 tons. No correction for condensing condition is necessary (liquid temperature is $105 - 15 = 90°F$).

The original pipe selected was $2\frac{1}{8}$ in. O.D., so it is satisfactory.

If the riser size proves too large to entrain oil at minimum load, there are two possible solutions. The first approach should be to consider reducing the riser size, while leaving the rest of the line the size originally selected. This will increase the pressure drop through the riser. The new total pressure drop through the line should be recalculated. If it does not exceed the allowed design pressure drop at full load then this is a feasible solution. The designer may even accept an increased design pressure drop if the energy penalty is small.

If reducing the riser size is unacceptable, then a double riser is the solution. Often at lower evaporating temperatures or with many steps of unloading, a double suction riser is required. The small riser is sized for the minimum load. The larger riser is sized so that the areas of both risers is at least equal to the total area required. The following example illustrates the procedure.

*Example 11.7* A refrigeration system with R-22 has a design load of 65 tons. Saturated suction and condensing temperatures are 40°F and 120°F. Minimum load is 20 percent. The suction line arrangement is as shown in Figure 11.22. Design pressure drop is 2°F. Size the suction line and risers. Piping is type L copper tubing. Suction gas and liquid temperatures are 70°F and 90°F.

*Solution* The procedure is carried out as follows:

1. Estimate the equivalent length of piping. Straight length (through riser B) is 62 ft. Assume 70 percent additional length of piping for fittings.

$$\text{E.L.} = 1.7 \times 62 = 105 \text{ ft}$$

2. At 40°F the pressure drop equivalent to 2°F is 2.8 psi (Table 11.1). This is corrected to 100 feet of length, in order to use Figure 11.19.

$$\text{Pressure drop} = 2.8 \times \frac{100}{105}$$
$$= 2.7 \text{ psi per } 100 \text{ ft}$$

Carrying out the usual construction with Figure 11.19, the required suction line size is found to be 3⅛ in. O.D. The E.L. of the fittings should be checked and the calculations repeated if necessary.

3. Determine if the riser size is small enough for oil return.

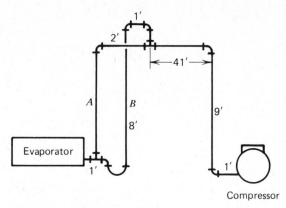

**FIGURE 11.22** Sketch of piping arrangement for Example 11.7.

Minimum load = $0.2 \times 65 = 13$ tons

From Table 11.3 a 3⅛ in. O.D. riser has a minimum capacity of only 20.4 tons. It might be considered to reduce the riser size to 2⅝ in. O.D., if the increased pressure drop is acceptable. A double riser will be used in this example, however, for illustration.

4. From Table 11.3 the minimum load riser required is 2⅝ in. O.D. Its minimum capacity is 12.9 tons.

5. The second riser is now sized so that the combined areas equal that of the suction line, at 3⅛ in O.D. The pipe cross-sectional areas are shown in Table 11.5.

$$\text{Area of } 3\tfrac{1}{8} \text{ in. O.D.} = 6.81 \text{ in.}^2$$
$$\text{Area of } 2\tfrac{5}{8} \text{ in. O.D.} = \underline{4.77 \text{ in.}^2}$$
$$\text{Difference} = 2.04 \text{ in.}^2$$

The nearest pipe size that has an area greater than this is a 2⅛ in. O.D. line. This is the size of the second riser.

## 10.10 Liquid Line Sizing

The main concern in sizing liquid lines is that the pressure drop be kept low enough to prevent flashing. The following example illustrates the procedure.

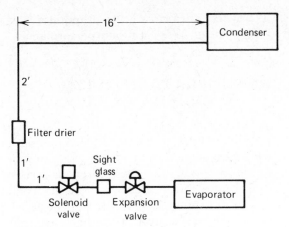

**FIGURE 11.23** Sketch for Example 11.8

***Example 11.8*** Determine the liquid line size and required subcooling to prevent flashing for the arrangement shown in Figure 11.23. Design load is 55 tons. Refrigerant is R-22. Evaporating temperature is 40°F, condensing temperature is 105°F. Tubing is type L copper. Design pressure drop is 2°F.

*Solution*

1. The straight length of pipe is 20 feet. Using a trial value of 100 equivalent feet for fittings and valves, the equivalent length is

$$\text{E.L.} = 100 + 20 = 120 \text{ ft}$$

2. The pressure drop equivalent to 2°F at 105°F is 6.1 psi. The pressure drop for 100 feet is

$$\text{Pressure drop} = 6.1 \text{ psi} \times \frac{100}{120} = 5.0 \text{ psi}$$

Using Figure 11.19 a required pipe size of 1⅛ in. O.D. is found.

3. The equivalent length can now be checked. The E.L. from Table 11.2 is

$$
\begin{array}{lr}
\text{solenoid valve} = & 87 \text{ ft} \\
\text{sight glass} = & 2.5 \\
\text{4 ells} = & 7.6 \\
\text{pipe} = & \underline{20} \\
\text{E.L.} = & 117.1 \text{ ft}
\end{array}
$$

This is close to the original estimate (120 ft). No correction is needed. However the pressure drop through the filter-drier must be added. Assume the manufacturer has furnished this information, at 2 psi.

There is a static head pressure gain, however, from the three-foot vertical leg, which must be subtracted from the pressure drop. Since each two feet of vertical height of liquid refrigerant exerts a pressure of about 1 psi, the pressure to be subtracted is 1.5 psi. The net pressure drop in the liquid line is

$$6.1 - 1.5 + 2 = 6.6 \text{ psi}$$

4. The amount of subcooling required to prevent flashing is now determined. The condensing pressure at 105°F is 210.8 psig. The pressure at the expansion valve is therefore

$$210.8 - 6.5 = 204.3 \text{ psig}$$

To prevent flashing, the refrigerant must be below the boiling point corresponding to this pressure, 103°F. Therefore the minimum amount of subcooling required in the condenser is

$$105°F - 103°F = 2°F$$

As mentioned previously, condensers are generally selected with considerably more subcooling than this.

## 11.11 Condensate Line Sizing

When a receiver is used, the line from the condenser to the receiver (called the condensate line) is connected as shown in Figure 11.24. The line is sized so that the static head in the vertical leg X is enough to overcome the friction loss. Recommended sizes are shown in Figure 11.24.

## 11.12 Energy Use

The major considerations in refrigerant piping that affect energy use are summarized here.

1. Suction and hot gas lines should be sized for reasonably low recommended pressure drops, since compressor power increases with pressure differential.

2. Pressure drop in the liquid line should be low enough to prevent flashing. Flash gas will reduce the expansion valve capacity and thus affect system capacity.

3. If a liquid-suction heat exchanger is used for subcooling, it will also improve compressor energy efficiency.

4. Follow recommended practices for oil return. Excess oil in the system will coat heat

transfer surfaces of the evaporator and condenser, reducing their performance.

## REFRIGERATION SYSTEM ACCESSORIES AND VALVES

A number of devices and valves installed in refrigerant lines, or at equipment, have useful functions. Some devices improve system performance, others may have safety or service functions. A few devices have been discussed in other chapters because their purposes relate closely to the subjects covered. Flow con-

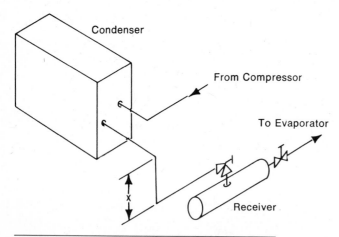

| Condensate Line Size (O.D. In.) | Refrigeration, Maximum Tons | | | "X" Minimum, in.[a] |
|---|---|---|---|---|
| | Refrigerant 12 | Refrigerant 22 | Refrigerant 500 | |
| ½ | 1.2 | 1.4 | 1.2 | 8 |
| ⅝ | 2.3 | 2.5 | 2.4 | |
| ⅞ | 6.4 | 7.7 | 6.8 | |
| 1⅛ | 13.3 | 15.9 | 14.0 | 15 |
| 1⅜ | 22.5 | 26 | 23.6 | |
| 1⅝ | 34.6 | 41 | 36 | |
| 2⅛ | 69.0 | 83 | 72 | 18 |
| 2⅝ | 119 | 143 | 125 | |
| 3⅛ | 184 | 220 | 194 | |
| 3⅝ | 261 | 312 | 274 | |

[a]This is the minimum elevation required between a condenser coil outlet and a receiver inlet for the total load when receiver is vented to coil outlet header (based on 10 ft of horizontal pipe, 1 valve and 2 elbows).

FIGURE 11.24 Recommended condensate line sizes.

trol devices are covered separately in Chapter 8. Devices closely associated with the compressor, such as crankcase heaters and suction line strainers, are discussed in Chapter 5.

## 11.13 Filter–Driers

This device (Figure 11.25), installed in the liquid line, removes both water (moisture) and foreign particles. Water can cause corrosion of metal parts. It can wet the windings of hermetic motors and result in a motor burn-out. It may also freeze in the expansion valve orifice. Foreign particles can collect in the expansion valve and interfere with its movement, can contaminate the oil so that lubrication is affected adversely, and can score the piston or cylinder walls.

The filter–drier contains a desiccant, a material that has a high affinity for water. Solid particles are also removed by a strainer or filter in the device. Filter–driers may be disposable or they may have a replaceable core. Commonly used desiccants include silica gel and activated alumina.

Although separate strainers (filters) and driers can be used, the filter-drier is obviously more convenient. Additional strainers are used before automatic valves and in the suction line of a compressor that does not have an integral strainer.

## 11.14 Sight Glasses

This device (Figure 11.26), installed in the liquid line, is used to observe refrigerant flow. Its purpose is to determine if the refrigerant charge is adequate, or if there is a restriction in

FIGURE 11.26 Refrigerant sight glass.

the liquid line. When liquid refrigerant is flowing through the line, the sight glass will be clear. If bubbles appear, gas is present, and inadequate liquid is flowing. Sight glasses also generally have a moisture indicator, which indicates the presence of moisture in the refrigerant; in this case some action should immediately be taken to remove the moisture, such as changing the filter–drier.

The sight glass is often used on small systems to determine if the system is adequately charged when adding refrigerant.

The sight glass should always be installed just ahead of the expansion valve so that it is not affected by other devices in the liquid line.

## 11.15 Oil Separators

Since oil and liquid ammonia do not mix, oil reaching the evaporator would foul the heat transfer surface. Their immiscibility also reduces the ability of the refrigerant to carry the oil back to the compressor. For these reasons discharge line oil separators are always used with ammonia systems.

In many halocarbon systems oil separators

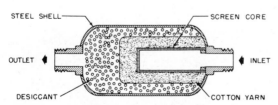

FIGURE 11.25 Refrigerant filter–drier.

are not required. Correct piping practice can take advantage of the natural oil–refrigerant miscibility to produce good oil return. The types of systems in which oil separators may be needed are low temperature systems, certain types of flooded evaporators, and systems with wide and sudden changes in load (a situation often encountered in process cooling).

A halocarbon oil separator is shown in Figure 11.27. Hot gas and oil entering the shell are separated by a reduction in velocity, gravity effects, and baffles or screens. When the oil level rises (oil is lighter than halocarbons), a float valve opens the return and oil is forced out by gas pressure to the suction line.

If the separator is in a cool location, halocarbon refrigerants may migrate to the separator during shutdown, liquify, and flood back to the compressor. To prevent this, the oil separator should be located close to the hot gas discharge and drained to the suction line, not the crankcase. It may also be desirable to insulate the separator and heat the oil. A temperature-controlled valve in the oil return outlet can also be used.

Since oil is heavier than liquid ammonia, it is drained from the bottom of the separator. An ammonia oil separator is located far from the compressor discharge. The cooler temperature reduces the gas volume, improving separation.

Oil separators will pass a slight amount of oil which collects and builds up in the system and must be returned. In ammonia systems, where oil is heavier, oil is drained from the bottom of evaporators and other required locations. With those flooded halocarbon evaporators that collect oil, the oil will rise to the top, since it is lighter than these refrigerants. It is bled (skimmed) from the top by a properly located connection.

## 11.16 Discharge Mufflers

On systems where noise from compressor discharge gas pulsations must be reduced, a muffler (Figure 11.28) is installed in the hot gas line. Internal baffle plates dampen the noise. A muffler should be installed in a vertical downflow or horizontal line so that it does not trap oil.

## 11.17 Receivers

This device (Figure 11.29) is a tank used to store liquid refrigerant not being used in operation, and the total liquid charge during shutdown. If the condenser has an adequate storage volume, a separate receiver is usually not required.

Storage space is needed to accommodate large load changes and resulting changes in flow rates. This aids in preventing the opposite effects of liquid floodback and starving of

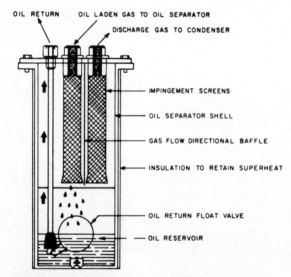

FIGURE 11.27 Oil separator. (Reprinted with permission from the 1979 Equipment ASHRAE Handbook & Product Directory)

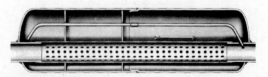

FIGURE 11.28 Discharge muffler.

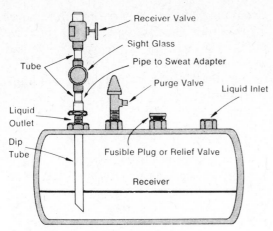

FIGURE 11.29 Receiver and connections.

**FIGURE 11.30** Liquid-suction heat exchanger (shell-and-coil type).

the evaporator. Capillary tube systems with very small charges that do not have a large load variation are generally designed so as not to require a receiver.

The receiver also serves to hold the whole charge, if necessary, when "pumping down" the system—pumping all the refrigerant into the receiver and isolating it with valves. This prevents any refrigerant migration during shutdown, and allows servicing of equipment without losing any refrigerant.

## 11.18 Liquid-Suction Heat Exchangers

This device (Figure 11.30) subcools the liquid refrigerant leaving the condenser by transferring heat from it to the suction gas leaving the evaporator, which in turn becomes superheated.

A liquid-suction heat exchanger is used for one or more of the following purposes:

1. To prevent flash gas from forming in the liquid line, by subcooling the refrigerant.

2. To prevent liquid floodback to the compressor, by superheating the suction gas.

3. To improve system efficiency by subcooling the refrigerant (Chapter 4).

A heat exchanger should be used with caution in an R-22 system because excess suction superheat may result in overheating the compressor discharge.

## 11.19 Suction Accumulators

This device (Figure 11.31) is used on systems with inherent floodback problems. It is installed in the suction line. Liquid refrigerant is collected in the accumulator and metered to the compressor at a controlled, safe rate. Oil is returned to the compressor crankcase.

**FIGURE 11.31** Suction accumulator.

A suction line accumulator is used on some heat pumps and systems with hot gas defrost. On changeover in a heat pump, the air cooled outdoor condenser, which has been feeding liquid refrigerant to the expansion valve, suddenly dumps it into the suction line when the condenser changes to the evaporator. In a system with hot gas defrost, hot high pressure gas is used to defrost the evaporator coil. This may force liquid in the evaporator into the suction line. A suction accumulator will alleviate the problem in both cases.

The types of valves that are used in the refrigeration system for such purposes as safety, service, or for control of pressure or temperature are discussed here. Expansion valves and condenser water regulating valves are covered elsewhere.

## 11.20 Solenoid Valves

This is an electrically operated valve (Figure 11.32) that is either in a fully open or closed position—it does not modulate. The valve has a solenoid coil with an iron rod in its core. When electric current energizes the coil an electromagnetic force is created that moves the iron rod. The rod is attached to the valve plunger, which opens the valve. Solenoid valves are used where it is desired to stop refrigerant flow, as in liquid lines with pump-down control.

## 11.21 Suction Pressure Regulator

This valve (Figure 11.33), also called a *crankcase pressure regulator* or *holdback* valve, limits the suction pressure to a maximum set value. It is used on low temperature installations to prevent high suction pressure on pull down or defrost. Since compressor power use increases with suction pressure, motor overloading might occur if suction pressure were allowed to increase freely.

The valve is installed in the suction line between the evaporator and compressor. Spring pressure tends to open the valve, whereas outlet (suction) pressure tends to close it. When suction pressure increases beyond a set spring pressure value, the valve throttles to a more closed position, decreasing suction pressure.

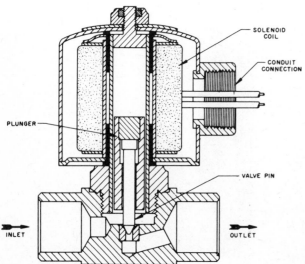

**FIGURE 11.32** Solenoid valve.

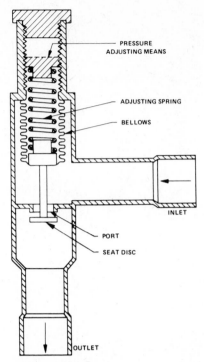

FIGURE 11.33 Suction pressure regulator. (Reprinted with permission from the 1979 Equipment ASHRAE Handbook & Product Directory)

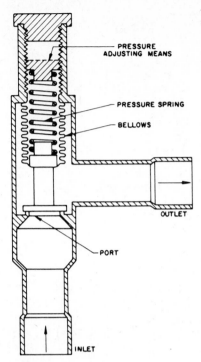

FIGURE 11.34 Evaporator pressure regulator. (Reprinted with permission from the 1979 Equipment ASHRAE Handbook & Product Directory).

## 11.22 Evaporator Pressure Regulator

This valve (Figure 11.34) limits the evaporator pressure to a preset minimum value. It is used in applications where the evaporator temperature must be kept above a certain level. One example is water chillers, to prevent freezeup. Another is air cooling coils where frosting is to be prevented. On systems with a multiple number of evaporators, evaporator pressure regulators might be used to control each evaporator at a different temperature (see Section 12.7).

The evaporator pressure regulator is constructed similarly to the suction pressure regulator, and is installed in the suction line at the evaporator outlet. The inlet pressure operates to open the valve, (rather than the outlet pressure, as with the suction pressure regula-

tor). When evaporator pressure rises above a preset spring pressure the valve opens wider, relieving evaporator pressure.

## 11.23 Manual Shut-Off Valves

These valves are used to isolate parts of the system or equipment for service. Valves are usually constructed with packing around the valve stem to protect against leakage. When used for refrigeration service they are generally of *backseating* construction (Figure 11.35). When the valve is fully opened, the valve disc seats against a second (back) seat, which seals the valve stem from the refrigerant pressure, preventing leakage around the packing. Refrigerant shut-off valves are often provided with seal caps that also protect against leakage.

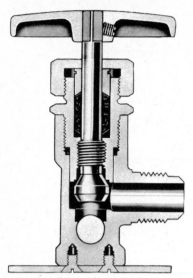

FIGURE 11.35 Refrigerant manual shut-off valve, backseating type.

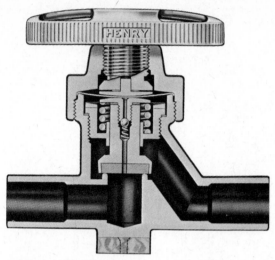

FIGURE 11.36 Refrigerant manual shut-off valve, packless diaphragm type.

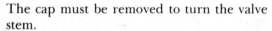

The cap must be removed to turn the valve stem.

A packless diaphragm type refrigerant shut-off valve (Figure 11.36) is also available. There is no packing around the valve stem; the diaphragm forms a seal between the stem and flow area to prevent leakage.

*Compressor Service Valves.* These are manual shut-off valves (Figure 11.37) that are located at both the suction and discharge connections of the compressor for service purposes. The valve is of the backseating type with a back-seat port. This connection can be used to attach a test pressure gage without losing the refrigerant charge. When the valve is fully open the gage part is closed. When the valve is front seated the line connection is closed and the gage port is open to the compressor. To read the gage pressure during operation, the normal procedure is to back seat the valve, attach the gage, and then turn the valve slightly.

A manual shut-off valve is also usually installed in the liquid line at the condenser, so

that the refrigerant charge can be isolated there. Another manual valve may be installed in the liquid line for charging refrigerant into the system.

## 11.24 Schrader Valves

This valve (Figure 11.38) is used for reading pressure when a compressor valve with gage port is not used or is inconvenient and is also used for charging refrigerant into the system. It is constructed similarly to a tire valve with a pin. A hose connection is available with a special adapter that fits the valve.

## 11.25 Check Valves

Check valves are used in refrigerant lines in cases where it is necessary to prevent backflow. Spring loaded valves (Figure 11.39) are used, which open when pressure is exerted in the direction of flow. An application already discussed is to prevent migration of refrigerant from the condenser to the compressor through the hot gas line, which might occur on shutdown if the compressor is colder than the condenser.

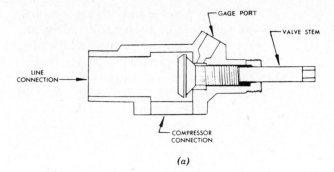

(a)

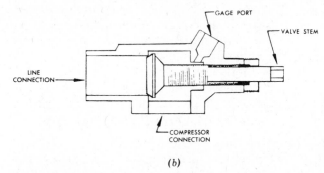

(b)

**FIGURE 11.37** Compressor service valve. (a) Valve backseated. (b) Valve frontseated.

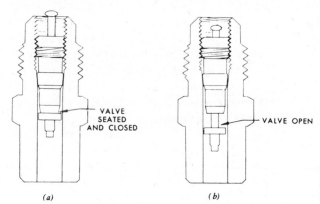

(a)                    (b)

**FIGURE 11.38** Schrader valve. (a) Valve in closed position. (b) Valve in open position—stem depressed.

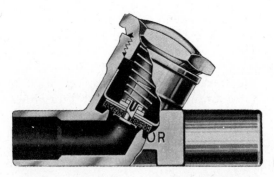

**FIGURE 11.39** Check valve, spring loaded type.

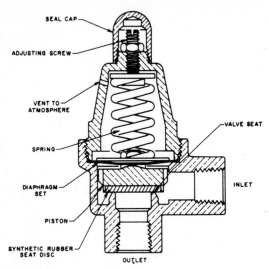

SEAL CAP

ADJUSTING SCREW

VENT TO ATMOSPHERE

VALVE SEAT

SPRING

INLET

DIAPHRAGM SET

PISTON

SYNTHETIC RUBBER SEAT DISC

OUTLET

**FIGURE 11.40** Pressure relief valve. (Reprinted with permission from the 1979 Equipment ASHRAE Handbook & Product Directory)

## 11.26 Relief Valves

Relief valves (Figure 11.40) are safety devices that open on high pressure to prevent excess pressure in the system or equipment. They are connected to the condenser or receiver. The valve outlet is sometimes vented to the low side of the system, and sometimes must be vented to the outdoors, depending on code requirements.

Spring loaded relief valves have a spring that holds the valve closed against normal pressures. There is also the rupture disc type that breaks on excess pressure.

A *fusible plug* is another safety device used on high pressure refrigeration equipment. This device melts at high temperature, thus relieving the pressure in the vessel. It is not a pressure safety device, since it opens only on temperature, but is used as a fire safety protection.

## 11.27 Reversing Valves

Refrigerant reversing valves are used in heat pump applications and for hot gas defrosting.

A four-way reversing valve is used in heat pump operation to change the refrigerant flow path between the heating and cooling cycle. Three-way reversing valves are used for hot gas defrosting. The valve temporarily diverts the compressor hot gas discharge from the condenser to the evaporator for defrost. These types of valves and their operation are discussed in detail in Chapter 12.

Figure 11.41 shows the arrangement and location of accessories in a halocarbon DX system. Each accessory is used only when required, of course. For instance, the oil separator, muffler, and heat exchanger are frequently not used. Control devices that might be required, such as pressure regulating valves, are also not shown in Figure 11.41.

## 11.28 Refrigerant Piping Materials

Both copper and steel are commonly used for the refrigerant piping for halocarbon refrigerants. Copper tubing is available in three different wall thicknesses, designated types K, L, and M. Type L is most often used in refrigeration work. Type M has a wall thickness too thin for the pressures generally encountered. Type K has a wall thickness heavier than necessary for most applications. Specifications for type L copper tubing are shown in Table 11.5. In the refrigeration industry the tubing diameter is specified by its outside diameter (O.D.).

Copper tubing is available in either *soft* or *hard temper*. Hard temper is more rigid. Soft temper tubing can be worked more easily, but may sag and distort, depending on how it is supported. Both tempers are used in refrigeration work, depending on the application.

Installed costs of piping tend to be less with copper tubing in the smaller diameters, and less for steel piping in the larger diameters. Aluminum tubing is also commonly used in small equipment, particularly household refrigerators.

For ammonia, steel piping is used. Copper is not suitable, since it is chemically attacked by ammonia.

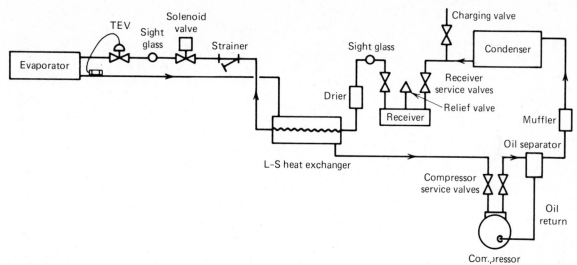

**FIGURE 11.41** Location of accessories in a halocarbon DX system. Accessories are used only when required. Piping is schematic. Traps, pitching, and the like, additional service or control valves, bypasses, and the like not shown.

TABLE 11.5 Specifications of Copper Tubing (Type L)

| Nominal Size, In. | Outside Diameter, In. | Inside Diameter, In. | Wall Thickness | Weight, lbs/ft | Volume, gal/ft |
|---|---|---|---|---|---|
| 3/8 | 1/2 | 0.430 | 0.035 | 0.198 | 0.00753 |
| 1/2 | 5/8 | 0.545 | 0.040 | 0.285 | 0.0121 |
| 5/8 | 3/4 | 0.660 | 0.042 | 0.362 | 0.0181 |
| 3/4 | 7/8 | 0.785 | 0.045 | 0.0455 | 0.0250 |
| 1 | 1 1/8 | 1.025 | 0.050 | 0.655 | 0.0442 |
| 1 1/4 | 1 3/8 | 1.265 | 0.055 | 0.884 | 0.0655 |
| 1 1/2 | 1 5/8 | 1.505 | 0.060 | 1.140 | 0.0925 |
| 2 | 2 1/8 | 1.985 | 0.070 | 1.750 | 0.1610 |
| 2 1/2 | 2 5/8 | 2.465 | 0.080 | 2.480 | 0.2470 |
| 3 | 3 1/8 | 2.945 | 0.090 | 3.330 | 0.3540 |
| 3 1/2 | 3 5/8 | 3.425 | 0.100 | 4.290 | 0.4780 |
| 4 | 4 1/8 | 3.905 | 0.110 | 5.380 | 0.6230 |
| 5 | 5 1/8 | 4.875 | 0.125 | 7.610 | 0.9710 |
| 6 | 6 1/8 | 5.845 | 0.140 | 10.200 | 1.3900 |
| 8 | 8 1/8 | 7.725 | 0.200 | 19.300 | 2.4300 |
| 10 | 10 1/8 | 9.625 | 0.250 | 30.100 | 3.7900 |
| 12 | 12 1/8 | 11.565 | 0.280 | 40.400 | 5.4500 |

Two common methods of joining copper tubing in refrigeration systems are *soldering* (also called *sweating*) and using *flared* joints. For soldering, the tube slips inside a joining fitting (coupling, elbow, etc.) A low temperature melting metal (solder) is melted and run into the slip joint. It forms a suitable pressure resistant joint when it solidifies. A pastelike material called flux is used to prevent oxidation and improve the flow of solder. The term *brazing* is used to refer to the soldering procedure with solders that melt at high (about 1000°F) temperatures. Brazing makes a stronger joint.

To make flared joints, the tube end is flared out, and a special set of flare fittings are screwed together against the flared tube to make a pressure-tight joint. Although a flared joint is more expensive, it is desirable for connections to equipment, since separation is easy.

Steel piping is joined either by welding or by using threaded (screwed) fittings and pipe. Further details on all these procedures may be found in service and installation manuals.

## 11.29 Vibration Isolation

The forces created by motion of the compressor produce vibrations that may be transmitted to the piping system, the building structure, or both. In some cases the magnitude of the vibration is quite small and has no harmful effect. In other cases, without treatment the vibrations may damage or break equipment or piping, or may produce unacceptable noises.

There are two general approaches to prevent vibrations from the compressor from being transmitted to the building structure. One is to mount the compressor rigidly on a massive concrete base. The concrete effectively absorbs the vibration energy. The other approach is to mount the compressor on flexible *vibration isolators,* which in turn are attached to the concrete floor or base. Coil springs and rubber mounts, or rubber or cork pads are among the types of isolators used. Regardless of the type, the transmitted vibration is reduced to a negligible amount.

Compressor vibrations may also be transmitted to the refrigerant piping. These vibrations can often be effectively reduced by making offsets or loops in the suction and discharge piping close to the compressor. Another technique is to use flexible connectors. This is a short section of manufactured flexible hose; it is installed in the pipe lines close to the compressor.

In some incidences it may also be necessary to use flexible pipe hangers. A curved section of rubber or cork inserted in a conventional rigid hanger may be adequate. In others, spring hangers may be used. Airborne noise directly produced by a compressor, when it is unacceptable, is usually reduced by acoustical enclosures or acoustical treatment of room surfaces. Both vibration and noise problems should be discussed with the compressor manufacturer concerning effects and recommended solutions.

## REVIEW QUESTIONS

1. What are the functions of the refrigerant piping?

2. What is the general effect of excessive pressure drop in any refrigerant line?

3. Describe the typical flow of oil and refrigerant through each part of the system.

4. What physical effects in the piping are used to return oil?

5. Sketch three correct installations for a hot gas line: with the condenser above, on the same level, and below the compressor.

6. What precaution should be taken if the condenser is in a warmer location than the compressor?

7. Sketch the arrangement of a vertical hot gas riser over eight feet in height, and explain the flow of refrigerant and oil.

8. What problem with hot gas risers occurs when a compressor has unloaders? What are two possible solutions?

9. Sketch and describe the operation of a double hot gas riser.

10. Sketch the arrangement of a discharge line oil separator.

11. Sketch three correct installations for a suction line: with the evaporator above, on the same level, and below the compressor.

12. What effect may excess pressure drop in the liquid line have? Why is this undesirable? What steps can be taken to prevent this problem?

13. What is "equivalent temperature change"? Why is it a useful way of expressing pressure drop?

14. What energy conservation practices in the design and installation of refrigerant pipe lines should be followed?

15. What are the functions of a filter–drier?

16. What are the functions of a sight glass? Where should a sight glass be located? Why?

17. What problem may occur with use of an oil separator?

18. What are the purposes of a receiver? When is it not required?

19. What is a liquid-suction heat exchanger used for?

20. Explain the functions and applications of a suction accumulator.

21. Describe the operation and purpose of a suction pressure regulator.

22. Describe the operation and purpose of an evaporator pressure regulator.

23. What is a backseating valve? What is its purpose?

24. Describe the operation of a compressor service valve.

25. Describe the purpose and operation of a Schrader valve.

26. What is the purpose of a refrigerant relief valve? Where are they installed?

27. Describe the application of a four-way reversing valve.

28. What piping materials are used for halocarbon refrigerants and for ammonia?

## PROBLEMS

11.1 Refrigerant R-22 leaves a condenser at 210 psig and 100°F. The evaporator is 22 ft above the condenser. Friction loss in the liquid line and its accessories is 8 psi. Will flashing occur in the liquid line?

11.2 A refrigeration system using R-502 operates at a condensing pressure of 250 psig. The evaporator is 30 ft above the condenser. Friction loss in the liquid line and its accessories is 8 psi. How much liquid subcooling is required to prevent flashing in the liquid line?

11.3 The evaporating temperature in a refrigeration unit using R-22 is 30°F. The suction line pressure drop is equivalent to 4°F. What is the suction line pressure drop in psi?

11.4 An R-22 system has a design refrigera-

tion load of 46 tons. Saturated suction and condensing temperatures are 40°F and 105°F, respectively. Piping is type L copper tubing. Find the required suction line size, if the design pressure drop is equivalent to 2°F. The equivalent length of the hot gas line is 58 ft.

11.5 An R-12 system has a design refrigeration load of 36 tons. Saturated suction and condensing temperatures are 14°F and 102°F, respectively. Piping is type L copper tubing. Find the required suction line size, if the design pressure drop is equivalent to 2°F. The equivalent length of the suction line is 38 ft.

11.6 An R-22 system has a design refrigeration load of 52 tons. Saturated suction and condensing temperatures are 32°F and 115°F, respectively. Piping is type L copper tubing. Find the required suction line size, if the design pressure drop is equivalent to 3°F. The equivalent length of the suction line is 46 ft.

11.7 A system uses R-22 and has a design capacity of 38 tons. The suction line consists of 32 ft of straight pipe and four 90° long radius ells, of type L copper tubing. Saturated suction and condensing temperatures are 40°F and 120°F, respectively. The design pressure drop is equivalent to 2°F. Find the required suction line size.

11.8 An R-22 system has a design refrigeration load of 27 tons. The compressor has unloading capacity down to 25 percent of the full load. Saturated suction and condensing temperatures are 20°F and 110°F, respectively. Suction superheat is 30°F and liquid subcooling is 10°F. Determine the maximum allowable suction riser size for adequate oil entrainment. Piping is type L copper tubing.

11.9 An R-12 refrigeration system has a design load of 78 tons. Saturated suction temperature is 20°F. Liquid temperature is 100°F. Minimum load is 20 percent. Design pressure drop is 2°F. Piping is type L copper tubing. The suction line arrangement is shown in Figure 11.42. Size the suction line and double risers. Suction gas is at 50°F.

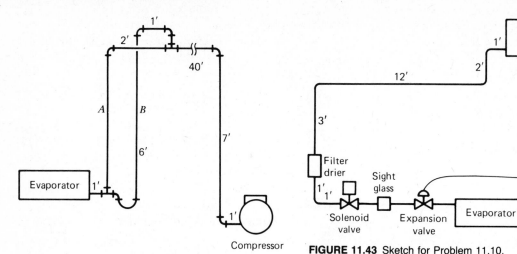

**FIGURE 11.42** Sketch for Problem 11.9.

**FIGURE 11.43** Sketch for Problem 11.10.

11.10 Determine the R-12 liquid line size and required subcooling to prevent flashing, for the arrangement shown in Figure 11.43. Design load is 34 tons. Tubing is type L copper. Design pressure drop is 2°F. Saturated suction and condensing temperatures are 40°F and 100°F, respectively. Use a filter-drier pressure drop of 2 psi.

# Chapter 12

## LOW TEMPERATURE REFRIGERATION. DEFROST METHODS. THE HEAT PUMP

Refrigeration systems that operate at low evaporating temperatures have special problems and features. Methods of defrosting evaporators, and the refrigeration features and defrosting of heat pumps are discussed in this chapter.

## OBJECTIVES

A study of this chapter will enable you to:
1. Identify the major concerns of refrigerating systems operating at low temperatures.
2. Sketch and describe compound and cascade multistage system arrangements.
3. Identify and describe defrosting methods.
4. Sketch and describe the operation of an air-to-air heat pump and reversing valve.
5. Identify refrigeration based heat pump problems and solutions.
6. Outline the heat pump defrost cycle.

### 12.1 Problems at Lower Temperature Refrigeration

Low evaporating temperatures lead to more difficult operating and maintenance problems and to increased energy use. High compressor discharge temperature, oil return, hermetic motor cooling, frost formation, increasing compressor size, and higher power consumption are among the problems to be considered.

*Discharge Temperature.* The temperature of the hot gas leaving the compressor increases as the evaporating pressure and temperature decrease. As explained in Chapter 4, this is because more energy is required to compress the gas over a greater pressure range. This increases the heat of compression and therefore, the refrigerant discharge temperature. Table 12.1 illustrates the comparison for different evaporating temperatures for an ideal cycle.

Excessive hot gas temperatures can result in a break-down of the lubricating oil, carbon deposit on valves, and acid formation. Increased maintenance and a shortened compressor life can be expected. Temperatures of 300 to 325°F at the discharge valves (about 275°F in the discharge line) are considered a limit.

Auxiliary cooling of the compressor is often used to prevent overheating at the discharge. Often fans are used on small units at low evaporating temperatures. Compressors with water cooled heads are commonly used with ammonia machines.

TABLE 12.1 The Effect of Decreasing Evaporating Temperature on Compressor Discharge Temperature[a]

| Evaporating Temperature, °F | Compression Ratio | Discharge Temperature, °F |
|---|---|---|
| 40 | 3.3 : 1 | 175 |
| −20 | 11 : 1 | 280 |
| −40 | 18 : 1 | 320 |

[a]Ideal Cycle, R-22, 120°F Condensing Temperature.

*Oil Return and Motor Cooling.* As the suction pressure decreases, the mass flow rate and density of the suction gas will decrease. This reduces the carrying ability of the suction gas to return oil to the crankcase. The increased viscosity at lower temperatures also makes the oil more difficult to return. In hermetic compressors, which rely on suction gas to cool the motor, the reduced flow rate may be inadequate to keep the motor temperature below safe limits.

Oil separators are used in the hot gas discharge, returning oil directly to the crankcase, when it is expected that oil return may be inadequate at low suction pressures.

*Frost Accumulation.* An air cooling evaporator will collect frost on the outside of the coil if the surface temperature is below 32°F. Periodic defrosting must be carried out to prevent buildup of frost. Methods of accomplishing this will be discussed later in this chapter.

*Compressor Size.* As the suction pressure decreases, the volumetric efficiency of a reciprocating compressor falls rapidly. That is, the volume of gas it can pump decreases (Chapter 5). Furthermore, the density of the suction gas decreases as its pressure decreases. The result is that the required compressor size (its displacement) for a given load increases as evaporating temperature decreases.

*Energy Use Efficiency.* With decreasing evaporating temperature more work is required to compress the gas, since the compression ratio increases. The refrigeration effect decreases at the same time. The combined result, as shown in Chapter 4, is a reduction in energy efficiency. That is, more power is required per unit of refrigeration capacity.

*Motor Overload.* Another problem that becomes more serious at low temperatures is the possibility of overloading the compressor motor. When the compressor is started, suction temperature and pressure are high. The compressor power requirement is much higher than at operating conditions (low suction pressure), and may result in a motor overload. A suction pressure regulating valve or pumpdown control may be used to limit compressor load.

## 12.2 Multistage Compression

Compression over the total pressure range in one step is called *single stage* compression. With decreasing refrigeration temperature a point is reached where it is impractical to achieve the required compression ratio in a single step for one or more of the reasons cited previously.

The solution to these problems is achieved by *multistage* compression—compression in two or more steps over the total pressure range. At typical condensing pressures single-stage compression is practical down to a temperature of about $-20°$ to $-30°F$ ($-29$ to $-34°C$). Below these temperatures multistage compression is used. Down to about $-70°F$ ($-57°C$) two-stage compression is used. From this temperature to about $-120°F$ ($-84°C$) three-stage compression is used. Below this temperature more stages can be used. However, other means of achieving refrigeration are often more practical at ultralow temperatures.

The temperature ranges listed are only approximate. Increasing the number of stages reduces energy use at low temperatures. As energy costs rise it is becoming economical to use multistaging at higher temperatures, even though the equipment costs are greater.

There are two types of multistage compression arrangements; *compound* and *cascade* systems.

## 12.3 Compound Compression System

An arrangement showing a typical two-stage compound compression system, also called di-

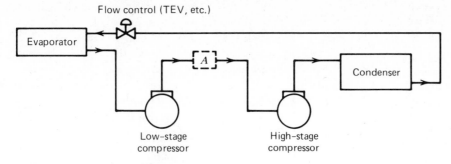

Note: Cooling of hot gas at A generally required.

**FIGURE 12.1** Two-stage compound compression (basic arrangement). Cooling of hot gas at A is usually required.

rect staging, is shown in Figure 12.1. The essence of this system is that a single refrigerant is compressed in two stages. The discharge from a low-stage compressor, at an intermediate pressure, is delivered to the suction of a high-stage compressor, which completes the compression over the total pressure range. Refrigerant from the evaporator is fed to the low-stage compressor suction, and discharge from the high-stage compressor is delivered to the condenser.

## 12.4 Desuperheating

The temperature of the discharge gas from the high stage compressor would be excessive

if it were not cooled (desuperheated) between stages. A water cooled heat exchanger is sometimes used to accomplish this, but frequently the water temperature is too high to reduce the temperature adequately. Another method is to use a desuperheating expansion valve, as indicated in Figure 12.2. Some liquid refrigerant is injected through an expansion valve into the hot gas line from the low-stage compressor. The liquid flashes to a gas at the lower pressure, cooling the whole mixture.

## 12.5 Liquid Subcooling

It is usual practice in compound systems to cool the liquid refrigerant leaving the conden-

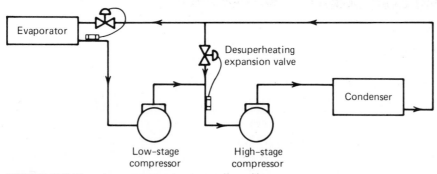

**FIGURE 12.2** Two-stage compound compression, with desuperheating expansion valve.

ser by use of a device called a *subcooler* or *intercooler,* which improves system performance, as will be explained. The subcooler is simply a heat exchanger. Two general types are used, the closed, and the flash or open type. A schematic arrangement of the closed type is shown in Figure 12.3.

A schematic arrangement of a closed intercooler in a two-stage compound system is shown in Figure 12.4a. The desuperheating function is often combined with the subcooling, as is true in this case. A *p–h* diagram showing the corresponding thermodynamic cycle is illustrated in Figure 12.4b. Discharge gas from the low-stage compressor (4) is delivered to the shell side of the intercooler, and from there to the high-stage suction (5). The intercooler is therefore maintained at the intermediate pressure. Some high pressure liquid refrigerant from the condenser (7) is delivered to the intercooler shell. The liquid flashes to gas as its pressure drops. The cool-

ing effect of the flashing cools (desuperheats) the discharge gas to point (5), the condition at which it enters the second stage suction. The gas is compressed to point (6) in the high-stage compressor. The main flow of high pressure liquid circulates through the intercooler coil before going to the expansion valve. This liquid is subcooled by the flashing effect, from point (7) to (1).

The improved performance of the two-stage system as compared to single staging results from a number of factors. Liquid subcooling increases the refrigeration effect. The flash gas that is formed in subcooling and desuperheating is compressed only across the high stage, reducing compressor power. Finally, the compression efficiency (ratio of theoretical power required to actual power required) is higher for each compressor, since it improves with lower compression ratios.

Total compressor displacement is also lower with a multistage system, since volumetric efficiency increases with decreasing compression ratio.

Minimum power is used when both compressors have the same compression ratio. That is, if the system compression ratio were 16 : 1, each stage should generally be chosen for a 4 : 1 compression ratio (unless there is a load at intermediate conditions requiring a different proportion of compressor capacities.)

Rotary compressors are often used as the low-stage or "booster" compressor because they handle large volumes of gas; refrigerant volume flow rate is much greater at evaporating pressure than at the intermediate pressure. For very large capacities, centrifugal compressors may be used.

For small loads two-stage reciprocating compressors are available (Figure 12.5). Discharge from one group of cylinders (the low stage) is delivered through an external manifold to the remaining (high stage) cylinders. The refrigerant is subcooled between stages by a desuperheating expansion valve.

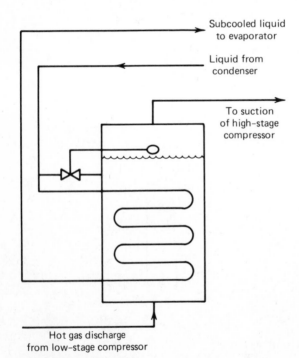

**FIGURE 12.3** Closed-type intercooler.

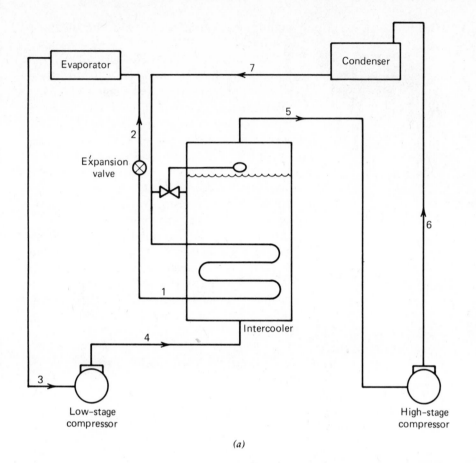

(a)

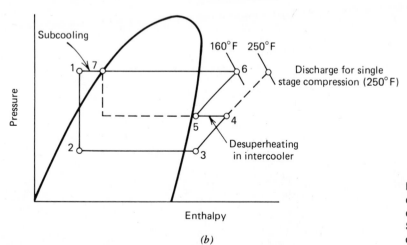

Enthalpy

(b)

**FIGURE 12.4** Two-stage compound compression with closed type intercooler. (a) System arrangement. (b) Cycle on p-h diagram.

**FIGURE 12.5** Two-stage reciprocating compressor. (Copeland Co.)

An intercooler may also be installed, as described previously.

In addition to the closed intercooler, an open flash intercooler is also available (Figure 12.6). All of the high pressure liquid refrigerant is delivered to the flash tank. Gas desuperheating and liquid subcooling takes place by flashing of a small quantity of the liquid, in the same way as with the shell and coil intercooler.

The flash type intercooler will subcool the liquid more than the closed type because there is no temperature difference between the liquid in the vessel and in the coil. On the other hand, the liquid to the expansion device is at intermediate pressure, not condensing pressure. This may necessitate use of a larger expansion valve, or in extreme cases the pressure differential may be inadequate to operate the expansion valve. Furthermore, liquid leaving the flash tank is not subcooled, and care must be taken that it does not flash before reaching the expansion valve. Addition of a separate heat exchanger may be required.

A three-stage system will be arranged in a manner similar to that of a two-stage system. Intercoolers would normally be used between each stage.

## 12.6 Typical Two-Stage System and Components

An arrangement of a two-stage compound direct expansion refrigeration system, with

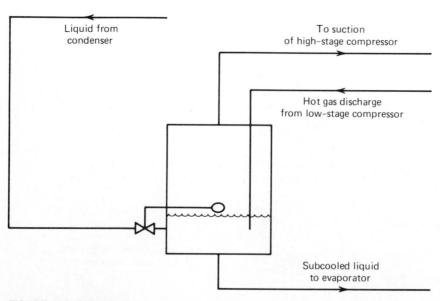

**FIGURE 12.6** Open (flash) intercooler.

typical required accessories, is shown in Figure 12.7. The use and features of these accessories have been described elsewhere in this book, but will be briefly reviewed here in relation to the low temperature system.

*A liquid line solenoid valve* is used for pump-down control. It is located ahead of the desuperheating expansion valve. Refrigerant is pumped from the evaporator to the condenser and receiver on shutdown and then isolated by the closed valve. This prevents high suction pressure and resulting motor overload on start-up.

*The desuperheating expansion valve* is used to flash some liquid and thereby cool the hot gas leaving the low stage compressor. The liquid in the circuit to the evaporator is also subcooled.

*A suction accumulator* is used to trap any liquid oil or refrigerant and prevent it from entering the compressor suction.

*A suction pressure regulating valve (holdback valve)* limits the maximum suction pressure, protecting against motor overload.

*A suction line strainer* removes any foreign particles before they reach the compressor.

*An oil separator* is used to return most of the oil directly to the crankcase, since oil return through the system is difficult at low temperatures.

*An oil equalizing line* with a high side float valve or trap is installed between compressor crankcases. This arrangement ensures that each compressor has a sufficient oil supply. The float valve is located to keep the proper oil level in the high stage compressor. Excess oil is drained to the low stage compressor when the float level rises, ensuring adequate oil for both compressors. If the oil equalizing line was used without the float valve, the difference in pressures might prevent oil return to one of the compressors.

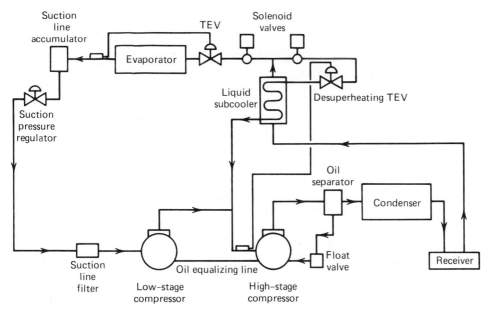

**FIGURE 12.7** Arrangement of two-stage compound system with closed intercooler and desuperheating expansion valve.

## 12.7 Multiple Temperature Systems

There are many applications where there are separate loads, each at different temperatures. The food processing and retailing industries frequently have such needs. To reduce the amount of equipment, two or more evaporators may be connected to one compressor, rather than using separate systems. This arrangement is called *multiplexing*. Figure 12.8 shows one method of connecting two evaporators to one compressor so that different temperatures can be maintained in each.

Individual expansion valves are used to supply each evaporator. An evaporator pressure regulator is installed at the outlet of the higher temperature evaporator, to maintain the suction pressure required by it. The compressor operation is controlled by a low pressure controller set to maintain the suction pressure required for the low temperature evaporator.

A check valve is installed in the suction line from the low pressure–temperature evaporator. This prevents high pressure suction gas from flowing back into the low pressure unit. This could raise the pressure to an unacceptable level. Furthermore, this gas could condense in the low temperature unit at shutdown and lead to liquid floodback on start-up.

The check valve creates an added problem, however. It will remain closed until the compressor pulls down the pressure in the high temperature unit. It is therefore necessary to limit to about one half the proportion of total capacity of the high temperature units connected to the system, so that the low temperature unit conditions are achieved in a reasonable time after each start-up. Another problem that can occur if the low temperature unit has too small a proportion of capacity is short cycling, if the load on the other units is satisfied. If the compressor has part load capacity control features this problem is less critical, of course.

Multiplexing is inherently an energy-wasteful means of arranging evaporators at different temperatures, since the compressor must operate at the lowest suction pressure required, with the evaporator pressure regulators (EPRs) providing the throttling from the higher pressure evaporators. Referring to Figure 5.18, the Bhp/ton for a compressor doubles for a change in suction temperature from about 30 to $-10°F$. It follows that if multiplexing is used, evaporators with large

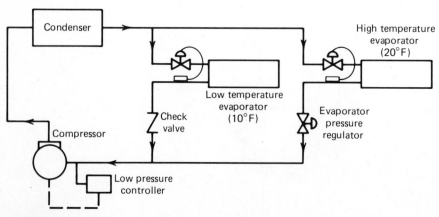

**FIGURE 12.8** Arrangement for two evaporators at different temperatures using one compressor (multiplexing).

differences in temperatures should not be mixed. For instance, in retail food operations, frozen food display cases (about 0°F) should not be multiplexed with meat cases (about 35°F)

## 12.8 Compound System for Two Temperatures

The compound compression system lends itself to applications where there is both a low and high temperature load. The arrangement is shown in Figure 12.9. It is sometimes called a booster system. Separately controlled low temperature and high temperature evaporators are used. The suction from the high temperature evaporator goes to the high pressure compressor. Compressor capacities are sized according to each load.

## 12.9 Cascade System

This method of multistage refrigeration for low temperatures uses two separate systems, each with its own refrigerant. The arrangement is shown in Figure 12.10.

The connection between the two stages of the overall system is that the evaporator of the high-stage system, called a *cascade condenser*, serves as the condenser for the low-stage system. The evaporating refrigerant in the cascade condenser, at an intermediate temperature, cools and condenses the refrigerant from the low-stage compressor to within a few degrees of the temperature corresponding to the intermediate pressure. The compression ratio of both low- and high-stage compressors is therefore kept low, resulting in an energy efficiency advantage over single stage compression.

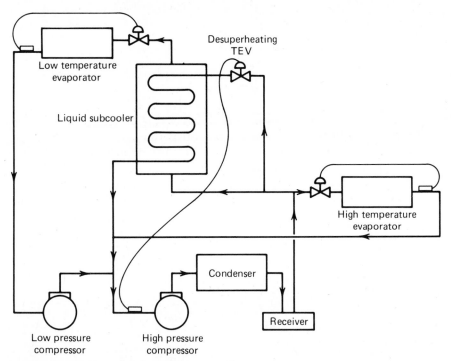

**FIGURE 12.9** Arrangement for two evaporators at different temperatures with low-stage and high-stage compressors (booster system).

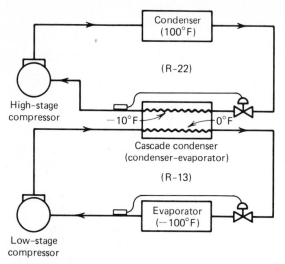

**FIGURE 12.10** Two-stage cascade system arrangement.

−50°F, whereas the specific volume of R-12 is 10 times greater.

An undesirable feature that results from using a refrigerant with a high pressure at low temperatures is that its pressure may be excessively high at ambient conditions. For instance, the pressure of R-13 in a saturated state at 80°F is 535 psia. This pressure would require extra strength equipment, raising costs unacceptably. To prevent excessive pressures when the system is shut down, a storage expansion tank is used. When the pressure rises, a relief valve vents the gas from the system into this tank.

Because there is a required temperature difference across the cascade condenser heat exchanger, the efficiency of the cascade system may not be quite as good as a comparable compound system.

## DEFROST METHODS

### 12.10 Defrost Requirements

Water vapor that is condensed out of the air by a cooling coil will collect on the coil surface. If the coil surface temperature is below 32°F the water will freeze and form ice or frost on the coil. In most refrigeration applications (as opposed to air conditioning) the refrigerant evaporating temperature is low enough so that frost will form on the tubing surface.

Frost has two undesirable effects that reduce cooling capacity. It increases the thermal resistance to heat transfer, and it collects on both tubing and fins, reducing the space between tubes. This causes a decrease in the air flow rate through the unit, which also results in reduced cooling capacity.

To prevent this problem from happening air cooling units subject to frost are periodically defrosted. Frost and ice must not only be removed from the coil surface, but from other parts of the unit where it may form, such as drain pans and air dampers.

The cascade system has some advantages over a compound system. Since separate refrigerants are used in each circuit, those whose properties are most suitable for each temperature range can be chosen for each stage. For example, R-12 has a reasonably low condensing pressure at the high stage (ambient) conditions, so extra strength high-side equipment is not required. At the low-stage evaporating conditions, however, its pressure would be less than atmospheric. This creates problems of possible air leakage into the system. In the compound compression system this situation would be unavoidable, and purging would be required. In the cascade system a refrigerant with a higher saturation pressure, such as R-13, can be used in the low-stage equipment. For instance, at −50°F the saturation pressure of R-13, is 71.7 psia, whereas R-12 has a saturation pressure of only 7.1 psia at −50°F.

Another advantage is that a low-stage refrigerant that has a low specific volume can be chosen in the cascade system, thereby keeping the required compressor displacement small. For instance saturated R-13 vapor has a specific volume of 0.5 cubic feet per pound at

***Defrost Methods.*** Defrosting is achieved by heating those parts of the unit requiring it, to melt the ice. The water is then drained off. There are a number of methods and sources by which the heat is furnished. They can be classified as follows:

1. Air (off-cycle.)
2. Heated air.
3. Liquid spray.
4. Warm brine.
5. Electric.
6. Hot gas.

Each of the methods has features that make it more or less suitble for different applications, as will be described. Defrost methods used with heat pumps will be discussed separately.

## 12.11 Air (Off-Cycle) Defrost

The simplest method of air defrost is to stop the refrigeration system and allow the evaporator to defrost by heat gains from outside the space, causing natural air convection across the tubing. This method, often used in household refrigerators, may take a long time.

In units with fans, the compressor is stopped but the fans continue to circulate room air through the evaporator. Air defrost is generally suitable only when the space temperature is greater than about 30°F; otherwise defrosting time is too slow and the temperature may increase too far above the design condition. Another limitation is that moisture on the coil will be returned to the space, increasing its humidity; where low humidity must be maintained this method might be unacceptable.

The off period for defrost may simply be the time during which the compressor is at normal off cycle due to the room thermostat control. Defrost periods may also be positively controlled from a clock timer set for a predetermined fixed length of time, or from temperature or pressure controls. Defrost controls will be discussed in more detail after each method is decribed.

## 12.12 Heated Air Defrost

To speed up the defrost process, heated air instead of recirculated space air can be used. If available, warm air from an adjacent space is sometimes used, connected to the unit through ductwork. Otherwise air is recirculated within the unit and heated by electric heaters or hot gas. The drain pan is also heated if the temperature is below 32°F (0°C).

## 12.13 Liquid Spray

In this method water or brine is sprayed onto the coils, melting the frost. Water is used if the space temperature is above 0°F ($-18$°C). Below this temperature the water might freeze on the coils, and brine is used. The water piping must be arranged to rapidly drain so that the water does not freeze in the piping.

When brine is used it will become diluted by the melted frost. It is usual practice to reconcentrate the brine for reuse. The diluted brine is collected and heated to evaporate the excess water.

## 12.14 Warm Brine Defrost

For a refrigeration system that uses chilled brine in an air cooling coil, defrosting can be accomplished by heating the brine and circulating it through the coil, after stopping the compressor. Any suitable heat source may be used. An energy conserving source of heat that should be considered is condenser water.

## 12.15 Electric Defrost

If electric resistance heating elements are used to defrost evaporators, the heating element may be attached to the outside finned tube surface. Another arrangement uses an inner rod that contains the heating element. This rod is inserted in the evaporator tubing and is attached to the tube wall by fins. The heat generated flows through the inner fins to the outside tube wall, melting the frost. Drain pans and drain lines are also heated by electric heating elements to prevent freezing in these components.

Electric defrost is an expensive, energy wasteful method. Its primary application is on household and small commercial refrigerators. Even here, its use is objectionable from an energy conservation viewpoint.

## 12.16 Hot Gas Defrost

In this method the heat available from the compressor discharge gas is used for defrost. The hot gas is circulated to the evaporator coil when defrosting is required. In some cases only the sensible superheat of the hot gas is used. In others the gas is condensed in the evaporator, making use of the additional heat available from the latent heat of condensation.

The basic circuit for a hot gas defrost system where the hot gas is condensed in the evaporator is shown in Figure 12.14. A hot gas bypass line is provided, going directly from the compressor to evaporator inlet. When de-

frosting is required a solenoid valve in the bypass line opens, and the hot gas flows to the evaporator, starting the defrost process. A check valve is located in the line to the condenser, to prevent reverse flow of high pressure liquid during defrost.

A suction line accumulator is recommended to trap the condensed hot gas and prevent liquid slugging to the compressor on start-up. A suction pressure regulator (holdback valve) is recommended to limit suction pressure and thus reduce motor load on start-up. Since this valve also serves as a pressure reducing device, liquid entering will flash to a gas; this aids in preventing liquid return to the compressor.

Other means are also often used to reevaporate any liquid leaving the evaporator during defrost. Some hot gas may be delivered directly to the suction line, or heat may be externally applied to the suction line. In this case electric resistance heating is convenient.

In the basic system described, the amount of heat available for defrost is limited to the heat of compression, since no heat is gained in the evaporator during defrost. Once all the refrigerant is condensed, there is no further heat available for defrost.

For a system with one evaporator using hot gas defrost, supplementary heat is often re-

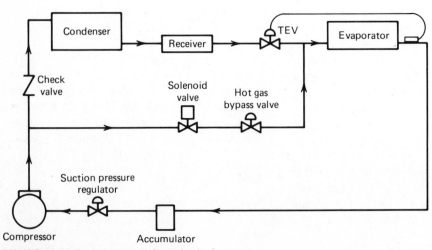

**FIGURE 12.11** Basic hot gas defrost circuit.

quired to provide sufficient defrost. Either an external heat source or storage of heat from within the system during the normal refrigeration cycle can be used. There are a number of variations used, usually proprietary with a certain manufacturer. We discuss two such methods for illustrative purposes. Although other methods are also well established, they are not described here, simply for the sake of brevity.

***Supplementary Heat Source Method.*** A hot gas defrost system that also uses a supplementary heat source is shown in Figure 12.12. It is sometimes called a two-pipe hot gas system.

The refrigerant flow circuit during the normal refrigeration cycle is shown in Figure 12.12 (*a*) and the flow circuit during the defrost cycle is shown in Figure 12.12 (*b*).

The refrigerant flows from the compressor to the condenser, receiver, and through the expansion valve to the evaporator during the refrigeration cycle. A three-way solenoid valve in the suction line is positioned so that the suction gas returns to the compressor suction.

A feature of this system is that during the defrost cycle the hot gas flows from the compressor through the suction line and the evaporator in reverse (reverse cycle). Note that there is a hot gas bypass line connecting

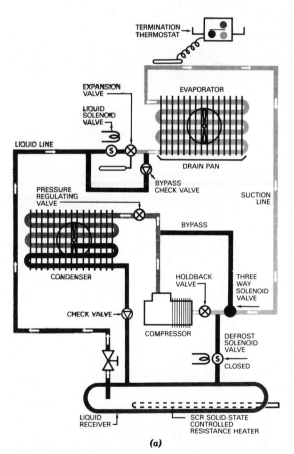

(*a*)

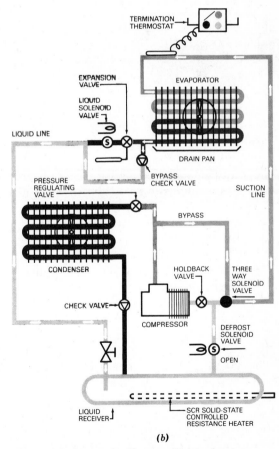

(*b*)

**FIGURE 12.12** Hot gas defrost system with supplementary (electric) heat source (*a*) Refrigeration cycle. (*b*) Defrost cycle. (Courtesy Halstead and Mitchell, A Division of Halstead Industries, Inc.)

the compressor discharge to the suction line. When the defrost cycle begins, usually on a time schedule, the position of the three-way solenoid valve in the suction line switches so that it is open to the bypass line and closed to the compressor suction. This reduces the pressure on the high side of the system. A pressure regulating valve located at the condenser inlet is set to close when this pressure drops. The compressor continues to operate and the hot gas is now diverted directly to the evaporator suction.

The gas condenses as it loses its defrosting heat; the liquid leaves the evaporator inlet and bypasses the expansion valve and filter–drier. A check valve is located in this bypass to prevent bypassing the expansion valve during the normal refrigeration cycle. The condensed liquid continues its flow through the liquid line in reverse to the receiver.

As seen in Figure 12.12, there is also a line connecting the receiver to the compressor suction, which has a defrost solenoid valve in it. This valve opens during the defrost cycle. The receiver also contains an electric resistance heater which is activated on defrost. The liquid returning to the receiver is vaporized by the heater and flows through the defrost valve back to the compressor suction; the hot gas defrost circuit is completed. When the defrost cycle ends, the solenoid valves switch back to their refrigeration cycle positions.

### Heat Storage Method.

This variation of hot gas defrosting stores heat energy from the normal refrigeration operation, and then makes use of this extra heat for defrost.

In Figure 12.13 (a) the system is shown operating in the refrigeration cycle mode. The discharge from the compressor (R) flows to a *heat bank* coil. This coil is immersed in a water storage tank (A). The hot gas gives up some of its superheat to the water; it then flows to the condenser (B), receiver (C), and evaporator (F) as in the normal refrigeration cycle.

Figure 12.13 (b) shows the system operating in the defrost cycle mode. When the defrost cycle starts, a discharge solenoid valve (G) at the condenser inlet closes. The discharge gas is forced to flow through a bypass line directly to the receiver. A hot gas solenoid (J) at the evaporator opens, so that high pressure warm liquid is forced through the drain pan heating coil and evaporator coil, defrosting the unit.

A suction solenoid valve (L) closes, so that the cool liquid refrigerant returning from the evaporator is diverted to a reevaporator coil in the heat bank storage tank. The liquid refrigerant absorbs heat from the water in the tank and evaporates, ensuring that vapor returns to the compressor suction. A holdback valve (P) at the reevaporator coil prevents excess suction pressure.

### Hot Gas Defrost of Multiplexed Evaporators.

In operations such as supermarkets, where a number of display cases and other evaporators may be connected to a central condensing unit, latent heat hot gas defrosting can be arranged to defrost one unit at a time. The defrosting evaporator serves as the condenser and furnishes the liquid for the remaining units. To furnish sufficient heat, the system can defrost only about one third of the total load at any one time. That is generally satisfactory, since the length of defrost is relatively short compared to intervals between defrosts.

An arrangement for sequential hot gas defrost is shown in Figure 12.14. Defrosting of each unit is initiated by a time clock control. The sketch shows a defrost cycle in operation, in evaporator 3.

When defrost of any unit is called for, the time control closes liquid line solenoid LS, and the system partially pumps down. The three-way hot gas bypass solenoid valve HGS 3 is positioned by the defrost time control to bypass hot gas from the compressor to evaporator 3 backwards, as shown. The other two hot gas bypass valves are in the position

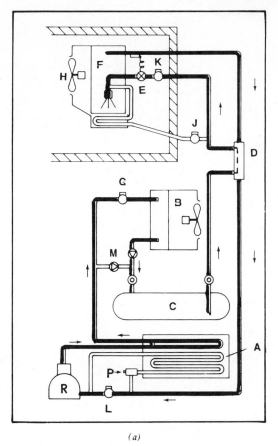

(a)

(b)

**FIGURE 12.13** Hot gas defrost with heat bank coil heat storage. (a) Refrigeration cycle. (b) Defrost cycle.

(Courtesy of Kramer Trenton Co., Copyrighted 1978 Kramer Trenton Co.)

for the normal refrigeration cycle to evaporators 1 and 2. The hot gas to evaporator 2 is condensed as it defrosts the coil. This liquid flows through check valve C3 and then to the other evaporator coils through their thermal expansion valves. The check valves are required to prevent refrigerant from bypassing the TEVs during refrigeration cycle operation.

A low pressure control is also located in the liquid line. If the high-side pressure drops too low to provide adequate pressure for operating the TEVs, this control opens the liquid line solenoid during defrost. When defrost is completed the control opens the liquid line sol-

enoid and positions HGS 3 for normal refrigeration cycle flow.

The same sequence of events occurs as the timer controls initiate defrost of the other evaporators, according to a predetermined schedule. Defrost is usually terminated by a temperature control (see Section 12.18). Evaporator pressure regulators (EPR) are used when different temperatures are maintained.

This system should be arranged so that a maximum of one third of the total load should be defrosted at any one time, so that enough heat is provided for defrosting within the time period required.

Legend

HGS     Hot gas solenoid
LS      Liquid line solenoid
C       Check valve
TEV     Thermal expansion valve
LPC     Low pressure control
EPR     Evaporator pressure regulator (when required)

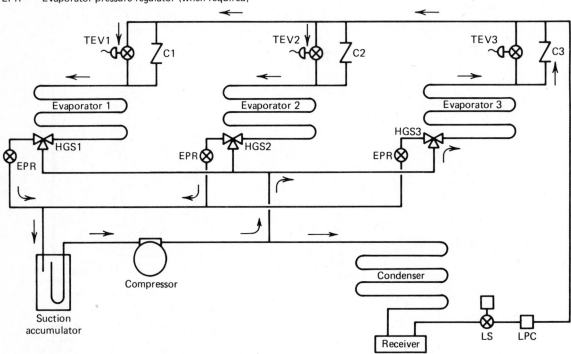

**FIGURE 12.14** Hot gas defrosting arrangement for multiplexed evaporators. Evaporator 3 is in defrost cycle.

## 12.17 Condensate Drain

The water that forms from defrosting must not be allowed to refreeze. A drain pan and piping should always be provided, pitched for rapid drainage. If subject to freezing, the drain pan and piping should be heated by supplementary means, such as electric heating. A seal trap should be provided in the drain line to prevent air from flowing back into the evaporator. The trap should be located outside of the refrigerated space if subject to freezing.

## 12.18 Defrost Control

Defrosting may be accomplished manually or automatically. Manual defrost requires extra labor and is subject to human error, and is not generally recommended. Automatic defrost may be time controlled, or may be controlled from temperature, pressure, or other signal.

*Time control* may be used to both start and terminate the defrost cycle. This uses a timer, a device that has a clock and switches whose positions are controlled by the clock. The cycle is set to begin at certain fixed periodic intervals, such as every three hours. If the cycle is also time terminated, the timer stops the defrost at a fixed interval, such as 10 minutes, and returns to the refrigeration cycle.

Frequently a time-started and signal-terminated defrost cycle is used, since the proper length of time for defrost cannot always be estimated beforehand, and may vary.

The *temperature termination* control usually consists of a thermostat that senses the evaporator coil surface temperature. When the temperature rises above a set point (about 40°F) the control switches to the refrigeration cycle.

The defrost cycle can also be terminated by *suction pressure* control. As the temperature rises the refrigerant suction pressure increases, and at a certain set point the control terminates the defrost.

When the defrost cycle terminates there is often a time delay feature that delays evaporator fan operation for a short period after the system switches to the refrigeration cycle. This prevents blowing warm air and water into the space.

In retail food store application, a demand-type defrost termination such as temperature termination is preferable to time termination. Varying surrounding conditions, such as store humidity, may change the amount of frost build-up and therefore the time required for proper defrost will vary. If the defrost time is too short then, of course, the cooling capacity may be inadequate. On the other hand, if the defrost time is set too long the condition of the product may deteriorate unacceptably.

There are other types of demand defrost controls available. One method is a control that senses air velocity or air pressure drop. Frost accumulation reduces the area across the coil and therefore reduces air flow rate. This type of control has been applied to retail food display cases and heat pumps (see Section 12.29). In the case of multiplexed units demand should be used for termination only,

to prevent the possibility of two or more units defrosting at the same time. The defrost starting timer is multicircuited and can be programmed at the desired starting intervals.

## THE HEAT PUMP

### 12.19 Principles

The term *heat pump* is used to describe a refrigeration system that is used for both cooling and heating. Heat pumps are generally used for air conditioning—that is, cooling or heating in the temperature range that provides comfortable space conditions for people. For this reason some of the features of heat pumps relate to the subject of air conditioning, rather than refrigeration. However, many of the special characteristics and most of the problems concerning use of heat pumps involve the refrigeration equipment and cycle. It is therefore appropriate to discuss these aspects in a refrigeration text. Comments related to air conditioning will be limited to those necessary to understand the material covered here. The reader should consult a suitable air conditioning text for a further knowledge of heat pump applications.

If we refer back to the explanation of the vapor compression refrigeration system (Chapters 3 and 4), it is noted that heat is rejected from the condenser to the surroundings. Air or water is generally used to carry the heat away. The air may be heated to temperatures in the order of 100°F (38°C) from the heat given up by the condensing refrigerant.

When the refrigeration plant is used for cooling, the heat rejected from the condenser is generally wasted to the environment; the system is operating in the *cooling mode*. This heat energy can be used for heating, however, and in this case the refrigeration plant is used as a heat pump; it is operating in the *heating mode*.

It follows from this explanation that there is no essential difference between a heat pump and any other vapor compression refrigeration system. The heat pump has the same essential components—evaporator, condenser, compressor, and flow control device—and operates on the same thermodynamic cycle.

Sometimes the term *reverse cycle* is used to describe the heat pump. This is incorrect, because it does not operate on a reverse thermodynamic cycle, but on the conventional refrigeration cycle. The term has arisen because in some heat pumps the refrigerant is made to reverse direction of flow between heating and cooling, and the evaporator and condenser may reverse their roles.

## 12.20 Applications and Advantages

Since the heat pump has the ability to accomplish both heating and cooling, it has the clear advantage of requiring one group of equipment for both functions rather than two separate units, such as a furnace or boiler and a refrigeration unit. This reduces space requirements and often decreases total initial costs.

It has been pointed out that the energy rejected in the condenser of a refrigeration system is equal to the sum of the energy absorbed from the load in the evaporator plus the heat of compression. This suggests why the heat pump is called by that name. It takes the heat energy absorbed by the system at a low temperature, raises it to a higher temperature in the compressor, and then utilizes it through the heat rejected in the condenser.

The heat pump has the advantage that the quantity of energy available for heating is much greater than the quantity of energy expended to drive the compressor (by the amount absorbed in the evaporator). The heating coefficient of performance (COP) of a heat pump is defined as the ratio of the useful heat output to the equivalent energy input to the compressor. This ratio may be in the order of 2 or 3 at a 20°F outdoor temperature. That is, two or three times as much energy is made available for heating as is expended in the energy source. This can be compared to a conventional heat source in which, at the most, all of the energy in the fuel can be converted into heat. That is, the best coefficient of performance is 1, one half to one third that of the heat pump.

Since the heat pump compressor is usually driven by an electric motor, this advantage is misleading when compared to a direct fuel fired boiler or furnace. This is because in generating the electricity from fuel at the power plant, about two thirds of the energy supplied in this way is lost. That is, the overall energy efficiency is roughly the same for a motor-driven heat pump and a furnace. However, the main operating cost advantage of the heat pump is over direct electric resistance heating, in which the direct coefficient of performance is 1, with the same losses in the power plant.

The use of heat operated heat pumps, solar assisted heat pumps, and combinations of furnaces and heat pumps may increase the energy efficiency advantage of the system. A discussion of these subjects is best left to the realm of air conditioning.

## 12.21 Types of Heat Pumps

Heat pumps may be classified into groups according to the type of heat source and heat sink that is used. The *heat source* is the medium from which heat is absorbed (in the evaporator) and the *heat sink* is the medium to which heat is rejected (in the condenser). Air and water are the most commonly used heat sources and sinks and the earth is occasionally used. Solar radiation has also been used as a heat source.

The most common heat pump is the *air-to-air* type, where air is used for both the heat source and sink. Other common types are the *water-to-air* type and *water-to-water* type. The air-to-air type will be explained in detail here and used as the basis for discussing heat pump refrigeration features and problems in general. A few comments will be offered about other types.

## 12.22 The Air-to-Air Heat Pump: Refrigerant Changeover

In this type of heat pump the two heat exchanger coils that are used as the evaporator and condenser have their roles reversed between the cooling and heating mode of operation. One coil is located indoors and one coil is located outdoors. Two methods can be used to change from the cooling to heating mode, called *refrigerant changeover* and *air changeover*. Figure 12.15 shows the system arrangement with refrigerant changeover.

The coils are called the indoor coil and outdoor coil, referring to their location. A *four-way reversing valve* is used to switch direction of refrigerant flow to the coils. This valve derives its name from the fact that it has four ports (Figure 12.16). One port is connected to the compressor discharge and another to the compressor suction. These ports are always open. The third and fourth ports are connected to the indoor and outdoor coil.

The reversing valve is a hollow cylinder with an internal floating slide that has openings through it. When the slide is in the position shown in Figure 12.15(a) the discharge port is connected to the outdoor coil and the suction port is connected to the indoor coil. The unit is now operating in the cooling mode. The discharge gas flows to the outdoor coil which serves as an air cooled condenser. The liquid refrigerant then flows through the expansion device to the indoor coil which serves as an evaporator, cooling room air. The gas then

flows through the reversing valve to the compressor suction.

When operating in the heating mode the reversing valve slide is in the position shown in Figure 12.15(b). The discharge gas now flows to the indoor coil. The room air circulating over the coil is heated as the hot discharge gas is condensed. The liquid refrigerant flows from the indoor coil (now serving as condenser) through the expansion device to the outdoor coil, where the refrigerant evaporates, absorbing heat from the outdoor air. This occurs because the outdoor air temperature is higher than the refrigerant temperature. The refrigerant gas then flows through the reversing valve to the compressor suction. Note that the outdoor coil is now the evaporator.

## 12.23 The Reversing Valve

One type of four-way reversing valve that controls the direction of refrigerant flow is shown in detail in Figure 12.17. The main body of the valve has a slide with a piston at each end. The slide has two large passages through it from bottom to top, one on each end. Two small orifices through it extend from the compressor discharge opening to each end of the valve cylinder.

The valve also has a solenoid coil and pilot chamber alongside the main valve body. The chamber contains a small piston which is attached to the solenoid armature. When the solenoid is energized it pulls the piston to the right. At each end of the chamber there is a small tube that connects to each end of the valve cylinder. Another tube connects from the center of the chamber to the suction line port.

The operation of the valve in the cooling mode is shown in Figure 12.17(a). The solenoid is not energized when cooling is desired, so the pilot piston is at the left of the chamber. Compressor discharge gas bleeds through the orifice in the slide to the right side of the main

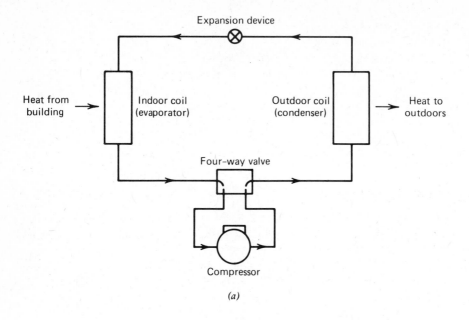

Expansion device

Heat from
building

Indoor coil
(evaporator)

Outdoor coil
(condenser)

Heat to
outdoors

Four-way valve

Compressor

(a)

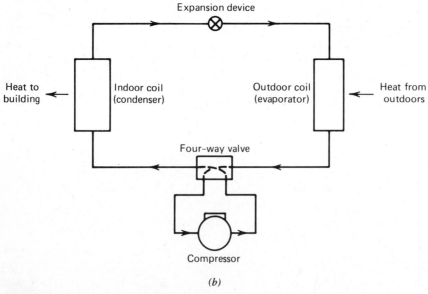

Expansion device

Heat to
building

Indoor coil
(condenser)

Outdoor coil
(evaporator)

Heat from
outdoors

Four-way valve

Compressor

(b)

**FIGURE 12.15** Air-to-air heat pump arrangement with
refrigerant changeover. (a) Cooling or defrosting mode.
(b) Heating mode.

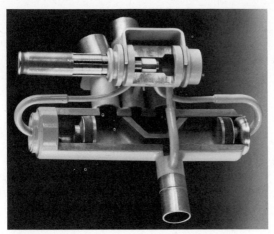

**FIGURE 12.16** A four-way refrigerant reversing valve. (Courtesy Alco Controls)

## 12.24 Flow Control Devices

With refrigerant changeover, special flow control device arrangements are necessary, since the refrigerant flows in opposite directions and pressures change between heating and cooling modes.

One method is to use two separate expansion valves, one at each coil (Figure 12.18). A bypass line is provided around each valve. For the valve that is not in use the bypass prevents flow in the wrong direction through the valve. A check valve is located in each bypass line to prevent the refrigerant from bypassing the expansion valve that is in active use. Each expansion valve can be selected for the conditions of service it is subject to. For instance the valve used with the outdoor coil may be of the cross-charge type because of the low temperature (Chapter 8).

The pressure difference across the flow control device may be greater for heating than cooling, since the temperature difference is greater. If a single capillary tube is used as the flow control device, its performance may not be satisfactory under one of the conditions. Some heat pumps use separate capillaries for heating and for cooling, with the heating capillary having a greater resistance to flow. A check valve arrangement can be used to bypass a capillary that is not used.

## 12.25 Air Changeover

This method uses ducts and dampers to change between the cooling and heating modes (Figure 12.19). The refrigerant circuit does not change, nor does the function of each coil.

In Figure 12.19(a) the system is operating in the cooling mode. The dampers are positioned so that indoor air is circulated through the evaporater coil. Outdoor air is directed through the condenser coil. Figure 12.19(b) shows the system operating in the heating mode. The dampers are now positioned so that indoor air is circulated through the con-

valve cylinder. The gas is trapped there because the pilot piston seals the opening through the tube. Discharge pressure is therefore exerted on the right side of the slide. At the same time the suction pressure acts through the center tube to the pilot chamber, then through the opening at the left side of the chamber to the left side of the valve cylinder. The result is that the slide is held to the left side of the valve cylinder by the pressure difference. In this position the refrigerant flow direction is from the compressor to the outdoor coil—the heat pump is functioning in the cooling mode.

The operation of the reversing valve in the heating mode is shown in Figure 12.17(b). When the control is switched to heating, the solenoid valve is energized and the pilot position moves to the right. The suction pressure now acts through the chamber to the right side of the valve cylinder. The discharge pressure gas bleeds through the orifice on the left and is trapped there because of the position of the pilot piston. The pressure difference moves the slide to the right. In this position the refrigerant flow direction is from the compressor to the indoor coil—the heat pump is functioning in the heating mode.

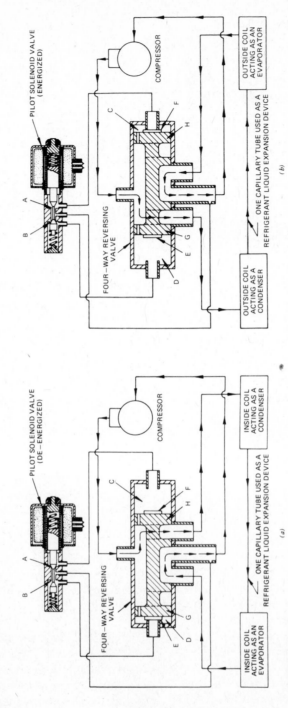

**FIGURE 12.17** Operation of a four-way reversing valve in a heat pump system (a) Cooling or defrosting mode. (b) Heating mode. (Reprinted with permission from the 1979 Equipment ASHRAE Handbook & Product Directory)

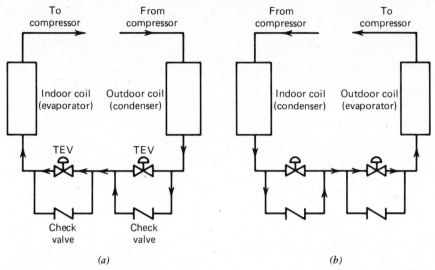

**FIGURE 12.18** Heat pump arrangement using two separate expansion valves to handle the problem of there being different conditions in the heating and the cooling mode. (a) Cooling mode. (b) Heating mode.

denser and heated. Outdoor air is now directed through the evaporator coil.

Because of its compactness, the refrigerant changeover arrangement is more suitable than the air changeover scheme for small unitary equipment.

Water–air and water–water heat pumps are more commonly used for larger systems, assembled in the field. (The air-to-air arrangement is applicable to larger as well as smaller systems). The choice is influenced by the availability of a particular heat source and sink and the end use of the system. For instance, if a building is to have a chilled water and hot water air conditioning system, the water-to-water heat pump might be selected. Description of each type will not be included here, since this does not bear directly on the subject of refrigeration.

## 12.26 Features of Heat Pump Equipment

Considerable operating and service problems were frequent in the earlier periods of heat pump history. Some of the problems resulted from an unawareness of the special requirements of the conditions of service; refrigeration equipment and practices that were satisfactory for conventional air conditioning cooling service were applied, with sometimes unpleasant results—equipment failure.

We have already discussed some of the special features of heat pump refrigeration equipment: the reversing valve and the flow control devices. Other equipment features and operating procedures will be discussed now. Many of these practices are normally carried out for commercial (lower temperature) refrigeration. Liquid floodback, oil return, and high discharge temperatures are all problems of concern associated with heat pumps.

*Compressors.* Compressors used with heat pumps commonly have lower clearance volume than those used for comfort cooling only. At the lower suction pressures encountered during heating, the lower clearance volume results in there being additional capacity. Compressors used must also be de-

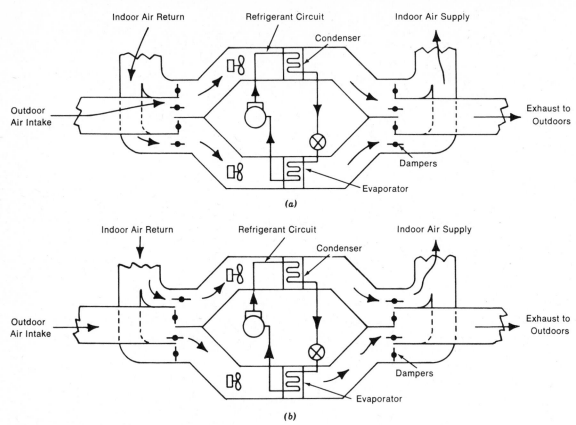

**FIGURE 12.19** Air-to-air heat pump arrangement with air changeover. (a) Cooling mode. (b) Heating mode.

signed for the high compression ratios that may occur at low outside temperatures.

***Accumulators.*** A suction line accumulator (Chapter 11) is generally installed at the compressor suction to prevent liquid refrigerant from reaching the compressor. There are a few reasons why an accumulator is needed.

During the heating cycle less refrigerant is needed, especially at lower temperatures, than during the cooling cycle. The conditions are such that the outdoor coil may not evaporate all the refrigerant. The accumulator will collect the excess liquid.

Liquid floodback can also occur when switching between cooling and heating modes. The coil that has been serving as the condenser, which is filled with liquid, is suddenly exposed to low suction pressure at the outlet, causing liquid to be forced into the suction line.

When the heat pump defrost cycle is initiated, high pressure hot gas is diverted to the evaporator; this may force liquid refrigerant in the evaporator into the suction line. A similar situation may occur at the end of defrost if liquid condenses in the cold evaporator coil. The suction accumulator will trap and store liquid refrigerant entering the suction line from these possible causes.

***Crankcase Heaters.*** At the low suction temperatures often encountered in the heating season during the off cycle, refrigerant migration to the compressor crankcase is rapid. On start-up the problems cited earlier in the text may occur—refrigerant foaming and loss of lubrication. A crankcase heater is used to maintain adequate temperature and pressure to prevent refrigerant migration.

*Receiver.* Because of the considerable difference in conditions between heating and cooling mode, the refrigerant flow rate through the system also varies. A receiver is useful to store the excess charge when not needed. The suction accumulator also serves as a receiver in some package units.

## 12.27 Heat Pump Practices

In addition to the special component features discussed, certain operating practices are special to the conditions of service that heat pumps encounter.

Unlike the usual situation when a refrigeration system is used for comfort cooling, the heat pump might be operated at very high evaporating temperatures. This could occur in mild weather if the unit were operated in the heating mode, since the outdoor coil is then the evaporator. High suction pressures result in greater compressor power, which at some point could overload the motor. It is generally recommended that a unit not be operated in the heating mode at outdoor temperatures above approximately 65°F.

A heat pump operates at a relatively high compression ratio in cold climates. For instance, on a 0°F day the evaporating temperature might be −20°F. If the condensing temperature were 100°F the compression ratio would be about 8.5 for refrigerant R-22. This is somewhat high for some compressor strength design limits. In addition, high discharge temperatures accompany high compression ratios. At the conditions just listed, the discharge temperature would be approaching a maximum acceptable limit. Therefore, a reduction in air flow rate over the indoor coil during the heating season,

which will increase the discharge temperature, must be avoided. This can occur from dirty filters, blocked air diffusers, or incorrect balancing.

Certain precautions must be taken concerning the outdoor coil installation to prevent poor performance of the unit. It must be located so that snow does not block air flow. It should be shielded from direct wind across the coil; but on the other hand, it should not be located where air can recirculate over the coil.

## 12.28 Supplementary Heating

The heating capacity (heat rejected from condenser) of a heat pump decreases with a decrease in evaporating temperature, because the heat absorbed in the evaporator decreases. Since the outdoor coil is the evaporator, the heating capacity decreases as outdoor temperature decreases. For typical heating and cooling load requirements, if the heat pump is sized to handle the maximum cooling load, its heating capacity will be inadequate below outdoor temperatures often encountered in many climates. For residential applications, an outside temperature of 30°F is a typical temperature at which the heating capacity of the unit will just match the load. This is called the *balance point*. For a further discussion of the balance point and its determination, a suitable air conditioning text should be consulted.

At any temperatures below the balance point, supplementary heating must be furnished. This is often accomplished by using one or more electric resistance heaters. As the outdoor temperature decreases, the amount of supplementary heat required increases, since both the load is increasing and the heat pump capacity is decreasing. Controls are arranged to activate the resistance heaters in steps as the outdoor temperature drops.

The supplementary heaters should always be located downstream of the indoor coil in the ductwork so that the heat does not affect the condensing temperature.

## 12.29 Heat Pump Defrost

Frost will collect on the outdoor (evaporator) coil of a heat pump during colder winter operation, and therefore defrosting is required with a heat pump. Hot gas defrosting is conveniently used. The unit is switched to the cooling mode operation for a short period of time and the hot gas defrosts the outdoor coil which is now acting as the condenser. The outdoor coil fan is stopped during defrost, so that cold air is not blown across the coil. This would only result in an increase in the amount of heat required for defrost.

The methods available for initiating and terminating defrost with a heat pump are similar to those we have discussed for other equipment. In a typical air-to-air heat pump defrost cycle, preparation for defrost is usually initiated by a timer which approximately every 90 minutes closes a set of contacts in an electrical control circuit. A device that senses the need for defrost operates another set of contacts in the same control circuit. It may be a thermostat that senses coil surface temperature, or a device that senses suction pressure, or the air pressure drop across the coil. If the conditions indicate frost accumulation, the thermostat (or pressurestat) closes the circuit, and the controls switch the unit from heating to cooling. The controls also stop the outdoor coil fan, for reasons previously explained.

The timer opens its circuit about 10 seconds after closing; if the sensing device does not signal a need for defrost within this time, the unit will remain in the heating mode. If the unit does go into defrost, the 10-second timer circuit is bypassed so that it does not affect the length of defrost.

The defrost cycle is terminated either by temperature or time. If the sensing element indicates defrost is completed, it opens the circuit and the controls switch the unit to the heating mode. If the unit is still on defrost after about 10 minutes, another set of contacts in the timer opens the defrost cycle circuit and the unit switches to heating. The time termination on limit serves as a safety back-up of the temperature sensor, in case the sensor fails to signal an end to defrost. It is also common to have one stage of supplementary heating automatically cycle on during defrost, so that cold air is not discharged into occupied spaces.

## REVIEW QUESTIONS

1. What undesirable effects may occur if the temperature of the refrigerant gas leaving the compressor is too high?

2. List two methods used to reduce the hot gas discharge temperature in the compressor.

3. How is oil returned to the crankcase? Why may oil return decrease at lower evaporating temperatures?

4. What can be done to resolve the problem of insufficient oil return to the crankcase?

5. What effect may low suction pressure have on hermetic compressors, and which does not occur with open compressors?

6. Explain why motor overload may occur in start-up of a low temperature system. How can this be prevented?

7. Describe and sketch a two-stage compound compression system.

8. Explain the use of and sketch an arrangement of a desuperheating expansion valve.

9. Describe and sketch the two kinds of intercoolers.

10. What are the advantages of multistage compression? Explain why each advantage occurs.

11. What is a booster compressor? What characteristic should it have? What type is often used as a booster?

12. What are the relative advantages and disadvantages of flash versus closed intercoolers?

13. List the accessories used in a typical two-stage compound system, and their function.

14. Describe the purpose and sketch the arrangement of a multiplexing system.

15. What are the functions of the evaporator pressure regulator system and the check valve in a multiplexing system.?

16. Describe and sketch a cascade refrigeration system.

17. Explain the relative advantages and disadvantages of compound versus cascade refrigeration.

18. Describe two physical effects of frost formation. What is the result of either effect?

19. How is defrosting accomplished? What methods of defrosting are possible?

20. Describe and sketch a hot gas defrost system.

21. Describe a time started, temperature terminated defrost cycle with time delay. What is the function of the time delay?

22. Describe and sketch an air-to-air heat pump system with refrigerant change-over, operating in both cooling and heating mode.

23. Explain how a four-way reversing valve functions.

24. Discuss the problems and solutions of using expansion valves and capillary tubes with heat pumps.

25. Explain the special features of heat pump refrigeration equipment.

26. What accessories are often used with heat pump refrigeration systems? What are their purposes?

27. Explain the problems that may occur at mild and at low outdoor air temperatures with heat pumps. Discuss the solutions to each problem.

28. What is the balance point? How does it affect the selection and operation of a heat pump?

29. Describe a heat pump defrost control cycle.

# Chapter 13

## ABSORPTION REFRIGERATION

Previously we have been concerned with the vapor compression system method of achieving refrigeration. In this chapter we discuss another method of producing refrigeration that is used on a large scale, absorption refrigeration. It is used especially for chilling water for air conditioning uses, but it also has applications for industrial refrigeration. A modern absorption refrigeration water chiller is shown in Figure 13.1

We will first explain how the absorption system functions, and then discuss equipment, controls, operation, and energy use.

## OBJECTIVES

A study of this chapter will enable you to:
1. Sketch and describe the absorption system used in large lithium bromide–water chillers.
2. Explain crystallization and its causes, and ways to prevent or eliminate it.
3. Describe how capacity control of the absorption chiller is accomplished.
4. Explain the difference between single effect and double effect absorption machines.

### 13.1 The Absorption and Vapor Compression Systems

There are both similarities and differences between the vapor compression and absorption systems. The useful refrigeration is achieved in the same way in both systems—by the evaporation of a liquid in an evaporator, using the latent heat of vaporization to achieve

a cooling effect. Both systems also use a condenser, to remove heat from the high pressure refrigerant vapor, and thus return it to its original liquid state. They both use a flow control or expansion device.

The systems differ, however, in the means by which the evaporated refrigerant is recovered and how its pressure is increased. In the first place, the forms of energy used to operate the system are different. In the vapor compression system, mechanical energy is used to drive a compressor. The operation of the compressor maintains the low evaporator pressure and also raises the pressure to the high-side pressure.

In the absorption system, heat energy is used to raise the refrigerant pressure. Low evaporator pressure is maintained by use of a second substance called an absorbent. Two components, the *absorber* and *generator,* serve a function similar to the compressor. Often auxiliary components, such as pumps, are used in the absorption system. Their functions will be explained later.

One reason the absorption system is popular and versatile is that it operates directly on heat energy. Wherever waste steam, hot water, or combustion gases are available, absorption refrigeration is an especially good candidate for consideration.

### 13.2 The Absorption Process

It is important to understand the process of absorption and some of the terms related to it, since they are essential to the understanding of the refrigeration system to be discussed.

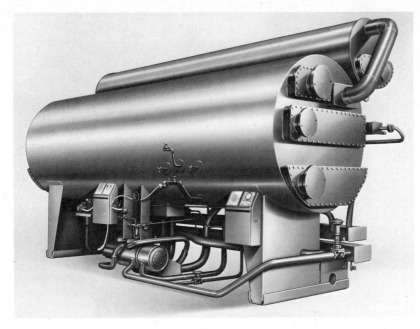

**FIGURE 13.1** A (two-stage) absorption refrigeration water chiller. (The Trane Co., La Crosse, WI)

Some pairs of substances have an affinity or attraction for each other such that when they come in contact one becomes absorbed by the other. The substance that absorbs the other is called an *absorbent.* A well-known example of such a pair of substances is common table salt (sodium chloride) and water vapor. Table salt acts as an absorbent with considerable affinity to absorb water vapor in the atmosphere. Thus on humid days we notice that salt has absorbed moisture from the air and will not pour.

Absorbents may be solids, liquids, or gases, and substances for which they have an affinity may be liquids or gases. In absorption refrigeration, the absorbent is a liquid and the other substance, which serves as the system refrigerant, is in a gaseous (vapor) state when it is absorbed. Two pairs of substances have been successfully used in absorption systems. One pair is water and ammonia. Water is the absorbent and ammonia is the refrigerant. The other pair is lithium bromide (chemical symbol LiBr) and water. In this case lithium bromide is the absorbent and water is the refrigerant. Note that water is the absorbent in one case and the refrigerant in the other.

The mixture of the two substances is normally in a liquid state in refrigeration systems. When the proportion of absorbent in the mixture is high and the proportion of refrigerant is low, it is called a *concentrated* or strong solution and when the proportion of absorbent is low and the proportion of refrigerant is high, it is called a *dilute* or weak solution. Concentration is usually expressed as percentage by weight of the absorbent. A more concentrated solution can absorb a greater quantity of refrigerant, and will do it at a faster rate. There is a maximum amount of refrigerant that a solution can absorb: when it becomes too dilute it will no longer absorb any refrigerant.

In this explanation of the absorption refrigeration system, we will use the lithium bromide–water cycle. When specific equipment is referred to, we will describe the arrangement commonly used in large capacity machines for air conditioning. Other equipment arrangements will be discussed afterwards.

## 13.3 The Absorber and Evaporator

As explained in Chapter 3, the evaporating temperature of the refrigerant depends on its saturation pressure–temperature characteristics. That is, the temperature at which the refrigerant will vaporize (boil) will vary with the evaporator pressure. The pressure must be low enough so that the resulting evaporating temperature will be at a value needed for the refrigeration application.

In the vapor compression systems, the low pressure in the evaporator is maintained by the suction pumping action of the compressor, as in Figure 13.2(a), which removes refrigerant as fast as it evaporates, thus preventing pressure from rising. Suitable refrigerants are chosen whose pressure–temperature characteristics correspond to the performance of the compressor and other components. For example, if R-12 is used, and an evaporating temperature of 40°F is desired, the pressure in the evaporator must be maintained at 51.7 psia. If R-11 is used, the pressure in the evaporator

would have to be maintained at 7.0 psia (14.3 in. Hg$_a$), a pressure well below atmospheric.

If water is to be used as a refrigerant evaporating at 40°F, the pressure must be kept extremely low, at 0.12 psia (0.25 in. Hg$_a$), according to Appendix 3. Figure 13.2(b) shows schematically how the absorption process is used to maintain this low pressure. The *evaporator* contains the refrigerant (water). The *absorber* is an adjoining vessel containing a strong (concentrated) solution of lithium-bromide–water. The two vessels are connected so that vapor may flow freely between them. The vessels are evacuated of any air to an extremely low pressure. Water in the evaporator will begin to flash to a gas, that is, it will boil. The cooling affect of the latent heat of vaporization will cool the unevaporated water, achieving refrigeration.

The water vapor produced will fill the evacuated space in both vessels. The pressure in the evaporator would continually increase as more refrigerant evaporates. The corresponding evaporating temperature would therefore also increase, and refrigeration at an acceptably low temperature would be lost. This is prevented by the action of the ab-

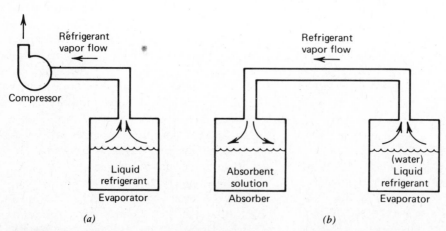

**FIGURE 13.2** Comparison of how suction and flow of refrigerant from the evaporator is achieved in both the absorption and vapor compression systems. (a) Vapor compression system, low-side pressure achieved. (b) Absorption system, low-side pressure achieved.

sorbent, however. The water vapor filling the vessels will contact the surface of the strong absorbing solution in the absorber, and will be absorbed by it. This reduces the pressure in the space. A slight pressure gradient is created from the surface of the evaporating refrigerant to the absorber, which promotes the flow of water vapor.

That is, the absorber will draw off the water vapor as it is produced, thereby maintaining the low pressure and temperature in the evaporator. This action of the absorber replaces the suction effect created by the compressor.

Since the evaporator has to be kept at a very low pressure the equipment must be sealed very tightly. This would be physically impractical if the refrigerant water were circulated externally through piping and coils to the load. Therefore the refrigerant is used to chill water circulating in a tube bundle in the evaporator (Figure 13.3). The chilled water is then circulated to the load. The refrigerant water is also continuously recirculated by an evaporator pump through spray header nozzles into the chilled water tubing. The heat from the system water (at a slightly higher temperature than the refrigerant) evaporates the refrigerant water. This cools the system water.

A pump and spray nozzle arrangement is also used to spray the strong absorber solution into the absorber space. This increases the surface area contact between the solution and the water vapor, increasing the effectiveness of the absorption process.

The system shown in Figure 13.2(b) would not operate satisfactorily for very long because the absorbing solution becomes more dilute as it absorbs water vapor and soon would be ineffective. The rate of absorption of water vapor would decrease, raising the pressure and evaporating temperature to an unacceptable level. At some point the solution would stop absorbing water vapor completely.

## 13.4 Recovery of the Refrigerant

Obviously some means of recovery of the refrigerant must be arranged for, if the system is to be used more than once. Two basic steps are needed. First, the refrigerant must be separated from the solution. This is accomplished by heating the weak solution, to a temperature at which the water boils off from it, in a component called the generator. Second, the water vapor must be condensed to a liquid so that it is ready for use in the evaporator again.

The equipment arrangement shown in Figure 13.2(b) is not suited for practical recovery

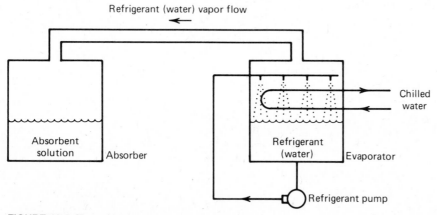

**FIGURE 13.3** The refrigerant pump and chilled water distribution coil added to the evaporator.

of the refrigerant on a continual basis, but it is an interesting historical note that it actually was once used as a household refrigeration unit, appropriately called a "dumbbell." The evaporator was placed in an insulated box used to cool foods. For a while the evaporating effect was satisfactory to produce reasonably cold water which then cooled the surrounding space. After the process became ineffective, the unit was removed.

A gas heater was then applied to the absorber to boil off the water, increasing the solution concentration. The absorber thus served also as a generator. The evaporator was simultaneously put in a bath of water, which condensed the refrigerant water vapor. The dumbbell was then ready for use again.

## 13.5 The Generator and Condenser

A practical arrangement for recovery of the refrigerant so that the system can be operated continuously is shown in Figure 13.4. The weak solution is pumped from the absorber to a vessel called either the *generator* or *concentrator*. Heat is applied to the solution, resulting in boiling off of the water. The now reconcentrated strong solution is returned to the absorber and sprayed into the surrounding refrigerant water vapor, where the absorption takes place. The heat source is often steam or hot water circulating in a coil, as shown. Direct firing from hot combustion gases can also be used, although the apparatus would be physically different, of course.

The generator space is connected to a fourth component, the *condenser*. The water vapor fills the space in the vessels. A source of cooling water is circulated through tubing in the condenser. The water temperature is lower than the condensing temperature of the water vapor at the condensing pressure. The water vapor therefore gives up its heat of condensation and condenses to a liquid, collecting at the bottom of the condenser.

The evaporator and absorber are at an extremely low pressure and can be considered the low side of the system. The pressure developed in the generator and condenser by the heating process is higher; these two components can be considered the high side of the system. (Even though the pressure is higher in the generator and absorber, it is still well below atmospheric.)

In order to maintain the high-side and low-side pressure differential, and to cause a flash cooling effect of the refrigerant, an orifice is provided between the condenser and evaporator. This serves as an expansion device, similar to that in the vapor compression system. This completes the cycle.

## 13.6 The Heat Exchanger and Cooling Water Circuits

An energy saving feature that is included in the actual system is a heat exchanger provided between the weak and strong solutions (Figure 13.4). The weak solution from the absorber is preheated by the hot strong solution leaving the generator. This saves part of the energy to bring the weak solution up to the boiling point temperature, which would otherwise come from the heat source. The cooling of the strong solution in the heat exchanger also reduces the cooling requirement in the absorber to reduce the solution to proper operating temperature.

In addition to the need of cooling water in the condenser, heat must be removed in the absorber. There are three sources of heat released in the absorber. First, the refrigerant vapor when it is absorbed becomes liquid. The latent heat of condensation of this effect must be removed. Second, the absorption process itself generates heat from chemical effects, called the heat of dilution. Finally, despite the heat exchanger, further sensible heat must be removed from the returning strong solution to bring it down to operating temperature.

The cooling water circuit is usually connected in series, going first to the absorber and then the condenser (Figure 13.4). Any of the usual sources of cooling water, such as a cool-

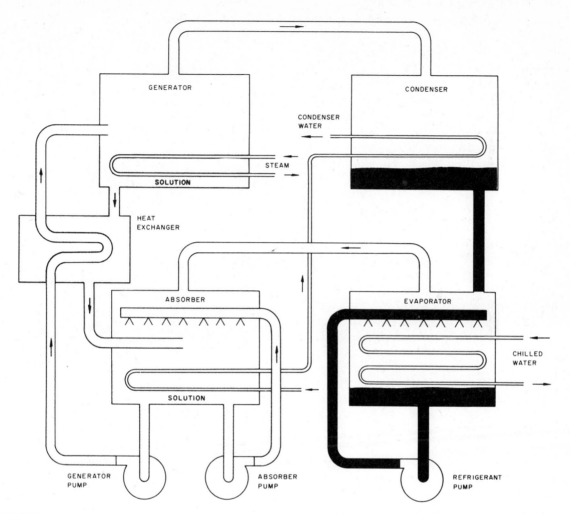

**FIGURE 13.4** Schematic of LiBr–water absorption system arrangement.

ing tower, may be used. The total amount of heat that must be rejected from the system is about double that in the vapor compression system.

## 13.7  Absorbent and Refrigerant Characteristics: Crystallization

Both the absorbent and refrigerant should have certain desirable characteristics. The lithium bromide–water pair are quite satisfac-

tory in most respects. They are low in cost, chemically stable, and nontoxic. Lithium bromide will absorb large quantities of water, therefore only a relatively small amount of lithium bromide must be pumped between the absorber and generator. The boiling point of water is considerably lower than that of lithium bromide, therefore it is easy to separate the two in the generator.

The vapor pressure–temperature characteristics of water are such that pressures in the vessels will be extremely low. This is undesirable, since air will leak in through any poorly sealed joints. This would raise the pressure, and the resulting increased evaporating temperature would be unacceptable. In early absorption machines this was often a problem. Equipment today is reliably pressure tight, however.

The applications of the lithium bromide–water system are limited to relatively high temperatures, since the refrigerant freezes at 32°F.

*Crystallization.*   The lithium bromide–water solution has one property that can cause difficulty. If a strong (concentrated) solution at a high temperature is cooled, solid crystals will precipitate out of the liquid. This process is called *crystallization.* The resultant mixture has a consistency like slush. If crystallization occurs in an absorption machine, refrigeration will cease, since the pumps cannot move the slushlike mixture around. We will discuss causes and prevention of crystallization shortly.

The water–ammonia pair are also low in cost and chemically stable. Equipment location is restricted, however, because ammonia vapor is a toxic substance. The pressure–temperature characteristics of ammonia result in high pressures in the vessels (at 40°F the evaporator pressure is 73.3 psia). Air leakage inward is therefore no problem during operation. The high pressures, particularly in the high-side equipment, may require greater strength equipment than in the lithium bromide–water machine. The water–ammonia system can, of course, be used for low temperatures, since the refrigerant does not freeze except at ultra-low temperatures.

A problem that exists with the water–ammonia absorption system is that some water boils off with the ammonia in the generator, because the volatilities of ammonia and water are not that much different from each other. The fluids then have to be separated, in equipment called a *rectifier.*

## 13.8 Large Lithium Bromide Absorption Machines

The lithium bromide absorption cycle described in the previous sections is essentially how most large absorption refrigeration machines operate. These machines are primarily used to chill water for air conditioning systems, in capacities ranging from about 100 to 1500 tons of refrigeration.

The actual physical arrangement of the equipment is quite different from the schematic arrangement that was shown in Figure 13.4. The four components are generally combined either in two or even one cylindrical shell.

A cross-sectional view through a one shell machine is shown in Figure 13.5. The one shell machine will be used to describe the cycle and its operation, and some physical features of the equipment. Typical temperature conditions are shown.

*The Evaporator.*   Cross-sectional and cutaway views of the evaporator components are shown in Figure 13.6. The liquid refrigerant (water) flows from the condenser through the orifice restriction to the evaporator. Due to the pressure drop some flashing occurs and the refrigerant is cooled to 40°F. The unevaporated refrigerant falls to the evaporator pan. The *evaporator pump* continuously circulates this water to the spray nozzles onto the system chilled water tube bundle. Heat from the system water evaporates the refrigerant, and the system water is in turn cooled, from 54 to 44°F in this case.

*The Absorber.*   Cross-sectional and cutaway views of the absorber components are shown in Figure 13.7. An *intermediate* concentration solution is sprayed into the absorber space by the *absorber pump.* The solution absorbs the surrounding refrigerant water vapor, which fills the open space in the evaporator and absorber part of the shell. This maintains the low pressure required (0.25 in. Hg$_a$). Due to a

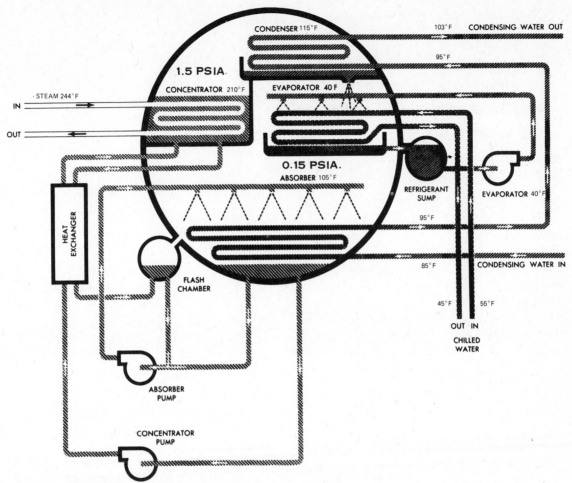

**FIGURE 13.5** Sectional view through a single shell LiBr–water absorption chiller showing typical operating pressures and temperatures. (The Trane Co., La Crosse, WI)

very small pressure gradient, refrigerant vapor flows continually to the absorber.

The diluted (weak) solution is collected in a well at the bottom of the shell. The weak solution is mixed with the strong solution returning from the generator, at the absorber pump suction, to make the intermediate solution.

There are two reasons a solution of intermediate concentration is used in the absorber. The strong solution might crystallize at the temperatures it is cooled to. Also, the quantity of strong solution alone would not be enough

to thoroughly wet the cooling water tube bundle.

Heat is generated in the absorber from the condensation of the absorbed refrigerant, from the heat of dilution, and from the sensible heat of the strong solution. This heat is removed by the cooling water circulating through a tube bundle. The absorber temperature is maintained at 105°F. The cooling water is heated from 85 to 95°F.

***The Generator (Concentrator).*** Cross sectional and cut-away views of the generator

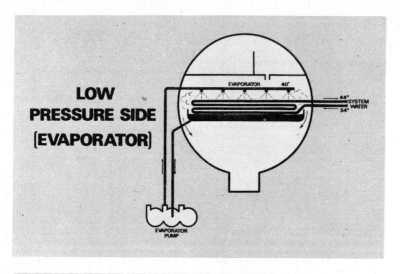

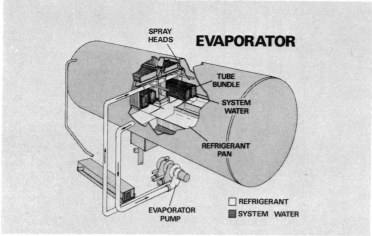

**FIGURE 13.6** Operation and construction of the evaporator. (The Trane Co., La Crosse, WI)

components are shown in Figure 13.8. The weak solution from the absorber is pumped to the generator by the *solution pump*. A heat source, in this case a steam coil, heats the solution to a temperature at which the water boils off (210°F), leaving a strong solution. The weak solution is preheated in a heat exchanger (from 105 to 175°F) by the returning strong solution, which in turn is cooled to 135°F. The strong solution mixes with the weak solution at the absorber pump suction.

*The Condenser.*   Cross sectional and cut-away views of the condenser are shown in Figure 13.9. Refrigerant water vapor from the generator passes over to the condenser. A cooling water tube bundle in the condenser desuperheats and then condenses the refrigerant (at 113°F). The refrigerant collects in the condenser pan and flows through the orifice to the evaporator, flashing and cooling itself as the pressure drops. The cooling water circuit is connected in series from the absorber, en-

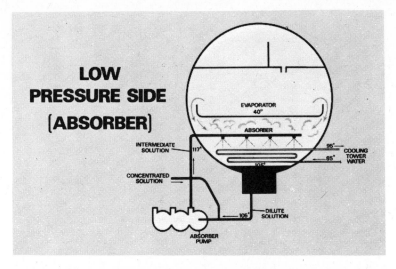

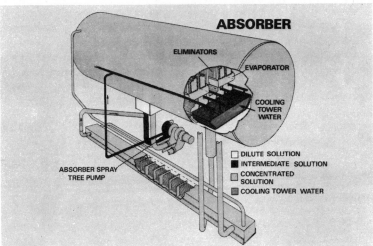

**FIGURE 13.7** Operation and construction of the absorber. (The Trane Co., La Crosse, WI)

tering at 95°F and leaving at 103°F. It then goes to the cooling tower to be recooled.

## 13.9 Capacity Control

Capacity control of lithium bromide–water absorption chillers is achieved by varying the concentration of the solution in the absorber. If the concentration is reduced, the solution has less affinity to absorb water vapor. This raises the pressure and temperature in the evaporator. The temperature difference between the system chilled water and the refrigerant therefore decreases, and the cooling capacity decreases.

Modern absorption machines use a *heat source throttling control* to modulate refrigeration capacity. A two-way throttling valve located in the steam or hot water supply line is controlled by the system leaving chilled-water

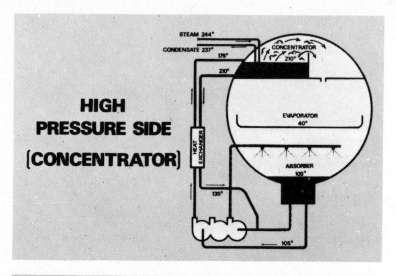

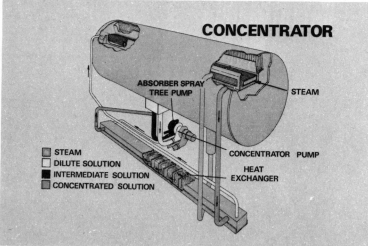

**FIGURE 13.8** Operation and construction of the concentrator. (The Trane Co., La Crosse, WI)

temperature. When the refrigeration load decreases the chilled water temperature will drop. This throttles the control valve, so less heat is supplied to the generator. Less refrigerant is boiled off, and the return solution is less concentrated. This reduces the concentration of solution pumped to the absorber, and the cooling capacity decreases, as just explained.

*Condenser water control* was previously used as a way of controlling absorption machine capacity. Throttling of condenser water flow raises condenser pressure and temperature, and less refrigerant boils off in the generator. The returning solution is therefore less concentrated, and the same effect occurs as previously explained. This method is no longer used, however. One problem with it is that the higher condensing water temperature results in increased scale formation in the tubes.

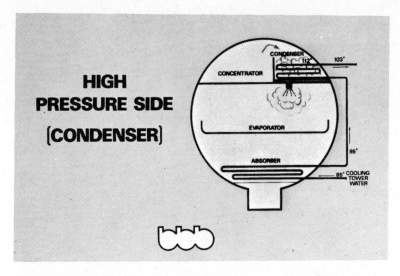

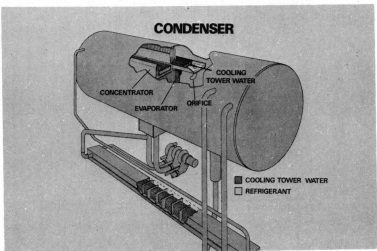

**FIGURE 13.9** Operation and construction of the condenser. (The Trane Co., La Crosse, WI)

## 13.10 Part-Load Performance and Energy Requirements

The relative energy consumption requirements of the absorption chiller are shown in Figure 13.10, for a few different entering condenser water temperatures. At 85°F, the energy requirement decreases approximately in the same proportion as the capacity.

At one time it was necessary to control con-

denser water temperature close to the design value at part load. A slight reduction in temperature could result in the solution temperature dropping to the crystallization point. In modern machines, however, the design permits condenser water temperature to vary down to about 55°F. This will usually occur naturally, since at part loads less heat is rejected to the cooling tower, and the cooling water temperature decreases. Weather condi-

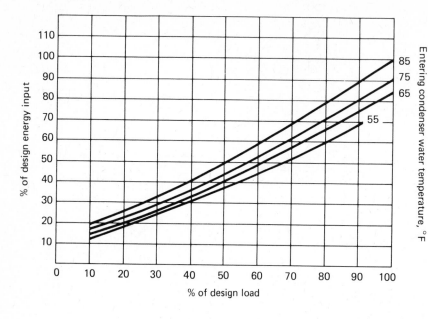

**FIGURE 13.10** Part-load performance energy requirements of a single-stage absorption chiller. (The Trane Co., La Crosse, WI)

tions generally lead to the same result. As seen from Figure 13.10, part load energy use is considerably less when condenser water temperature is allowed to drop.

A *part load economizer* arrangement (Figure 13.11) is available that reduces energy consumption at any given condenser water temperature. A throttling valve is located in the weak solution line from the absorber to the

generator. When the load drops, the valve throttles so that less solution is pumped to the generator. This reduces the heat input required and saves energy. For example, with 85°F condenser water, the energy input at 50 percent load is 40 percent of full load energy input.

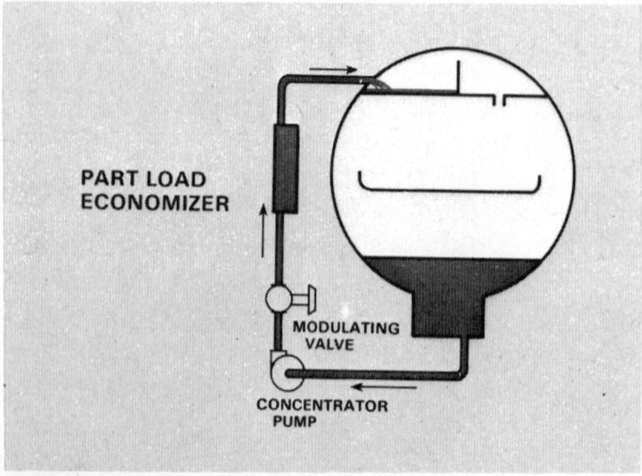

## 13.11 The Equilibrium Chart

The physical properties of absorbent–refrigerant solutions can be graphically shown on an *equilibrium chart*. One is shown for lithium bromide–water in Figure 13.12. The equilibrium chart is valuable in understanding how the cycle functions, and in checking if operating conditions are satisfactory. It is also useful in checking if crystallization may occur.

In the chart shown, the solution temperature is plotted along the horizontal axis. The vapor pressure and corresponding refrigerant saturation temperature are plotted on the vertical axis. The solution concentration is shown by the lines sloping from upper right to lower left.

**FIGURE 13.11** The part-load economizer arrangement. (The Trane Co., La Crosse, WI)

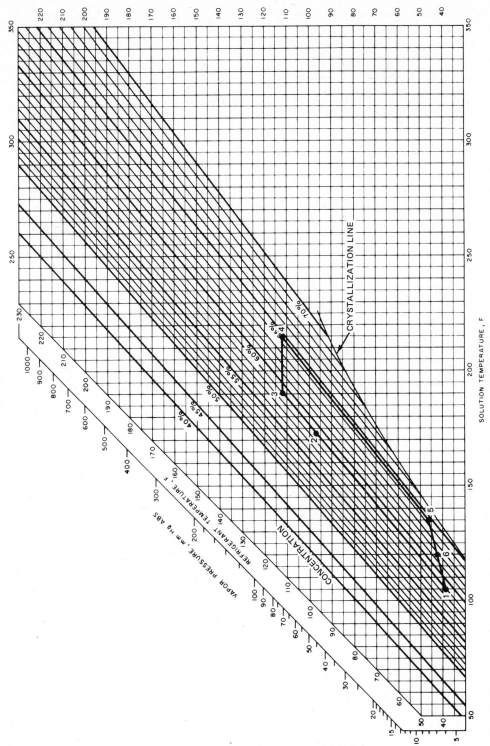

**FIGURE 13.12** The equilibrium chart for LiBr–water. A typical solution cycle is shown.

The crystallization line, the heavy sloping line at the right of the diagram, indicates the limiting conditions under which crystallization takes place. To the left of this line the solution remains all liquid. If its condition changes to a point to the right of the line, precipitation of some lithium bromide out of the solution as a solid will occur.

The solution cycle for a set of typical conditions is shown in Figure 13.12 by the lines 1–2–3–4–5–6–1. This shows the changes in temperature and concentration of the solution as it circulates between the absorber and generator.

The evaporating temperature in the example is 40°F. This establishes the vapor pressure in the evaporator and absorber at 6 mm $Hg_a$ (0.25 in. $Hg_a$). The weak solution, at 59 percent concentration and 105°F, leaves the absorber at point 1.

Line 1–2 is the temperature increase in the heat exchanger, and 2–3 is the further sensible heat increase in the generator (no change in concentration). Point 3 is determined by the conditions in the condenser. In this example it is assumed that the cooling water results in the refrigerant condensing at 112°F. The corresponding saturation pressure is 70 mm $Hg_a$ (6.0 in. $Hg_a$). This is the pressure in the condenser and generator.

Line 3–4 represents the increase in concentration in the generator as the refrigerant boils off. For the example shown, the solution is heated to 215°F and a strong concentration of 64 percent.

Line 4–5 represents the cooling of the strong solution in the heat exchanger, to 135°F.

Line 5–6 represents the mixing of strong and weak solution to make the intermediate solution at 62 percent.

The intermediate solution is pumped into the absorber. Line 6–1 represents the dilution of the solution as it absorbs the refrigerant vapor.

## 13.12 Crystallization Problems

As the equilibrium chart shows, if a highly concentrated solution is cooled, the new condition may be beyond the crystallization line, resulting in formation of solids and loss of refrigeration.

***Example 13.1*** In the operating cycle shown in Figure 13.5, the solution is concentrated to 67 percent instead of 65 percent in the generator. Will crystallization occur?

*Solution* Point 5 is now as shown in Figure 13.13. Following a new line 4–5 as the strong solution is cooled in the heat exchanger, it crosses the crystallization line at about 167°F. Since the solution is cooled to 135°F in the heat exchanger, crystallization will occur, the heat exchanger tubes will be blocked, and the machine will stop functioning.

The design and controls in modern absorption machines generally prevent crystallization occurring in the way described in this example. However, there are sometimes other unexpected problems that should be understood. Three possible causes of crystallization are:

1. Air in the machine.
2. Low condensing water temperature.
3. Electric power loss.

If air leaks into the machine, the evaporator pressure and therefore temperature increases. This reduces the refrigeration capacity. The controls respond by increasing the heat input, which raises the solution concentration. As seen in the example, subsequent cooling may lead to crystallization. Routine purging of air is carried out in absorption machine operation, which should prevent this problem.

If condensing water temperature drops ex-

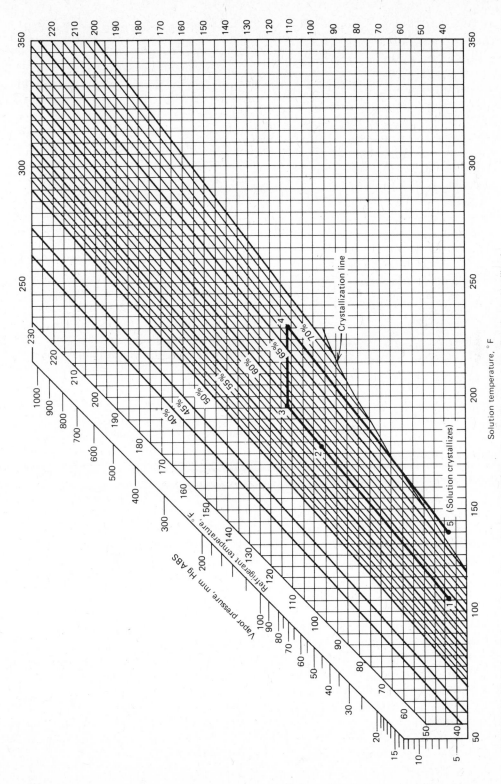

**FIGURE 13.13** The solution cycle for Example 13.1 plotted on the equilibrium chart, showing crystallization.

279

tremely low, it is possible that the weak solution to the heat exchanger could be cold enough to cool the strong solution below the crystallization temperature.

If an unexpected power loss occurs when load is high (at high load there is a highly concentrated strong solution), the solution may cool below its crystallization temperature.

There are methods available both for preventing crystallization and for decrystallizing the system, if it occurs. Prevention of crystallization can be achieved by a device that senses concentration level, and, in response to excess concentration, opens a valve that mixes dilute solution with the concentrated solution. Decrystallization can be achieved by sending hot solution through the heat exchanger, so that the crystallized cool solution in the other circuit is heated above its crystallization temperature.

An automatic dilution cycle is normally part of the absorption machine operation controls. The pumps operate for a few minutes after the machine shuts down, mixing the solution so that concentrated solution does not remain in any location.

## 13.13 Purging

Air or other noncondensable gases must not be allowed to leak into the absorption machine. Special attention must be paid to this problem, since the extremely low pressures in the lithium bromide machine enhance the possibility of air leakage inward. During manufacture, air is completely removed and the machine is sealed. All pumps are hermetic to prevent leakage through seals. Regular purging is still required during operation, however. Air in the system will reduce refrigeration capacity and promote crystallization. Purging may be done manually at intervals or continually by automatic means. Devices used are either mechanical vacuum pumps or jet pumps.

## 13.14 Performance and Application

The lithium bromide–water absorption chiller that we have been describing is called a *single-stage* or *single effect* machine, referring to the fact that the refrigerant is boiled off a single time in the generator.

The energy use efficiency of the single-effect absorption machine is quite poor. This machine is designed to operate with low pressure steam at about 12 psig (244°F saturation temperature) or hot water at 270°F. At these conditions the energy input requirement at full load is about 17,000 to 18,000 Btu/hr per ton of refrigeration produced, for typical chilled water and cooling water temperatures. The corresponding coefficient of performance (COP) is quite low, about 0.65 to 0.70. This compares to a COP of about 3 to 4 for a vapor compression machine water chiller. That is, the absorption machine requires about five to six times as much energy!

The situation is not as one sided as this when the energy source for the electric driven compressor is considered. Only about one third of the heat energy in the fuel in the power plant is converted into electricity. Actually, the absorption machine uses about twice as much of the amount of heat energy in the original fuel as the compressor driven machine.

This still would make the absorption machine noncompetitive, except for other practical factors. Particularly in industrial applications, there often is a source of otherwise wasted low pressure steam or hot combustion gases. This energy can be considered to be available at no cost.

Aside from this, the single-effect absorption machine has been used in the past despite its energy inefficiency because of certain conveniences. Its noise and vibration level are lower than equipment using compressors, and it therefore is desirable when located on upper floors of buildings. Also, it is a low pressure steam operated machine; in some localities this means that the people who operate it do not require the special licenses that may be required with other types of equipment.

Despite these considerations, there are fewer applications today, with high energy costs, where the single-stage absorption machine is competitive. More attractive, however, is the *two-stage,* or *double effect* machine, which is more energy efficient.

## 13.15 The Two-Stage Absorption Machine

The basic absorption principle is the same in the two-stage machine as has been described previously; and the equipment is similar, except that the refrigerant is boiled off in two stages in two generators (concentrators).

The two-stage (or double effect) absorption machine uses about 30 to 40 percent less energy than the single-stage machine. Less heat is rejected to the cooling water, resulting in a smaller cooling tower. The machine described in this section uses steam at about 150 psig or hot water at 400°F.

A cross-sectional view of the generators is shown in Figure 13.14. The high pressure steam heat source (at about 150 psig) boils off some of the refrigerant vapor from the dilute solution entering the first-stage generator, at about 320°F. The vapor, at about 5 psig (20 psia), then flows to a coil in the second-stage generator. The partially concentrated solution from the first-stage generator flows to the second-stage generator after passing through a high temperature exchanger. The dilute solution flows through the other circuit of this heat exchanger before entering the first-stage generator, and is thus preheated (to about 270°F).

The refrigerant vapor in the second-stage generator coil boils off refrigerant vapor at about 208°F from the entering partially concentrated solution. The resulting concentrated solution flows back to the absorber through a low temperature heat exchanger, as it does in the single stage machine.

A view of the complete two-stage arrangement is shown in Figure 13.15. Note that the first-stage generator is in a separate shell, and that the components in the second shell are similar to those of the one-stage machine.

## 13.16 The Direct Fired Two-Stage Absorption Machine

Large absorption water chillers are also available that use the combustion of natural gas or

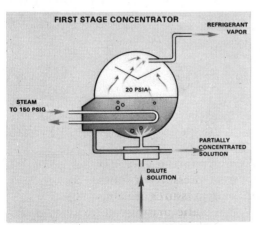
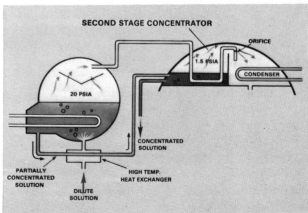

**FIGURE 13.14** Operation of the two-stage concentrator. (The Trane Co., La Crosse, WI)

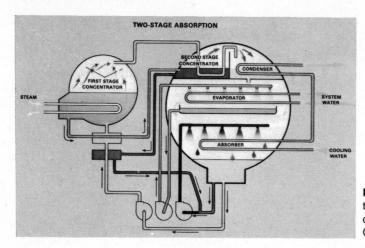

**FIGURE 13.15** Arrangement of the two-stage absorption chiller. (The Trane Co., La Crosse, WI)

No. 2 fuel oil as the heat source (Figure 13.16). The cycle is identical to that described for the steam or hot water fired machine, and the component arrangements are similar. The energy efficiencies are also approximately equal.

This machine is manufactured as a combination water chiller and heater. During the heating cycle the first-stage generator serves as a gas or oil fired steam heating boiler. The refrigerant vapor flows to a space heating system hot water heat exchanger and a domestic hot water heat exchanger, where it gives up its latent heat and condenses.

The direct fired two-stage absorption chiller–heater is a viable competitor where gas or oil are available and both cooling and heating are needed. Initial costs may be less then for purchasing separate cooling and heating equipment, and space requirements usually are much less. There is also an exhaust gas heat recovery version of this machine. Wherever otherwise wasted hot combustion gases are available, this machine can be a very useful energy conservation measure.

### 13.17 Small Capacity Lithium Bromide Absorption Chillers

Absorption refrigeration water chillers are also made in small units, ranging from about 3 to 25 tons capacity (Figure 13.17). These units operate on the same absorption principle as described previously, with evaporator, absorber, generator, and condenser. They are made for a steam heat source or direct fired use.

The unit shown in Figure 13.17 has a direct fired generator. The solution flows from the generator to a separator. Here the refrigerant vapor separates from the concentrated solution and flows to the condenser, and the solution flows back to the absorber. In some units flow is accomplished by slight differences in density and pressure in the system, so that pumps are not required.

### 13.18 The Water–Ammonia Absorption System

In the water–ammonia absorption refrigeration cycle, ammonia is the refrigerant, and water is the absorbent. The system operates at high pressures. For example if the evaporating temperature is 38°F, the corresponding saturation pressure of ammonia is 59 psig. High-side pressures are about 300 psig.

A schematic arrangement of a water–ammonia absorption system is shown in Figure 13.18. Liquid ammonia from the condenser at high pressure flashes to the low

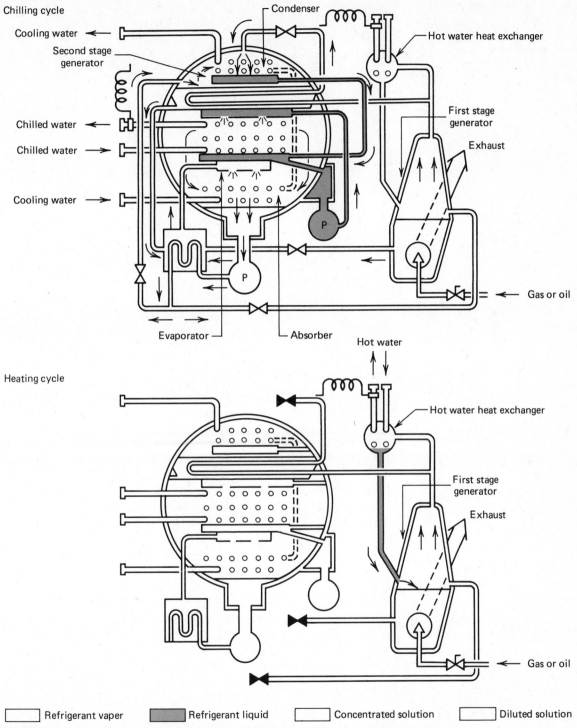

**Chilling cycle**

Cooling water ←

Second stage generator

Condenser

Hot water heat exchanger

Chilled water ←

Chilled water →

First stage generator

Exhaust

Cooling water →

P

P

Gas or oil

Evaporator

Absorber

**Heating cycle**

Hot water

Hot water heat exchanger

First stage generator

Exhaust

Gas or oil

☐ Refrigerant vaper  ▣ Refrigerant liquid  ☐ Concentrated solution  ☐ Diluted solution

**FIGURE 13.16** The direct fired two-stage combination absorption chiller and heater. (Gas Energy Inc.)

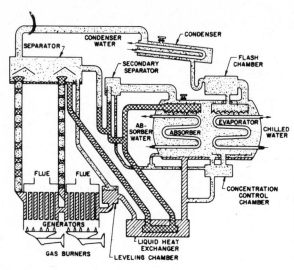

**FIGURE 13.17** Small capacity direct fired LiBr–water absorption chiller. (Reprinted with permission from the 1979 Equipment ASHRAE Handbook & Product Directory)

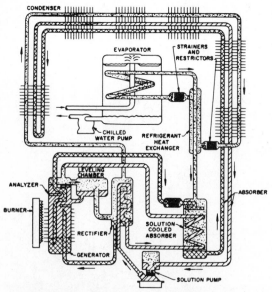

**FIGURE 13.18** Arrangement of a water–ammonia absorption water chiller. (Reprinted with permission from the 1979 Equipment ASHRAE Handbook & Product Directory)

pressure and temperature in the evaporator. The refrigerant evaporates as it gains heat from the load. The solution in the absorber absorbs the ammonia vapor, maintaining the low evaporator pressure. A heat exchanger is provided between the absorber and generator.

Thus far the system is identical to the lithium bromide–water system. However, when the weak water–ammonia solution is heated in the generator some of the water will boil off with the ammonia, since both fluids are volatile. The water must be separated so that it does not flow with the refrigerant to the condenser and evaporator. If this occurred, refrigeration capacity would be reduced, since the water would not evaporate at the evaporator conditions.

The water vapor that is present with the ammonia vapor leaving the generator is removed in two steps, by two devices, called the *analyzer* and the *rectifier*. The analyzer is a heat exchanger mounted in the generator. Cool solution from the absorber flows through the analyzer, cooling the leaving water vapor–ammonia vapor mixture. This condenses some of the water vapor.

The vapor leaving the generator then flows to another heat exchanger, the rectifier. Here the vapor mixture is cooled with cooling water, which condenses any remaining water vapor. The water is then returned to the generator, and the refrigerant flows to the condenser.

## 13.19 Energy Conservation

The absorption machine uses considerably more energy per unit of refrigeration produced than compressor driven units. The performance can be improved considerably by using two-stage absorption machines, but usually the advantage is still in favor of the compressor unit. When waste heat is available, however, the absorption machine is very practical, since no new energy is being used. For the same reason, the use of solar energy should be considered as an alternative heat source for absorption machines.

Energy consumption is reduced at part loads by allowing cooling water temperature to drop, except that it must not fall so low that crystallization occurs.

A part load economizer arrangement, which reduces solution flow rate, will improve energy efficiency significantly.

Regular purging of air from the machine is required to prevent loss of capacity.

## REVIEW QUESTIONS

1. How is refrigeration achieved in an absorption system?

2. What type of energy sources are particularly suited for use with absorption machines?

3. What is an absorption process?

4. What pairs of substances have been found practical for absorption systems? Which are used in absorption machines for air conditioning? Which one is the refrigerant?

5. Explain what is meant by a concentrated and a dilute solution.

6. What are the four basic components of an absorption machine?

7. Describe the action in the evaporator and absorber.

8. Describe the action in the generator and condenser.

9. How is expansion from high to low pressure achieved?

10. What is the function of the heat exchanger? Sketch its circuiting.

11. Sketch the cooling water circuit. What are sources of heat in the absorber?

12. What are desirable and undesirable features of lithium bromide–water and water–ammonia for absorption refrigeration?

13. What is crystallization? What effect can it have?

14. What pumps are used in large lithium bromide machines?

15. Why is an intermediate concentration solution used in the absorber?

16. Describe how refrigeration capacity is controlled in the absorption chiller.

17. Describe the action of a part load economizer.

18. What is the equilibrium chart? What purpose can it be used for?

19. What are the possible causes of crystallization? How can it be controlled?

20. What is a two-stage absorption machine? Why is it used? What is the advantage of a direct fired two-stage machine?

21. What problem exists in using water–ammonia in the absorption refrigeration cycle? How is this resolved?

# Chapter 14

## THE REFRIGERATION LOAD. COMPONENT BALANCING

This chapter explains the procedures for calculating the refrigeration load. Both detailed calculations and a simplified method often used in refrigeration are covered. How the refrigeration load is used to select the refrigeration equipment, and matching and balancing of equipment components are also discussed.

## OBJECTIVES

A study of this chapter will enable you to:
1. Calculate the refrigeration load for a given application.
2. Select unit coolers.
3. Find the balance condition for refrigeration system components.

## 14.1 The Refrigeration Load

*The **refrigeration load** is the rate of heat removal from the refrigerated space required to keep the space or product at the conditions desired.*

The load is a result of heat gains from a number of possible sources, which may be classified conveniently into the following categories:

1. Heat transmission through walls, floors, and ceiling or roof.
2. Heat from warm air infiltration through refrigerator doors.
3. Heat from the product to be refrigerated.
4. Internal source heat gains other than the products. This usually includes heat from people, lights, and motors.

## 14.2 Heat Transmission

The heat transmission gain to the refrigerated space is a result of conduction and convection through the enclosing surfaces as a result of a temperature difference. It is calculated from the heat transfer equation (6.5), discussed in Chapter 6.

For convenience in refrigeration load calculations, however, the heat transmission gains from Equation 6.5 have been calculated for various temperatures and heat transfer coefficients, and presented in Table 14.1.

The heat gains in Table 14.1 are presented in Btu per square foot of outside surface, per 24 hour period. To find the total heat transmission gain through any surface (walls, ceiling, or floor), multiply the heat gain per square foot by its area. The gains are listed for 24 hours rather than 1 hour because this simplifies equipment selection, as explained later. The thermal conductivity $k$ of different insulating materials used in the walls is shown in the notes following the table. Recommended minimum insulation thicknesses are shown in Table 14.2.

The heat gains shown do not include any effect of solar radiation (sun effect), which will be discussed later.

*Example 14.1*  A walk-in refrigerator has outside dimensions of 10 ft width × 12 ft

## TABLE 14.1 Heat Transmission Gains (Btu/ft² per 24 hours)[a]

| Thickness, Inches | k Factor[c] | 1 | 10 | 20 | 30 | 40 | 45 | 50 | 55 | 60 | 65 | 70 | 75 | 80 | 85 | 90 | 95 | 100 | 105 | 110 | 115 | 120 | 125 |
|---|---|---|---|---|---|---|---|---|---|---|---|---|---|---|---|---|---|---|---|---|---|---|---|
| 1 | 0.30 | 7.2 | 72 | 144 | 216 | 288 | 324 | | | | | | | | | | | | | | | | |
| | 0.25 | 6.0 | 60 | 120 | 180 | 240 | 270 | 300 | 330 | | | | | | | | | | | | | | |
| | 0.20 | 4.8 | 48 | 96 | 144 | 192 | 216 | 240 | 264 | 288 | 312 | | | | | | | | | | | | |
| | 0.16 | 3.84 | 38 | 77 | 115 | 154 | 173 | 192 | 211 | 230 | 250 | 269 | 288 | 307 | | | | | | | | | |
| | 0.14 | 3.36 | 34 | 67 | 101 | 134 | 151 | 168 | 185 | 202 | 218 | 235 | 252 | 269 | 286 | 302 | | | | | | | |
| 2 | 0.30 | 3.6 | 36 | 72 | 108 | 144 | 162 | 180 | 198 | 216 | 234 | 252 | 270 | 288 | 306 | | | | | | | | |
| | 0.25 | 3.0 | 30 | 60 | 90 | 120 | 135 | 150 | 165 | 180 | 195 | 210 | 225 | 240 | 255 | 270 | 285 | 300 | | | | | |
| | 0.20 | 2.4 | 24 | 48 | 72 | 96 | 108 | 120 | 132 | 144 | 156 | 168 | 180 | 192 | 204 | 216 | 228 | 240 | 252 | 264 | 276 | 288 | 300 |
| | 0.16 | 1.92 | 19 | 38 | 58 | 77 | 86 | 96 | 106 | 115 | 125 | 134 | 144 | 154 | 163 | 173 | 182 | 192 | 202 | 211 | 221 | 230 | 240 |
| | 0.14 | 1.68 | 17 | 34 | 50 | 67 | 76 | 84 | 92 | 101 | 109 | 118 | 126 | 134 | 143 | 151 | 160 | 168 | 176 | 185 | 193 | 202 | 210 |
| 3 | 0.30 | 2.4 | 24 | 48 | 72 | 96 | 108 | 120 | 132 | 144 | 156 | 168 | 180 | 192 | 204 | 216 | 228 | 240 | 252 | 264 | 276 | 288 | 300 |
| | 0.25 | 2.0 | 20 | 40 | 60 | 80 | 90 | 100 | 110 | 120 | 130 | 140 | 150 | 160 | 170 | 180 | 190 | 200 | 210 | 220 | 230 | 240 | 250 |
| | 0.20 | 1.6 | 16 | 32 | 48 | 64 | 72 | 80 | 88 | 96 | 104 | 112 | 120 | 128 | 136 | 144 | 152 | 160 | 168 | 176 | 184 | 192 | 200 |
| | 0.16 | 1.28 | 13 | 26 | 38 | 51 | 58 | 64 | 70 | 77 | 83 | 90 | 96 | 102 | 109 | 115 | 122 | 128 | 134 | 141 | 147 | 154 | 160 |
| | 0.14 | 1.13 | 11 | 23 | 34 | 45 | 50 | 56 | 62 | 67 | 73 | 78 | 84 | 90 | 95 | 101 | 106 | 112 | 118 | 123 | 129 | 134 | 140 |
| 4 | 0.30 | 1.8 | 18 | 36 | 54 | 72 | 81 | 90 | 99 | 108 | 117 | 126 | 135 | 144 | 153 | 162 | 171 | 180 | 189 | 198 | 207 | 216 | 225 |
| | 0.25 | 1.5 | 15 | 30 | 45 | 60 | 68 | 75 | 83 | 90 | 98 | 105 | 113 | 120 | 128 | 135 | 143 | 150 | 158 | 165 | 173 | 180 | 188 |
| | 0.20 | 1.2 | 12 | 24 | 36 | 48 | 54 | 60 | 66 | 72 | 78 | 84 | 90 | 96 | 102 | 108 | 114 | 120 | 126 | 132 | 138 | 144 | 150 |
| | 0.16 | 0.96 | 10 | 19 | 29 | 38 | 43 | 48 | 53 | 58 | 62 | 68 | 72 | 77 | 82 | 87 | 91 | 96 | 101 | 106 | 111 | 115 | 120 |
| | 0.14 | 0.84 | 9 | 17 | 25 | 34 | 38 | 42 | 46 | 50 | 55 | 59 | 63 | 68 | 71 | 75 | 80 | 84 | 88 | 92 | 97 | 101 | 105 |
| 5 | 0.30 | 1.44 | 14 | 29 | 42 | 58 | 65 | 72 | 79 | 87 | 94 | 101 | 108 | 115 | 122 | 130 | 137 | 144 | 151 | 159 | 166 | 172 | 180 |
| | 0.25 | 1.2 | 12 | 24 | 36 | 48 | 54 | 60 | 66 | 72 | 78 | 84 | 90 | 96 | 102 | 108 | 114 | 120 | 126 | 132 | 138 | 144 | 150 |
| | 0.20 | 0.96 | 10 | 19 | 29 | 38 | 43 | 48 | 53 | 58 | 62 | 67 | 72 | 77 | 82 | 87 | 91 | 96 | 101 | 106 | 110 | 115 | 120 |
| | 0.16 | 0.76 | 8 | 15 | 23 | 31 | 35 | 38 | 42 | 46 | 50 | 54 | 58 | 61 | 65 | 69 | 73 | 77 | 81 | 84 | 88 | 92 | 96 |
| | 0.14 | 0.67 | 7 | 13 | 20* | 27 | 30 | 34 | 37 | 40 | 44 | 47 | 50 | 54 | 57 | 60 | 64 | 67 | 71 | 74 | 77 | 81 | 84 |
| 6 | 0.30 | 1.2 | 12 | 24 | 36 | 48 | 54 | 60 | 66 | 72 | 78 | 84 | 90 | 96 | 102 | 108 | 114 | 120 | 126 | 132 | 138 | 144 | 160 |
| | 0.25 | 1.0 | 10 | 20 | 30 | 40 | 45 | 50 | 55 | 60 | 65 | 70 | 75 | 80 | 85 | 90 | 95 | 100 | 105 | 110 | 115 | 120 | 125 |
| | 0.20 | 0.8 | 8 | 16 | 24 | 32 | 36 | 40 | 44 | 48 | 52 | 56 | 60 | 64 | 68 | 72 | 76 | 80 | 84 | 88 | 92 | 96 | 100 |
| | 0.16 | 0.64 | 6 | 13 | 19 | 26 | 29 | 32 | 35 | 38 | 42 | 45 | 48 | 51 | 54 | 58 | 61 | 64 | 67 | 70 | 74 | 77 | 80 |
| | 0.14 | 0.56 | 6 | 11 | 17 | 22 | 25 | 28 | 31 | 34 | 36 | 39 | 42 | 45 | 48 | 50 | 53 | 56 | 59 | 62 | 64 | 67 | 70 |
| 7 | 0.30 | 1.02 | 10 | 20 | 30 | 41 | 46 | 52 | 57 | 62 | 67 | 72 | 77 | 82 | 88 | 93 | 98 | 103 | 108 | 113 | 118 | 124 | 129 |
| | 0.25 | 0.85 | 9 | 17 | 26 | 34 | 39 | 43 | 47 | 51 | 56 | 60 | 64 | 68 | 73 | 77 | 81 | 86 | 90 | 94 | 99 | 103 | 107 |
| | 0.20 | 0.68 | 7 | 14 | 21 | 27 | 31 | 34 | 38 | 41 | 45 | 48 | 51 | 55 | 58 | 62 | 65 | 69 | 72 | 75 | 79 | 82 | 86 |
| 8 | 0.30 | 0.90 | 9 | 18 | 27 | 36 | 41 | 45 | 50 | 54 | 59 | 63 | 68 | 72 | 77 | 81 | 86 | 90 | 95 | 99 | 104 | 108 | 113 |
| | 0.25 | 0.75 | 8 | 15 | 23 | 30 | 34 | 38 | 41 | 45 | 49 | 53 | 56 | 60 | 64 | 68 | 71 | 75 | 79 | 83 | 86 | 90 | 94 |
| | 0.20 | 0.60 | 6 | 12 | 18 | 24 | 27 | 30 | 33 | 36 | 39 | 42 | 45 | 48 | 51 | 54 | 57 | 60 | 63 | 66 | 69 | 72 | 75 |
| 9 | 0.30 | 0.80 | 8 | 16 | 24 | 32 | 36 | 40 | 44 | 48 | 52 | 56 | 60 | 64 | 68 | 72 | 76 | 80 | 84 | 88 | 92 | 96 | 100 |
| | 0.25 | 0.67 | 7 | 13 | 20 | 27 | 30 | 34 | 37 | 40 | 44 | 47 | 50 | 54 | 57 | 60 | 64 | 67 | 70 | 74 | 77 | 80 | 84 |
| 10 | 0.30 | 0.72 | 7 | 14 | 21 | 29 | 32 | 36 | 40 | 43 | 47 | 50 | 54 | 58 | 61 | 65 | 68 | 72 | 76 | 79 | 83 | 86 | 90 |
| | 0.25 | 0.60 | 6 | 12 | 18 | 24 | 27 | 30 | 33 | 36 | 39 | 42 | 45 | 48 | 51 | 54 | 57 | 60 | 63 | 66 | 69 | 72 | 75 |
| 11 | 0.30 | 0.65 | 6.5 | 13 | 19.5 | 26 | 30 | 33 | 36 | 40 | 43 | 46 | 50 | 53 | 56 | 60 | 63 | 66 | 69 | 73 | 76 | 79 | 82 |
| | 0.25 | 0.55 | 5.5 | 11 | 17 | 22 | 25 | 28 | 30 | 33 | 36 | 39 | 41 | 44 | 47 | 50 | 52 | 55 | 58 | 61 | 63 | 66 | 69 |
| 12 | 0.30 | 0.60 | 6 | 12 | 18 | 24 | 27 | 30 | 33 | 36 | 39 | 42 | 45 | 48 | 51 | 54 | 57 | 60 | 63 | 66 | 69 | 72 | 75 |
| | 0.25 | 0.50 | 5 | 10 | 15 | 20 | 23 | 25 | 28 | 30 | 33 | 35 | 38 | 40 | 43 | 45 | 48 | 50 | 53 | 55 | 58 | 60 | 63 |
| Single glass | | 27 | 270 | 540 | 810 | 1080 | 1220 | 1350 | 1490 | 1620 | | | | | | | | | | | | | |
| Double glass | | 11 | 110 | 220 | 330 | 440 | 500 | 500 | 610 | 660 | 715 | 770 | 825 | 880 | 936 | 990 | 1050 | 1100 | 1160 | 1210 | 1270 | 1320 | 1375 |
| Triple glass | | 7 | 70 | 140 | 210 | 280 | 320 | 350 | 390 | 420 | 454 | 490 | 525 | 560 | 595 | 630 | 665 | 700 | 740 | 770 | 810 | 840 | 875 |
| Floor under 144 sq. ft. | | 6 | 60 | 120 | 180 | 240 | 270 | | | | | | | | | | | | | | | | |
| Floor over 144 sq. ft. | | 4.5 | 45 | 90 | 135 | 180 | 203 | | | | | | | | | | | | | | | | |

[a]For 6 or 8 inch concrete floor on the ground, not insulated use the TD between the average summer ground temperature and box temperature. (Note: Not for freezers or for coolers operated close to freezing. Insulated floors recommended for all coolers and freezers (use insulation thickness and TD room to slab temperature).

[b]Insulation *k = 0.30, corkboard, mineral wool
    k = 0.25, fiberglass styrofoam, expanded polystyrene
    k = 0.20, molded polystyrene
    k = 0.16, sprayed urethane, foam urethane sheets, slabs, and panels
    k = 0.14, urethane panels (foamed in place).

[c]k factor in Btu/Hr.Ft.²/°F/in.

Courtesy Dunham–Bush, Inc.

**TABLE 14.2** Recommended Minimum Insulation Thicknesses

| Storage Temperature °F | Cork or Equivalent Thickness (Inches) | |
|---|---|---|
| | Northern United States | Southern United States |
| 15 to 60 | 2 | 3 |
| 40 to 50 | 3 | 4 |
| 25 to 40 | 4 | 5 |
| 15 to 25 | 5 | 6 |
| 0 to 15 | 6 | 7 |
| 0 to −15 | 7 | 8 |
| −15 to −40 | 9 | 10 |

Courtesy Dunham–Bush, Inc.

**TABLE 14.3** Allowance for Sun Effect[a]

| Type of Surface | East Wall | South Wall | West Wall | Flat Roof |
|---|---|---|---|---|
| Dark colored surfaces such as: <br> Slate roofing <br> Tar roofing <br> Black paints | 8 | 5 | 8 | 20 |
| Medium colored surfaces, such as: <br> Unpainted wood <br> Brick <br> Red tile <br> Dark cement <br> Red, gray, or green paint | 6 | 4 | 6 | 15 |
| Light colored surfaces, such as: <br> White stone <br> Light colored cement <br> White paint | 4 | 2 | 4 | 9 |

[a]Farenheit degrees to be added to the normal temperature difference for heat leakage calculations to compensate for sun effect—not to be used for air conditioning design.
Courtesy Dunham–Bush, Inc.

length × 8 ft height. The temperature difference between the outside and the refrigerator is 60°F. The walls and ceiling are insulated with 4 in. of molded polystyrene. What is the 24-hour heat gain through walls and ceiling? There is no sun effect.

*Solution* Table 14.1 shows that molded polystyrene has a thermal conductivity $k = 0.20$. The heat gain is listed as 72 Btu per square ft per 24 hours. The total area of walls and ceiling is

$$2 (10 \times 8) + 2 (12 \times 8)$$
$$+ 10 \times 12 = 472 \text{ ft}^2$$

The heat gain is

$$Q = 72 \text{ Btu/ft}^2 \text{ per 24 hr} \times 472 \text{ ft}^2$$
$$= 33,980 \text{ Btu per 24 hr}$$

If the walls or roof are exposed to the sun, a correction to the actual temperature difference must be made, using Table 14.3. This accounts for the increased heat transmission from the solar heat gain.

***Example 14.2*** The roof of a refrigerated room is exposed to the sun. The actual temperature difference between the outside and the room is 70°F. The roof is painted green.

What temperature difference should be used for Table 14.1 in calculating the roof heat transmission?

*Solution* From Table 14.3, the roof surface falls in the medium color class, and the temperature correction for the sun effect is 15°F. The corrected temperature difference is therefore 70 + 15 = 85°F.

Table 14.1 also lists heat gains for glass refrigerator doors.

For refrigerator room floors that are insulated concrete slabs on the ground, Table 14.1 can be used, but the exterior temperature is the summer ground temperature, unless the floor slab is heated. For freezer rooms the ground slab is often heated to prevent freezing of ground water (expansion of the ice might heave and break the concrete slab). When the floor is heated, a ground temperature of 55°F should be used. Uninsulated floor slabs are not recommended.

Table 14.4 lists outdoor conditions recommended for refrigeration calculations.

***Example 14.3*** An unheated floor slab on the ground has 3 in. of corkboard insulation. The

**TABLE 14.4** Outdoor Design Conditions for Refrigeration[a]

| | | Summer | | Winter | |
| | | Dry Bulb °F | Wet Bulb °F | Dry Bulb °F | Eleva-tion Ft. |
|---|---|---|---|---|---|
| State | City | | | | |
| Alabama | Birmingham | 97 | 79 | 19 | 610 |
| | Mobile | 96 | 80 | 26 | 211 |
| Alaska | Fairbanks | 82 | 64 | −53 | 436 |
| | Juneau | 75 | 66 | − 7 | 17 |
| Arizona | Phoenix | 108 | 77 | 31 | 1117 |
| | Tucson | 105 | 74 | 29 | 2584 |
| Arkansas | Fort Smith | 101 | 79 | 15 | 449 |
| | Little Rock | 99 | 80 | 19 | 257 |
| California | Bakersfield | 103 | 72 | 31 | 495 |
| | Fresno | 101 | 73 | 28 | 326 |
| | Los Angeles | 94 | 72 | 42 | 312 |
| | Oakland | 85 | 65 | 35 | 3 |
| | San Francisco | 80 | 64 | 32 | 8 |
| Colorado | Denver | 92 | 65 | − 2 | 5283 |
| Connecticut | Hartford | 90 | 77 | 1 | 15 |
| | New Haven | 88 | 77 | 5 | 6 |
| Delaware | Dover | 93 | 79 | 13 | 38 |
| | Wilmington | 93 | 79 | 12 | 78 |
| District of Columbia | Washington | 94 | 78 | 15 | 14 |
| Florida | Jacksonville | 96 | 80 | 29 | 24 |
| | Key West | 90 | 80 | 55 | 6 |
| | Miami | 92 | 80 | 44 | 9 |
| | Tampa | 92 | 81 | 36 | 19 |
| Georgia | Atlanta | 95 | 78 | 15 | 1005 |
| | Savannah | 95 | 81 | 24 | 42 |
| Hawaii | Honolulu | 87 | 75 | 60 | 7 |
| Idaho | Boise | 96 | 68 | 4 | 2842 |
| Illinois | Chicago | 94 | 78 | − 3 | 594 |
| | Peoria | 94 | 78 | − 2 | 652 |
| | Springfield | 95 | 79 | − 5 | 587 |
| Indiana | Evansville | 96 | 79 | 6 | 381 |
| | Fort Wayne | 93 | 77 | 0 | 791 |
| | Indianapolis | 93 | 78 | 0 | 793 |
| | Terre Haute | 95 | 79 | 3 | 601 |
| Iowa | Des Moines | 95 | 79 | − 7 | 948 |
| | Sioux City | 96 | 79 | − 10 | 1095 |
| Kansas | Dodge City | 99 | 74 | 3 | 2594 |
| | Topeka | 99 | 79 | 3 | 877 |
| | Wichita | 103 | 77 | 5 | 1321 |
| Kentucky | Louisville | 96 | 79 | 8 | 474 |
| Louisiana | New Orleans | 93 | 81 | 32 | 3 |
| | Shreveport | 99 | 81 | 22 | 252 |
| Maine | Bangor | 88 | 75 | − 8 | 162 |
| | Portland | 88 | 75 | − 5 | 61 |
| Maryland | Baltimore | 94 | 79 | 16 | 14 |

(continued)

**TABLE 14.4** Continued

Design Temperatures, United States

| State | City | Summer Dry Bulb °F | Summer Wet Bulb °F | Winter Dry Bulb °F | Eleva-tion Ft. |
|-------|------|--------------------|--------------------|--------------------|----------------|
| Massachusetts | Boston | 91 | 76 | 6 | 15 |
| | Springfield | 86 | 74 | − 3 | 247 |
| Michigan | Detroit | 92 | 76 | 4 | 633 |
| | Grand Rapids | 91 | 76 | 2 | 601 |
| | Lansing | 89 | 76 | 2 | 652 |
| Minnesota | Duluth | 85 | 73 | − 19 | 1426 |
| | Minneapolis | 92 | 77 | − 14 | 822 |
| Mississippi | Vicksburg | 97 | 80 | 23 | 234 |
| Missouri | Kansas City | 100 | 79 | 4 | 742 |
| | St. Louis | 96 | 79 | 7 | 465 |
| Montana | Billings | 94 | 68 | − 10 | 3367 |
| | Helena | 90 | 65 | − 17 | 3893 |
| Nebraska | Lincoln | 100 | 78 | − 4 | 1150 |
| | Omaha | 97 | 79 | − 5 | 978 |
| Nevada | Reno | 95 | 64 | 12 | 4490 |
| New Hampshire | Concord | 91 | 75 | − 11 | 339 |
| New Jersey | Atlantic City | 91 | 78 | 14 | 11 |
| | Newark | 94 | 77 | 11 | 11 |
| | Trenton | 92 | 78 | 12 | 144 |
| New Mexico | Albuquerque | 96 | 66 | 14 | 5310 |
| | Sante Fe | 90 | 65 | 7 | 7045 |
| New York | Albany | 91 | 76 | 1 | 19 |
| | Buffalo | 88 | 75 | 3 | 705 |
| | New York | 93 | 77 | 11 | 132 |
| North Carolina | Asheville | 91 | 75 | 13 | 2770 |
| | Charlotte | 96 | 78 | 18 | 735 |
| | Raleigh | 95 | 79 | 16 | 433 |
| | Wilmington | 93 | 52 | 23 | 30 |
| North Dakota | Bismarck | 95 | 74 | − 24 | 1647 |
| Ohio | Cincinnati | 94 | 78 | 8 | 761 |
| | Cleveland | 91 | 76 | 2 | 777 |
| | Columbus | 92 | 77 | 2 | 212 |
| | Dayton | 92 | 77 | 0 | 997 |
| | Toledo | 92 | 72 | 0 | 900 |
| Oklahoma | Oklahoma City | 102 | 78 | 11 | 1280 |
| | Tulsa | 102 | 79 | 12 | 650 |
| Oregon | Portland | 91 | 69 | 26 | 57 |
| Pennsylvania | Erie | 88 | 76 | 7 | 732 |
| | Philadelphia | 93 | 78 | 11 | 7 |
| | Pittsburg | 90 | 75 | 7 | 749 |
| | Scranton | 89 | 75 | 2 | 940 |
| Rhode Island | Providence | 89 | 76 | 6 | 55 |
| South Carolina | Charleston | 95 | 81 | 26 | 9 |
| | Greenville | 95 | 77 | 19 | 957 |
| South Dakota | Huron | 97 | 77 | − 16 | 1282 |
| | Rapid City | 96 | 72 | − 9 | 3165 |
| | Sioux Falls | 95 | 77 | − 14 | 1430 |

**TABLE 14.4** Continued

Design Temperatures, United States

| State | City | Summer Dry Bulb °F | Summer Wet Bulb °F | Winter Dry Bulb °F | Elevation Ft. |
|-------|------|-----------|-----------|-----------|-----------|
| Tennessee | Chattanooga | 97 | 78 | 75 | 670 |
| | Knoxville | 95 | 77 | 13 | 980 |
| | Memphis | 98 | 80 | 17 | 263 |
| | Nashville | 97 | 79 | 12 | 577 |
| Texas | Amarillo | 98 | 72 | 8 | 3607 |
| | Corpus Christi | 95 | 32 | 32 | 43 |
| | Dallas | 101 | 79 | 19 | 481 |
| | El Paso | 100 | 70 | 21 | 3918 |
| | Galveston | 91 | 32 | 32 | 5 |
| | Houston | 96 | 80 | 29 | 158 |
| | San Antonio | 99 | 77 | 25 | 792 |
| Utah | Salt Lake City | 97 | 67 | 5 | 4220 |
| Vermont | Burlington | 88 | 74 | −12 | 331 |
| Virginia | Norfolk | 94 | 79 | 20 | 26 |
| | Richmond | 96 | 79 | 14 | 152 |
| | Roanoke | 94 | 76 | 15 | 1174 |
| Washington | Seattle | 81 | 69 | 28 | 14 |
| | Spokane | 93 | 66 | −2 | 2357 |
| West Virginia | Charleston | 92 | 76 | 9 | 939 |
| | Parkersburg | 93 | 77 | 8 | 615 |
| Wisconsin | Green Bay | 88 | 75 | −12 | 683 |
| | Madison | 92 | 77 | −9 | 858 |
| | Milwaukee | 90 | 77 | −5 | 672 |
| Wyoming | Cheyenne | 89 | 63 | −6 | 6128 |

Design Temperatures, Canada

| Province | Station City | Summer Dry Bulb °F | Summer Wet Bulb °F | Winter Dry Bulb °F | Elevation Ft. |
|----------|--------------|-----------|-----------|-----------|-----------|
| Alberta | Calgary | 87 | 66 | −29 | 3540 |
| British Columbia | Vancouver | 80 | 68 | 15 | 60 |
| Manitoba | Winnipeg | 90 | 78 | −28 | 786 |
| Newfoundland | Gander | 85 | 69 | −5 | 482 |
| Northwest Territories | Fort Smith | 85 | 67 | −49 | 665 |
| Nova Scotia | Halifax | 83 | 69 | 0 | 136 |
| Ontario | Toronto | 90 | 77 | −3 | 578 |
| Prince Edward Island | Charlottetown | 84 | 71 | −6 | 186 |
| Quebec | Montreal | 88 | 75 | −16 | 98 |
| | Quebec | 86 | 75 | −19 | 245 |
| Saskatchewan | Regina | 92 | 73 | −34 | 1884 |
| Yukon | White Horse | 78 | 62 | −45 | 2289 |

Courtesy Dunham–Bush, Inc.

[a]Summer design DB & WB temperatures equal to or exceeded 1% of four summer months (about 30 hours), and winter DB temperatures 99% of three winter months (about 22 hours).

Ground temperatures (GT) for cold storage room calculations may be approximated for range −30 to +30°F. Winter design dry bulb (WDB) by GT, °F = 65 + WDB/2.

cold storage room, located in Des Moines, Iowa, is maintained at 40°F. What is the floor heat gain per square foot of area?

*Solution* The summer temperature is 60°F, according to Table 14.4. The temperature difference is therefore 60 − 40 = 20°F.

From Table 14.1, for the type and thickness of insulation listed, the heat gain is 48 Btu/ft$^2$ per 24 hr.

## 14.3 Air Infiltration

Whenever refrigerator doors are open air infiltration from the exterior will occur. The enthalpy (heat content) of this air in summer will be greater than that of the refrigerated space. The difference between the enthalpy of the infiltrating air and the space is a heat load that must be removed by the refrigeration equipment. This load includes the sensible heat of the infiltrating air and the latent heat of condensation of the water vapor in the air. Equations for calculating the load are developed in air conditioning texts. For refrigeration use the results have been arranged in a convenient form, shown in Tables 14.5 and 14.6.

Table 14.5 lists the air infiltration rate into the room, in air changes per 24 hours. This is

**TABLE 14.5** Air Infiltration into Cold Storage Rooms

| Average Air Changes Per 24 Hours for Storage Rooms Above 32°F Due to Door Opening and Infiltration[a] | | | | | | | |
|---|---|---|---|---|---|---|---|
| Volume Cu. Ft. | Air Changes Per 24 Hr. | Volume Cu. Ft. | Air Changes Per 24 Hr. | Volume Cu. Ft. | Air Changes Per 24 Hr. | Volume Cu. Ft. | Air Changes Per 24 Hr. |
| 200 | 44.0 | 800 | 20.0 | 5000 | 7.2 | 25,000 | 3.0 |
| 250 | 38.0 | 1000 | 17.5 | 6000 | 6.5 | 30,000 | 2.7 |
| 300 | 34.5 | 1500 | 14.0 | 8000 | 5.5 | 40,000 | 2.3 |
| 400 | 29.5 | 2000 | 12.0 | 10,000 | 4.9 | 50,000 | 2.0 |
| 500 | 26.0 | 3000 | 9.5 | 15,000 | 3.9 | 75,000 | 1.6 |
| 600 | 23.0 | 4000 | 8.2 | 20,000 | 3.5 | 100,000 | 1.4 |
| | | | | | | 350,000 | 1.13* |
| | | | | | | 700,000 | 0.97* |

| Average Air Changes Per 24 Hours for Storage Rooms Below 32°F Due to Door Opening and Infiltration[b] | | | | | | | |
|---|---|---|---|---|---|---|---|
| Volume Cu. Ft. | Air Changes Per 24 Hr. | Volume Cu. Ft. | Air Changes Per 24 Hr. | Volume Cu. Ft. | Air Changes Per 24 Hr. | Volume Cu. Ft. | Air Changes Per 24 Hr. |
| 200 | 33.5 | 800 | 15.3 | 5000 | 5.6 | 25,000 | 2.3 |
| 250 | 29.0 | 1000 | 13.5 | 6000 | 5.0 | 30,000 | 2.1 |
| 300 | 26.2 | 1500 | 11.0 | 8000 | 4.3 | 40,000 | 1.8 |
| 400 | 22.5 | 2000 | 9.3 | 10,000 | 3.8 | 50,000 | 1.6 |
| 500 | 20.0 | 3000 | 7.4 | 15,000 | 3.0 | 75,000 | 1.3 |
| 600 | 18.0 | 4000 | 6.3 | 20,000 | 2.6 | 100,000 | 1.1 |
| | | | | | | 150,000 | 0.88*c |
| | | | | | | 200,000 | .77 |

[a]For heavy usage multiply the above values by a service factor of 2. For long storage multiply the above values by 0.6
[b]For heavy usage multiply the above values by a service factor of 2. For long storage multiply the above values by 0.6. For 2 doors in same wall multiply by 1.25. For 2 doors in opposite walls multiply by 2.5, but two open doors on adjacent or opposite walls should not be tolerated.
[c]Extrapolated.
Courtesy Dunham–Bush, Inc.

**TABLE 14.6** Heat Removed in Cooling Outside Air to Storage Room Temperature, Btu/ft$^3$

| Storage Room Temperature °F | Temperature of Outside Air, °F | | | | | | | | Storage Room Temperature °F | Temperature of Outside Air, °F | | | | | | | |
|---|---|---|---|---|---|---|---|---|---|---|---|---|---|---|---|---|---|
| | 85 | | 90 | | 95 | | 100 | | | 40 | | 50 | | 90 | | 100 | |
| | Relative Humidity, % | | | | | | | | | Relative Humidity, % | | | | | | | |
| | 50 | 60 | 50 | 60 | 50 | 60 | 50 | 60 | | 70 | 80 | 70 | 80 | 50 | 60 | 50 | 60 |
| 65 | 0.65 | 0.85 | 0.93 | 1.17 | 1.24 | 1.54 | 1.58 | 1.95 | 30 | 0.24 | 0.29 | 0.58 | 0.66 | 2.26 | 2.53 | 2.95 | 3.35 |
| 60 | 0.85 | 1.03 | 1.13 | 1.37 | 1.44 | 1.74 | 1.78 | 2.15 | 25 | 0.41 | 0.45 | 0.75 | 0.83 | 2.44 | 2.71 | 3.14 | 3.54 |
| 55 | 1.12 | 1.34 | 1.41 | 1.66 | 1.72 | 2.01 | 2.06 | 2.44 | 20 | 0.56 | 0.61 | 0.91 | 0.99 | 2.62 | 2.90 | 3.33 | 3.73 |
| 50 | 1.32 | 1.54 | 1.62 | 1.87 | 1.93 | 2.22 | 2.28 | 2.65 | 15 | 0.71 | 0.75 | 1.06 | 1.14 | 2.80 | 3.07 | 3.51 | 3.92 |
| 45 | 1.50 | 1.73 | 1.80 | 2.06 | 2.12 | 2.42 | 2.47 | 2.85 | 10 | 0.85 | 0.89 | 1.19 | 1.27 | 2.93 | 3.20 | 3.64 | 4.04 |
| 40 | 1.69 | 1.92 | 2.00 | 2.26 | 2.31 | 2.62 | 2.67 | 3.06 | 5 | 0.98 | 1.03 | 1.34 | 1.42 | 3.12 | 3.40 | 3.84 | 4.27 |
| 35 | 1.86 | 2.09 | 2.17 | 2.43 | 2.49 | 2.79 | 2.85 | 3.24 | 0 | 1.12 | 1.17 | 1.48 | 1.56 | 3.28 | 3.56 | 4.01 | 4.43 |
| 30 | 2.00 | 2.24 | 2.26 | 2.53 | 2.64 | 2.94 | 2.95 | 3.35 | − 5 | 1.23 | 1.28 | 1.59 | 1.67 | 3.41 | 3.69 | 4.15 | 4.57 |
| | | | | | | | | | −10 | 1.35 | 1.41 | 1.73 | 1.81 | 3.56 | 3.85 | 4.31 | 4.74 |
| | | | | | | | | | −15 | 1.50 | 1.53 | 1.85 | 1.92 | 3.67 | 3.96 | 4.42 | 4.86 |
| | | | | | | | | | −20 | 1.63 | 1.68 | 2.01 | 2.09 | 3.88 | 4.18 | 4.66 | 5.10 |
| | | | | | | | | | −25 | 1.77 | 1.80 | 2.12 | 2.21 | 4.00 | 4.30 | 4.78 | 5.21 |
| | | | | | | | | | −30 | 1.90 | 1.95 | 2.29 | 2.38 | 4.21 | 4.51 | 4.90 | 5.44 |

Courtesy Dunham–Bush, Inc.

the number of times that the volume of room air is changed in 24 hours. Note that the infiltration rate is different for rooms above and below 32°F. The infiltration also varies according to the frequency of door usage, as noted.

Table 14.6 lists the heat removed in cooling one cubic foot of air from outside conditions to storage room conditions. The use of the tables in calculating the infiltration air heat load is illustrated by the following example.

**Example 14.4** A cold storage room kept at 20°F has a volume of 1500 ft$^3$. Outside air conditions are 90°F and 50 percent RH (relative humidity). The product is kept in short storage. Calculate the infiltration heat load through the door.

*Solution* From Table 14.5, there are 11 room air changes per 24 hr. Expressed in cubic feet of air, this is

ft$^3$ of air = number of air changes

$$\times \text{ room volume, ft}^3$$

$$= 11.0 \times 1500$$

$$= 16,500 \text{ ft}^3 \text{ per 24 hr}$$

Using Table 14.6, 2.62 Btu are removed in cooling each cubic foot of air from outside to room conditions. The infiltration heat load is therefore

$$\text{Heat load} = 2.62 \text{ Btu/ft}^3$$

$$\times 16,500 \text{ ft}^3 \text{ per 24 hrs}$$

$$= 43,230 \text{ Btu per 24 hr}$$

## 14.4 Product Pull-Down Load

The products being refrigerated become part of the refrigeration load from two effects. First, heat must be removed from the product to bring it to storage conditions. This is called the *pull-down load*. Second, some products (fruits and vegetables) continue to give off heat at storage conditions.

Calculation of the heat removed from the products to bring them to storage condition depends upon the initial and final conditions. If the product is cooled to a temperature above freezing, the load is the sensible heat above freezing:

$$Q = m \times c_1 \times TC_1 \qquad (14.1)$$

where

$Q$ = amount of heat removed from product, Btu per 24 hr

$m$ = quantity of product cooled, lb/24 hr

$c_1$ = specific heat of product above freezing, Btu/lb-°F

$TC_1$ = temperature change of product above freezing from initial to final temperature, °F

If the product is to be frozen then the load also consists of the latent heat of fusion and the sensible heat of cooling the frozen product below the freezing temperature.

The latent heat removal to freeze the product is determined from the following equation:

$$Q = m \times h_{if} \qquad (14.2)$$

where $Q$ and $m$ are as in Equation 14.1 and $h_{if}$ is the latent heat of fusion of product, Btu/lb.

To find the sensible heat removal in cooling the product after it is frozen to the storage temperature, an equation of the same form as Equation 14.1 is used, except that the specific heat is that of the frozen product, and the temperature change is from the freezing point to the final storage temperature. This is expressed in Equation 14.3.

$$Q = m \times c_2 \times TC_2 \qquad (14.3)$$

where

$Q$ and $m$ are as in Equation 14.1

$c_2$ = specific heat of product below freezing, Btu/lb-°F

$TC_2$ = temperature change of product from freezing point to final temperature, °F

Table 14.7 lists the properties required for calculating the heat removal to cool products, using any of Equations 14.1, 14.2, or 14.3.

**Example 14.5**   A freezing room receives 12,000 lb of fish at 60°F, to be frozen to − 10°F in 24 hours. Calculate the product pull-down load.

*Solution*   The load is calculated in three steps. The data are obtained from Table 14.7.

Using Equation 14.1, the sensible heat above freezing is

$$Q = m \times c_1 \times TC_1$$
$$= 12{,}000 \times 0.86 \times (60 - 28)$$
$$= 330{,}240 \text{ Btu/24 hr}$$

Using Equation 14.2, the latent heat of fusion is

$$Q = m \times h_{if}$$
$$= 12{,}000 \times 122$$
$$= 1{,}464{,}000 \text{ Btu/24 hr}$$

Using Equation 14.3, the sensible heat below freezing is

$$Q = m \times c_2 = TC_2$$
$$= 12{,}000 \times 0.45 \times (28 - (-10))$$
$$= 205{,}200 \text{ Btu/24 hr}$$

Product pull-down load
$$= 1{,}999{,}440 \text{ Btu/24 hr.}$$

If the product is to be cooled down to storage conditions in less than 24 hr this increases the daily (24 hr) load in the system. This is accounted for by using an "equivalent" daily product quantity in calculations, as follows:

$$\text{Equivalent daily lb} = \text{actual lb} \qquad (14.4)$$
$$\times \frac{24 \text{ hr}}{\text{pull-down hr}}$$

**Example 14.6**   If the fish to be frozen in Example 14.5 is to be cooled down to storage conditions in 9 hr, what should be the equivalent pounds used in calculating the 24 hr pull-down load?

# TABLE 14.7 Storage Requirements and Properties of Perishable Products

| Commodity (Alphabetical Listing) | Storage Conditions | | | Water Content, % | Highest Freezing Point, °F | Specific Heat Above Freezing Btu/Lb/°F | Specific Heat Below Freezing Btu/Lb/°F | Latent Heat of Fusion Btu/Lb |
| | Storage Temperature °F | Relative Humidity % | Approximate Storage Life[a] | | | | | |
|---|---|---|---|---|---|---|---|---|
| Apples | 30–40 | 90 | 3– 8 months | 84.1 | 29.3 | 0.87 | 0.45 | 121 |
| Apricots | 31–32 | 90 | 1– 2 weeks | 84.5 | 30.1 | 0.88 | 0.46 | 122 |
| Artichokes (globe) | 31–32 | 95 | 2 weeks | 83.7 | 29.9 | 0.87 | 0.45 | 120 |
| Asparagus | 32–36 | 95 | 2– 3 weeks | 93.0 | 30.9 | 0.94 | 0.48 | 134 |
| Avocados | 45–55 | 85–90 | 2– 3 weeks | 65.4 | 31.5 | 0.72 | 0.40 | 94 |
| Bananas | — | 85–95 | — | 74.8 | 30.6 | 0.80 | 0.42 | 108 |
| Beans (green or snap) | 40–45 | 90–95 | 7–10 days | 88.9 | 30.7 | 0.91 | 0.47 | 128 |
| Lima | 32–40 | 90 | 1 week | 66.5 | 31.0 | 0.73 | 0.40 | 94 |
| Beer, keg | 35–40 | — | 3– 8 weeks | 90.2 | 28.0 | 0.92 | — | 129 |
| bottles, cans | 35–40 | 65 or below | 3– 6 months | 90.2 | — | — | — | — |
| Beets, topped | 32 | 95–100 | 4– 6 months | 87.6 | 30.1 | 0.90 | 0.46 | 126 |
| Blackberries | 31–32 | 95 | 3 days | 84.8 | 30.5 | 0.88 | 0.46 | 122 |
| Blueberries | 31–32 | 90–95 | 2 weeks | 82.3 | 29.7 | 0.86 | 0.45 | 118 |
| Bread, baked | 0 | — | 1– 3 months | 32–37 | 16–20 | 0.70 | 0.34 | 46–53 |
| Dough | 35–40 | 85–90 | 3–72 hours | 58.0 | — | 0.75 | — | — |
| Broccoli, sprouting | 32 | 95 | 10–14 days | 89.9 | 30.9 | 0.92 | 0.47 | 130 |
| Brussels sprouts | 32 | 95 | 3– 5 weeks | 84.9 | 30.5 | 0.88 | 0.46 | 122 |
| Cabbage, late | 32 | 95–100 | 3– 4 months | 92.4 | 30.4 | 0.94 | 0.47 | 132 |
| Carrots, topped, mature | 32 | 98–100 | 5– 9 months | 88.2 | 29.5 | 0.90 | 0.46 | 126 |
| Cauliflower | 32 | 95 | 2– 4 weeks | 91.7 | 30.6 | 0.93 | 0.47 | 132 |
| Celery | 32 | 95 | 1– 2 months | 93.7 | 31.1 | 0.95 | 0.48 | 135 |
| Cherries, sour | 31–32 | 90–95 | 3– 7 days | 83.7 | 29.0 | 0.87 | — | 120 |
| Sweet | 30–31 | 90–95 | 2– 3 weeks | 80.4 | 28.8 | 0.84 | — | — |
| Chocolate (coating) | 50–65 | 40–50 | 2– 3 months | 55.0 | 95–85 | 0.30 | 0.55 | 40 |
| Cocoa | 32–40 | 50–70 | 1 year, plus | — | — | — | — | — |
| Coconuts | 32–35 | 80–85 | 1– 2 months | 46.9 | 30.4 | 0.58 | 0.34 | 67 |
| Coffee (green) | 35–37 | 80–85 | 2– 4 months | 10–15 | — | 0.30 | 0.24 | 14–21 |
| Collards | 32 | 95 | 10–14 days | 86.9 | 30.6 | 0.90 | — | — |
| Corn, sweet (fresh) | 32 | 95 | 4– 8 days | 73.9 | 30.9 | 0.79 | 0.42 | 106 |
| Cranberries | 36–40 | 90–95 | 2– 4 months | 87.4 | 30.4 | 0.90 | 0.46 | 124 |
| Cucumbers | 50–55 | 90–95 | 10–14 days | 96.1 | 31.1 | 0.97 | 0.49 | 137 |
| Currants | 31–32 | 90–95 | 10–14 days | 84.7 | 30.2 | 0.88 | 0.45 | 120 |
| Dairy products | | | | | | | | |
| Cheddar cheese | 40 | 65–70 | 6 months | 37.5 | 8.0 | 0.50 | 0.31 | 53 |
| Processed cheese | 40 | 65–70 | 12 months | 39.0 | 19.0 | 0.50 | 0.31 | 56 |
| Butter | 40 | 75–85 | 1 month | 16.0 | −4–31 | 0.50 | 0.25 | 23 |
| Cream | 35–40 | — | 2–3 weeks | 55–75 | 31.0 | 0.66–0.80 | 0.36–0.42 | 79–107 |
| Ice cream | −20 to −15 | — | 3–12 months | 58–63 | 21.0 | 0.66–0.70 | 0.37–0.39 | 86 |
| Milk, fluid whole | | | | | | | | |
| Pasteurized, Grade A | 32–34 | — | 2–4 months | 87.0 | 31.0 | 0.93 | 0.46 | 125 |
| Condensed, sweetened | 40 | — | 15 months | 28.0 | 5.0 | 0.42 | 0.28 | 40 |
| Evaporated | 40 | — | 24 months | 74.0 | 29.5 | 0.79 | 0.42 | 106 |
| Dates (dried) | 0 or 32 | 75 or less | 6–12 months | 20.0 | 3.7 | 0.36 | 0.26 | 29 |
| Dewberries | 31–32 | 90–95 | 3 days | 84.5 | 29.7 | 0.88 | — | — |
| Dried fruits | 32 | 50–60 | 9–12 months | 14.0–26.0 | — | 0.31–0.41 | 0.26 | 20–37 |
| Eggplant | 45–50 | 90–95 | 7–10 days | 92.7 | 30.6 | 0.94 | 0.48 | 132 |
| Eggs, shell | 29–31 | 80–85 | 5– 6 months | 66.0 | 28.0 | 0.73 | 0.40 | 96 |
| Shell, farm cooler | 50–55 | 70–75 | 2– 3 weeks | 66.0 | 28.0 | 0.73 | 0.40 | 96 |
| Frozen, whole | 0 or below | — | 1 year plus | 74.0 | 28.0 | 0.73 | 0.42 | 106 |
| Endive (escarole) | 32 | 95 | 2– 3 weeks | 93.3 | 31.9 | 0.94 | 0.48 | 132 |
| Figs, dried | 32–40 | 50–60 | 9–12 months | 24.0 | — | 0.39 | 0.27 | 34 |
| Fresh | 31–32 | 85–90 | 7–10 days | 78.0 | 27.6 | 0.82 | 0.43 | 112 |
| Fish, fresh | 33–35 | 90–95 | 5–15 days | 62–85 | 28.0 | 0.70–0.86 | 0.38–0.45 | 89–122 |
| Smoked | 40–50 | 50–60 | 6–8 months | — | — | 0.70 | 0.39 | 92 |
| Shellfish, fresh | 30–33 | 85–95 | 3– 7 days | 80–87 | 28.0 | 0.83–0.90 | 0.44–0.46 | 113–125 |
| Furs and fabrics | 34–40 | 45–55 | several years | — | — | — | — | — |

(continued)

**TABLE 14.7** Continued

| Commodity (Alphabetical Listing) | Storage Temperature °F | Relative Humidity % | Approximate Storage Life[a] | Water Content, % | Highest Freezing Point, °F | Specific Heat Above Freezing Btu/Lb/°F | Specific Heat Below Freezing Btu/Lb/°F | Latent Heat of Fusion Btu/Lb |
|---|---|---|---|---|---|---|---|---|
| Garlic, dry | 32 | 65–70 | 6– 7 months | 61.3 | 30.5 | 0.69 | 0.40 | 89 |
| Gooseberries | 31–32 | 90–95 | 2– 4 weeks | 88.9 | 30.0 | 0.90 | 0.46 | 126 |
| Grapefruit | 50–60 | 85–90 | 4– 6 weeks | 88.8 | 30.0 | 0.91 | 0.46 | 126 |
| Grapes, American type | 31–32 | 85–90 | 2– 8 weeks | 81.9 | 29.7 | 0.86 | 0.44 | 116 |
| European type | 30–31 | 90–95 | 3– 6 months | 81.6 | 28.1 | 0.86 | 0.44 | 116 |
| Greens, leafy | 32 | 95 | 10–14 days | — | — | — | — | — |
| Guavas | 45–50 | 90 | 2– 3 weeks | 83.0 | — | 0.86 | — | — |
| Honey | 38–50 | 50–60 | 1 year, plus | 18.0 | — | 0.35 | 0.26 | 26 |
| Horseradish | 30–32 | 95–100 | 10–12 months | 73.4 | 28.7 | 0.78 | 0.42 | 104 |
| Kale | 32 | 95 | 3– 4 months | 86.6 | 31.1 | 0.89 | 0.46 | 124 |
| Kohlrabi | 32 | 95 | 2– 4 weeks | 90.1 | 30.2 | 0.92 | 0.47 | 128 |
| Leeks, green | 32 | 95 | 1– 3 months | 85.4 | 30.7 | 0.88 | 0.46 | 126 |
| Lemons | 32 or 50–58 | 85–90 | 1– 6 months | 89.3 | 29.4 | 0.91 | 0.46 | 127 |
| Lettuce, head | 32–34 | 95–100 | 2– 3 weeks | 94.8 | 31.7 | 0.96 | 0.48 | 136 |
| Limes | 48–50 | 85–90 | 6– 8 weeks | 86.0 | 29.1 | 0.89 | 0.46 | 122 |
| Maple sugar | 75–80 | 60–65 | 1 year, plus | 5.0 | — | 0.24 | 0.21 | 7 |
| Mangoes | 55 | 85–90 | 2– 3 weeks | 81.4 | 30.3 | 0.85 | 0.44 | 117 |
| Meat | | | | | | | | |
| Bacon, cured (farm style) | 60–65 | 85 | 4– 6 months | 13–29 | — | 0.30–0.43 | 0.24–0.29 | 18–41 |
| Game, fresh | 32 | 80–85 | 1– 6 weeks | 47–54 | 28–29 | 0.80 | 0.42 | 115 |
| Beef, fresh | 32–34 | 88–92 | 1– 6 weeks | 62–77 | 28–29 | 0.70–0.84 | 0.38–0.43 | 89–110 |
| Hams and shoulders, fresh | 32–34 | 85–90 | 7–12 days | 47–54 | 28–29 | 0.58–0.63 | 0.34–0.36 | 67–77 |
| Cured | 60–65 | 50–60 | 0– 3 years | 40–45 | — | 0.52–0.56 | 0.32–0.33 | 57–64 |
| Lamb, fresh | 32–34 | 85–90 | 5–12 days | 60–70 | 28–29 | 0.68–0.76 | 0.38–0.51 | 86–100 |
| Livers, frozen | −10– 0 | 90–95 | 3– 4 months | 70.0 | — | — | 0.41 | 100 |
| Pork, fresh | 32–34 | 85–90 | 3– 7 days | 32–44 | 28–29 | 0.46–0.55 | 0.30–0.33 | 46–63 |
| Smoked sausage | 40–45 | 85–90 | 6 months | 60.0 | — | 0.68 | 0.38 | 86 |
| Fresh | 32 | 85–90 | 1– 2 weeks | 65.0 | 26.0 | 0.89 | 0.56 | 93 |
| Veal, fresh | 32–34 | 90–95 | 5–10 days | 64–70 | 28–29 | 0.71–0.76 | 0.39–0.41 | 92–100 |
| Melons, cantaloupe | 36–40 | 90–95 | 5–15 days | 92.0 | 29.9 | 0.93 | 0.48 | 132 |
| Honeydew and honey ball | 45–50 | 90–95 | 3– 4 weeks | 92.6 | 30.3 | 0.94 | 0.48 | 132 |
| Watermelons | 40–50 | 80–90 | 2– 3 weeks | 92.1 | 31.3 | 0.97 | 0.48 | 132 |
| Mushrooms | 32 | 90 | 3– 4 days | 91.1 | 30.4 | 0.93 | 0.47 | 130 |
| Nectarines | 31–32 | 90 | 2– 4 weeks | 81.8 | 30.4 | 0.90 | 0.49 | 119 |
| Nuts (dried) | 32–50 | 65–75 | 8–12 months | 3–6 | — | 0.22–0.25 | 0.21–0.22 | 4–8 |
| Okra | 45–50 | 90–95 | 7–10 days | 89.8 | 28.7 | 0.92 | 0.46 | 128 |
| Oleomargarine | 35 | 60–70 | 1 year, plus | 15.5 | — | 0.32 | 0.25 | 22 |
| Olives, fresh | 45–50 | 85–90 | 4– 6 weeks | 75.2 | 29.4 | 0.80 | 0.42 | 108 |
| Onions (dry) and onion sets | 32 | 65–70 | 1– 8 months | 87.5 | 30.6 | 0.90 | 0.46 | 124 |
| green | 32 | 95 | 3– 4 weeks | 89.4 | 30.4 | 0.91 | — | — |
| Oranges | 32–48 | 85–90 | 3–12 weeks | 87.2 | 30.6 | 0.90 | 0.46 | 124 |
| Orange juice, chilled | 30–35 | — | 3– 6 weeks | 89.0 | — | 0.91 | 0.47 | 128 |
| Papayas | 45 | 85–90 | 1– 3 weeks | 90.8 | 30.4 | 0.82 | 0.47 | 130 |
| Parsley | 32 | 95 | 1– 2 months | 85.1 | 30.0 | 0.88 | 0.45 | 122 |
| Parsnips | 32 | 98–100 | 4– 6 months | 78.6 | 30.4 | 0.84 | 0.44 | 112 |
| Peaches and nectarines | 31–32 | 90 | 2– 4 weeks | 89.1 | 30.3 | 0.90 | 0.46 | 124 |
| Pears | 29–31 | 90–95 | 2– 7 months | 82.7 | 29.2 | 0.86 | 0.45 | 118 |
| Peas, green | 32 | 95 | 1– 3 weeks | 74.3 | 30.9 | 0.79 | 0.42 | 106 |
| Peppers, sweet | 45–50 | 90–95 | 2– 3 weeks | 92.4 | 30.7 | 0.94 | 0.47 | 132 |
| Peppers, chili (dry) | 32–50 | 60–70 | 6 months | 12.0 | — | 0.30 | 0.24 | 17 |
| Persimmons | 30 | 90 | 3– 4 months | 78.2 | 28.1 | 0.84 | 0.43 | 112 |
| Pineapples, ripe | 45 | 85–90 | 2– 4 weeks | 85.3 | 30.0 | 0.88 | 0.45 | 122 |
| Plums, including fresh prunes | 31–32 | 90–95 | 2– 4 weeks | 82.3 | 30.5 | 0.88 | 0.45 | 118 |
| Pomegranates | 32 | 90 | 2– 4 weeks | 77.0 | 26.6 | 0.87 | 0.48 | 112 |
| Popcorn, unpopped | 32–40 | 85 | 4– 6 months | 13.5 | — | 0.31 | 0.24 | 19 |
| Potatoes, early crop | 50–55 | 90 | 0– 2 months | 81.2 | 30.9 | 0.85 | 0.44 | 116 |
| Late crop | 38–50 | 90 | 5– 8 months | 77.8 | 30.9 | 0.82 | 0.43 | 111 |

**TABLE 14.7** Continued

| Commodity (Alphabetical Listing) | Storage Conditions | | | Water Content, % | Highest Freezing Point, °F | Specific Heat Above Freezing Btu/Lb/°F | Specific Heat Below Freezing Btu/Lb/°F | Latent Heat of Fusion Btu/Lb |
|---|---|---|---|---|---|---|---|---|
| | Storage Temperature °F | Relative Humidity % | Approximate Storage Life[a] | | | | | |
| Poultry, fresh chicken | 32 | 85–90 | 1 week | 74.0 | 27.0 | 0.79 | 0.42 | 106 |
| Fresh goose | 32 | 85–90 | 1 week | 47.0 | 27.0 | 0.57 | 0.34 | 67 |
| Fresh turkey | 32 | 85–90 | 1 week | 55.0 | 27.0 | 0.64 | 0.37 | 79 |
| Pumpkins | 50–55 | 70–75 | 2– 3 months | 90.5 | 30.5 | 0.92 | 0.47 | 130 |
| Quinces | 31–32 | 90 | 2– 3 months | 85.3 | 28.4 | 0.88 | 0.45 | 122 |
| Radishes, spring, prepackaged | 32 | 95 | 3– 4 weeks | 93.6 | 30.7 | 0.95 | 0.48 | 134 |
| Raisins (dried) | 40 | 60–70 | 9–12 months | 35.0 | — | 0.47 | 0.32 | 43 |
| Rabbits, fresh | 32–34 | 90–95 | 1– 5 days | 68.0 | — | 0.74 | 0.40 | 98 |
| Raspberries, black | 31–32 | 90–95 | 2– 3 days | 80.6 | 30.0 | 0.84 | 0.44 | 122 |
| Red | 31–32 | 90–95 | 2– 3 days | 84.1 | 30.9 | 0.87 | 0.45 | 121 |
| Rhubarb | 32 | 95 | 2– 4 weeks | 94.9 | 30.3 | 0.96 | 0.48 | 134 |
| Rutabagas | 32 | 98–100 | 4– 6 months | 89.1 | 30.1 | 0.91 | 0.47 | 127 |
| Salsify | 32 | 98–100 | 2– 4 months | 79.1 | 30.0 | 0.83 | 0.44 | 113 |
| Spinach | 32 | 95 | 10–14 days | 92.7 | 31.5 | 0.94 | 0.48 | 132 |
| Squash, summer | 32–50 | 85–95 | 5–14 days | 94.0 | 31.1 | 0.95 | 0.48 | 135 |
| Winter | 50–55 | 70–75 | 4– 6 months | 88.6 | 30.3 | 0.91 | 0.48 | 127 |
| Strawberries, fresh | 31–32 | 90–95 | 5– 7 days | 89.9 | 30.6 | 0.92 | 0.42 | 129 |
| Sugar, maple | 75–80 | 60–65 | 1 year, plus | 5.0 | — | 0.24 | 0.21 | 7 |
| Sweet potatoes | 55–60 | 85–90 | 4– 7 months | 68.5 | 29.7 | 0.75 | 0.40 | 97 |
| Syrup, maple | 31 | 60–70 | 1 year, plus | 35.5 | — | 0.48 | 0.31 | 51 |
| Tangerines | 32–38 | 85–90 | 2– 4 weeks | 87.3 | 30.1 | 0.90 | 0.46 | 125 |
| Tobacco, cigarettes | 35–46 | 50–55 | 6 months | — | 25.0 | — | — | — |
| Cigars | 35–50 | 60–65 | 2 months | — | 25.0 | — | — | — |
| Tomatoes, mature green | 55–70 | 85–90 | 1– 3 weeks | 93.0 | 31.0 | 0.95 | 0.48 | 134 |
| Firm ripe | 45–50 | 85–90 | 4– 7 days | 94.1 | 31.1 | 0.94 | 0.48 | 134 |
| Turnips, roots | 32 | 95 | 4– 5 months | 91.5 | 30.1 | 0.93 | 0.47 | 130 |
| Vegetables (mixed) | 32–40 | 90–95 | 1– 4 weeks | 90.0 | 30.0 | 0.90 | 0.45 | 130 |
| Yams | 60 | 85–90 | 3– 6 months | 73.5 | 28.5 | 0.79 | 0.40 | 105 |
| Yeast, compressed baker's | 31–32 | — | — | 70.9 | — | 0.77 | 0.41 | 102 |

[a]Not based on maintaining nutritional value.
Courtesy McQuay Group, McQuay–Perfex, Inc. Extracted by permission from 1974 ASHRAE Applications Handbook.

*Solution*  Using Equation 14.4

Equivalent daily lb = 12,000 lb

$$\times \ \frac{24 \text{ hr}}{9 \text{ hr}}$$

$$= 32,000 \text{ lb}/24 \text{ hr}$$

This quantity would be used instead of the actual when calculating the pull-down load on a 24-hour basis.

## 14.5 Heat of Respiration

As mentioned before, fruits and vegetables give off heat continually at storage conditions,

called the *heat of respiration*. This heat is generated from the life processes that are still occurring in them. Heats of respiration are listed in Table 14.8. In those cases where a range of values is given, the average should be used if no further information about the product is known.

***Example 14.7***  A storage room contains 8000 lb of mushrooms at 40°F. What is the daily load due to the heat of respiration?

*Solution*  Table 14.8 lists the heat of respiration as 7.80 Btu/lb per 24 hr for mush-

**TABLE 14.8** Heat of Respiration of Products[ab]

| | Btu/Lb/24Hr | | | |
|---|---|---|---|---|
| | Storage Temperature, °F | | | |
| Product | 32°F | 40°F | 60°F | °F Other |
| **Fruits** | | | | |
| Apples | 0.25–0.450 | 0.55–0.80 | 1.5–3.4 | |
| Apricots | 0.55–0.63 | 0.70–1.0 | 2.33–3.74 | |
| Avacados | — | — | 6.6–15.35 | |
| Bananas | — | — | 2.3–2.75 | @ 68° 4.2–4.6 |
| Blackberries | 1.70–2.52 | 5.91–5.00 | 7.71–15.97 | |
| Blueberries | 0.65–1.10 | 1.0–1.35 | 3.75–6.5 | @ 70° 5.7–7.5 |
| Cherries | 0.65–0.90 | 1.4–1.45 | 5.5–6.6 | |
| Cherries, sour | 0.63–1.44 | 1.41–1.45 | 3.0–5.49 | |
| Cranberries | 0.30–0.35 | 0.45–0.520 | — | |
| Figs, mission | — | 1.18–1.45 | 2.37–3.52 | |
| Gooseberries | 0.74–0.96 | 1.33–1.48 | 2.37–3.52 | |
| Grapefruit | 0.20–0.50 | 0.35–065 | 1.1–2 | |
| Grapes, American | 0.30 | 0.60 | 1.75 | |
| Grapes, European | 0.15–0.20 | 0.35–0.65 | 1.10–1.30 | |
| Lemons | 0.25–0.45 | 0.30–0.95 | 1.15–2.50 | |
| Limes | — | 0.405 | 1.485 | |
| Melons, cantaloupes | 0.55–0.63 | 0.96–1.11 | 3.70–4.22 | |
| Melons, honey dew | — | 0.45–0.55 | 1.2–1.65 | |
| Oranges | 0.20–0.50 | 0.65–0.8 | 1.85–2.6 | |
| Peaches | 0.45–0.70 | 0.70–1.0 | 3.65–4.65 | |
| Pears | 0.35–0.45 | — | 4.40–6.60 | |
| Plums | 0.20–0.35 | 0.45–0.75 | 1.20–1.40 | |
| Raspberries | 1.95–2.75 | 3.40–4.25 | 9.05–11.15 | |
| Strawberries | 1.35–1.90 | 1.80–3.40 | 7.80–10.15 | |
| Tangerines | 1.63 | 2.93 | — | |
| **Vegetables** | | | | |
| Artichokes (globe) | 2.48–4.93 | 3.48–6.56 | 8.49–15.90 | |
| Asparagus | 2.95–6.60 | 5.85–11.55 | 11.0–25.75 | |
| Beans, green or snap | — | 4.60–5.7 | 16.05–22.05 | |
| Beans, lima | 1.15–1.6 | 2.15–3.05 | 11.0–13.7 | |
| Beets, topped | 1.35 | 2.05 | 3.60 | |
| Broccoli | 3.75 | 5.50–8.80 | 16.9–25.0 | |
| Brussels sprouts | 1.65–4.15 | 3.30–5.50 | 6.60–13.75 | |
| Cabbage | 0.60 | 0.85 | 2.05 | |
| Carrots, topped | 1.05 | 1.75 | 4.05 | |
| Cauliflower | 1.80–2.10 | 2.10–2.40 | 4.70–5.40 | |
| Celery | 0.80 | 1.20 | 4.10 | |
| Corn, sweet | 3.60–5.65 | 5.30–6.60 | 19.20 | |
| Cucumbers | — | — | 1.65–3.65 | |
| Garlic | 0.33–1.19 | 0.63–1.08 | 1.18–3.0 | |
| Horseradish | 0.89 | 1.19 | 3.59 | |
| Kohlrabi | 1.11 | 1.78 | 5.37 | |
| Leeks | 1.04–1.78 | 2.15–3.19 | 9.08–12.82 | |

**TABLE 14.8** Continued

| | Btu/Lb/24Hr | | | |
|---|---|---|---|---|
| | Storage Temperature, °F | | | |
| Product | 32°F | 40°F | 60°F | °F Other |
| Lettuce, head | 1.15 | 1.35 | 3.95 | |
| Lettuce, leaf | 2.25 | 3.20 | 7.20 | |
| Mushrooms | 3.10–4.80 | 7.80 | — | @ 50° 11.0 |
| Okra | — | 6.05 | 15.8 | |
| Olives | — | — | 2.37–4.26 | |
| Onions, dry | 0.35–0.55 | 0.90 | 1.20 | |
| Onions, green | 1.15–2.45 | 1.90–7.50 | 7.25–10.70 | |
| Peas, green | 4.10–4.20 | 6.60–8.0 | 19.65–22.25 | |
| Peppers, sweet | 1.35 | 2.35 | 4.25 | |
| Potatoes, immature | — | 1.30 | 1.45–3.4 | |
| Potatoes, mature | — | 0.65–0.90 | 0.75–1.30 | |
| Potatoes, sweet | — | 0.85 | 21.5–3.15 | |
| Radishes with tops | 1.59–1.89 | 2.11–2.30 | 7.67–8.5 | |
| Radishes, topped | 0.59–0.63 | 0.85–0.89 | 3.04–3.59 | |
| Rhubarb, topped | 0.89–1.44 | 1.19–2.0 | 3.41–4.97 | |
| Spinach | 2.10–2.45 | 3.95–5.60 | 18.45–19.0 | |
| Squash, yellow | 1.3–1.41 | 1.55–2.04 | 8.23–9.97 | |
| Tomatoes, mature green | — | 0.55 | 3.10 | |
| Tomatoes, ripe | 0.50 | 0.65 | 2.8 | |
| Turnips | 0.95 | 1.10 | 2.65 | |
| Vegetables, mixed | 2.0 | — | — | |
| Miscellaneous | | | | |
| Caviar, tub | — | — | 1.91 | |
| Cheese, | | | | |
| American | — | — | 2.34 | |
| Camembert | — | — | 2.46 | |
| Limburger | — | — | 2.46 | |
| Roquefort | — | — | — | @45° 2.0 |
| Swiss | — | — | 2.33 | |
| Flowers, cut | 0.24 Btu/24 Hr/Ft$^2$–Floor area | | | |
| Honey | — | 0.71 | — | |
| Hops | — | — | — | @ 35° 0.75 |
| Malt | — | — | — | @ 50° 0.75 |
| Maple sugar | — | — | — | @ 45° 0.71 |
| Maple syrup | — | — | — | @ 45° 0.71 |
| Nuts | 0.074 | 0.185 | 0.37 | |
| Nuts, dried | — | — | — | @ 35° 0.50 |

[a]All fruits and vegetables are living and give off heat in storage: If heat of respiration is not given, an approximate value or average value should be used.
[b]For Btu/24 hr/Ton/°F multiply by 2000.
Courtesy Dunham Bush, Inc.

rooms at 40°F. The daily load is

Daily load = 8000 lb

$$\times \ 7.80 \ \text{Btu per 24 hr}$$

$$= 62,400 \ \text{Btu per 24 hr}$$

## 14.6 Occupant, Lighting, and Motor Loads

The bodily heat generated per occupant in the refrigerated room is listed in Table 14.9.

The heat equivalent of the electrical energy of lights or heaters is 1 W = 3.4 Btu/hr.

The heat equivalent of the motor horsepower is listed in Table 14.10. There are three possible conditions listed: the motors and connected load (such as fan, pump, fork lift) both located in the space, the motor outside the space and the load inside the space, and the load outside. Some small fan motors are rated in watts. In this case the proper conversion factor from watts to Btu/hr is used.

For occupant, lighting, and motor loads not

**TABLE 14.9** Body Heat of Occupants

| Cooler Temperature, °F | Heat Equivalent Per Person, Btu/hr |
|---|---|
| 50 | 720 |
| 40 | 840 |
| 30 | 950 |
| 20 | 1050 |
| 10 | 1200 |
| 0 | 1300 |
| −10 | 1400 |

Courtesy Dunham–Bush, Inc.

operating full time or not in the space continually, the 24-hr load is the hourly heat generated multiplied by the hours of use per day.

## 14.7 Refrigeration Load Calculation Form

To facilitate the refrigeration load calculations it is useful to use a load form that includes spaces for all the necessary data. A

**TABLE 14.10** Heat Equivalent of Electric Motors[a]

| Evaporator Fan Motor hp | Connected Load in Refrigerated Space, Btu/hp/hr | Motor Losses Outside Refrigerated Space Btu/hp/hr | Connected Load Outside Refrigerated Space Btu/hp/hr |
|---|---|---|---|
| 1/20 | 6400 | 2545 | |
| 1/15 | 5700 | 2545 | |
| 1/12 | 5300 | 2545 | |
| 1/10 | 4950 | 2545 | |
| 1/8 | 4650 | 2545 | |
| 1/6 | 4350 | 2545 | |
| 1/4 | 4000 | 2545 | 1455 |
| 1/3 | 3850 | 2545 | 1305 |
| 1/2 | 3700 | 2545 | 1155 |
| 3/4 | 3600 | 2545 | 1055 |
| 1 | 3500 | 2545 | 955 |
| 2 | 3300 | 2545 | 755 |
| 3 | 3200 | 2545 | 655 |
| 5 | 3100 | 2545 | 555 |
| 7 1/2 | 3050 | 2545 | 505 |
| 10 to 20 | 3000 | 2545 | 455 |

[a]For motors rated in watts (input) multiply watts by 3.41 Btu/W/hr.
Courtesy Dunham–Bush, Inc.

blank form is shown in Figure 14.1, and a worked out example is shown in Figure 14.2.

The student should study the worked out example and check the data taken from the appropriate tables. A few features of the load form and example will be explained.

The necessary design data are listed in the first part of the form (temperatures, construction, product). This is obtained from a job survey with the customer.

The heat transmission load is calculated for each exposed surface, taking into account any sun effect.

The infiltration load is calculated based on the air changes.

The product load is calculated in the steps listed, depending on whether or not freezing occurs. The equivalent product pounds are used if the pull down is in less than 24 hours.

Occupant, lighting, and motor daily loads are calculated based on hours of use per day.

A 10 percent safety factor is then added to give the total net 24 hour refrigeration load, a common practice in the refrigeration industry.

The next step is to determine the required refrigeration equipment capacity. The hourly equipment capacity will be greater than one twenty-fourth of the daily load because the compressor does not run continuously; it cycles off and on in response to the space thermostat. A further load is imposed on the refrigeration equipment from the evaporator fan heat, and in some cases from the defrost heat. Space is included in Figure 14.1 for these loads. The procedures by which they are determined will be discussed later in this chapter.

An example will illustrate a complete refrigeration load calculation. The student should check all of the data listed in the example.

**Example 14.8** Calculate the refrigeration load for the walk-in meat cooler described in load form Figure 14.2.

*Solution* Data for the cooler are selected from appropriate tables and listed in the form. The daily load is calculated. The hourly load is calculated by correcting for compressor running time and evaporator fan load.

## 14.8 Simplified Load Determination Methods

Experience has led to the use of many abbreviated methods for determining refrigeration loads. These methods are usually based on the size of the refrigerated space. Those that are based on room volume rather than surface area are considered by most authorities as being more reliable. In any case, simplified methods should not be used to replace the detailed calculations, unless it is not possible to obtain the required design data. A simplified method is useful as a preliminary estimate in determining costs, however. Table 14.11 presents one of the approximate rapid load determination methods, based on the volume of the room.

**Example 14.9** A freezer 18 ft wide × 20 ft long × 9 ft high at −20°F has a product load of 700 lb/day, entering at 40°F. Insulation is 6 in. of glass fiber. What is the approximate hourly refrigeration load? Ambient temperature is 95°F.

*Solution* From Table 14.11, the load is approximately 21,000 Btu/hr. If conditions differed significantly from those listed in the table, use of it would be very questionable.

## 14.9 Refrigeration Equipment Selection

The refrigeration daily (24 hour) load is used as the basis of selecting the refrigeration equipment for the application. However, the hourly required refrigeration capacity of the equipment is not one twenty-fourth of the

# REFRIGERATION LOAD ESTIMATE FORM
## FOR ROOMS ABOVE AND BELOW FREEZING

### - LOAD SURVEY & ESTIMATING DATA -

DESIGN AMBIENT:_____°FDB, _____°FWB _____%RH, _____°F SUMMER GROUND TEMP.
(USE 55°F FOR INSULATED FREEZE FLOOR SLAB)

ROOM DESIGN: _____°FDB, _____°FWB, _____%RH _____°F WINTER DESIGN AMBIENT

ACCESS AREA: _____°FDB, _____°FWB, _____%RH, (ANTE-RM/LOADING DOCK/OTHER)

ROOM DIM. OUTSIDE: _____FT. W_____FT. L _____FT. H _____TOTAL SQ. FT. (OUTSIDE SURFACE)

| | | Insulation | | | Wall Thick-ness | Adj. Area °F | Effective Wall TD | °F Sun Effect | Total TD | Overall Wall Heat Gain BTU/24 HRS/Sq. Ft. |
| | Type | Inches Thick | K Factor | U* Factor | | | | | | |
|---|---|---|---|---|---|---|---|---|---|---|
| N. Wall | | | | | | | | | | |
| S. Wall | | | | | | | | | | |
| E. Wall | | | | | | | | | | |
| W. Wall | | | | | | | | | | |
| Ceiling | | | | | | | | | | |
| Floor | | | | | | | | | | |

\* 'U' - Factor = $\dfrac{K}{\text{Insul. Thickness (in.)}}$

REFRIG. DOOR(S): _____ VENT. FAN(S): _____

ROOM INT. VOL: _____W x _____L x _____H = _____CU. FT.
(INSIDE ROOM DIMENSION = OUTSIDE DIMENSION - WALL THICKNESSES)
FLOOR AREA _____W x _____L = _____SQ. FT.
ELECTRICAL POWER_____VOLTS,_____PH._____HERTZ; CONTROL _____VOLTS

TYPE CONTROL:_____

PRODUCT DATA AND CLASS OF PRODUCT: _____

| Type Product | Amount of Product | | | Product Temp °F | | Specific Heat | | Lat. Ht. Freeze Btu/lb. | Highest Product Freeze Temp. | Heat or Respir'n Btu/lb. 24 Hr. | ( ) Pull-Down ( ) Freezing Time Hrs. |
| | Amount Storage | Daily Turn-Over | Freezing or Cooling | Enter -ing | Final | Above Freeze | Below Freeze | | | | |
|---|---|---|---|---|---|---|---|---|---|---|---|
| | | | | | | | | | | | |

EVAP. TD_____, TYPE DEFROST □ AIR, □ HOT GAS, □ ELECTRIC,
CLASS PRODUCT_____,
NO. OF DEFROSTS & TOTAL TIME PER 24 HRS._____NO.,_____HRS.
COMPRESSOR RUNNING TIME_____HRS.
BOX USAGE □ AVERAGE, □ HEAVY, □ EXTRA HEAVY
PRODUCT LOAD AND ADDITIONAL INFORMATION:_____
_____
_____
_____
_____

PACKAGING_____CONTAINERS_____WGT._____SP. HT._____(CONTAINER)
PALLETS: NO._____SIZE _____WGT. EA._____ SP. HT._____
PRODUCT RACKS: NO._____MAT'L_____WGT. EA._____ SP. HT._____

### ESTIMATING PRODUCT LOADING CAPACITY OF ROOM

ESTIMATED PRODUCT LOADING = 0.40 x_____CU. FT. x_____LBS./CU. FT. =_____LBS:
(ROOM VOLUME)  (LOADING DENSITY)

MISCELLANEOUS LOADS
PEOPLE NO._____HRS._____

MOTORS (OTHER THAN EVAP. FAN)
USE: _____, _____HP,_____HRS.
_____, _____HP,_____HRS.

FORK LIFTS_____NO.,_____HP ,_____HRS./DAY, OTHER_____

LIGHTS_____WATTS/SQ. FT.

**FIGURE 14.1** Refrigeration load survey and estimating form. (Courtesy Dunham–Bush, Inc.)

## CALCULATIONS

**I  WALL LOSS (TRANSMISSION LOAD)**

| SURFACE | TD | AREA OF SURFACE | WALL HEAT GAIN FACTOR | BTU/24 HR |
|---------|-----|-----------------|------------------------|-----------|
| N. Wall | | _____ Ft. L x _____ Ft. H = _____ Sq. Ft. x _____ = | | |
| S. Wall | | _____ Ft. L x _____ Ft. H = _____ Sq. Ft. x _____ = | | |
| E. Wall | | _____ Ft. L x _____ Ft. H = _____ Sq. Ft. x _____ = | | |
| W. Wall | | _____ Ft. L x _____ Ft. H = _____ Sq. Ft. x _____ = | | |
| Ceiling | | _____ Ft. L x _____ Ft. W = _____ Sq. Ft. x _____ = | | |
| Floor | | _____ Ft. L x _____ Ft. W = _____ Sq. Ft. x _____ = | | |
| Box | | Total: Surface = _____ Sq. Ft. x _____ = | | |

| **I** | Total Wall Transmission Load BTU/24 HRS. = | |

**II$_{SF}$ (SHORT FORM) USAGE HEAT GAIN ( ) AVG. ( ) HVY. ( ) EX. HVY.**
COOLERS ONLY

_____ CU. FT. x _____ BTU/24 HR./CU. FT. (@ ____ TD) =
(INT. BOX VOLUME)          (USAGE HEAT GAIN)

NOTE:  IF PRODUCT LOADS ARE UNUSUAL USE THE LONG FORM
EX. HVY. = 1½ x HVY. USAGE

| TOTAL I + II$_{SF}$ = | |

IF USAGE HEAT GAIN ABOVE IS USED DO NOT USE ( II$_{LF}$ III & IV )

**II$_{LF}$ (LONG FORM) INFILTRATION (AIR CHANGE LOAD)**
_____ CU. FT. x _____ AIR CHANGES/24 HRS. x _____ SRVC. FACTOR x _____ BTU/CU. FT=

| **II** | INFILTRATION LOAD BTU/24 HRS. = | |

**III  PRODUCT LOAD**

PRODUCT TEMP. REDUCTION ABOVE FREEZING (SENSIBLE HEAT)
_____ *LBS./DAY x _____ °F TEMP. REDUCTION x _____ SP. HT. =

PRODUCT FREEZING (LATENT HEAT LOAD)
_____ *LBS./DAY x _____ BTU/LB. LATENT HEAT =

PRODUCT TEMP. REDUCTION BELOW FREEZING (SENSIBLE HEAT)
_____ *LBS./DAY x _____ °F TEMP. REDUCTION x _____ SP. HT. =

HEAT OF RESPIRATION
_____ LBS. PRODUCT (STORAGE) x _____ BTU/LB./24 HRS. =

MISCELLANEOUS PRODUCT LOADS (1) CONTAINERS (2) PALLETS (3) OTHER
_____ LBS./DAY x _____ °F TEMP. REDUCTION x _____ SP. HT. =
_____ LBS./DAY x _____ °F TEMP. REDUCTION x _____ SP. HT. =

| **III** | TOTAL PRODUCT LOAD BTU/24 HRS. = | |

**IV  MISCELLANEOUS LOADS**
(a) LIGHTS _____ Ft.² Floor Area x _____ Watts/Ft.² x 3.41 Btu/Watt x _____ HRS/24 HRS =
(1 TO 1½ WATTS/SQ. FT. IN STORAGE AREAS & 2 TO 3 FOR WORK AREAS)
(b) OCCUPANCY _____ NO. OF PEOPLE x _____ BTU/HR. x _____ HRS. =
(c) MOTORS _____ BTU/HP/HR. x _____ HP x _____ HRS./ 24 HRS =
_____ BTU/HP/HR. x _____ HP x _____ HRS./24 HRS. =

(d) MATERIAL HANDLING
_____ FORK LIFT(S) x _____ EQUIV. HP x 3100 BTU/HR./HP. x _____ HRS. OPERATION =
OTHER _____ =

| **IV** | TOTAL MISCEL. LOADS BTU/24 HRS. = | |

*IF THE PRODUCT PULL-DOWN IS ACCOMPLISHED IN LESS THAN 24 HRS. THE DAILY PRODUCT WILL BE :

LBS. PRODUCT x $\dfrac{\text{24 HRS.}}{\text{PULLDOWN HRS.}}$

| TOTAL BTU LOAD I TO IV BTU/24 HRS. = | |
| ADD 10% SAFETY FACTOR = | |

TOTAL BTU/24 HRS. WITH SAFETY FACTOR
(NOT INCLUDING EVAP. FAN OR DEFROST HEAT LOADS) =
24 HR. BASE REFRIGERATION LOAD

**FIGURE 14.1** Continued

---

### EQUIPMENT SELECTION FROM LOAD CALCULATION FORM

1. DETERMINE EVAP. TD REQUIRED FOR CLASS
   OF PRODUCT AND ROOM TEMP._____°F (TD) (FROM LOAD SURVEY DATA)

2. DETERMINE COMPRESSOR RUNNING TIME BASED ON OPERATING TEMPERATURES
   AND DEFROST REQUIREMENTS_____HRS. (FROM LOAD SURVEY DATA)

3. EVAPORATOR TEMP.°F = _____ - _____ = _____°F
                  (ROOM TEMP) (EVAP. TD**)  **FROM LOAD SURVEY DATA

4. COMP. SUCT. TEMP.°F     = _____ - _____ = _____°F
                  (EVAP. SUCT. TEMP)   (SUCT. LINE LOSS)

     BTU/24 HR. BASE REFRIGERATION LOAD WITH SAFETY FACTOR = _____
        (NOT INCLUDING EVAPORATOR FAN OR DEFROST HEAT)

PRELIMINARY HOURLY LOAD =  _____   BTU/24 HR. (BASE LOAD)   = _____ BTU/HR.
                      HRS./DAY (COMP' RUNNING TIME)

FAN HEAT LOAD ESTIMATE BTU/HR. =

     _____ x _____ WATTS EA. x 3.41 BTU/WATT x_____HRS. = _____ BTU/24 HRS.
        (MOTORS)      (INPUT)

OR   _____ x _____ HP EA. x_____ BTU/HP/HR. x_____HRS. = _____ BTU/24 HRS.
        (MOTORS)          (TABLE 13)

DEFROST HEAT LOAD ESTIMATE BTU/HR =

     _____QTY. EVAPS. x_____WATTS EA. x_____HRS. x 3.41 BTU/WATT x_____DEFROST LOAD FACTOR*

= _____ BTU/24 HRS.

                *USE 0.50 FOR ELECTRIC DEFROST 0.40 FOR HOT GAS DEFROST

BTU/24 HR. TOTAL LOAD = _____ + _____ + _____ = _____ BTU/24 HRS.
                  (BASE LOAD)' (FAN HEAT) (DEFROST HEAT)

     OR       _____ x _____ = _____ BTU/24 HRS.
             (BASE LOAD) (BASE LOAD MULT.)

ACTUAL HOURLY LOAD  = _____   BTU/24 HRS. (TOTAL LOAD)   = _____ BTU/HR.
                     HRS/DAY (COMP. RUNNING TIME)

**FIGURE 14.1** Continued

---

daily load, but is greater. This is due to three factors: the compressor running time, the evaporator fan load and running time, and the possible defrost load.

***Compressor Running Time.*** The compressor does not run continuously because the thermostat control has a differential. That is, over a small range of satisfactory space temperatures the compressor cycles off, and does not cycle on until the maximum allowed temperature is reached. The system may also be stopped for defrost.

For rooms at 35°F or above it is common practice to use 16 hours as the compressor running time with defrost, and 18 to 20 hours without defrost. For rooms under 35°F, 18 to 20 hours is usually selected as the total compressor running time. This increases the ac-

tual hourly load on the equipment, which is calculated as follows:

$$\text{Hourly load} = \frac{\text{daily load}}{\text{running time, hr}} \quad (14.5)$$

***Example 14.10*** The daily refrigeration load in a cooler kept at 40°F without defrost has been calculated to be 360,000 Btu/24 hr. What is the hourly equipment load?

*Solution* The hourly load is found from Equation 14.5, using 16 hours running time

$$\text{Hourly load} = \frac{\text{daily load}}{\text{running time, hr}}$$

$$= \frac{36,000 \text{ Btu}}{16 \text{ hr}}$$

$$= 22,500 \text{ Btu/hr}$$

SURVEY BY _PETE HARRIS_ ___ OFFICE _CHICAGO_ DATE _4-1-79_
CUSTOMER _COLD STORAGE INC_ ADDRESS _133 RIVER RD. CHICAGO_
JOB NAME _LOU'S DELI_ ADDRESS _75 STEWART ST. CHICAGO_
APPLICATION _WALK-IN COOLER_

## - LOAD SURVEY & ESTIMATING DATA -

DESIGN AMBIENT _95_ FDB · FWB _50_ RH ___ F SUMMER GROUND TEMP
(USE 55 F FOR INSULATED FREEZE FLOOR SLAB)

ROOM DESIGN _35_ FDB · FWB _90_ RH ___ F WINTER DESIGN AMBIENT
ACCESS AREA _85_ FDB · FWB _50_ RH (ANTE RM/LOADING DOCK/OTHER)
ROOM DIM OUTSIDE _8_ FT W _14_ L _9_ FT H _620_ TOTAL SQ FT (OUTSIDE SURFACE)

| | Type | Insulation (Table 6) | | | Wall Thickness | Adj Area F | Effective Wall TD | F Sun Effect (Table 8) | Total TD | Overall Wall Heat Gain BTU/24 HRS/Sq Ft (Table 6) |
| | | Inches Thick | K Factor | U* Factor | | | | | | |
|---|---|---|---|---|---|---|---|---|---|---|
| N Wall | CORKBOARD | 4" | 0.3 | .075 | 6" | 95 | 60 | | 60 | 108 |
| N Wall | | | | | | | | | | |
| E Wall | | | | | | | | | | |
| W Wall | | | | | | | | | | |
| Ceiling | | | | | | | | | | |
| Floor | | | | | | | | | | |

REFRIG DOOR(S) _(1) 7' x 4'_ ___ VENT FAN(S) ___

ROOM INT VOL _7_ W x _13_ L x _8_ H = _728_ CU FT
(INSIDE ROOM DIMENSION = OUTSIDE DIMENSION - WALL THICKNESSES)
FLOOR AREA _7_ W x _13_ L = _91_ SQ FT
ELECTRICAL POWER _208_ VOLTS _3_ PH _60_ HERTZ CONTROL _115_ VOLTS
TYPE CONTROL

PRODUCT DATA AND CLASS OF PRODUCT

| Type Product | Amount of Product (Refer to Pg 2 Item 3) | | | Product Temp F | | Specific Heat | | | | Table 42 | | (1) Pull Down (1) Freezing Time Hrs |
| | Amount Storage | 3 Lbs/Cu Ft Daily Turn Over | Freezing or Cooling | Entering | Final | Above Freeze | Below Freeze | Lat Ht Freeze Btu/lb | Highest Product Freeze Temp | Heat of Respir n Btu/lb 24 Hr | |
|---|---|---|---|---|---|---|---|---|---|---|---|---|
| Mixed Veg | 3500 | 2184 | Cooling | 45 | 35 | .9 | | | | 2 | 24 |

EVAP TD _10_ TYPE DEFROST (AIR, HOT GAS, ELECTRIC)
CLASS PRODUCT _II_
NO OF DEFROSTS & TOTAL TIME PER 24 HRS ___ NO. ___ HRS
COMPRESSOR RUNNING TIME _16_ HRS.
BOX USAGE AVERAGE, HEAVY, EXTRA HEAVY
PRODUCT LOAD AND ADDITIONAL INFORMATION _MIXED VEGETABLE BOX_

PACKAGING _PAPER CARTONS_ CONTAINERS ___ WGT _100 LBS_ SP HT _.34_ (CONTAINER)
PALLETS NO. ___ SIZE ___ WGT. EA. ___ SP HT ___
PRODUCT RACKS NO ___ MAT'L ___ SIZE ___ SP HT ___

### ESTIMATING PRODUCT LOADING CAPACITY OF ROOM
ESTIMATED PRODUCT LOADING = 0.40 x _728_ CU FT x _12_ LBS/CU FT = _3490_ LBS
(ROOM VOLUME) (LOADING DENSITY)

MISCELLANEOUS LOADS
PEOPLE NO. _1_ HRS _12_

MOTORS (OTHER THAN EVAP FAN)
USE ___ HP ___ HRS.
___ HP ___ HRS.

FORK LIFTS ___ NO. ___ HP ___ HRS./DAY. OTHER ___
LIGHTS _1½_ WATTS/SQ. FT

## CALCULATIONS

### I WALL LOSS (TRANSMISSION LOAD)

| SURFACE | TD | AREA OF SURFACE | | WALL HEAT GAIN FACTOR | BTU/24 HRS. |
|---|---|---|---|---|---|
| N Wall | | Ft L x Ft H = Sq Ft x | | | |
| S Wall | | Ft L x Ft H = Sq Ft x | | | |
| E Wall | | Ft L x Ft H = Sq Ft x | | | |
| W Wall | | Ft L x Ft H = Sq Ft x | | | |
| Ceiling | | Ft L x Ft W = Sq Ft x | | | |
| Floor | | Ft L x Ft W = Sq Ft x | | | |
| Box | 60 | ∴ Surface = 620 Sq Ft x 108 | | | 66,960 |

| | I Total Wall Transmission Load BTU/24 HRS | 66,960 |

### II SF (SHORT FORM) USAGE HEAT GAIN ( ) AVG. ( ) HVY. ( ) EX. HVY. COOLERS ONLY
Refer to II LF (Long Form) ___ CU FT x ___ BTU/24 HR /CU FT (@ ___ TD) =
if application exceeds (INT. BOX VOLUME) (TABLE 14) (USAGE HEAT GAIN) (TABLE 15)
data shown in Table 15
NOTE: IF PRODUCT LOADS ARE UNUSUAL USE THE LONG FORM | TOTAL I + II SF |
EX HVY = 1" HVY USAGE

IF USAGE HEAT GAIN ABOVE IS USED DO NOT USE ( II LF, III & IV)

### II LF (LONG FORM) INFILTRATION (AIR CHANGE LOAD)
_728_ CU FT x _21_ AIR CHANGES/24 HRS x _1_ SRVC FACTOR _1.86_ BTU/CU FT = 28,433

| | II INFILTRATION LOAD BTU/24 HRS | 28,433 |

### III PRODUCT LOAD
PRODUCT TEMP. REDUCTION ABOVE FREEZING (SENSIBLE HEAT)
_2180_ LBS/DAY x _10_ F TEMP REDUCTION x _0.9_ SP HT = 19,620
PRODUCT FREEZING (LATENT HEAT)
___ LBS/DAY x ___ BTU/LB LATENT HEAT =
PRODUCT TEMP. REDUCTION BELOW FREEZING (SENSIBLE HEAT)
___ LBS/DAY x ___ F TEMP REDUCTION x ___ SP HT =
HEAT OF RESPIRATION
_3500_ LBS PRODUCT (STORAGE) x _2_ BTU/LB /24 HRS = 7,000
MISCELLANEOUS PRODUCT LOADS (1) CONTAINERS (2) PALLETS (3) OTHER
___ LBS/DAY x ___ F TEMP REDUCTION x ___ SP HT =

| | III TOTAL PRODUCT LOAD BTU/24 HRS | 26,620 |

### IV MISCELLANEOUS LOADS
(a) LIGHTS _91_ Ft² Floor Area x _1_ Watts Ft² x 3.41 Btu/Watt x _12_ HRS/24 HRS = 3,723
(1 TO 1. WATTS/SQ FT IN STORAGE AREAS & 2 TO 3 FOR WORK AREAS)
(b) OCCUPANCY _1_ NO OF PEOPLE x _900_ BTU/HR x _12_ HRS = 10,800
(c) MOTORS ___ BTU HP/HR x ___ HP x ___ HRS / 24 HRS =
___ BTU HP/HR x ___ HP x ___ HRS / 24 HRS =
(d) MATERIAL HANDLING
FORK LIFTS x ___ EQUIV HP x 3100 BTU/HR /HP x ___ HRS. OPERATION =
OTHER ___

| | IV TOTAL MISCEL. LOADS BTU/24 HRS | 14,523 |

*IF THE PRODUCT PULL DOWN IS ACCOMPLISHED IN LESS THAN 24 HRS THE DAILY PRODUCT WILL BE

LBS. PRODUCT x ___24 HRS___
PULLDOWN HRS

| TOTAL BTU LOAD I TO IV BTU/24 HRS | 136,538 |
| ADD 10% SAFETY FACTOR | 13,650 |
| TOTAL BTU/24 HRS. WITH SAFETY FACTOR (NOT INCLUDING EVAP. FAN OR DEFROST HEAT LOADS) 24 HR. BASE REFRIGERATION LOAD | 150,188 |

### EQUIPMENT SELECTION FROM LOAD CALCULATION FORM

1. DETERMINE EVAP. TD REQUIRED FOR CLASS OF PRODUCT AND ROOM TEMP _10_ F (TD) (FROM LOAD SURVEY DATA)

2. DETERMINE COMPRESSOR RUNNING TIME BASED ON OPERATING TEMPERATURES AND DEFROST REQUIREMENTS _16_ HRS (FROM LOAD SURVEY DATA)

3. EVAPORATOR TEMP °F = _35_ - _10_ = _25_ F
(ROOM TEMP) (EVAP TD**) **FROM LOAD SURVEY DATA

4. COMP. SUCT. TEMP. F = _25_ - _2_ = _23_ F
(EVAP SUCT TEMP) (SUCT LINE LOSS)

BTU/24 HR BASE REFRIGERATION LOAD WITH SAFETY FACTOR = _150,188_
(NOT INCLUDING EVAPORATOR FAN OR DEFROST HEAT)

PRELIMINARY HOURLY LOAD = ___150,188___ BTU/24 HR (BASE LOAD) = _9,386_ BTU/HR
16 HRS/DAY (COMP. RUNNING TIME)

FAN HEAT LOAD ESTIMATE BTU/HR.
___ QTY x ___ WATTS EA. x 3.41 BTU/WATT x ___ HRS. ___ BTU/24 HRS
(MOTORS) (INPUT)
OR _1_ QTY x _½_ HP EA. x _4350_ BTU/HP/HR. x _24_ HRS _17,400_ BTU/24 HRS
(MOTORS)

DEFROST HEAT LOAD ESTIMATE BTU/HR
___ QTY. EVAPS x ___ WATTS EA x ___ HRS x 3.41 BTU/WATT x ___ DEFROST LOAD FACTOR*
___ BTU/24 HRS.

*USE 0.50 FOR ELECTRIC DEFROST 0.40 FOR HOT GAS DEFROST

BTU/24 HR. TOTAL LOAD = _150,188_ + _17,400_ + ___-___ = _167,588_ BTU/24 HRS
(BASE LOAD) (FAN HEAT) (DEFROST HEAT)

FL = 1 x ½ x 4350 = _____ OR _150,188_ x _1.10_ = _165,206_ BTU/24 HRS
12000/1000 (BASE LOAD) (BASE LOAD MULT.)
= 60.4

ACTUAL HOURLY LOAD = ___167,588___ BTU/24 HR (TOTAL LOAD) = _10,474_ BTU/HR
16 HRS/DAY (COMP. RUNNING TIME)

**FIGURE 14.2** Refrigeration load form and calculations for Example 14.8. (Courtesy Dunham–Bush, Inc.)

**TABLE 14.11** Simplified Load Determination for Walk-in Refrigerators[a,b]

95°F (35°C) Ambient Air Temperature Surrounding Box

Column groups:
- **Walk-in Coolers, 3 in. Glass Fiber Insulation or Equivalent — Btuh Load** — +35°F (1.7°C) Room[c] (Average Usage, Heavy Usage); +30°F (−1.1°C) Room[d] (Average Usage, Heavy Usage)
- **0°F (−17.8°C) Walk-in Freezers, 4 in. Glass Fiber Insulation or Equivalent — Btuh Load[d]** — Storage Only—No Product Freezing; Food Freezing—Lb./24 Hr. Product Entering at +40°F (+4.4°C): 750, 1500, 3000
- **−20°F (−28.9°C) Walk-in Freezers, 6 in. Glass Fiber Insulation or Equivalent — Btuh Load[d]** — Storage Only—No Product Freezing; Food Freezing—Lb./24 Hr. Product Entering at +40°F (+4.4°C): 750, 1500, 3000

| Outside Dimensions of Walk-in Cooler or Freezer W × L × H | +35°F (1.7°C) Room[c] Average Usage | +35°F (1.7°C) Room[c] Heavy Usage | +30°F (−1.1°C) Room[d] Average Usage | +30°F (−1.1°C) Room[d] Heavy Usage | 0°F Storage Only—No Product Freezing | 0°F 750 | 0°F 1500 | 0°F 3000 | −20°F Storage Only—No Product Freezing | −20°F 750 | −20°F 1500 | −20°F 3000 |
|---|---|---|---|---|---|---|---|---|---|---|---|---|
| 6 × 6 × 9 | 3,050 | 3,650 | 2,950 | 3,500 | 3,550 | 8,800 | | | 3,500 | 9,500 | 15,000 | 27,500 |
| 6 × 7 × 9 | 3,500 | 4,200 | 3,450 | 4,050 | 4,100 | 9,350 | | | 4,000 | 10,000 | 16,000 | 28,000 |
| 6 × 8 × 9 | 3,800 | 4,650 | 3,650 | 4,450 | 4,350 | 9,600 | | | 4,500 | 10,500 | 16,500 | 28,500 |
| 6 × 9 × 9 | 4,200 | 5,100 | 4,050 | 4,900 | 4,650 | 9,900 | | | 4,850 | 10,900 | 16,900 | 28,900 |
| 6 × 10 × 9 | 4,600 | 5,600 | 4,400 | 5,400 | 4,950 | 10,200 | | | 5,100 | 11,100 | 17,100 | 29,100 |
| 7 × 7 × 9 | 3,900 | 4,750 | 3,750 | 4,550 | 4,400 | 9,650 | | | 4,550 | 10,600 | 16,600 | 28,600 |
| 7 × 8 × 9 | 4,350 | 5,300 | 4,200 | 5,100 | 4,800 | 10,000 | | | 4,900 | 10,900 | 16,900 | 28,900 |
| 7 × 9 × 9 | 4,750 | 5,800 | 4,550 | 5,600 | 5,050 | 10,300 | 15,600 | | 5,250 | 11,300 | 17,300 | 29,300 |
| 7 × 10 × 9 | 5,150 | 6,400 | 4,950 | 6,150 | 5,550 | 10,800 | 16,100 | | 5,750 | 11,800 | 17,800 | 29,800 |
| 7 × 12 × 9 | 5,900 | 7,350 | 5,700 | 7,050 | 6,100 | 11,400 | 16,700 | | 6,350 | 12,400 | 18,400 | 30,400 |
| 8 × 8 × 9 | 4,800 | 5,850 | 4,600 | 5,600 | 5,150 | 10,400 | 15,700 | | 5,300 | 11,300 | 17,300 | 29,300 |
| 8 × 9 × 9 | 5,250 | 6,450 | 5,050 | 6,200 | 5,600 | 10,900 | 16,200 | | 5,800 | 11,800 | 17,800 | 29,800 |
| 8 × 10 × 9 | 5,700 | 7,100 | 5,500 | 6,800 | 6,000 | 11,300 | 16,600 | | 6,150 | 12,200 | 18,200 | 30,200 |
| 8 × 12 × 9 | 6,600 | 7,950 | 6,350 | 7,650 | 6,600 | 11,900 | 17,200 | | 6,800 | 12,800 | 18,800 | 30,800 |
| 8 × 14 × 9 | 7,500 | 9,300 | 7,200 | 8,950 | 7,400 | 12,700 | 18,000 | | 7,450 | 13,500 | 19,500 | 31,500 |
| 9 × 9 × 9 | 5,750 | 7,150 | 5,500 | 6,850 | 6,000 | 11,300 | 16,600 | | 6,200 | 12,200 | 18,200 | 30,200 |
| 9 × 10 × 9 | 6,250 | 7,750 | 6,000 | 7,450 | 6,350 | 11,600 | 16,900 | | 6,600 | 12,600 | 18,600 | 30,600 |
| 9 × 12 × 9 | 7,300 | 9,050 | 7,000 | 8,700 | 7,100 | 12,400 | 17,700 | | 7,300 | 13,300 | 19,300 | 31,300 |
| 9 × 14 × 9 | 8,200 | 10,500 | 7,900 | 10,100 | 7,850 | 13,100 | 18,400 | | 8,000 | 14,000 | 20,000 | 32,000 |
| 9 × 16 × 9 | 9,050 | 11,700 | 8,700 | 11,200 | 8,500 | 13,800 | 19,100 | | 8,800 | 14,800 | 20,800 | 32,800 |
| 10 × 10 × 9 | 6,850 | 8,400 | 6,700 | 8,050 | 6,700 | 12,000 | 17,300 | 27,700 | 7,000 | 13,000 | 19,000 | 31,000 |
| 10 × 12 × 9 | 7,800 | 9,650 | 7,500 | 9,250 | 7,650 | 12,900 | 18,200 | 28,700 | 7,750 | 13,800 | 19,800 | 31,800 |
| 10 × 14 × 9 | 8,900 | 11,200 | 8,550 | 10,800 | 8,350 | 13,600 | 18,900 | 29,400 | 8,550 | 14,600 | 20,600 | 32,600 |
| 10 × 16 × 9 | 9,650 | 12,300 | 9,300 | 11,800 | 9,000 | 14,300 | 19,600 | 30,000 | 9,400 | 15,400 | 21,400 | 33,400 |
| 10 × 18 × 9 | 10,600 | 13,400 | 10,200 | 12,900 | 10,000 | 15,300 | 20,600 | 31,000 | 10,100 | 16,100 | 22,100 | 34,100 |
| 12 × 12 × 9 | 9,050 | 11,100 | 8,700 | 10,700 | 8,450 | 13,700 | 19,900 | 29,500 | 8,850 | 14,900 | 20,900 | 32,900 |
| 12 × 14 × 9 | 10,000 | 12,700 | 9,600 | 12,200 | 9,350 | 14,600 | 20,700 | 30,400 | 9,650 | 15,700 | 21,700 | 33,700 |
| 12 × 16 × 9 | 11,000 | 13,900 | 10,600 | 13,400 | 10,100 | 15,400 | 21,700 | 31,100 | 10,400 | 16,400 | 22,400 | 34,400 |
| 12 × 18 × 9 | 12,100 | 15,300 | 11,600 | 14,700 | 11,100 | 16,400 | 22,300 | 32,100 | 11,300 | 17,300 | 23,300 | 35,300 |
| 12 × 20 × 9 | 13,200 | 16,200 | 12,200 | 15,600 | 11,700 | 17,000 | | 32,700 | 12,200 | 18,200 | 24,200 | 36,200 |

| Box size | | | | | | | | | | | | |
|---|---|---|---|---|---|---|---|---|---|---|---|---|
| 12 × 22 × 9 | 14,200 | 17,600 | 13,600 | 16,900 | 12,500 | 17,800 | 23,100 | 33,500 | 13,100 | 19,100 | 25,100 | 37,100 |
| 14 × 14 × 9 | 11,150 | 14,100 | 10,700 | 13,600 | 10,200 | 15,500 | 20,800 | 31,200 | 10,500 | 16,500 | 22,500 | 34,500 |
| 14 × 16 × 9 | 12,350 | 15,500 | 11,900 | 14,900 | 11,200 | 16,500 | 21,800 | 32,200 | 11,400 | 17,400 | 23,400 | 35,400 |
| 14 × 18 × 9 | 13,500 | 16,900 | 13,000 | 16,300 | 12,100 | 17,350 | 22,600 | 33,100 | 12,300 | 18,300 | 24,300 | 36,300 |
| 14 × 20 × 9 | 14,750 | 18,100 | 14,200 | 17,400 | 12,800 | 18,100 | 23,400 | 33,800 | 13,100 | 19,100 | 25,100 | 37,100 |
| 14 × 22 × 9 | 15,750 | 19,500 | 15,100 | 18,700 | 13,400 | 18,700 | 24,000 | 34,400 | 14,200 | 20,200 | 26,200 | 38,200 |
| 14 × 24 × 9 | 16,700 | 20,900 | 16,000 | 20,100 | 14,300 | 19,600 | 24,900 | 35,300 | 15,000 | 21,000 | 27,000 | 39,000 |
| 16 × 16 × 9 | 13,500 | 17,100 | 13,000 | 16,400 | 12,200 | 17,500 | 22,800 | 33,200 | 12,500 | 18,500 | 24,500 | 36,500 |
| 16 × 18 × 9 | 14,850 | 18,000 | 14,300 | 17,300 | 13,000 | 18,300 | 23,600 | 34,000 | 13,300 | 19,300 | 25,300 | 37,300 |
| 16 × 20 × 9 | 16,100 | 20,000 | 15,500 | 19,200 | 13,900 | 19,200 | 24,500 | 34,900 | 14,000 | 20,000 | 26,000 | 38,000 |
| 16 × 22 × 9 | 17,300 | 21,400 | 16,600 | 20,500 | 14,800 | 20,100 | 25,400 | 35,800 | 14,800 | 21,500 | 27,500 | 39,500 |
| 16 × 24 × 9 | 17,800 | 22,800 | 17,100 | 21,900 | 15,600 | 20,900 | 26,200 | 36,600 | 16,300 | 22,300 | 28,300 | 40,300 |
| 18 × 18 × 9 | 16,300 | 20,200 | 15,700 | 19,400 | 14,000 | 19,300 | 24,600 | 35,000 | 14,200 | 20,200 | 26,200 | 38,200 |
| 18 × 20 × 9 | 17,500 | 21,700 | 16,800 | 20,800 | 15,100 | 20,400 | 25,700 | 36,100 | 15,000 | 21,000 | 27,000 | 39,000 |
| 18 × 22 × 9 | 18,900 | 22,700 | 18,200 | 21,800 | 15,800 | 21,100 | 26,400 | 36,800 | 16,400 | 22,400 | 28,400 | 40,400 |
| 18 × 24 × 9 | 19,900 | 24,800 | 19,100 | 23,800 | 16,600 | 21,900 | 27,200 | 37,600 | 17,300 | 23,300 | 29,300 | 41,300 |
| 20 × 20 × 9 | 19,300 | 23,100 | 18,500 | 22,200 | 16,000 | 21,300 | 26,600 | 37,000 | 15,800 | 21,800 | 27,800 | 39,800 |
| 20 × 22 × 9 | 20,200 | 26,600 | 19,400 | 25,600 | 16,700 | | 27,300 | 37,700 | 17,400 | | 29,400 | 41,400 |
| 20 × 24 × 9 | 21,400 | 28,600 | 20,500 | 27,500 | 17,400 | | 28,000 | 38,400 | 18,000 | | 30,000 | 42,000 |
| 22 × 22 × 9 | 21,100 | 28,200 | 20,300 | 27,100 | 17,300 | | 27,900 | 38,300 | 17,600 | | 29,600 | 41,600 |
| 22 × 24 × 9 | 22,400 | 30,100 | 21,500 | 28,900 | 18,400 | | 29,000 | 39,400 | 18,800 | | 30,800 | 42,800 |
| 24 × 24 × 9 | 24,100 | 32,300 | 23,100 | 31,000 | 19,500 | | 30,100 | 40,500 | 20,000 | | 32,000 | 44,000 |

[a] Enter the table under the appropriate cooler or freezer application and determine the Btuh load at the desired walk-in box size.
[b] For ice cream hardening rooms use food freezing selections with 750 lb = 250 gal, 1500 lb = 500 gal, 3000 lb = 1000 gal.
[c] Based on 16 hr compressor operation.
[d] Based on 20 hr compressor operation.
Courtesy McQuay Group, McQuay–Perfex, Inc.

If the daily load had simply been divided by 24 hr the hourly load would appear to be

$$\frac{360,000}{24} = 15,000 \text{ Btu/hr}$$

which is much less than the required equipment capacity.

**Evaporator Fan Load.** The evaporator fan and motor, generally both located in the refrigerated space, add to the required equipment capacity. This load has not been included as part of the other motor loads on the refrigeration load calculation form. The reason for this is that it depends on the equipment capacity, which is not known until the total load is calculated.

After the hourly load is determined, the evaporator fan motor load can be determined from the manufacturer's rating data. This load must also be corrected for running time in those situations where the unit does not operate continually. For rooms above 35°F the fan usually runs continually. For rooms at lower temperatures, the fan is often shut down during defrosting periods and pulldown time. A total of two hours is a typical daily allowance. This is not a rigid figure, however, and needs to be determined in each case, depending on application, equipment, and similar concerns. Table 14.12 shows typical unit cooler ratings. The evaporator fan load can be determined from it.

**Defrost Load.** For rooms with coil surface temperatures below about 32°F, frost will accumulate on the cooling coil. In some cases where the temperature is close to 32°F a simple off cycle time period may be adequate to defrost the coil. Otherwise heat input is required to defrost the coil surface in a short period of time, using hot gas or electric heat. This imposes an additional load on the refrigeration equipment. Figure 14.1 lists approximate defrost load correction factors.

## 14.10 Evaporator Temperature Difference and Room Humidity

In refrigeration applications the evaporator temperature difference (TD) is defined as the design temperature difference between the air in the refrigerated room and the evaporating refrigerant. The humidity in the room will decrease as the TD increases, since a lower coil temperature will condense more moisture out of the air. Each type of product requires a certain range of humidity in the surrounding room air for proper preservation, taste, appearance, and other factors. Table 14.13 lists recommended TD values that will result in satisfactory humidity levels for different classes of product. This table should be used in selecting a forced air unit. For freezer applications a TD of 8 to 10°F is often recommended, to keep dehydration of the product to a minimum.

The following example illustrates equipment selection.

**Example 14.11** A fruit storage cooler at 35°F has a calculated refrigeration load of 280,000 Btu/day. Determine the equipment load and select a unit cooler with off-cycle defrost.

*Solution* The recommended compressor running time is 16 hours. The corrected

**TABLE 14.12** Unit Cooler Capacity Ratings

| Model Size | Btu/hr | | | Motor Power Watts |
|---|---|---|---|---|
| | 10°F TD | 12°F TD | 15°F TD | |
| A | 4500 | 5400 | 6750 | 110 |
| B | 5400 | 6480 | 8100 | 120 |
| C | 6300 | 8160 | 10,000 | 220 |
| D | 8700 | 10,440 | 13,050 | 240 |
| E | 10,600 | 12,720 | 15,900 | 240 |
| F | 13,500 | 16,200 | 20,250 | 360 |
| G | 18,000 | 21,600 | 27,000 | 480 |
| H | 22,500 | 27,000 | 33,750 | 600 |
| I | 27,000 | 32,400 | 40,500 | 720 |

TABLE 14.13 Recommended Evaporator TD[a] for Different Classes of Foods[b]

| Class of Coils | Forced Air Coils, °F | Gravity Coils, °F |
| --- | --- | --- |
| 1 | 6–9 | 14–18 |
| 2 | 9–12 | 18–22 |
| 3 | 12–20 | 21–28 |
| 4 | Above 20 | 27–37 |

[a]Temperature difference is defined as average fixture temperature minus average refrigerant temperature.

[b]Classes of Food:

*Class 1.* Such products as eggs, unpackaged butter and cheese and most vegetables held for comparatively long periods of time. These products require very high relative humidity because it is necessary to effect a minimum of moisture evaporation during storage.

*Class 2.* Such foods as cut meats, fruits and similar products. These require high relative humidities but not as high as Class 1.

*Class 3.* Carcass meats and fruit such as melons which have tough skins. These products require only moderate relative humidities because they have surfaces whose rate of moisture evaporation is moderate.

*Class 4.* Canned goods, bottled goods, and other products which have a protective covering. These are products which need only low relative humidities or which are unaffected by humidity. Products from whose surfaces there is a very low rate of moisture evaporation or none at all, fall into this class. Courtesy Dunham-Bush, Inc.

hourly load is

$$\text{Hourly load} = \frac{280,000 \text{ Btu}}{16 \text{ hr}}$$

$$= 17,500 \text{ Btu/hr}$$

A TD of 12°F is chosen, recommended for fruits in Table 14.13. Using Table 14.12, this indicates a Model G unit cooler, as a tentative solution.

The evaporator fan motors have a total of 480 watts. This adds to the load, calculated as

$$\begin{aligned}\text{Evaporator} \\ \text{fan load}\end{aligned} = \frac{480 \text{ W} \times 3.41 \text{ Btu/hr}}{1 \text{ W}}$$

$$= 1640 \text{ Btu/hr}$$

No correction to running time of the fan is made; it runs continuously, since the room is above freezing. There is also no defrost load. The actual load is therefore

$$\text{Actual load} = 17,500 + 1,640$$

$$= 19,140 \text{ Btu/hr}$$

The Model G is still adequate for the load, and is the unit selected.

## COMPONENT BALANCING

### 14.11 System Component Balancing

The selection of each component of the refrigeration system is generally based on the design cooling load and design conditions. These conditions include the space temperature and perhaps humidity, and conditions of the condenser cooling medium.

Because equipment is manufactured in incremental capacities, it is extremely unlikely that each component selected will have the capacity that exactly matches the design load at the required conditions. In addition to this fact, when the components (compressor, condenser, and evaporator) are installed and operate as a system, each has an effect on the performance of the other. The result of this is that the refrigeration system operates at some fixed condition of capacity and temperatures (for a given set of external conditions). This condition is called the *balance* (or equilibrium) condition or point.

It is necessary to determine the balance point to see if it is close enough to the required conditions, according to the application. If not, a change in equipment selection may be necessary; sometimes a change in required conditions is permissible.

Finding the balance condition is important not only at design (full load) conditions, but often at part load conditions. This is not a question of capacity. A study of the balanced operation at part load is useful in determining if the system will operate without performing erratically, or in a way that could damage equipment.

A study of the component balance conditions is not only useful when selecting proper equipment, but it can also serve in diagnosing unsatisfactory performance, to find which component is the source of the trouble, and perhaps what corrections are needed.

## 14.12 Individual Component Performance

The effect that changing conditions has on the capacity of the compressor, condenser, and evaporator has been discussed in detail in the chapters covering those components. However, a review of some of these effects will aid in understanding component balancing. In the following, the use of the word *capacity* refers to the system refrigeration capacity, regardless of which component is being discussed.

The compressor capacity will decrease with decreasing suction pressure and therefore with corresponding decreasing saturated suction temperature (SST). The compressor capacity will decrease with increasing condensing temperature. For a given compressor operating at a certain speed these effects on performance can be plotted graphically, as shown in Figure 14.3. The evaporating tem-

perature is sometimes plotted instead of the saturated suction temperature, because this is of more interest in relation to evaporator conditions. It is just as correct to use evaporator temperature, since it differs from the saturated suction temperature by a constant value—the suction line equivalent temperature drop (see Chapters 4 and 11).

The capacity of an air cooled condenser increases with an increasing difference between the surrounding air (dry bulb) temperature and the condensing temperature.

For an air cooled condensing unit (compressor and condenser operating as a single unit) the capacity increases with decreasing surrounding air temperature and decreases with decreasing saturated suction (or evaporating) temperature. Typical performance curves are shown in Figure 14.4.

The capacity of an evaporator increases with decreasing refrigerant evaporating temperature. For an air cooling coil, if there is dehumidification, the capacity increases with increasing air wet bulb temperatures. This is the usual situation in comfort air conditioning work. If there is little dehumidification (only sensible cooling), the capacity increases with increasing air dry bulb temperature. This is frequently the situation in commercial refrigeration. The capacity variation of a typical air cooling coil for refrigeration applications is shown in Figure 14.5, at a given CFM.

## 14.13 Procedures for Component Balancing

The determination of component balance conditions by calculation would prove difficult. It involves development of suitable equations and their solution. A computer is generally needed to solve the equations handily.

However, a graphical analysis can be carried out quite simply. It has the advantage of indicating quickly what happens to performance when conditions change. The general proce-

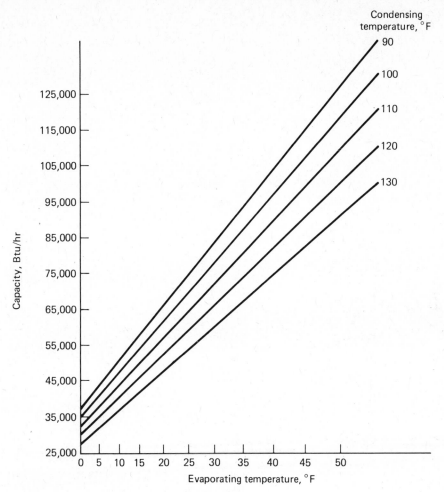

**FIGURE 14.3** Performance curves of a reciprocating compressor (typical).

dure is to plot the performance curves of each component on the same graph. The intersection point of the curves of two components is the balance point. That is, that point will be the capacity and operating condition of the components when operating together as a system. We will carry out the analysis here for the combination of a condensing unit and air cooling coil. If a separate compressor and condenser are used, the graphical procedure is first applied to these two components, and then to the resulting condensing unit and cooling coil.

Figure 14.6 shows the graphical performance of a specific air cooled condensing unit together with a forced air evaporator used for commercial refrigeration. The evaporator capacity varies with entering air dry bulb temperature, since there is little dehumidification. Notice that the horizontal scale, which shows evaporating temperature, is not linear. (The temperature scale is based on the corresponding saturated suction pressure (because this results in straight-line performance curves for the equipment). An assumed suction line

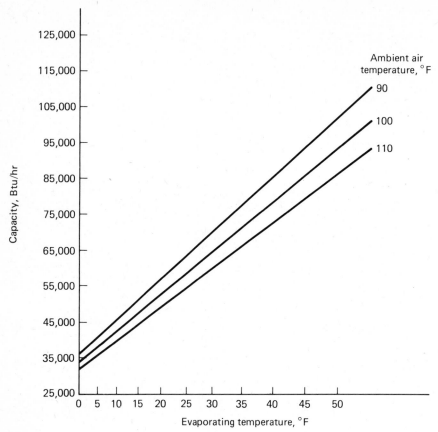

**FIGURE 14.4** Performance curves of an air cooled condensing unit (typical).

pressure drop equivalent to 2°F has been used in plotting performance. An example illustrates use of the performance diagram.

***Example 14.12*** Air cooled condensing unit C and forced air evaporator M (performance curves shown in Figure 14.6) are used together in a walk-in refrigerator. The ambient air temperature is 95°F and the temperature in the space is 35°F. What is the system capacity and evaporating temperature?

*Solution* The intersection of the performance curves for the specified conditions is the balance point. Figure 14.7, a detail of Figure 14.6, shows the solution. Reading from the diagram

Capacity = 24,200 Btu/hr

Evaporating temperature = 21°F

The capacity variation of water cooled and evaporative condensers and liquid chillers will not be discussed in relation to component balancing. The procedures can be developed in a manner similar to that for air cooled condensers and air cooling coils.

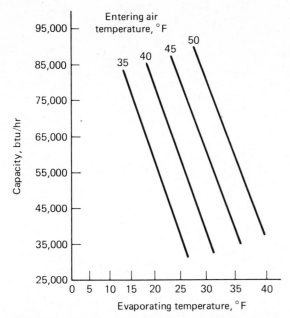

**FIGURE 14.5** Performance curves of a forced air evaporator (typical).

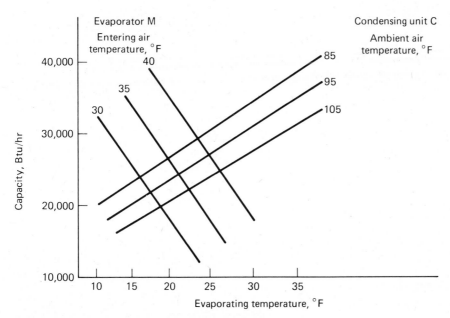

**FIGURE 14.6** Performance of an air cooled condensing unit and forced air evaporator plotted together (typical).

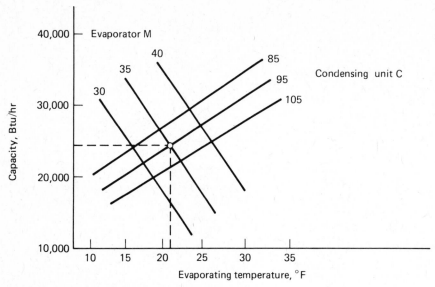

**FIGURE 14.7** Sketch of solution for Example 14.12

## 14.14 Component Unbalance and Space Conditions

The system performance diagram can also be used for diagnostic troubleshooting, especially to determine if the components are unbalanced—that is, if one is oversized compared to another. In many food refrigeration applications the space humidity must be kept at a certain level to preserve the food quality. For a given required space dry bulb temperature, the lower the evaporating temperature, the lower will be the space relative humidity. This is because the lower coil surface temperature will condense more water vapor from the air. The difference between the space temperature and refrigerant evaporating temperature is called evaporator temperature difference, or simply TD. Suggested TD values to produce different relative humidities are shown in Table 14.14.

Component unbalance can create unsatisfactory space humidity conditions, as illustrated in the following example.

*Example 14.13* A storage space holding fresh strawberries is to be kept at 32°F and 90 percent RH (relative humidity). The ambient air temperature is 85°F. The refrigeration

**TABLE 14.14** Suggested Evaporator TD for Desired Relative Humidity

| Temperature Range, °F | Desired Relative Humidity, % | TD (Refrigerant to Air), °F |
|---|---|---|
| 25–45 | 90 | 8–12 |
| 25–45 | 85 | 10–14 |
| 25–45 | 80 | 12–16 |
| 25–45 | 75 | 16–22 |
| 10 and below | — | 15 or less |

load is 23,000 Btu/hr. The air cooled condensing unit and forced air evaporator shown in Figure 14.6 are used. Is this a satisfactory combination?

*Solution* From Figure 14.6 it is seen that the balance point results in an adequate refrigeration capacity of 25,000 Btu/hr. However, the evaporating temperature is about 17°F. This results in a TD of 32 − 17 = 15°F. According to Table 14.15 the TD is too high for the humidity specified, and will cause the product to lose moisture.

The fault shown in the system in Example 14.13 is that the evaporator is undersized. The refrigeration capacity is achieved by increasing the evaporator TD. For a 90 percent RH the maximum TD = 12°F. With this TD the evaporating temperature, ET, is 20°F, and at that temperature the evaporator cooling capacity is only 21,000 Btu/hr. A larger evaporator is required.

In Figure 14.8 the conditions are shown for both the undersized evaporator M and larger evaporators N and P. Their capacities are plotted for the design space condition of 32°F, so as not to complicate the figure. The balance point for unit N is at point 2, with a capacity of 27,000 Btu/hr, an evaporating temperature of 20°F and a TD = 12°F. This is a satisfactory condition.

An oversized evaporator can also result in unsatisfactory space conditions. If evaporator P shown in Figure 14.8 is used, the balance point is 3, with a refrigeration capacity of 30,000 Btu/hr, and a smaller evaporator TD. The higher capacity will result in the unit being in the off cycle for longer periods of time. Both this and the smaller TD will result in a higher space humidity. Although in this particular example a high humidity is desirable, in many applications the humidity might rise to an unacceptable level, causing spoilage of the product.

In the previous discussion the effect of an incorrectly sized condensing unit has not been considered. In Figure 14.9 point (1) shows a satisfactory balance of an evaporator R and condensing unit E for a load of 43,000 Btu/hr, with a space temperature of 35°F and an evaporator TD = 14°F, for a desired humidity of 80 percent RH. The evaporating tempera-

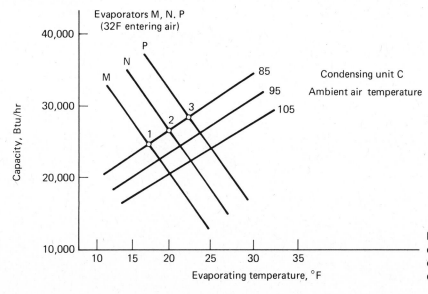

**FIGURE 14.8** Illustration of the effect of an incorrect size evaporator on space conditions.

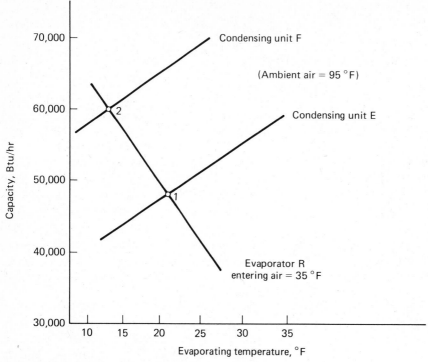

**FIGURE 14.9** Illustration of the effect of an incorrect size condensing unit on space conditions.

ture ET = 21°F. The condenser ambient air temperature is 95°F. The system capacity is 48,000 Btu/hr, about 12 percent above the design load.

If an oversized condensing unit F is used, the new balance point (2) results in a refrigeration capacity of 60,000 Btu/hr, about 40 percent excess capacity. The system will be operating for much too short a period of time. While the system is off, humidity may rise too high. On the other hand, while the system is operating the evaporating temperature will be too low, resulting in too low a humidity. If the oversized condensing unit has capacity reduction features the situation might be resolved by operating it at part load. Of course this is not the best solution. An unnecessary higher cost was spent for the oversized unit. Furthermore, the energy use at part load is usually higher than for a unit selected at its design capacity.

## REVIEW QUESTIONS

1. What is the meaning of the term *refrigeration load?*

2. What are the sources of heat gains to the refrigerated space?

3. What is the pull-down load? Of what does it consists?

4. What is the heat of respiration? What causes it?

5. In what ways does the location of a motor affect the refrigeration load?

6. Explain the term *balance condition* and its importance.

7. What are the possible effects of an oversized (undersized) evaporator on refrigerated space conditions?

8. What are the possible effects of an oversized (undersized) condenser on refrigerated space conditions?

# PROBLEMS

14.1 A walk-in refrigerator has outside dimensions of 12 ft wide × 14 ft long × 12 ft high. The temperature difference between the outside and the refrigerator is 80°F. The walls and ceiling are insulated with 6 in. of corkboard. What is the 24-hr heat gain through the walls and roof?

14.2 The red tile roof of a refrigerated room is exposed to the sun. The difference between inside and outside temperatures is 60°F. What temperature difference should be used to calculate the roof heat transmission gain?

14.3 A cold storage room has an unheated floor slab on the ground, with 3 in. of styrofoam insulation. The building is in New Orleans, Louisiana. The floor dimensions are 20 ft long × 16 ft wide. The room is kept at 38°F. What is the 24-hr heat gain through the floor slab?

14.4 A cold storage room kept at 40°F has a volume of 8000 ft$^3$. Outside air conditions are 95°F and 50 percent RH. Calculate the infiltration heat load through a door with heavy usage.

14.5 A freezing room receives 800 lb of beef at 50°F, to be frozen to −10°F in 12 hr. Calculate the 24 hr product pull-down load.

14.6 A storage room contains 32,000 lb of corn at 32°F. What is the daily load from the heat of respiration?

14.7 A 10 ft wide × 12 ft long × 9 ft high walk-in cooler at 35°F has an average usage. Using the rapid load determination procedure, what is the hourly refrigeration load?

14.8 The daily refrigeration load in a cooler kept at 35°F, with defrost, is 670,000 Btu/24 hr. What is the hourly equipment load?

14.9 A cooler at 40°F has a refrigeration load of 240,000 Btu/day. The evaporator TD is 15°F. Determine the equipment load and select a unit cooler without defrost.

14.10 Air cooled condensing unit C and forced air evaporator M (Figure 14.6) are used together for a walk-in cooler. The ambient air temperature is 100°F and the cooler space temperature is 40°F. What is the system capacity and the evaporating temperature?

14.11 Calculate the refrigeration load for the walk-in freezer described in Table 14.15.

**TABLE 14.15** Freezer Specifications for Problem 14.11

## REFRIGERATION LOAD ESTIMATE FORM
### FOR ROOMS ABOVE AND BELOW FREEZING

— LOAD SURVEY & ESTIMATING DATA —

DESIGN AMBIENT __90__ °FDB. __77__ °FWB. __60__ %RH. __65__ °F SUMMER GROUND TEMP.
(USE 55°F FOR INSULATED FREEZE FLOOR SLAB)

ROOM DESIGN: __-10__ °FDB. _____ °FWB. __90__ %RH _____ °F WINTER DESIGN AMBIENT

ACCESS AREA: __80__ °FDB. _____ °FWB. __60__ %RH. (ANTE-RM/LOADING DOCK/OTHER)

ROOM DIM. OUTSIDE: __30__ FT. W __40__ FT. L __12__ FT.H __4080__ TOTAL SQ. FT. (OUTSIDE SURFACE)

| | Insulation | | | | Wall Thick-ness | Adj. Area °F | Effective Wall TD | °F Sun Effect | Total TD | Overall Wall Heat Gain |
| --- | --- | --- | --- | --- | --- | --- | --- | --- | --- | --- |
| | Type | Inches Thick | K Factor | U* Factor | | | | | | Btu/24 Hrs/Sq. Ft. |
| N. Wall | Moulded | 6 | .2 | 0.033 | 8" | 90 | 100 | ■ | 100 | 80 |
| S. Wall | Polystyrene | 6 | ↑ | " | " | 80 | 90 | — | 90 | 72 |
| E. Wall | | 6 | | " | " | 80 | 90 | — | 90 | 72 |
| W. Wall | | 6 | | " | " | 90 | 100 | 6 | 106 | 0.8 × 106 = 84.8 |
| Ceiling | | 8 | | 0.025 | 10" | 90 | 100 | 20 | 120 | 72 |
| Floor | | 4 | ↓ | 0.025 | 6" | 55 | 65 | ■ | 65 | 78 |

*'U' Factor: $\dfrac{K}{\text{Insul. Thickness (in.)}}$ _____

REFRIG. DOOR(S): __(1) 7'×4'__ VENT. FAN(S): _____

ROOM INT. VOL: __28⅔__ W × __38⅔__ L × __10⅔__ H = __11,823__ CU. Ft.
(INSIDE ROOM DIMENSIION = OUTSIDE DIMENSION − WALL THICKNESSES)

FLOOR AREA __28⅔__ W × __38⅔__ L = __1108__ SQ. FT.

ELECTRICAL POWER __440__ VOLTS. __3__ PH. __60__ HERTZ; CONTROL __115__ VOLTS

TYPE CONTROL: _____

PRODUCT DATA AND CLASS OF PRODUCT: __FROZEN FOODS (PACKAGED)__ _____

| | Amount of Product | | | Product Temp. °F | | Specific Heat | | | | | |
| --- | --- | --- | --- | --- | --- | --- | --- | --- | --- | --- | --- |
| Type product | TONS Amount Storage | TONS Daily Turn-over | Freezing or Cooling | Enter-ing | Final | Above Freeze | Below Freeze | Lat. Ht. Freeze Btu/lb. | Highest Product Freeze Temp. | Heat or Respir'n Btu/lb. 24 Hr. | (  ) Pull Down (  ) Freezing Time Hrs. |
| FROZEN FOODS | 50 | 12 | FREEZING | +5 | -10 | — | 0.46 | — | — | — | — |
| | | | | | | | | | | | |

EVAP. TD __10°__ , TYPE DEFROST ☐ AIR, ☐ HOT GAS, ☑ ELECTRIC.

CLASS PRODUCT __—__ .

318

**TABLE 14.15** Continued

NO. OF DEFROSTS & TOTAL TIME PER 24 HRS. _6_ NO. _2_ HRS.

COMPRESSOR RUNNING TIME _18_ HRS.

BOX USAGE ☐ AVERAGE, ☐ HEAVY, ☐ EXTRA HEAVY

PRODUCT LOAD AND ADDITIONAL INFORMATION: _PRODUCT ARRIVES IN REFRIGERATED TRUCKS, ALLOW_ _15° F PULLDOWN TO FREEZER TEMPERATURE. PRODUCT PACKAGED AND SEALED IN CARTONS._

PACKAGING: _CARTONS_ CONTAINERS _—_ WGT. _1500 LBS._ SP. HT. _.32_ (CONTAINER)

PALLETS: NO. _24_ SIZE _____ WGT. EA. _35 LBS_ SP. HT. _.6_  _840 LBS TOTAL_

PRODUCT RACKS: NO. _____ MAT'L _____ WGT. EA. _____ SP. HT. _____

ESTIMATING PRODUCT LOADING CAPACITY OF ROOM

ESTIMATED PRODUCT LOADING = 0.40 × _____ CU. FT. × _____ LBS./CU. FT. = _____ LBS. _____

(ROOM VOLUME)        (LOADING DENSITY)

MISCELLANEOUS LOADS                                    MOTORS (OTHER THAN EVAP. FAN)

PEOPLE NO. _4_ HRS. _10_                              USE: _____ , _____ HP, _____ HRS.

FORK LIFTS _2_ NO., _4_ HP. _8_ HRS./DAY, OTHER _____

LIGHTS _1½_ WATTS/SQ. FT.

# Chapter 15

## ELECTRICAL SERVICE SYSTEMS. MOTORS

This chapter describes electrical service systems used to supply power for motors, and offers information on types of motors used to drive refrigeration compressors and accessory equipment. A review of some electrical fundamentals is presented first. Explanations will be brief, but will be adequate for our purposes.

## OBJECTIVES

A study of this chapter will enable you to:
1. Explain the meaning of the basic terms used in electrical service systems.
2. Sketch and describe electrical service system arrangements.
3. Identify and explain the use of circuit overcurrent protection devices.
4. Identify and describe motor characteristics.
5. Sketch the circuit and describe the operation of single-phase motors.
6. Identify and describe the types of three-phase motors.

### 15.1 Voltage, Current, Resistance

Electrons are elementary particles that carry a negative electric charge. The flow of electrons in a circuit, called electric *current,* is caused by an electromotive *force* (EMF). This force is also called by the names electric *potential* and *voltage.* The name *voltage* derives from the unit of measurement of electric force, the volt (E).

A voltage exists when there is an excess of electrons in one part of a circuit in relation to another part. That is, a potential difference is created. Electrons are particles that have a negative ($-$) electric charge. When there is a deficiency of electrons, a positive ($+$) charge exists. The terms *negative polarity* and *positive polarity* are used to describe the conditions of negative and positive charge. The behavior of electrical charges is such that a potential difference (voltage) exists when there is an opposite polarity between two points. If a complete circuit or loop is provided, electrons will flow from the negative ($-$) to the positive ($+$) polarity. Batteries and generators are typical electric devices that can develop a voltage.

The rate of flow of electricity is called *current.* It is measured by the unit called the *ampere,* or simply amp (I). In order for current to continuously flow there must be a complete *circuit* or path for the electricity to flow through. The flow of current is opposed by a property of the material through which it is flowing, called *resistance.* Some substances, such as copper, have a very low electrical resistance; they are called *conductors.* Materials that have a high electrical resistance to current flow are called *resistors.* Tungsten is an example. Materials that do not conduct any significant current are called nonconductors or *insulators.* Glass is an example. There is also a group of materials called *semiconductors,* that conduct electricity only under certain conditions.

### 15.2 Direct and Alternating Current

Electric current that always flows in one direction is called *direct current* (dc). This results when the voltage (force) is always applied in one direction in the circuit, as from a battery. That is, the voltage does not change polarity. DC voltage is constant in value when delivered from a source such as a battery, but can be made to vary in value by use of appropriate devices.

Current that reverses its direction of flow periodically is called *alternating current* (ac). This is caused by a voltage that changes direction. Electricity for power use is almost always generated and distributed as ac current, primarily because overall costs are lower. Direct current is used in some controls, electronic circuits, and other special applications.

## 15.3 Alternating Current Characteristics

The voltage produced by a battery is constant in value and does not change in polarity. That is, the force is always in the same direction in the circuit, see Figure 15.1(*a*). As a result the current always flows in one direction.

In an alternating current system the electrical generator produces a voltage that varies both in value and reverses direction periodically with time. The voltage rises to a peak, falls to zero, then rises and falls again, but in the opposite direction, as in Figure 15.1(*b*).

That is, the polarity of the voltage is reversed. The shape of the voltage curve is called a sine wave.

The curve in Figure 15.1(*b*) is shown for one complete cycle or period, which is repeated continuously with time. The rate at which the complete cycle is repeated is called the *frequency*. In the United States the frequency is usually 60 cycles per second, abbreviated 60 Hz (Hertz). That is, the polarity of the voltage is reversed 60 times a second, and one cycle would take one-sixteenth of a second. It is convenient to define the length of one complete cycle as 360°, the number of degrees of angle in a full circle. This coincides with the fact that the voltage generator is a rotating device, and one voltage cycle occurs with one complete rotation of the generator. The position on the cycle time axis is called the *phase angle*. For instance, referring to Figure 15.1(*b*), the voltage peaks at 90°, drops off to zero at 180°, and then peaks again (in the opposite direction) at 270°, then falls to zero at 360° as one cycle is completed.

The current also rises and falls, as well as reverses direction, as a result of the way the voltage is applied in an ac circuit. The current is said to be *in phase* with the voltage when it rises and falls in step with the voltage, as seen in Figure 15.2. That is, in this situation the

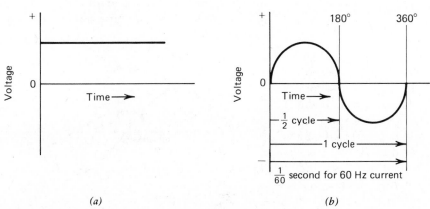

(*a*)                                 (*b*)

**FIGURE 15.1** A comparison of (*a*) direct (dc) and (*b*) alternating (ac) current.

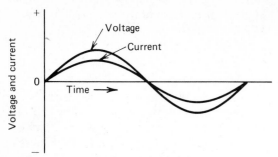

**FIGURE 15.2** Voltage and current in phase.

current peaks, falls to zero, and reverses at the same time as the voltage. Another way of expressing this relation is to say that the phase angle (between voltage and current) is zero.

## 15.4 Inductance and Capacitance

The equipment to which the current is delivered is called the *load*. For the purposes of the following discussion, we can assume that practically all of the opposition to flow is in the load, temporarily neglecting any in the wire conductors. The property of resistance has been mentioned previously. *When the load has resistance only, the current and voltage are in phase.*

There are two other characteristics that the load may have, besides resistance, that also affect the flow of current. They are called *inductance* and *capacitance*. These characteristics exist only with alternating current flow.

*Inductance.* The flow of electric current through a wire creates a magnetic force field around the wire. This force is used in electromechanical devices such as relays and contactors to open and close circuits, and to make motors function. We are more interested at this time in discussing another effect that may occur. If the current rises and falls (alternating current) the magnetic field builds up and collapses in a manner similar to the current. If a second wire is adjacent to the energized circuit, the changing magnetic field will induce a voltage and current in the second wire.

This effect is called *inductance*. It is the basis by which transformers and induction motors function. These devices will be discussed later.

When ac current flows through a coil of wire, the changing field induces a voltage in that wire itself (called *self-inductance*), in the *opposite* direction to the applied voltage. (This is often called a.counter EMF). The opposing voltage delays the rise of the current: The current *lags* behind the applied voltage. This is shown in Figure 15.3. *The current is no longer in phase with the voltage,* unlike the case when there is a pure resistance load. This phase lag is important, because it results in a loss of useful power. Motors and other devices with coils have an inductance as well as a resistance load.

*Capacitance.* A capacitor is a device constructed of two metallic plates separated by insulation. The insulation is called a dielectric. By applying a voltage, an electric charge can be stored in the capacitor. This is called *capacitance.* When an ac voltage is applied, the capacitor alternately charges and discharges. The effect of capacitance when installed in series with a load in an ac circuit is to retard the voltage in relation to the current. That is, the *current leads the voltage,* the opposite effect to that of an inductance. The uses to which this effect can be applied will be discussed later. The combined effect on current flow of resistance, inductance, and capacitance in an ac

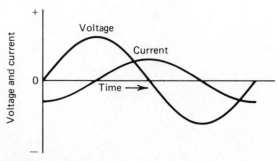

**FIGURE 15.3** voltage and current out of phase (current lags).

circuit is called *impedance*. In a dc circuit, of course, resistance is the only effect that can exist.

## 15.5 Electrical System Relationships

The voltage, current, resistance, and power of electrical systems are related by equations that are used in electrical calculations. It is not our purpose here to engage in this work, but since these relations also demonstrate the general performance of systems, they will be discussed.

*Ohm's Law.* The relation between voltage, current, and resistance in both dc and ac circuits is expressed by the following equation, called Ohms law:

$$I = \frac{E}{R} \qquad (15.1)$$

where

> $I$ = current, amps
> $E$ = voltage, volts
> $R$ = resistance (or impedance), ohms

*Power.* Electricity is a form of energy. Power ($P$), the *rate* at which energy is used, is generally of more immediate concern than energy when dealing with motors. Power is measured in the unit of watts (W) or kilowatts (kW). In a dc circuit, and in an ac circuit where the current and voltage are in phase, the power consumed is expressed by the following equation:

$$P = E \times I \qquad (15.2)$$

where

> $P$ = power, watts
> $E$ = voltage, volts
> $I$ = current, amps

*Power Factor.* In an ac circuit where the current and voltage are not in phase, Equation 15.2 does not express the power used. The actual power consumed in this case is given by the following equation for single phase:

$$P = E \times I \times PF$$

where

> $P, E, I$ are as before     (15.3)
> $PF$ = power factor

The actual power is usually measured at the load by a power measuring instrument, a watt-meter. The product of the current and voltage is the "apparent power," and is expressed as

$$P_{app} = E \times I \qquad (15.4)$$

The power factor is expressed by the following relation:

$$PF = \frac{P}{P_{app}} = \frac{P}{E \times I} \qquad (15.5)$$

where

> $PF$ = power factor
> $P$ = actual power
> $P_{app}$ = apparent power

Mathematically, the power factor is the cosine of the angle representing the phase shift of the current from the voltage. When there is an inductive load the actual power is less than the apparent power. The explanation of this can be seen from Figure 15.4.

In Figure 15.4(*a*) the power is plotted for the case where the current and voltage are in phase. In Figure 15.4(*b*) the power is plotted for the situation where current lags behind voltage. Note that there is actually a period of time when there is negative power. This power does not do useful work in driving the motor. It is undesirable because more current must be transmitted, which increases line losses. Since capacitance causes current to lead voltage—that is, it raises the power factor—it can be used to improve a low power factor.

*Line ($I^2R$) Losses.* Some power is lost in overcoming the resistance of the wire conductors,

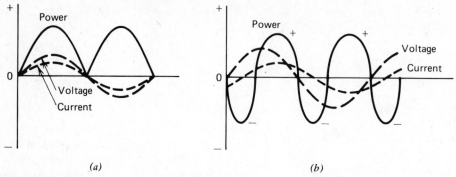

*(a)*

*(b)*

**FIGURE 15.4** The effect of power factor on useful power. (*a*) Voltage and current in phase—power is all positive. (*b*) Current lags behind power—some power is negative.

and is converted into heat. This loss can be expressed by the equation

$$P = E \times I = I^2 R \qquad (15.6)$$

where

$P$ = power lost in wiring, watts
$I$ = current, amps
$R$ = resistance of wiring, ohms
$E$ = voltage

It is apparent from this equation that it is desirable to reduce the current so as to minimize line losses, which is wasted energy, and which in extreme cases can overheat the wiring dangerously. This is one reason electricity is transmitted long distances at very high voltages.

***Single and Three-Phase Power.*** Figure 15.1 illustrates the voltage–time characteristic for *single phase* alternating current. A single voltage is used to deliver current through one conductor. Large-scale electric power is actually generated as *three-phase* power. The electric generator is constructed to develop three separate (single phase) voltages, each 120° apart, as seen in Figure 15.5. The current from each phase is transmitted in a separate conductor, resulting in three-phase power.

The power delivered in a three-phase system is expressed by the relation

$$P = 1.73 \times E \times I \times PF \qquad (15.7)$$

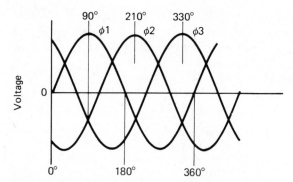

**FIGURE 15.5** Voltage in a three-phase system. Symbol φ means phase.

## 15.6 Transformers

A transformer is a device that changes ac voltage in one circuit to a higher or lower ac voltage in another circuit. A simple transformer is shown in Figure 15.6. It consists of two coils wound on an iron core. The coil carrying the source voltage is called the *primary* and the other coil is called the *secondary*.

The alternating current in the primary produces a magnetic field with lines of force that cut through the secondary coil, inducing a voltage in it. The ratio of voltages is directly proportional to the ratio of the number of turns in the two coils. Thus, if the primary coil has 1000 turns and the secondary has 500 turns, the secondary voltage would be one half the primary voltage. A transformer that de-

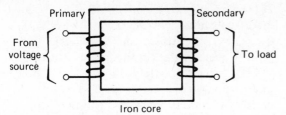

**FIGURE 15.6** Basic elements of a transformer.

creases voltage is called a *step-down* transformer and one that increases voltage is called a *step-up* transformer.

## 15.7 Electric Service Characteristics

Alternating current is distributed at very high voltages from the utility company and gradually stepped down according to the remaining distance to be covered and the customer's requirements.

There are many possible secondary service voltages and arrangements. We will discuss only a few of the most popular types here. First we should distinguish between service (or nominal) voltage and utilization voltage, a point that sometimes causes confusion. *Service voltage* is the voltage supplied from the utility under normal conditions, whereas *utilization voltage* is the voltage available at the motor or other device. The utilization voltage is lower than the service voltage because of "voltage drop" due to line losses. For example, when voltages of 115 V, 120 V, and 110 V are referred to, the service voltage is usually 120 V. The lower voltages refer to the voltage available at the equipment, or to the equipment voltage rating. We will specify service voltages in this section, and motor rating voltages when motors are discussed.

*Single Phase, Three-Wire, 120/240 V.* A schematic diagram of this service is shown in Figure 15.7. It is used commonly for residential and some small commercial applications.

This service furnishes single phase current at either 120 V or 240 V (written 120/240 V). The connections to the transformer secondary are as shown. Connections across the two outer conductors, called the "hot legs," furnish 240 V. Connections between either outer conductor and the center conductor furnishes 120 V.

The center conductor, called the *neutral*, is *grounded*. This means that it is directly connected to the ground (earth) or to a pipe, rod, or other conducting object that is then connected to the earth. This conductor is at approximately zero voltage, the voltage of the ground. It does not carry any current if the loads are balanced (equal) between it and the two hot legs. This is why it is called a "neutral." The use of a neutral wire allows smaller size wiring to be used. Each hot leg conductor carries only the load between it and the neutral. Without the neutral, both of any two conductors carry the total load between them.

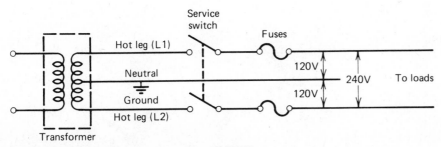

**FIGURE 15.7** A single phase, three-wire, 120/240V service.

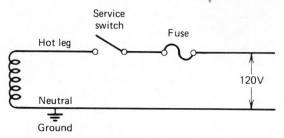

**FIGURE 15.8** A single phase, two-wire, 120V service.

Grounding is used to protect the system from a sudden high voltage and to protect people against electrical shock. In addition to grounding the system, equipment must also be connected to a ground to protect against shock.

A simple 120 V, single phase, two-wire service is found in older residential installations (Figure 15.8), but it is limited to very small loads, since the conductors must be larger. Furthermore, devices wired for 220 V, such as electric ranges and large air conditioning units, could not be used.

For larger loads, three-phase current is normally furnished. This is both because larger motors are of the three-phase type, and conductor sizes are smaller than required for single phase.

***Three Phase, Four-Wire, 120/208 V.*** A schematic diagram of this service is shown in Figure 15.9. The transformer is called a "wye" type because of the arrangement of its coils.

This service has four conductors—three phase (hot) wires and a neutral wire. Connection between any phase and the neutral furnishes 120 V single phase current for lighting, receptacles, and small single-phase motors. Connection between two phases supplies 208 V single phase current, and connection across all three phases supplies 208 V three-phase current for larger motors. This service is widely used in commercial applications, and has been installed in some residential areas where central air conditioning is widespread, so that three-phase motors can be used for the refrigeration compressors.

***Three Phase, Four-Wire, 120/240 V.*** A schematic diagram of this service is shown in Figure 15.10. A "delta" type transformer is used, called so because of the coil arrangement.

Single-phase, 120 V service is available between either phase leg (L1 or L3) and the neutral. Single-phase, 240 V is fed between L1 and L3. Three-phase, 240 V is fed from all three phases L1, L2, and L3. Connection from the transformer tap that feeds L2 and the

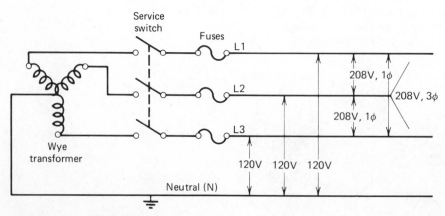

**FIGURE 15.9** A three-phase, four-wire, 120/208V service. Symbol φ means phase.

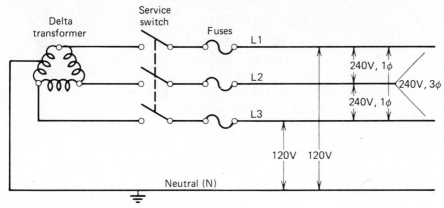

**FIGURE 15.10** A three-phase, four-wire, 120/240V service. Symbol φ means phase.

neutral will furnish 208 V. Referred to as the "wild leg," it is not generally used.

***Three Phase, Four-Wire, 277/480 V.*** A schematic diagram of this service is shown in Figure 15.11. It is very desirable for large commercial installations. Large motors are served with 480 V three-phase current and the fluorescent lighting with 277 V single phase current. The higher voltages allow a considerable savings in conductor sizes.

Single-phase, 277 V current is supplied between any phase and the neutral, and three-phase, 480 V is supplied from the three phases. The building can also be furnished with 120/240 V current by installing a step-down transformer, using 480 V single phase from two phases for the transformer primary.

Three-phase, three-wire service without a neutral also exists, but four-wire service is generally installed in modern systems.

## 15.8 Circuit Protection

Excess current (overcurrent) through any part of an electrical circuit can overheat the conductors, due to increased $I^2R$ resistance heating. Overheating can melt the wiring, or even start fires.

Overcurrent can also damage motors and other equipment, through the same effects (overheating, melting, and fire). The third possible result is injury and even fatality to people, resulting from electrical shock caused if high currents pass through an individual's body.

Special protective devices and certain wiring arrangements are required to protect against these hazards. Combinations of switches and overcurrent protective devices are used for circuit protection. Two types of circuit protective devices are available, *fuses* and *circuit breakers*. Additional devices also used to protect only motors will be discussed, more appropriately, later.

Overcurrent can result either from an overload in equipment, which will result in its drawing too much current, or from a system fault, either a short circuit or ground fault. A *short circuit* is a condition in which the circuit takes a "short" path (low resistance) between two hot wires rather than through a load. As a result a very high current results. A *ground fault* is a short circuit to the ground or neutral.

Overcurrent devices operate by sensing an excess current and respond by simply opening the circuit. This is called "clearing" the fault. Generally the circuit remains open until it is

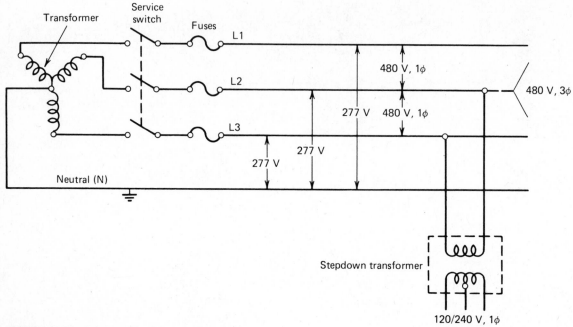

**FIGURE 15.11** A three-phase, four-wire, 277/480V service. Symbol ϕ means phase.

manually closed. That is, the device is not constructed to automatically close, except under special circumstances.

Requirements for types and locations of circuit protection devices and grounding procedures are governed by various codes and standards, particularly the National Electric Code (NEC) in the United States. Some familiarity with this code is an absolute must for the technologist who deals with electrical systems.

## 15.9 Fuses

The fuse is a simple yet very effective overcurrent protection device. It contains a metal link with a low melting point temperature, in series with the line. When a current significantly above the rated value of the fuse flows through the metal, its resistance causes it to overheat and melt ("blow"), breaking the circuit.

Fuses are available in two physical arrange-

ments, the *plug* type and the *cartridge* type (Figure 15.12). The plug fuse is commonly used in residences, and is available up to 30 amps rating. The cartridge type, used in both residential and other installations, is available in sizes over 30 amps.

Cartridge fuses can be either renewable or nonrenewable. The metal link can be replaced in a blown fuse of the renewable type. Since only the metal element is changed, the renewable type can save costs. An objection, however, is that a link of the wrong capacity may inadvertently be used as a replacement.

A *time delay* fuse has an element that will take a current overload for a short period of time before melting. This type is used as a motor protective device. Motors may draw a very large current for a very short period of time when starting. This current does not last long enough to overheat, and of course the fuse should not blow during this normal function.

Fuses are often combined as part of a *discon-*

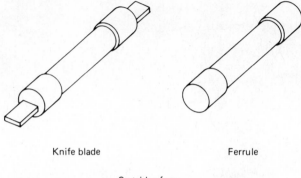

Knife blade                     Ferrule

Cartridge fuses

Plug fuse

**FIGURE 15.12** Basic fuse types.

*nect switch* (Figure 15.13), a switch that is used to isolate a circuit. Fuses are placed in series with each leg of the switch.

## 15.10 Circuit Breakers

The fuse is clearly a somewhat inconvenient device since it must be removed and replaced. The circuit breaker is an overcurrent protection device that remains permanently in the circuit and which, after clearing the fault, can be reset (reclosed). This is considerably more convenient to have than a fuse.

A circuit breaker (Fig. 15.14) is a switch that operates automatically. It contains a mechanical latch mechanism that holds the electrical contacts closed. A spring tends to pull the contact open. An overcurrent releases the latch causing the switch to open, or trip. There are two types of circuit breakers, the *magnetic trip* and the *thermal trip*.

The thermal trip breaker contains a bimetal strip. Overcurrent heats the strip which then bends due to the different expansion effects of the metals in the strip. This releases the latch and the breaker trips.

The magnetic trip breaker contains a solenoid coil. When an overcurrent passes through the coil the electromagnetic field created around the coil becomes strong enough to pull an armature which trips the breaker contacts.

The circuit breaker can be manually reset by a switch handle after the overcurrent has passed. (A short period of time is required for the bimetal strip to cool down in the thermal type.) A circuit breaker in some cases can also double as a manual disconnect switch. Code requirements spell out when this is permissible. Circuit breakers are made in both single pole or multipole arrangements, as needed.

Although a circuit breaker is more convenient than a fuse, it is subject to abuse, wear, and dirt, and therefore requires inspection and possible maintenance. It is also more ex-

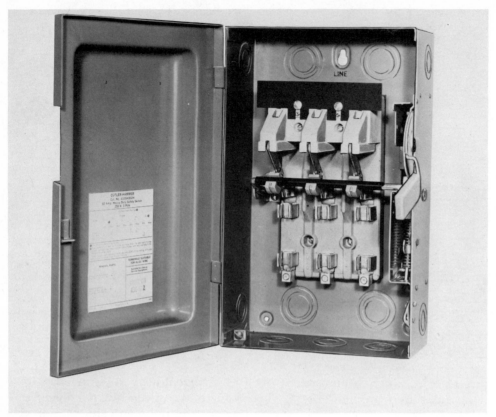

**FIGURE 15.13** A fused disconnect switch. (EATON Corp., Cutler–Hammer Products)

pensive than a fuse. Furthermore, for heavy service, fuses have certain features for interrupting excess current that are superior to circuit breakers. This is a specialized subject which there is no further need to examine here.

Manual disconnect means and fuses or circuit breakers are generally installed in main service lines and in each branch circuit, so that each part of the system is protected from what happens in the next part toward the power source. As pointed out before, the disconnect and fuses are often combined into one unit. The circuit breaker can also serve as a combination manual disconnect and overcurrent device. The main and branch devices are often arranged and mounted together on switchboards or panelboards for convenience. A typical service arrangement for a residence is shown in Figure 15.15.

# MOTORS

## 15.11 Motor Types

Alternating current motors are classified as either single phase or polyphase (multiphase) and as either nonhermetic or hermetic.

Single phase motors are constructed to use single phase current supply. Most polyphase motors are the three-phase type, designed to

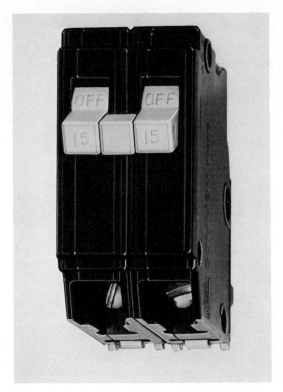

**FIGURE 15.14** A circuit breaker. (EATON Corp., Cutler–Hammer Products)

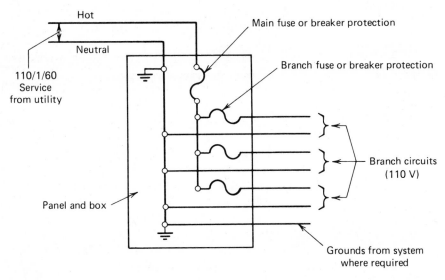

**FIGURE 15.15** Circuit protection arrangement for residential service.

use three-phase current. Single phase motors are available from very small fractional horsepower sizes (about .01 hp) to small integral sizes. Three-phase motors are available from ½ hp up to hundreds of horsepower, and even higher for special applications.

Refrigeration compressors and most other associated equipment (pumps, fans) are driven by ac motors. DC motors are occasionally used in rare locations where only dc current is available. The main application of dc motors is in operating control devices, in which small special types are used.

Motors can also be classified according to their enclosures. Nonhermetic motors used in refrigeration applications are generally of the *open* type. There are openings in the frame surrounding the motor to permit circulation of air for cooling of the motor windings. Other types may be needed in special circumstances. The *splashproof* motor has an enclosure that protects it from rain. The *totally enclosed fan cooled* motor (TEFC) is used where very dusty or dirty atmosphere is encountered. An *explosion proof* motor is required where explosive gases are present that might be ignited by a spark in the motor.

*Motor Construction.* The type of motor that is generally used in driving refrigeration equipment is called an *induction* motor. A nonhermetic induction motor is shown in Figure 15.16. The motor has two main functional parts, a *stator* and a *rotor*. The stator does not move, and forms a part of the motor housing. The stator consists of the field poles. These are electromagnets—iron bars wound with insulated copper wiring. The rotor is a rotating iron cylinder centered inside the stator. It has a layer of copper bars around its circumference. The motor shaft is attached to the rotor. Connection to a compressor shaft is made with a coupling. The frame has two end bells that attach to the stator housing and enclose the motor. The shaft bearings fit in each end bell.

Hermetic motors have only a stator and a rotor. The compressor shaft is the motor shaft. The hermetic compressor housing serves both the motor and the compressor. A further discussion of hermetic motors can be found in Chapter 5.

## 15.12 Motor Characteristics

Nonhermetic motors used in most applications in industry are called *general purpose* motors. They have features that are standard throughout the motor industry. These standards are set by the National Electrical Manufacturer's Association (NEMA). They include construction and performance standards, allowable temperature rise, overload factors, and horsepower ratings. These standards can be found in NEMA publications. A few general motor characteristics are described here.

*Current.* Single phase motors are usually constructed for 115 V or 230 V use. This is called nameplate or use voltage. Typical voltages of three-phase motors are 200 V, 230 V, and 460 V. Higher voltage motors are available but are used only occasionally such as in driving a large centrifugal compressor. Motors generally will perform satisfactorily within ± 10 percent of rated voltage.

When the circuit to a motor is closed, there is momentarily very low resistance to current flow in the motor windings. The resulting current is about four to five times the normal full load running current, unless special starting equipment is used. This initial current is called the *starting, inrush,* or *locked rotor* current. The motor nameplate usually indicates the rated locked rotor amps (LRA) and the rated full load amps (FLA). The inrush current is normally not harmful, because it lasts for a very brief time if the motor comes up to speed quickly.

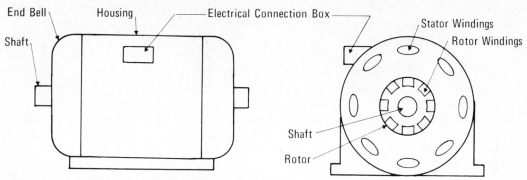

**FIGURE 15.16** Basic components of an ac induction motor.

**Speed.** When using 60 Hz current, the synchronous speed of two-pole induction motors is 3600 rpm. Actual speed is approximately 3450 to 3500 rpm. Four-pole motors have a speed of 1725 to 1750 rpm (1800 rpm synchronous speed).

**Torque.** The torque of a motor is its twisting or turning force capability. The starting torque, also called *locked rotor* torque, is the force necessary to start the driven device moving. The *full load running* torque is the force needed to keep the device turning at full speed under load. Starting torque required for refrigeration compressors can sometimes be quite high if the compressor starts under load. The starting or inrush current is also usually quite high, because there is little electrical resistance when starting.

**Power and Service Factor.** The full load power that a motor is rated at is based on the acceptable temperature of the coil windings and insulation. Increased power raises the line losses in the windings, which increases the heat generated. Motors are designed to safely take an overload, however. This is called the *service factor*. The service factor is dependent on the ambient temperature, and is specified at 40°C (104°F). For example, a 10 hp motor that has a service factor rating of 1.15 could deliver 11.5 hp without overheating, if the ambient temperature were 40°C. At higher surrounding temperatures the allowable power would be less, of course. Service factors are shown on the motor nameplate.

## 15.13 Principles of Operation

A brief review of how ac motors function is useful as a background to discussing different types of single phase motors. This explanation will avoid some theoretical aspects which are not needed for the purposes intended here.

An electric motor is a device that converts electric energy into mechanical energy. It is constructed so that the mechanical energy produced is in the form of rotation. The means by which this energy conversion is carried out is through electromagnetism. When electric current flows through a coil of wire surrounding an iron core, the device becomes an electromagnet. A magnetic field is developed in the space surrounding the magnet. This field exerts a force, which will act on another magnet, if present. Electromagnets have opposite polarities at their two ends, called north (N) and south (S). The force of like polarities is repulsion and of opposite polarities is attraction. The polarity of the electromagnet changes with the polarity of the current. With a proper physical arrangement, the forces will act in a direction to cause the rotation of one of the electromagnets, and the desired result is achieved.

Figure 15.17 shows those essential elements of a simplified single phase motor that will be used to explain its operation. (An actual single phase motor has additional essential elements, for reasons that will become evident in our discussion.)

The stator consists of two separated stationary iron cores wrapped with a single coil of insulated wire. The two parts of the stator are called the field poles, and the coil is called the field winding. When current flows through the winding an electromagnet is developed. One pole will be N polarity and the other pole will be S. This polarity will periodically change as the ac current reverses direction.

The magnetic field developed by the ac current in the stator continually "cuts" the copper bars in the rotor, inducing a current in the rotor bars (the rotor bars act like a coil of wire). The rotor becomes an electromagnet, with its own magnetic field. With this arrangement, when the rotor is at rest, the magnetic

force developed acts directly through the axis of the rotor; no starting torque exists. If the rotor is turning however, the induced current lags behind the current in the stator. The resultant direction of the two magnetic fields in this case will produce a turning force (Figure 15.18) and the motor keeps running. The direction of the force keeps moving in a circular direction; that is, the magnetic field is said to rotate.

The problem with a single phase motor is therefore one of starting it. We will examine methods of accomplishing this in the following sections.

The basic type motor just described is called an *induction* motor, the name deriving from the fact that a current is induced in the rotor. This is the type of ac motor that we will be examining, in its various forms.

The speed that the magnetic field rotates at in a motor is called the *synchronous* speed. The magnetic field rotates at the same speed as the cycle change of the current. Therefore for 60 cycle per second current, for a two-pole motor, the synchronous speed is 3600 rpm. Motors are also available with four or more stator poles (Figure 15.19). For a four-pole motor the windings are arranged so that for one complete cycle of current the magnetic field rotates only one half turn. The synchronous speed is then 1800 rpm. The actual

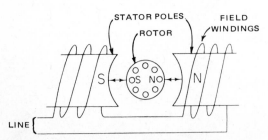

**FIGURE 15.17** Schematic arrangement of functional parts of a single-phase induction motor (no turning force produced when magnetic poles of rotor and stator are as shown).

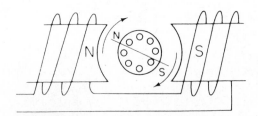

**FIGURE 15.18** Turning force produced in a single-phase motor from magnetic forces between rotor and stator.

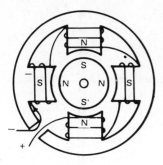

FOUR POLE MOTOR—
SYNCHRONOUS SPEED
IS 1800 RPM AT 60 HZ

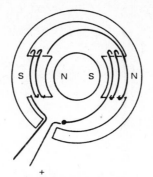

TWO POLE MOTOR—
SYNCH RONOUS
SYNCHRONOUS SPEED
IS 3600 RPM AT 60 H Z

**FIGURE 15.19** Single phase motor winding arrangements. (*a*) Four pole motor—synchronous speed is 1800 rpm at 60 Hz. (*b*) Two pole motor—synchronous speed is 3600 rpm at 60 Hz.

rotor speed in an induction motor is slightly less than synchronous speed, because of the drag caused by the load. This difference in speed is called *slip*.

## 15.14 Single Phase Motors

There are a number of types of single phase motors, differing from each other primarily in the way the motor is started. They also vary in their starting torque abilities, efficiency, and cost. The user chooses the most suitable type for the application. Generally the higher the starting torque and efficiency, the higher the cost.

The single phase motors that will be discussed here are the *split-phase,* the *permanent split capacitor* (PSC), *capacitor start* (CS), *capacitor-start–capacitor-run* (CSR), and *shaded pole* types. Slight variations in these names are used. A type called repulsion start will not be discussed here, since it is seldom used now.

All single phase motors have two separate sets of field windings, physically wound around the stator. One is called the *start* or

*auxiliary* winding, the other the *run* or *main* winding. The motor is constructed so that the currents in the windings are out of phase with each other. The result of this current displacement is that the magnetic force developed acts in a direction that creates a torque, and the rotor starts to turn. In a sense a two-phase current is temporarily produced. The difference between the various types of single phase motors is primarily in how the difference in phase angles between the two windings is achieved.

## 15.15 Split-Phase Motor

The electrical circuit for this type of single phase motor is shown in Figure 15.20

The stator has two windings, connected in parallel. The start winding is made of many turns of fine wire. This gives it a high resistance and therefore high power factor. The running winding has fewer turns of a heavy wire; it therefore has a low resistance and high inductance. The two currents will be out of phase. The result of this and the position of

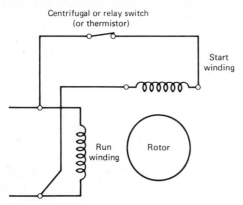

**FIGURE 15.20** Elecrical circuit of a split-phase motor, using a centrifugal switch in starting circuit (solid state thermistor may also be used).

the windings is that the direction of the magnetic force will provide a starting torque.

The start winding would overheat if left in the circuit too long, because of its high resistance. To prevent this, it is automatically disconnected when the motor reaches about 75 percent of running speed. There are two ways used to accomplish this, either with a *centrifugal switch* or a *starting relay*. A mechanical arm on the centrifugal switch opens the contacts due to the increasing centrifugal force as the motor speeds up. This device is not suitable in hermetic motors because the electric arc that occurs when the contacts open could cause a chemical breakdown of oil or refrigerant. For hermetic motors an externally located relay is used to disconnect the start winding circuit. These relays will be described later.

Split-phase motors have a low starting torque and relatively low efficiency. This makes them suitable for applications such as a household refrigerator with a capillary tube. Starting torque requirement is low since pressures are equalized with a capillary; since power consumption is small, the penalty for low efficiency may be acceptable.

## 15.16 Capacitors in Single Phase Motors

A *capacitor* is a device that stores electrical energy. In an ac circuit it alternately stores and releases the electric charge. Its effect is to cause a phase shift between the current and voltage so that the current leads the voltage. The power factor therefore increases.

The amount of electrical charge that a capacitor can store is called the *capacitance*. It is measured in a unit called the farad, or in the microfarad (one-millionth of a farad).

When a capacitor is installed in series with the start winding of a single phase motor, a phase shift between the windings results—the current in the start winding will lead the current in the main winding. This creates the displacement of the magnetic force required to provide a starting torque for the motor.

A large capacitance capacitor results in a large phase shift, high starting torque, and high current through the winding. A small capacitance results in a small phase shift, low starting torque, and low current through the winding. The power factor and motor efficiency improve as the capacitance increases. In the following sections we will see how capacitors are used in varied arrangements in single phase motors.

## 15.17 Permanent Split Capacitor (PSC) Motor

The circuit for this type of single phase motor is shown in Figure 15.21. The arrangement of the start and main windings is similar to that of the split-phase motor, except that a capacitor has been added in series with the start winding.

The capacitor causes a phase angle difference between the two windings, and this results in a starting torque to turn the rotor. In a permanent split capacitor motor the capacitor

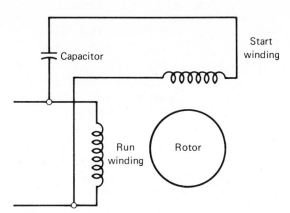

**FIGURE 15.21** Permanent split capacitor (PSC) motor circuit.

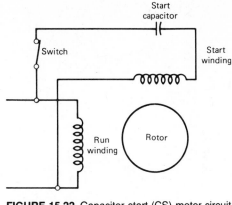

**FIGURE 15.22** Capacitor start (CS) motor circuit.

and start winding are left in the circuit after starting. The capacitor used must therefore have a relatively small capacitance, to limit the current in the start winding; otherwise overheating might occur. The result is that the phase angle change is small, and starting torque is low. Since the capacitor and start winding remain in the circuit, motor efficiency is higher than that of the split-phase motor. This results from an improved power factor and more even running torque. The absence of a switch or relay reduces the cost and service problems associated with those devices. The PSC motor can be used in small air conditioning and commercial units where high starting torque is not required, but good efficiency is desirable.

## 15.18 Capacitor Start (CS) Motor

The electrical circuit for the capacitor start (CS) motor, also called the capacitor start–induction run motor, is shown in Figure 15.22.

A starting capacitor with a large rating is used in series with the start winding to provide a high starting torque. Since this would result

in overheating if left in the circuit, a centrifugal switch or relay is used to disconnect the start circuit when the motor approaches running speed.

Because of the large rating capacitor the CS motor has a high starting torque. Its power factor and efficiency are lower than for a permanent split capacitor motor.

## 15.19 Capacitor-Start–Capacitor-Run (CSR) Motor

This motor is a combination of the permanent split capacitor and capacitor start types, and achieves the desirable characteristics of both. The electrical circuit wiring diagram is shown in Figure 15.23.

A high rating start capacitor and switch or relay are placed in the start winding circuit. This capacitor is disconnected as the motor approaches running speed. A running capacitor is located in parallel with the start capacitor. It remains in the circuit. High starting torque, a high power factor, and good motor efficiency are achieved. The cost of the motor is obviously higher than the cost of those with simpler arrangements.

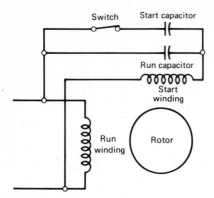

**FIGURE 15.23** Capacitor start, capacitor run (CSR) motor circuit.

## 15.20 Starting Relays

An electrical relay is a device in which the opening or closing (or other action) of one circuit is used to open or close (control) another circuit. That is, a relay is one form of an automatic switch. There are a variety of ways relays are constructed. One arrangement is shown in Figure 15.24. This type is a magnetic relay. Other types will be discussed later.

The relay consists of a magnetic coil and a contactor arm. The contacts may be normally-open (NO) or normally closed (NC). In the example illustrated the contacts are NO. The

normal position is the condition when no current is flowing through the coil. The contacts are held in this position by a spring or perhaps by the weight of the mechanism. When the coil is energized an electromagnetic force field is produced. This pulls the armature to close the contacts. This completes the circuit that is being controlled.

Relays used in single phase motor starting circuits (with hermetic units) are called *starting relays*. Two types of starting relays are used, the *potential* relay and the *current* relay. The coil of the potential relay is connected in parallel with the start winding (of a CSR motor) (Figure 15.25). The relay contacts, in series with the start capacitor, are normally closed (NC). As the motor approaches running speed the voltage across the start winding increases to a value that energizes the relay and the contacts are opened, removing the start capacitor from the circuit.

The coil of the current-type relay is connected in series with the run winding (Figure 15.26). The relay contacts are normally open (NO). Whe the motor starts the inrush current is very high, causing the coil to energize and the relay contacts to close. As the motor ap-

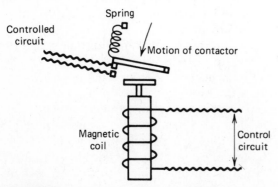

**FIGURE 15.24** A magnetic relay (the physical construction differs considerably among relays).

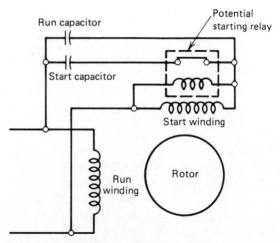

**FIGURE 15.25** Potential starting relay used with hermetic single-phase motor (CSR type).

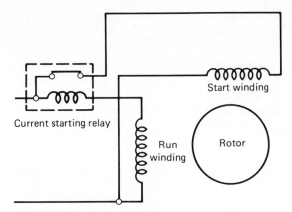

**FIGURE 15.26** Current starting relay used with hermetic single phase motor (split-phase type).

proaches running speed the current decreases and the coil is deenergized. The contacts open and the start winding is disconnected. This arrangement is suitable with a split phase or CSR motor.

A *thermal relay* can be used instead of an electromagnetic relay for starting single phase motors. A thermal bimetal element in the line heats as motor current is applied. By the time the motor approaches running speed the thermal element will move as a result of being heated, opening a set of contacts in the start winding.

Besides electromechanical switch relays, a solid state device can be used for starting. A positive temperature coefficient (PTC) thermistor is installed in series with the start winding of a split phase or CS motor. The resistance of a PTC thermistor increases greatly as its temperature increases. By the time the motor approaches running speed, the current has heated the thermistor to the extent that its resistance blocks out all but a very small acceptable current flow through the start winding. This current is enough to keep the thermistor temperature high, however. The thermistor can also be connected in parallel for use with a CSR motor.

As with all solid state devices, the advantage of a thermistor over relays with switches is that

there are no moving parts or contacts to fail or wear out.

Either relays or thermistors are suitable in starting circuits of hermetic units, since these devices can be mounted on the outside of the compressor.

## 15.21 Shaded Pole Motor

The electrical circuit wiring diagram for this type of single phase motor is shown in Figure 15.27. This motor has one stator field winding connected to the power source and wrapped around the pole pieces, creating a magnetic field. The two poles have a groove cut in them. A small band of metal is wrapped around each groove, creating another set of poles. The induction effect from the main poles causes the grooved poles to become an electromagnet. The direction of the resultant force field from the two sets of poles will produce a torque to turn the rotor.

The torque produced by a shaded pole motor is quite low, so it is not suitable for driving refrigeration compressors. It is mentioned here, however, because it is used to drive auxiliary equipment such as very small fans. Its main advantage is that it is low in cost.

## 15.22 Three-Phase Motors

Polyphase ("many" phase) induction motors are available in two- or three-phase arrange-

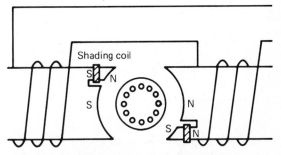

**FIGURE 15.27** Shaded pole motor construction.

ments; two-phase motors are rare and will not be discussed here.

The three-phase induction motor operates on the same principle as that of the single phase motor. However, since each of the phases are 120° apart, a starting torque exists, and no special starting means are needed. Furthermore, the starting torque is high. Motor efficiency is also high because the voltage is more even.

The three-phase motor may be wound either in a wye or delta arrangement, depending on the voltage service (Figure 15.28). There are also two special winding arrangements called *part winding* and *star–delta*, which are used to limit inrush current when starting.

The induction motor we have been describing is often called a *squirrel cage* induction motor (the turning rotor has the appearance of a pet animal exercise cage). There are two special variations on the squirrel cage induction motor, the *wound rotor* motor and the *synchronous* motor.

***Wound Rotor Motor.*** This is a variation of the induction motor; its speed can be varied. A set of resistances are introduced into the rotor winding circuit. The effect of the resistance is to cause a speed change. Large speed varia-

tions and good efficiency at low speeds are achieved. The cost of the motor increases considerably, however. This motor is used occasionally to drive large compressors when their capacity is to be varied by speed variation. Another method of varying motor speed that uses solid state electronic devices will be discussed in Chapter 16.

***Synchronous Motor.*** This is a variation of the induction motor that runs at synchronous speed, and has a high power factor. It is occasionally used to drive a machine when it is desirable to increase the overall power factor of an installation that has a number of induction motors. This effect can decrease energy costs, since utility companies often charge more for lower power factors.

A synchronous motor is an induction motor that has a means for supplying dc current to the windings as the motor approaches its normal induction motor speed (with slip). This develops an extra torque that pulls the motor up to synchronous speed.

## 15.23 High Efficiency Motors

Increased energy costs have stimulated a trend toward demand for and the manufacture of higher efficiency general purpose

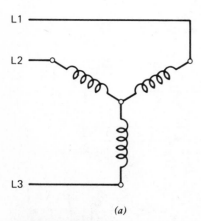

(a)

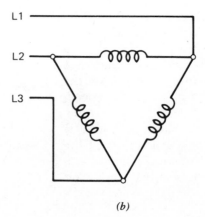

(b)

**FIGURE 15.28** Three-phase motor winding arrangements. (a) Wye. (b) Delta.

motors. The increased efficiency does not come from any major technological advance, but, for example, from use of materials that reduce electrical losses and heat buildup, from closer tolerances, and improved lubrication, among other changes. These motors are more expensive than "standard" efficiency motors. However, overall efficiency may increase by about 5 percent.

# REVIEW QUESTIONS

1. What is electrical polarity?
2. Describe and sketch the difference between dc and ac current.
3. Describe, with the aid of a sketch, cycle and frequency.
4. Explain inductance and capacitance. What are their effects on current and voltage in a circuit?
5. What is the significance of power factor? Draw a sketch to aid the explanation.
6. Describe and sketch what is meant by single-phase and three-phase power.
7. What is the meaning and importance of $I^2R$ losses?
8. What is a transformer used for? Sketch and label the essential parts of a transformer.
9. What do the terms *step-up* and *step-down* mean?
10. Explain the terms *hot leg, neutral,* and *ground,* with the aid of a sketch of a three-wire circuit.
11. Sketch a single phase three-wire service with commonly used voltages and label the essential features.
12. Sketch a three phase, four-wire service with commonly used voltage and label the essential features.
13. What is a short circuit; what is a ground fault? What effects do they have?
14. What are the possible causes and possible effects of overcurrent? What is done to protect against it, if it occurs?
15. Explain what is meant by a cartridge fuse and a time delay fuse.
16. What are the two types of circuit breakers? How does each function?
17. What are the relative advantages and disadvantages of circuit breakers versus fuses?
18. What are the different types of motor enclosures and where are they used?
19. List the major motor characteristics.
20. What voltages are common for single-phase and for three-phase motors? What speeds are common in the United States?
21. What is meant by running torque and starting torque? Why are they different? What effect do they have on current?
22. Explain the meaning and significance of motor service factor.
23. What is an induction motor? Sketch and describe how an elementary ac motor functions. Why will it not start?
24. What is synchronous speed and what is slip?
25. Sketch and describe the operation of split-phase, PSC, CS, and CSR single-phase motors.
26. Name and describe the two ways of disconnecting a start winding.
27. What is an electrical relay? Describe and sketch an electromagnetic relay.
28. Name and describe with sketches the two types of starting relays.
29. What is a capacitor? What effect does it have on an ac electric current?
30. Why does a three-phase motor start without auxiliary devices?
31. For what applications are wound rotor and synchronous motors used?
32. Why is a shaded pole motor not suitable for driving a refrigeration compressor?

# Chapter 16

## MOTOR CONTROLS AND PROTECTION. REFRIGERATION CONTROL SYSTEMS

Subjects covered in this chapter will include the equipment used for starting and stopping (controlling) motors and methods for protecting motors from overloads. We will also discuss devices used to control the performance of the refrigeration system, and a few of the ways these devices are used in combination.

## OBJECTIVES

A study of this chapter will enable you to:
1. Describe types of motor controllers and their applications.
2. Explain the causes of motor overloads.
3. Specify the types of motor overload protection devices and their features.
4. Identify and describe the basic refrigeration control devices.
5. Analyze motor control and simple refrigeration control schematic diagrams.
6. Explain the basic terms and describe applications of solid state electronics to controls.

## MOTOR CONTROLS

### 16.1 Motor Controllers

The term *motor controller*, more commonly called a motor *starter*, refers to the device used to start and stop a motor by connecting and disconnecting it from the power source. A motor controller is primarily a switch that makes and breaks electrical contacts. It may

also contain devices to perform additional functions, such as controlling motor speed. It may incorporate motor protection devices.

The type of motor controller used in each case depends on the size of motor, the relative location of motor and starter, and the way in which the operation of the refrigeration compressor (or other load) is to be controlled. These points will be discussed when the different motor controller types are described.

### 16.2 Motor Controls for Small Single Phase Motors

The simplest arrangement for starting and stopping a motor is with a set of contacts in the power circuit that are closed and opened either manually or automatically. The manual switch is usually a single lever (toggle) that is moved back and forth to close or open the power circuit. This type of manual switch is often found in small household appliance motor circuits. A light switch is of similar construction.

Control of small motors may also be automatic with a set of contacts in the power circuit that are closed and opened by a control device such as a thermostat. The contacts are usually part of the control device. A separate manual switch for initial starting may be provided in series with the control device switch (Figure 16.1). This arrangement might be suitable for a small refrigeration compressor circuit.

The contacts used in both the manual switch

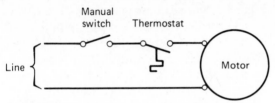

**FIGURE 16.1** A simple form of motor control suitable for a fractional hp refrigeration motor compressor. Thermostat operates compressor. Manual switch for service may even be omitted in some instances.

and in the automatic control devices described are small, and are capable of carrying only small currents. When the contacts open and close a large current may arc across the air gap and damage the contacts. For this reason, this method of motor control is limited to small fractional hp single phase motors.

It may be worth pointing out that the use of the terms *motor controller* or *starter* is perhaps an exaggeration in reference to the simple switches described so far. The more conventional use of these terms will be described shortly.

## 16.3 Contactors and Starters

It was noted in the last section that very small fractional hp motors may sometimes use only a small line switch or control device contacts to start and stop the motor. For motors drawing larger currents, heavier duty motor controllers, either contactors or motor starters, are required.

> *A* **contactor** *is a heavy duty switch mounted in an enclosed box. A* **starter** *is a contactor that also includes motor overload protection devices as part of the assembly.*

In some cases, particularly with smaller motors, a contactor is satisfactory, with the motor overload devices furnished as part of the motor. In other cases, motor overload protection in the starter and perhaps at the motor are furnished. This subject will be discussed later.

Some types of starters serve additional motor control functions, such as controlling inrush current, starting torque, and speed.

The required size of a starter or contactor depends on the amount of current it is to handle and the number of times it is to be switched in an expected lifetime. Standard sizes have been adopted by the electrical industry and may be determined from appropriate handbooks or manufacturer's catalogs.

*Manual and Magnetic Starters.* Motor starters can be either of the *manual* or *magnetic* type. The line contacts in the manual type (Figure 16.2) are closed and opened by hand, using a toggle switch or push buttons located in the starter cover. Manual full voltage starters are limited to about five to seven and one half hp motor size. One reason for this is that the high arcing current across the opening switch gaps can be hazardous to both equipment and operator, if the switching action is slow. The switching action in a magnetic starter is automatic, faster, and more positive.

The magnetic starter (Figure 16.3) has a magnetic relay coil, called a *holding coil*, which

**FIGURE 16.2** A small manual starter with a toggle switch. (Courtesy of Square D Co.)

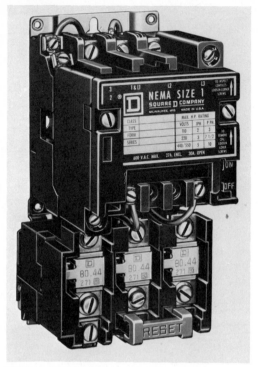

**FIGURE 16.3** A magnetic starter (enclosure removed). Note the reset button. (Courtesy of Square D Co.)

operates the switch contacts. The contacts are normally held open, either by a spring or by the force of gravity. When the holding coil circuit is energized, the coil pulls the power contacts closed. The coil circuit may be energized manually or automatically.

If the motor is to be controlled manually from the starter location, the magnetic starter can be furnished with start and stop push-button switches in the starter cover. Since the holding coil circuit only draws the small control current, not the motor current, the operator is safer. Opening of the live contacts mechanically is also a faster, more positive, and therefore safer operation than that with a manual starter.

Other important features of the magnetic starter (not possible with a manual starter), are that the motor may be controlled from a remote location away from the starter, and that

it may be controlled by pilot devices (thermostats, safety switches, etc.), through the control circuit. For these reasons, even though the magnetic starter is considerably more expensive than the manual starter, it is more commonly used in refrigeration applications.

*Two-Wire and Three-Wire Control.* Magnetic motor control circuits can be grouped into two types, called *two-wire control* and *three-wire control*. The names derive from the fact that there are either two or three wires in the basic control circuit between the control device and the starter.

In the two-wire control system, Figure 16.4(*a*), there is one circuit through the control device. The control device, a manual or automatic switch (a knife switch, maintained contact push button, thermostat, etc.), closes to energize the holding coil. When the control device contacts open, the coil is deenergized and the motor stops.

If the circuit loses power, or the voltage drops momentarily during operation, the motor will stop and then start again automatically when full voltage is returned, since the holding coil control circuit remains closed. This feature is called *undervoltage release*. It may be undesirable, since the cause of the low voltage may be damaging to the motor when it is restarted; furthermore, the type of problem may cause the motor to cycle off and on repeatedly. As will be seen, the three-wire control system protects the motor from this type of event.

The three-wire control system, Figure 16.4(*b*) has two circuits through the holding coil. One circuit is through a normally open start push button and a normally closed stop push button; the other circuit is through the start push button and a set of auxiliary contacts in the starter, controlled by the holding coil. The start push button is of the momentary contact type. This means that the contacts open when pressure is released from the button (through action of a spring).

When the start button is pushed, a circuit

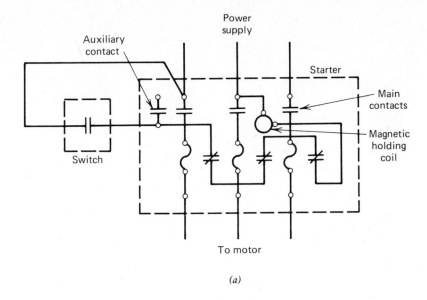

(a)

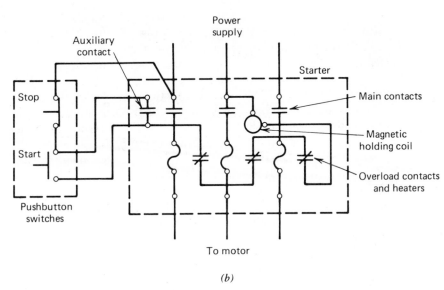

(b)

**FIGURE 16.4** (a) Two-wire and (b) three-wire motor controls.

through the normally closed stop button and holding coil is completed, the coil is energized, the main contacts are closed, and the motor starts. The auxiliary contacts also are closed by the holding coil. When the start button is released, the circuit through it is opened, but the second circuit through the auxiliary con-

tacts remains closed, and the motor continues to run.

If the line voltage drops, the holding coil will be weakened or deenergized and both the main and auxiliary contacts will open. The motor stops, but does not restart when full voltage is restored since both circuits through

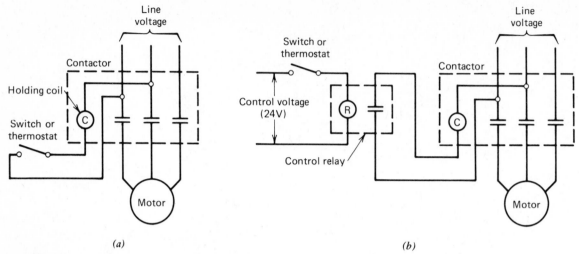

**FIGURE 16.5** (a) Direct and (b) indirect motor control circuits.

the holding coil are open. The motor must be restarted manually by the operator, who will presumably investigate the cause of the problem. This feature is called *undervoltage protection.*

The overload protection devices that are an integral part of the starters, as well as additional devices often used in motor control circuits, will be described later.

***Direct and Indirect Motor Control.*** When the motor control circuit is connected directly to the line as shown in Figure 16.5(a), it is called *direct motor control.* A separate relay circuit can also be used to control the motor indirectly, as in Figure 16.5(b). The relay is also a magnetic coil with contacts in the starter holding coil circuit. When the relay coil switch is closed it closes the holding coil contacts, which in turn energizes the holding coil, and the starter contacts close. Called *indirect motor control,* this offers an advantage when control from a remote location is desired; the control circuit is usually at a low voltage (e.g., 24 volts) through a transformer. This enables smaller and less expensive wiring and control to be used, and is also safer.

Manual starters cost considerably less than magnetic starters. However, if remote or automatic control of the motor is required, as is usually true with refrigeration compressors, a magnetic starter must be used.

A manual contactor or starter should not be confused with a disconnect switch, discussed earlier. However, a disconnect switch and starter are sometimes combined in one unit for convenience. This is called a *combination starter.* If the motor is in sight of the starter, electrical codes may permit this arrangement. Otherwise a separate disconnect is generally required in sight of the motor.

## 16.4 Magnetic Starters

Magnetic starters are widely used for controlling the operation of motors of all sizes in driving refrigeration and air conditioning equipment.

Magnetic starters are classified into two main groups: *across-the-line,* also called *full voltage,* and *reduced voltage* types. The full voltage starter is connected directly and immediately to the line voltage. The full motor inrush current flows; this may be from 400 to 600 percent of full load current. Large starting currents can cause voltage dips in the system, which may affect other equipment adversely. For this reason utility companies may limit inrush current, and for larger motors reduced voltage starters may be required. Note that the purpose of a reduced voltage starter is to limit inrush current, not voltage.

Four types of reduced voltage starters will be mentioned here:

1. Autotransformer.
2. Primary resistor.
3. Part winding.
4. Star–delta.

The last two types also require motors with special windings, as will be explained.

***Auto Transformer Starter.*** This type of starter contains an *autotransformer,* one that has only one coil. The full coil serves as the primary. By tapping off part of the coil for the secondary, a reduced secondary voltage is achieved. The starter has two sets of contactors. When the motor is started it is connected across the transformer secondary tap. As the motor comes up to speed a timer switches the motor across the line.

Since starting voltage to the motor is reduced, inrush current is also reduced. It should be noted that starting torque will also be reduced.

***Primary Resistor Starter.*** This starter has external resistances in series with the stator windings to reduces the starting voltage at the windings. A timer is used to switch the resistors out of the circuit when the motor comes up to speed.

***Part Winding Starter.*** This type of starter requires use with a motor that has two windings. The starter has two sets of contactors. The motor starts with one set of windings (part winding) energized. This reduces the inrush current. After a time delay the complete set of windings is connected in the circuit.

The part winding starter is less expensive than most other reduced voltage types. It is often used for reciprocating refrigeration compressors that have unloaders for unloaded starting.

***Star–Delta Starter.*** This type of starter is used with a motor that is wound so that the windings can be changed from a star (wye) to a delta connection. The starter has two sets of contactors. The motor is connected in star on starting and after a time delay it is switched to delta circuiting. The star arrangement draws about one-third the inrush current as the delta connection. Starting torque is also consequently reduced, however. The star–delta starter and suitable motor are often used in hermetic centrifugal refrigeration machines, since a centrifugal compressor can be started in an unloaded condition.

## 16.5 Motor Overload Protection

A motor must be protected against *motor overloads.* This term refers to the excessive current and overheating which can damage the motor. Excessive current through the motor windings results in increased $I^2R$ losses (resistance heating) which can damage or break down the effectiveness of the winding insulation, leading to motor failure and probable damage, sometimes called burnout.

Before discussing means of motor overload protection, it is worthwhile to examine some of the conditions that cause overloads. This will aid in understanding why a number of different types of overload protection devices are available.

***Locked Rotor Current.*** At the moment a motor starts it draws a very large current, called *locked rotor* or *inrush* current. This may be four to six times full load running current.

The high current drops very rapidly as the motor speeds up, and normally not enough heat is generated to do any damage. If the motor fails to start or stalls, however, the high current flow will continue and overheat the motor. This could be caused by too large a load, low voltage, or single phasing of a three-phase motor. In any of these events the motor starting torque may be too low to turn the load.

If the motor short cycles on and off continually, that could also cause a build up of excess heat from starting current. This could happen from faulty controls.

Excess current may also be drawn while the motor is running, from a number of possible causes.

1. Both abnormally low and high voltage cause excessive current.

2. If there is a break in one line to a three-phase motor, the motor will operate on two feeders as a single phase motor (this is called single phasing). A higher current is drawn through each line and winding than when the motor operates normally.

3. If there is a voltage imbalance (inequality) between phases of a three-phase supply, excessive current occurs.

4. A high driven load may overload a motor. A number of possible causes of high refrigeration compressor loads have been discussed in other chapters.

Increased temperature of the motor may also occur directly from sources other than increased current. The ambient temperature of open motors may be above that planned for. In hermetic motors cooling from the suction gas may be inadequate under certain conditions (Chapter 5).

## 16.6 Motor Overload Protection Devices

The use of fuses and circuit breakers as circuit overload protection devices has been dis-cussed previously. These devices are also used to protect against overcurrent in branch circuits to motors. However they are not always adequate by themselves to protect motors from some of the problems discussed previously. For instance, fuses and circuit breakers will take a moderate current overload for an indefinite period of time. This may not immediately damage a motor, but it certainly can significantly shorten its life. In most cases additional motor protective devices are required.

*Current and/or Temperature Devices.* Motor overload protection devices operate either on the principle of responding to high current, or directly to high temperature, or to both current and temperature. All types of devices act by breaking the circuit to the motor.

*Line Duty or Pilot Duty Devices.* Overload devices may also be grouped into *line duty* or *pilot duty* types. The line duty protector contacts are wired in series with the motor, and therefore carry line current, as in Figure 16.6(*a*). Its contacts therefore must be relatively large. When an overload condition occurs the contacts in the device open, disconnecting the motor winding from the power source. The pilot duty protector is a relay device, Figure 16.6(*b*), with contacts located in a control circuit carrying a low current. On a motor overload the relay opens the contacts in the motor contactor (starter), through the starter holding coil. This disconnects the starter and motor. The pilot duty device has to take only its switch contact current, and not full line and locked rotor current. It thus can be made smaller, and is used with larger motors.

*Manual or Automatic Reset.* Another distinction between overload devices is whether they have *manual* or *automatic reset*. When a manual reset device breaks the circuit it must be reset by hand. This of course requires attendance

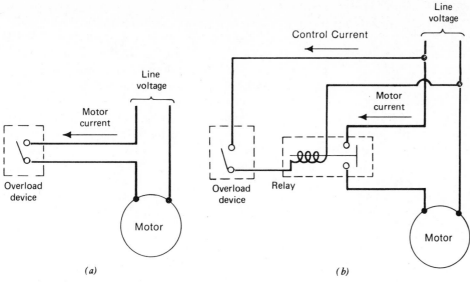

**FIGURE 16.6** (a) Line duty and (b) pilot duty overload protective device circuits.

by personnel. An automatic reset device will automatically reconnect the motor after the overload condition has been cleared. Some automatic devices will reset immediately. Others, if they function on high temperature, may not reset immediately, since it may take some time for the device to cool.

Automatic reset offers the convenience of not leaving the system shut down when there is a momentary overload, such as a brief voltage dip, which would usually not be harmful. These are called *nuisance trips*. On the other hand repeated restarting when there is a continual problem could lead to motor burnout. This is resolved by using a *restart relay*. When the circuit trips, the motor is restarted through the relay manually by a push button. In this way the operator is alerted to trouble.

Some types of motor protection devices are furnished as part of the motor or the hermetic motor–compressor unit. These are called *integral protection devices*. The may be located outside the motor or unit, in which case they are called *external* protectors, or inside the motor

or hermetic unit, in which case they are called internal *protectors*.

In addition to these integral types of devices, separate external protective devices are available that are not part of the motor. The protective devices to be used depend on the equipment and the application in each case. Generally the separate protective device is located in the circuit at the starter. This will respond to excess current in the line to the motor. One or more integral protective devices located at the motor will respond to current and/or temperature problems occurring there. We will describe some of these devices, without attempting to include all of the kinds available.

## 16.7 Thermal Overload Relays

This type of protector is a current sensing, usually pilot duty device. The sensing element is a small resistance heater connected in series with the motor. On excess current the heater temperature rises sharply.

A set of contacts and a device that responds to the heat from the heater is located in the starter holding coil control circuit. One type of sensor that is used is a bimetal element connected to a set of contacts (Figure 16.7). When the bimetal is heated and its temperature rises, it bends or twists due to the differing expansions of its two dissimilar metals. This opens the contacts it is connected to, and the motor contactor is disconnected. The overload device will automatically reset as the bimetal element cools and returns to its original position, closing the contacts.

A large change in ambient temperature may cause the overload to operate at too small or too great a current increase. This can be resolved by including a second bimetal element that is sensitive to ambient temperature change. It moves the main bimetal element slightly as ambient temperature changes. This is called a *compensating* overload device.

Another type of thermal overload relay has a low melting temperature alloy device in the contactor control circuit. The heater melts the alloy which releases a mechanism that opens the relay contacts, which then disconnects the contactor. This type must be manually reset by a push button connected to the overload contacts.

The thermal overload may be included in the contactor enclosure, in which case the complete unit is called a *starter*. The protection is usually provided in all three legs of a three-phase motor supply.

A magnetic thermal overload relay is available for similar service. The overload device circuit contacts are mounted on an iron coil. The contacts are held normally closed by a spring. The motor current flows through a coil wrapped around the iron core. If excess current flows the magnetic field produced is strong enough to pull the iron core and open the control contacts. This disconnects the contactor.

The overload devices described must have a time delay to allow a brief overload for motor starting. They may not furnish adequate protection for a sudden temperature increase at the motor, particularly in hermetic units, which will overheat rapidly when the cooling effect of suction gas is not available.

## 16.8 Internal and External Line Duty Overload Protectors

A sealed internal protector of the type shown in Figure 16.8 is often used in small hermetic units. It has a bimetal strip sensitive to both current and temperature. The overload device is wound in the motor windings; on overload the bimetal element opens its contacts. It automatically resets when it cools.

An external protector sensitive to both current and temperature is shown in Figure 16.9. It has a bimetal disc and is wired in series with the motor winding, usually in the common line to a single phase motor. The bimetal disc warps on overload, opening its contacts, and automatically resets on cooling. It is mounted on the outside of the unit, usually in the motor

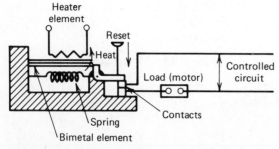

**FIGURE 16.7** A bimetal thermal overload relay.

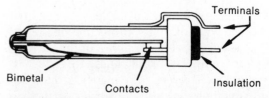

**FIGURE 16.8** An internal overload protector. The device is imbedded in the motor windings.

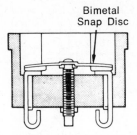

**FIGURE 16.9** An external overload protector. This device is mounted on the outside of the motor.

terminal box. It is sometimes called a Klixon, although this is a trade name of one manufacturer.

Variations of these types of devices are available for three-phase hermetic motors. The internal type is located in the center of a wye wound motor, and is used up to about 7 ½ hp.

## 16.9 Motor Thermostat Protectors

This type of device is sensitive to temperature only. It is available in internal or external versions. The internal protector is placed against the motor windings, but it is connected to a pilot circuit so that it can be used with large compressors. On overload the heat from the motor windings will open the control circuit. A bimetal element is used as the sensor. This type of protector does not respond rapidly enough to the effect of locked rotor current, and therefore must be supplemented by a current sensitive device.

There is a solid state thermostat protector, however, which is sensitive enough to respond quickly to a temperature increase in the windings resulting from locked rotor current. It uses a *thermistor* as a sensor. This is a semiconductor material whose electrical resistance changes with a change in temperature. The change in resistance is amplified by semiconductor devices (transistors) to break the contacts in the pilot circuit. This type of device will

protect against both excess running current and locked rotor current.

# REFRIGERATION CONTROLS

## 16.10 Purpose of Refrigeration Controls

The term *refrigeration controls* refers to the devices used to automatically control the operation and performance of the refrigeration system and to protect its equipment.

Control of the operation of the system includes the ability to automatically change its refrigeration capacity in response to the load demands. Sometimes this is a relatively simple task, such as starting or stopping a refrigeration compressor. Often, however the control system is more complicated. It may control speeds, open or close valves and dampers, or adjust temperatures, pressures, and flow rates of fluids in order to accomplish its purposes. The operation of different pieces of equipment may have to occur in a certain time sequence. The mode of operation of a piece of equipment may have to be periodically changed, as in defrosting, or switching a heat pump cycle.

Not only are controls required to change the refrigeration capacity of the system, but often they are required to do this in a manner that results in an efficient use of energy under varying conditions. Indeed, in almost all cases this is a requirement today.

Aside from controlling system performance and its use of energy, controls are also required to protect the equipment from abnormal conditions. These are called *safety* controls, whereas the controls that regulate the system performance are called *operating* controls.

## 16.11 Types of Control Systems

Control systems (and devices) in refrigeration and air conditioning can be classified according to the source of power by which they operate. There are two common types, pneumatic (compressed air) and electric. Systems that use some electronic devices in an overall electric system are sometimes called electronic, but this distinction is not of importance here. Refrigeration controls are usually electric, and therefore our discussion will be largely devoted to them. Pneumatic systems are used primarily in large air conditioning systems. Even here the refrigeration equipment controls are often electric. This presentation will be necessarily limited, and a further study of the subject of automatic controls is strongly recommended.

Some refrigeration control devices have been discussed in other parts of this text. Flow control devices, discussed in Chapter 8, are self-contained devices. That is, they do not require either pneumatic or electric power to operate. Motor controllers can also be considered part of the system controls. We will refer again briefly to motor controls and how they relate to the rest of the refrigeration system controls.

We have already discussed auxiliary devices such as relays, transformers, solenoid valves, and switches, which are often used in the refrigeration control system. We will refer to these devices when it is appropriate.

## 16.12 Control Device (Controller) Operation

All control devices function according to similar principles. The basic elements of a controller and its operation are illustrated in Figure 16.10. Examining this is worthwhile, for it can help in clarifying the operation of the many types of devices available.

The controller consists of two basic parts, the *sensing* element (*sensor*) and the *control* element. The sensor receives and responds to an external signal, such as temperature or pressure. The control element converts the response of the sensor to a useful output and

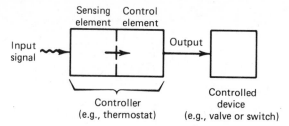

**FIGURE 16.10** The basic action of any automatic control.

sends this to a device to be controlled, such as a switch or valve. The output signal may be converted or amplified by auxiliary devices, but this does not affect the basics of the control device.

Control devices are usually named according to the type of input signal. The most common devices are temperature, pressure, and humidity controls.

## 16.13 Temperature Controls

This type of control device is also called a *thermostat*. It senses the temperature of a substance such as air, water, or refrigerant, and if it is an electric control device, it controls an electrical circuit.

A commonly used thermal sensor is a *bimetal* element. The element is composed of two different metal strips; the metals have different rates of expansion as their temperature changes. This causes the element to bend or curl as the temperature increases. Some common shapes of a bimetal element are a straight strip, a disc, and a spiral (Figure 16.11).

In the case of the straight bimetal strip and disc thermostats shown, the control element is simply a set of contacts. The contacts open or close a circuit on rise or fall of temperature, depending on the application. The resulting electric action is then used to carry out a desired action. For example, the thermostat may be sensing air temperature in a cooler. On rise in temperature the contacts close, com-

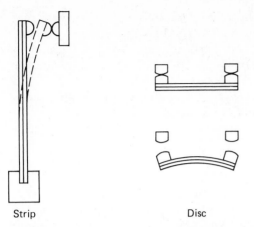

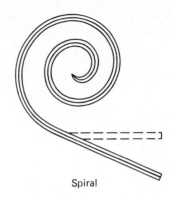

Strip                    Disc                    Spiral

**FIGURE 16.11** Some arrangements of bimetal sensing elements used in thermostats. (*a*) Strip. (*b*) Disc. (*c*) Spiral.

pleting the compressor motor electrical circuit, and the compressor starts.

The control mechanism that is commonly used with the spiral bimetal sensor is a mercury filled bulb with a set of contacts (Figure 16.12). The movement of the spiral element as temperature changes causes the bulb to tilt. The mercury flows from one end of the bulb to the other, making or breaking the electrical circuit.

Another type of sensor uses a bulb with a tube connecting it to a closed *bellows* (Figure 16.13). The bulb, tube, and bellows contain a fluid. As temperature changes the pressure of the fluid changes, causing the flexible bellows to expand or contract. This motion is used to

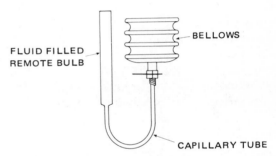

**FIGURE 16.13** Remote bulb thermostat with bellows.

open or close a circuit through a mechanical linkage (the control mechanism). This type of temperature control, called a *remote bulb thermostat,* has the advantage that the sensing bulb can be located in a separate place from the switch. For instance, the bulb can be placed in a refrigerated space whereas the switch and its adjusting mechanism can be located outside the room, by running the tube through the wall. The mechanism is not exposed to possible very low temperature in the space, which might affect its performance, and the room does not have to be entered to check operation or change settings.

In addition to the bellows type of temperature sensor, a flexible *diaphragm* can also be

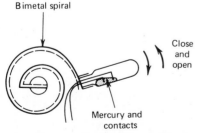

**FIGURE 16.12** Thermostat with spiral bimetal sensor and mercury filled bulb control element.

used with a bulb and connecting tube. The fluid causes flexing of the diaphragm, which through a linkage makes and breaks the electrical circuit.

## 16.14 Pressure Controls

This type of control device is also called a *pressurestat*. The sensor may be either a bellows or diaphragm, which is directly connected by an open tube to the fluid whose pressure supplies the signal (Figure 16.14). Pressure changes of the fluid cause the bellows (or diaphragm) to move; this motion opens or closes the electrical circuit through a linkage.

*Refrigerant Pressure Controls.* The type of pressure control devices that have been described can be used for refrigerant low pressure and high pressure control. The *low pressure* controller senses compressor refrigerant suction pressure. It makes contact when pressure rises and breaks contact when pressure falls. It is sometimes used as the operating control to control temperature with small units. However, since the control is indirect, the space temperature may fluctuate more than is acceptable for some applications.

The same type of device can also be used as a *low limit* safety control. In this case the pressure setting on the controller is set at a low limiting value. The operation of the controller is identical to that when it is used as an operating control, only the pressure setting is below the normal operating point. A low limit may be needed to prevent possible motor overheating, coil frosting, and other undesirable effects that could result from low suction pressure.

A *high pressure* controller is generally used as a safety control to sense discharge pressure, set to stop the compressor when the discharge pressure exceeds a safe limit. The controller may have either manual or automatic reset features.

The low pressure and high pressure controller are often combined for convenience in one housing; the combination is called a *dual pressure* controller (Figure 16.15). Two separate sensors are used, but they generally control only one switch.

## 16.15 Oil Pressure Failure Control

A pressure type safety controller is used to stop the compressor if there is inadequate oil pump pressure. This pressure control is designed to sense the pressure *differential* be-

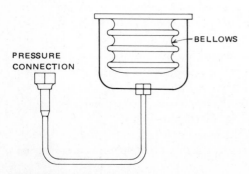

**FIGURE 16.14** Pressurestat—bellows type.

**FIGURE 16.15** Dual pressure controller (combines low- and high-pressure compressor controls).

FIGURE 16.16 Oil pressure failure control.

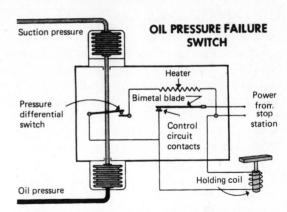

FIGURE 16.17 The operating circuit of an oil pressure failure control.

tween the oil pump discharge and refrigerant suction pressures, since that is the useful available pump pressure. This is true because the crankcase (the pump suction) is at refrigerant suction pressure, which may vary.

An *oil pressure failure* control is shown in Figure 16.16. It contains two remote bulb and bellows sensors. One senses oil pump discharge pressure, the other refrigerant suction pressure. Each bellows has a rod attached to it, opposing each other, and acting against a pressure differential switch. The switch is held closed by a spring (not shown) when there is no pressure differential, and opens at a preset pump pressure differential.

The control circuit of the oil pressure failure controller has a time delay arrangement. This allows the oil pressure to be less than the required value for a brief period of time before the compressor is stopped. It is needed during start-up, as will now be explained.

As seen in Figure 16.17 the compressor starter holding coil is wired in series with a bimetal element (NC) in the control. When this control circuit is energized the compressor starts, even though there is no oil pressure. (Except for very large compressors the oil pump is driven off of the compressor). It takes a short period of time for pump pressure to build up to the required value, perhaps one or

two minutes. A loss of lubrication for this brief period is not unsafe. However, if pressure is not reached in the appropriate time, the control will stop the compressor. Note that control power also goes through the pressure differential switch (NC) and a small resistance heater. After a short time, if the pressure differential switch does not open, enough heat is generated by the heater to cause the bimetal strip to warp, breaking the motor control circuit and stopping the compressor. If pump pressure builds up in normal time, however, the pressure differential switch opens and the heater has no effect.

The time delay serves the same function during operation. A momentary loss in oil pressure will not stop the compressor. However, since the pressure differential contacts close, the time delay heater circuit is energized and the compressor will be stopped in the required time. The pressure differential switch has a manual reset button.

## 16.16 Control Differential

Control devices that open and close a set of contacts are called *two position* or *on–off* controls. The value of the signal at which the control makes contact (closes) is called the *cut-in* point and the value at which it breaks (opens) the circuit is called the *cut-out* point.

The desired value of the condition to be maintained is called the *set point*. For instance a space temperature of 40°F may be desired. If the cut-in and cut-out points were both set at the set point, the compressor would start and then stop immediately, an impossible situation. The cut-in and cut-out points are therefore set at slightly different values. The difference between them is called the control *differential*.

For instance, a unit cooler thermostat may be set with a cut-in point of 40°F and a cut-out point of 37°F. When the temperature rises to 40°F the thermostat contacts close and the compressor starts. When the space temperature falls to 37°F the contacts open and the compressor stops. In this example the differential is 3°F.

A small differential results in less variation in conditions, but also means that the compressor will cycle on and off more frequently. This inevitably shortens the life of starter, motor, and compressor. On the other hand, a large differential may result in unacceptably large swings in temperature or other condition being controlled. Depending on the application, a satisfactory compromise is chosen. Most controls are constructed with adjustable control differentials. This might be accomplished with a screw that adjusts a spring tension holding the contacts apart.

Another related term is the control *range*. This is the minimum and maximum value between which the cut-in and cut-out points can be set, as recommended by the manufacturer. For instance if a pressurestat is said to have a range of 50 to 100 psig, this means that the cut-in and cut-out points can be set anywhere within those values, but not below or above them.

## 16.17 Proportional and Step Controls

In addition to two-position type controls, there are also controls that can produce an output signal that varies in value. In electric controls this is usual done with a variable resistance, called a *potentiometer*. The control contact moves, changing its position of contact along a coil of wire. This changes the length of wire to a circuit, changing its resistance, which changes the voltage to a controlled device, changing its action *proportionally*. Often the controlled device is a motor that adjusts the position of a valve. Another example is a *step* controller. The controlled motor may make a series of contacts with controls to each step of compressor cylinder unloader circuits.

## 16.18 Wiring Diagrams

Two types of wiring diagrams are commonly used to show the connections of electrical equipment and controls in refrigeration systems. One is usually called the pictorial or *connection* diagram, the other the *schematic* diagram. The connection diagram shows each component or its parts in approximately their real physical location with respect to each other; the wiring connections between and within each device are also shown realistically located. This type of wiring diagram is therefore quite pictorial; it is helpful in installing the wiring and in tracing wiring. However it is not useful for understanding how the control system functions, or as an aid in troubleshooting control problems.

The schematic wiring diagram is universally used as an aide to understanding how the control system functions. It does not show the control components in their physical location. Instead, each circuit is drawn in a straight horizontal line, and the control power lines to each circuit are shown as two vertical lines. Because of the resulting appearance, the schematic diagram is often called a *ladder* diagram. This arrangement makes it easier to follow the scheme or logic of how the control system operates. We will offer examples later to show how the schematic diagram is used.

## 16.19 Control Circuit Symbols

Control circuit wiring diagrams are drawn with graphical symbols to represent the devices included. Most symbols have the same meaning to all users in the air conditioning and refrigeration industry, but since this is not fully standardized, a symbol list is always necessary. An example is shown in Figure 16.18. This list does not include all possible devices, but is satisfactory for our purposes. Some of the items shown require discussion, since understanding the symbols is needed so that the control diagram can be understood.

We first note that all devices in any electrical circuit can be grouped either into *switches* or *loads*. Switches of course are used to make or break (open or close) circuits. They do not use power. Loads are devices that use power. They include lights, coils, resistances, motors, and any other current consuming equipment.

The symbol for a switch should always indicate its *normal* position. The normal position of an automatic switch is its position when it is

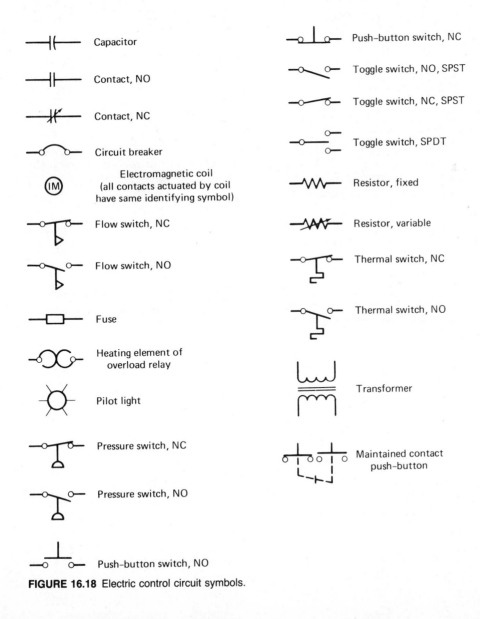

**FIGURE 16.18** Electric control circuit symbols.

not energized. The normal position of a manual switch generally means its position during normal operation of the equipment. The reader should keep these points in mind and should refer to the symbol list in Figure 16.18 as we discuss some of the symbols.

*Contacts* are circuit connections that close or open. We have discussed them often before, as part of a relay, a starter, or other devices. Note that the symbol for a normally closed (NC) contact uses a slash through the symbol to distinguish it from a normally open (NO) contact.

Note that for most manual switches the normal position can be shown in a realistic way in the symbol; that is, the circuit is shown either open or closed.

A *momentary* contact push button means that the changed position is maintained only for the moment that it is manually pushed. It returns to its original position as soon as pressure is released. A push button switch should be drawn in its normal position. In addition to ensure that there is no mistake in reading the diagram, the cross bar should be shown above the wiring for a normally open contact, and below the bar for a normally closed contact. This corresponds to the actual motion.

A *maintained* contact push button is also shown. It will remain in whichever of the two positions it is switched to, until manually changed again. The dashed line indicates that the two push buttons are mechanically linked to move together.

Switches can be described by the terms *pole* and *throw. Pole* refers to the number of circuits through the switch. If there is one circuit it is called single pole (SP) and if there are two circuits it is called double pole (DP). The throw refers to the number of closed positions the switch can take. If it has only one closed position it is called single throw (ST), and if it has two it is called double throw (DT). For example, looking at the symbol list, SPDT indicates a single pole, double throw type switch.

A magnetic coil is often represented by a circle symbol. It may be a starter or relay coil. In order to distinguish on a diagram that has more than one coil which contact is operated by a coil, the same lettering abbreviation should be used to identify both the coil and its contacts. The letters are placed beside both the coil and contacts. If one coil controls more than one set of contacts, a different number should follow each set of contacts. For example, if a coil is labeled CR, and it controls two sets of contacts, they would be labeled $CR_1$ and $CR_2$. A legend (list) is usually placed near a diagram to explain the abbreviations.

The same lettering cross-identification procedure is used for a thermal heater and the contacts it controls.

## 16.20 Motor Control Circuit

A basic control circuit for manual control of a three-phase motor using a magnetic starter is shown in Figure 16.19. The motor is started and stopped manually from push buttons, which may be a part of the starter or located separately. In this example we show both the connection diagram and schematic diagram, for comparison. Even for this very simple case it is more difficult to follow the control operation from the connection diagram.

Note that the schematic wiring diagram is a stretched out linear scheme of the connected control devices. A general rule on reading (and developing) the diagram is to read from left to right. Beginning at the left, the stop button is normally closed. The start button and auxiliary contact M is normally open, however, so current does not flow. When the start button is pushed control power reaches the starter coil M. The three starter overload contacts, OL, are normally closed, so the circuit is complete and will be energized. The starter coil will close the starter contacts and the motor will start.

The auxiliary contact M in the starter remains closed when the start button is released,

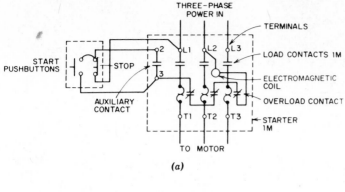

(a)

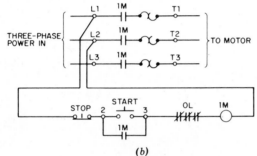

(b)

**FIGURE 16.19** (a) Connection and (b) Schematic (ladder) wiring diagrams for manual control of a three-phase motor with a magnetic starter.

so the motor continues to run. The motor may be stopped by pushing the stop button; this opens the circuit and de-energizes coil M, and the starter contacts drop out. Note that releasing the stop button has no effect on the broken circuit. The control circuit will also be broken if the motor draws too much current. In this case the overload heaters will act, opening one or more of the overload contacts in the control circuit.

In the example shown, control power was drawn from the power lines. A transformer could also have been used if low voltage control power was preferred. This does not change the internal control circuit.

The motor starter main contacts and heater coils were included in this example to show the relationship between its components and the control circuit. This will not be done in future examples. Remember however that the motor starter coil and its auxiliary contacts were

shown because they are electrically part of the control circuit.

## 16.21 Elementary Refrigeration Compressor Control

A simple control system for a small compressor that is automatically controlled for on–off operation is shown in the schematic diagram of Figure 16.20.

A manual switch is provided for disconnecting the control circuit. This switch would be manually closed to initiate operation, and would be left closed except for unusual conditions such as servicing the system. It may not be included in some cases. The thermostat makes contact on rise in temperature. The refrigerant dual pressure (high–low) control is normally closed. The compressor motor has a protective thermostat that is normally closed and the starter overloads are normally closed.

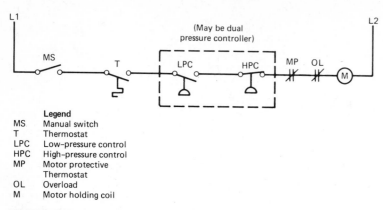

**Legend**

| | |
|---|---|
| MS | Manual switch |
| T | Thermostat |
| LPC | Low-pressure control |
| HPC | High-pressure control |
| MP | Motor protective |
| | Thermostat |
| OL | Overload |
| M | Motor holding coil |

**FIGURE 16.20** Schematic wiring diagram for simple on–off control of a refrigeration compressor.

On a rise in temperature the thermostat switch contacts close. Since all other switches are normally closed when the starter coil is energized, the motor contacts (not shown) close, and the motor runs. The compressor will cycle off normally when a fall in temperature opens the thermostat switch. An abnormal condition corresponding to the function of any of the other devices will of course break the circuit, stopping the compressor.

The thermostat may be a space temperature or refrigerant temperature controller. The operating control could also have been a suction pressure controller.

## 16.22 Pumpdown Control

*Pumpdown* control is used to remove refrigerant from the evaporator before the compressor stops, and to then isolate the evaporator so that it remains free of refrigerant during shutdown. As described in Chapter 5, this limits refrigerant migration to the crankcase and reduces the likelihood of liquid floodback to the compressor. A control circuit with pumpdown features is shown in Figure 16.21.

The first circuit (reading from the top) contains a thermostat and solenoid coil. This coil is part of a solenoid valve that is in the refriger-

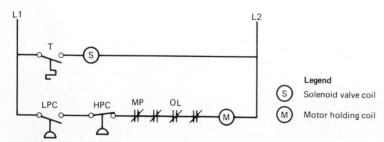

**Legend**

| | |
|---|---|
| S | Solenoid valve coil |
| M | Motor holding coil |

**FIGURE 16.21** Schematic wiring diagram for pump-down control of a refrigeration compressor.

ant liquid line to the evaporator. The second circuit contains the refrigerant high–low pressure control, starter coil M, overloads, and motor protective thermostat.

On a rise in temperature, the thermostat switch closes, energizing the solenoid coil; the valve opens and refrigerant flows to the evaporator. This increases suction pressure and the low pressure control switch closes. The safety devices are normally closed, so the motor starter coil M is energized and the compressor starts.

When the temperature condition is satisfied the thermostat breaks contact, and the solenoid valve closes. The compressor continues to operate for a brief period until the low pressure control point is reached. Refrigerant is pumped out of the evaporator, as desired.

The pumpdown arrangement described can lead to short cycling of the compressor. A small leak through the closed solenoid valve or through the compressor discharge valve will result in refrigerant migration to the crankcase. This raises the suction pressure and the compressor low pressure control will cause the compressor to cycle on, even though the thermostat does not call for cooling. This problem can be resolved by using a *nonrecycling* pumpdown control arrangement, also called *pumpout*. It will be described in the next section.

## 16.23  Control of a DX System

In this section we describe one possible control arrangement for a small direct expansion refrigeration system with evaporator fan and condenser fan. A nonrecycling pumpdown feature will be used. The schematic diagram is shown in Figure 16.22.

Beginning at the top of the ladder, the evaporator fan is started manually with a momentary start push button. This energizes the starter coil 1M and the fan starts. The coil auxiliary contact $1M_1$ closes so that the circuit

is maintained when the pushbutton is released.

In line 2, another evaporator fan auxiliary contact $1M_2$ closes. When the thermostat calls for cooling its contacts close and this circuit is completed. This energizes both the solenoid valve coil SV and a control relay coil CR. The solenoid valve opens and refrigerant is admitted to the evaporator.

In line 3 the control relay contacts $CR_1$ close. This energizes condenser fan starter coil 2M and the fan starts.

In line 4 another set of control relay contacts $CR_2$ close. If the refrigerant pressure controls and oil pressure failure switch OFS are closed the compressor starter coil 3M is energized and the compressor starts. There is another set of contacts 3M that close when coil 3M is energized. Contact $3M_2$, in the condenser fan circuit, closes.

The operating sequence will now be described. After the evaporator fan is started manually, when the thermostat calls for cooling the solenoid valve opens, and the condenser fan and compressor start. When the temperature conditions are satisfied the thermostat contacts open and the solenoid valve closes. Control relay CR also is de-energized.

The compressor continues to operate even though contact $CR_2$ opens, because of the parallel circuit through $3M_1$. When the low pressure control opens the compressor will stop and pumpdown is completed. The condenser fan has also continued to operate through contact $3M_2$, until the compressor stops, opening $3M_2$.

If the crankcase pressure rises due to leakage, the compressor will not cycle on even though the low pressure control closes, since both contacts $CR_2$ and $3M_1$ are open. Short cycling is prevented. When the thermostat calls for cooling, however, the sequence of events is repeated and the compressor starts.

Line 5 shows a crankcase resistance heater CCH. Contact $3M_3$ is normally closed so that

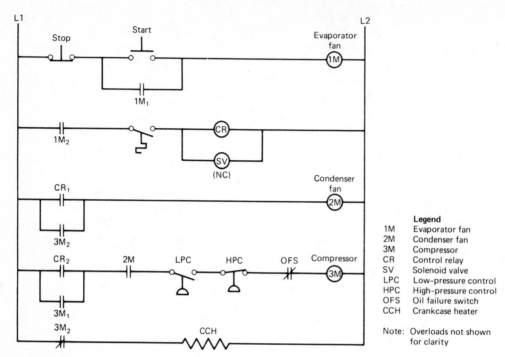

**FIGURE 16.22** Schematic wiring diagram for pumpout (nonrecycling pump-down) control of a refrigeration compressor. (Overloads not shown, for clarity.)

the heater functions when the compressor is not running. The contacts, controlled by the compressor starter coil, open when the compressor runs. In some systems the crankcase heater is energized at all times.

When nonrecycling pumpdown is used significant refrigeration migration to the crankcase can occur during the off periods. This could lead to foaming and lubrication loss on start-up. Use of a crankcase heater is therefore especially important to prevent migration with this control arrangement.

The control scheme shown in Figure 16.22 includes interlocks. An *interlock* is an arrangement in which one device is automatically prevented from operating until another device or sequence of events has become activated. Often the interlock is between motors. That is,

one motor cannot run until another motor is running. This is usually done for safety reasons. In the control scheme described, note that the compressor is interlocked with the condenser fan through contact 2M. That is, the compressor cannot run until the condenser fan runs. This protects against the high compressor discharge temperature that would occur without the condenser operation.

The control scheme described here is only one of many possibilities, which depend on the specifics on each installation. Some additional features that would often be used, such as compressor capacity control, timers, and condenser head pressure control were not shown so that the control system would not be too complex, which could detract from the learning process.

## 16.24 Solid State Controls

*Solid state* devices are electronic devices made of solid materials that have special properties which are extremely useful for control purposes. (They are called solid state because electronics originally used only gaseous devices, such as gas filled tubes, or vacuum tubes.)

Solid state devices are generally made from one or more substances called semiconductors. Silicon is an example. *Semiconductors* are materials that have certain special electrical properties. Some of them change electrical conductivity with a change in temperature, pressure, light, or other conditions. This makes them useful as control sensors.

Another extremely important characteristic of some semiconductor devices is that they can change between being either good conductors or good insulators. This property depends both on the type of device and the way they are arranged in circuits. These characteristics can be used to develop solid state control circuits that act as switches, relays, amplifiers, and virtually any other control function needed.

Solid state controls have many desirable features that result from the fact that the control function is carried out solely by electricity. There are no mechanical moving parts or electrical contacts. This increases reliability and life expectancy as compared to electromechanical devices. Maintenance is virtually nonexistent. The small size of solid state controls and their compactness when grouped together is another clear advantage. Their nature also lends to their use in programmed automatic control with computers.

## 16.25 Solid State Control Logic

A refrigeration control circuit for even a relatively simple system may include a series of steps for starting, stopping, varying capacity, interlocking, safety responses, change of operating modes, and many other features. This may include a number of kinds of equipment, including compressors, pumps, and fans. The plan of the possible sequence and alternates that the control system is designed to automatically perform is called the program, or *programming control.* The term *control logic* is also used to refer to the whole scheme. Control logic requirements are becoming more complex due to demands for more energy efficient operation, higher technology equipment, and more complex refrigeration systems. Solid state controls are often more convenient then electromechanical controls for more complex control. One reason is that it is relatively simple to accomplish complex control logic through varying the circuit design of the solid state devices. Further advantages are the small size, possible lower cost, and higher reliability of solid state devices.

## 16.26 Solid State Devices

It is not our intention in this brief discussion to attempt to explain the complex technology of solid state electronics. However, it is useful to introduce some terminology and describe how solid state devices are used in controls.

A *diode* is a device that permits electrons to flow through it in only one direction. It is therefore basically a switching device. In addition to being used as a simple switch, diodes are often used in rectifiers. A *rectifier* or *converter* is a device that converts alternating current to direct current. Since a diode only allows current to flow in one direction, if ac current is used as input to a diode, the output will be only dc current. An *inverter* is a solid state device that changes dc to ac current.

A *transistor* is a semiconductor device that can be used either as an electrical switch or as an amplifier.

*Thyristors* are semiconductor switching devices that are particularly useful for control of high power use, such as with motors. Two types of thyristors are the *silicon controlled rectifier* (SCR) and the *triac.* They are used to regulate the speed of motors. This can be accomplished by their switching ability. For instance, the triac can "trigger" (permit) current flow for only part of each ac voltage cycle. Less current flows, and the motor runs at lower speed. Thyristors are composed of circuits using diodes and other electronic devices.

## 16.27 Solid State Logic Circuits

Combinations of diodes and transistors are used to build circuits that by switching make certain decisions. These are called logic circuits. They are extremely useful as control circuits, because the functions of a control system are also just a set of decisions. For example, if a thermostat and a pressure controller are in a certain position then the decision might be to start a motor. If either device is not in that position, the decision would be to not start the motor.

All such switching decisions are built up from a simple "yes" or "no" decision. In electrical terms a switch is either closed (yes) or open (no), so that current would flow or not flow. Solid state device logic circuits carry out combinations of yes and no decisions that make up the complete control program. These circuits are built up of basic elements called *logic gates*. There are three types of logic gates, called AND, OR, and NOT. They can be combined into additional logic functions such as NAND (not–and) and NOR (not–or). We will mention only the AND and OR function here. Logic symbols have been devised for these functions. The symbols for AND and OR gates are shown in Figure 16.23.

The OR gate means that if a signal from

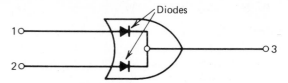

**FIGURE 16.24** Two diodes used to create an OR gate.

*either* input 1 or 2 is "yes," there will be an (electrical) output from 3, that is, a "yes." Or, to put it in practical terms, the switch will close.

The AND gate means that there must be a "yes" signal (a voltage, for instance) from *both* inputs 1 and 2 for there to be an output (circuit completed) at 3. If either 1 or 2 is not activated, the circuit will be open.

It is not possible in our discussion to explain in detail how semiconductor devices are arranged to create these functions. However, we can mention that the OR gate can be achieved by using two diodes in parallel. For instance, Figure 16.24 shows an OR gate. Input to either of the two diodes will result in current flow at the output.

An example of OR logic control is shown in Figure 16.25, with both the conventional schematic circuit diagram and the equivalent logic circuit diagram. Coil M will be energized when either pressure control switch contact

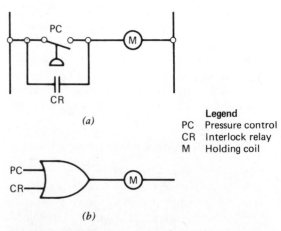

Legend
PC   Pressure control
CR   Interlock relay
M    Holding coil

**FIGURE 16.25** Use of an OR logic circuit to control a magnetic coil. (*a*) Schematic electric circuit diagram. (*b*) OR logic control circuit diagram.

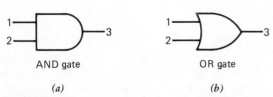

**FIGURE 16.23** Logic symbols for solid state AND and OR gates.

PC is closed or interlock relay switch CR is closed. The same control logic is achieved with the solid state OR gate shown. If the signal (voltage) from either the pressure control sensor through 1 or the relay circuit 2 is on ("yes"), the OR gate device will pass current to the output 3, energizing coil M.

An example of an AND control circuit is shown in Figure 16.26. Both thermostat switch T and pressure control PC must be closed for coil M to be energized. In this case we have also shown a transistor amplifier to the output. Amplification of the signal is frequently necessary with solid state control circuits, which use low voltages (5 or 12 V dc).

The development of solid state integrated circuits has made possible the microprocessor based *programmable controller* (PC), which can be used for more complex refrigeration control systems (Figure 16.27). The instructions

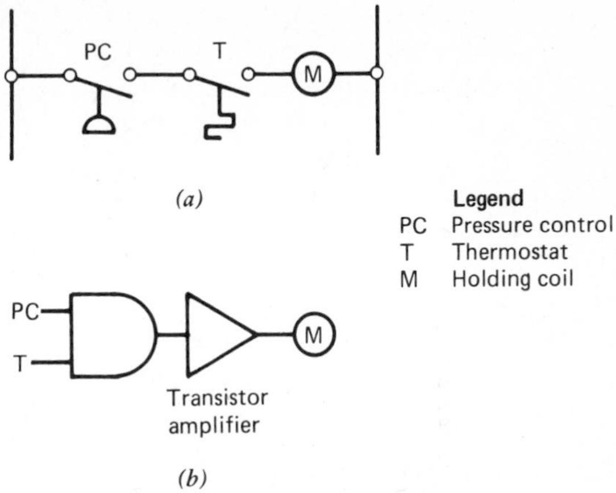

**Legend**
PC   Pressure control
T    Thermostat
M    Holding coil

*(a)*

Transistor amplifier

*(b)*

**FIGURE 16.26** Use of an AND logic circuit in refrigeration control. (*a*) Schematic electric circuit diagram. (*b*) AND logic control circuit diagram.

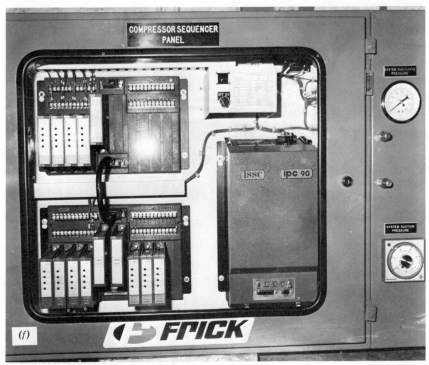

**FIGURE 16.27** A programmable controller for controlling the operations of a refrigeration compressor. (Courtesy of Frick Co., Waynesboro, Pa.)

for the equivalent logic of the ladder wiring diagram can be programmed into the PC, which receives inputs and sends the proper outputs to control the refrigeration equipment according to the program.

The programmable controller eliminates hardware such as relays as well as the interconnecting wiring. A further desirable feature is that the program (instructions) can be changed if a different control logic is wanted, without rewiring or changing hardware.

## REVIEW QUESTIONS

1. What is the main function of a motor controller? By what other name is it called?

2. What is the simplest arrangement for starting and stopping a motor? Why is it limited to very small motors?

3. What is a contactor? How does it differ from a starter?

4. Explain the difference between a manual and a magnetic starter.

5. Explain the difference between direct and indirect motor control and two-wire and three-wire control. Draw a sketch of each. What are the advantages of indirect control?

6. What is a combination starter?

7. Explain the difference between across-the-line and reduced voltage starters. What is the purpose of a reduced voltage starter?

8. Name and describe four types of reduced voltage starters.

9. What feature does a star–delta starter have that makes it acceptable for starting centrifugal refrigeration compressors?

10. Explain what is meant by motor overload and describe its possible effects.

11. What is locked rotor (inrush) current? When is it harmful?

12. What are possible causes of a motor failing to start (even though it has power)?

13. Explain some possible causes of motor overload.

14. Why are fuses and circuit breakers not always sufficient to protect motors against overloads?

15. What do motor overload devices protect against?

16. Explain the difference between line duty and pilot duty protective devices, using sketches.

17. Explain what is meant by the terms *manual reset* and *automatic reset*, and discuss relative advantages.

18. Explain what is meant by a nuisance trip, and a restart relay.

19. What is an integral protection device?

20. What are the two ways of sensing heat in a heater type thermal overload relay?

21. What is a compensating overload device?

22. Describe the operation of a magnetic thermal overload relay.

23. Describe the operation of two heater thermal overload relays.

24. Why do thermal overload relays have a time delay? Why is this a problem with hermetic unit motors?

25. What are two possible sensing devices for motor thermostat protectors?

26. What is the primary purpose of refrigeration controls? What other purposes may they serve?

27. What are the two possible sources of power used in most control systems?

28. Name and describe the function of the two elements of a controller.

29. Describe three methods of sensing temperature.

30. Describe the operation of a remote bulb thermostat. When is it used?

31. What are the functions of a low pressure and high pressure controller?

32. Describe the operation of an oil pressure failure control.

33. Explain the terms *cut-in, cut-out, differential,* and *range.*

34. Explain the use of a potentiometer with controls.

35. What are a connection diagram and a schematic diagram? What are their purposes?

36. Into what two categories can all electrical circuit devices be grouped? List three examples in each group.

37. Explain the terms, NO, NC, SP, DP, ST, DT.

38. What are momentary and maintained contact push buttons?

39. Describe a simple refrigeration control; a pumpdown control; a pumpout control. What are their relative advantages?

40. What is an interlock? Describe an example of its use.

41. What are solid state devices? What are the advantages of solid state controls?

42. How can ac motor speed be controlled using solid state devices?

43. What is a logic circuit? What are AND and OR gates? Describe an example of each used in controls.

# Glossary

**absolute pressure** See "pressure, absolute."

**absolute temperature** See "temperature, absolute."

**absolute zero temperature** Lowest temperature possible; temperature at which all molecular activity ceases ($-460°F$, $-273°C$).

**absorbent** A substance with the ability to take up (absorb) another substance.

**absorption** A process in which one substance absorbs another, resulting in a physical and/or chemical change.

**accumulator, suction (also called suction trap and surge drum)** A storage tank that receives liquid refrigerant from the evaporator and prevents it from flowing into the suction line.

**adiabatic process** A thermodynamic process in which no heat is added to or removed from the system.

**air, saturated** An air–water vapor mixture that contains the maximum amount of water vapor that the mixture can hold.

**air changes** The amount of air leakage into a space expressed in the number of times the space volume is changed per unit of time.

**air conditioning** The treatment to control one or more of the following conditions of air in a space: temperature, humidity, cleanliness, and distribution.

**algae** A plant growth; it may particularly contaminate water used in cooling towers and water cooled condensers.

**approach** The difference between the leaving water temperature and the entering air wet bulb temperature, as applied to a cooling tower or other evaporative cooler.

**automatic expansion valve** See "constant pressure expansion valve."

**azeotrope** A mixture of refrigerants that behaves as a homogeneous substance.

**back pressure** See "suction pressure."

**back-seat** A seat against which a valve disc seats when fully opened. By *backseating*, the fluid pressure cannot reach the valve packing, and connection can be made to a back-seat port.

**barometer** An instrument for measuring atmospheric pressure.

**Baudelot cooler** A cooling device in which a liquid to be cooled flows by gravity over the outside of tubes or plates containing the refrigerant.

**blowdown (bleed-off)** The removal of water from an evaporative cooling device to reduce mineral concentration.

**boiling point** The temperature at which a fluid will change from a liquid to a gas; it changes with the pressure exerted on the liquid.

**booster compressor** A term applied to the compressor used in the low stage of a two-stage compression system.

**bore** The internal diameter of a compressor cylinder.

**brake horsepower** The power required to drive a machine.

**brine** A solution of water and a salt, used as a coolant.

**British thermal unit (Btu)** A unit of (heat) energy; it is the heat required to change the temperature of one pound of water one degree F, at 60°F.

**capacitor** A device that stores an electric charge, used in some motor circuits.

**capacity, refrigerating** The rate of heat removal by the refrigeration system from the medium or space being cooled.

**capillary tube** A small diameter tube used (*a*) as a refrigerant flow control device, or (*b*) to transmit pressure from the bulb of a temperature controller.

**carbonization** The formation of carbon deposits on compressor parts as a result of lubrication oil decomposition.

**cascade system** An arrangement of two or more refrigerating systems in series to produce low temperatures. The evaporator of a higher temperature system serves as the condenser of the lower temperature system.

**Celsius (Centigrade)** A temperature scale in which the freezing point of water is 0°C and the boiling point 100°C, at 14.7 psia pressure.

**change of state** Change from one state (solid, liquid, or gas) to another.

**charge** Amount of refrigerant put in a system; or, the fluid in a TEV power element.

**check valve** A valve that permits flow in one direction only.

**circuit breaker** A safety device that automatically opens an electrical circuit that is overloaded.

**clearance volume** The space remaining in a compressor at the end of the piston compression stroke.

**coefficient of performance, refrigerating (COP)** The ratio of the rate of heat removed to the rate of energy input of a refrigeration system, expressed in the same units.

**compound compression** Compression of a refrigerant gas in two or more stages.

**compression ratio** The ratio of discharge to suction pressure in a compressor, expressed in absolute pressure units.

**compressor** A machine that raises the pressure of a gas.

**compressor, accessible hermetic (semihermetic)** A compressor and motor combination enclosed in a gasketed sealed housing that can be opened for service in the field.

**compressor, centrifugal** A compressor that raises the pressure of a gas by a centrifugal force.

**compressor, hermetic** A compressor and motor combination enclosed in a welded sealed housing that cannot be opened for service in the field.

**compressor, open** A compressor with a shaft extending through its casing for external drive.

**compressor, positive displacement** A compressor that raises the pressure of a gas by decreasing the volume of a chamber.

**compressor, reciprocating** A positive displacement compressor that has reciprocating pistons and cylinders.

**compressor, rotary** A positive displacement compressor that has an eccentric rotor.

**compressor, screw (helical rotary)** A positive displacement compressor that has intermeshing (male and female) rotors.

**compressor unit** An assembly consisting of compressor, motor, and accessories on a common base.

**condensation** The process of changing state from a gas to a liquid by the extraction of heat.

**condenser** A heat exchanger in which high pressure refrigerant gas is condensed by transferring heat to a cooling medium.

**condenser, air cooled** A condenser that uses surrounding air as a cooling medium, raising the temperature of the air.

**condenser, evaporative** A condenser that utilizes both the cooling effect of evaporating water and surrounding air.

**condenser, water cooled** A condenser that uses water as a cooling medium, raising the temperature of the water.

**condensing unit** An assembly consisting of compressor, motor, condenser, and accessories.

**conductance, thermal** The time rate of heat flow through a body, per unit area per degree temperature difference.

**conduction, thermal** The form of heat transfer through a body from particle to particle without displacement of the body.

**conductivity, thermal** The ability of a material to conduct heat.

**control** Regulation of equipment to maintain a desired condition.

**controller** A device used to automatically regulate equipment.

**convection** The transfer of heat by movement of a fluid obtaining thermal energy.

**cooling tower** A device used for cooling water by evaporating a portion of the water in air.

**copper plating** An abnormal condition in which copper deposits on compressor parts.

**corrosion** The deterioration of metals from chemical action.

**counterflow** The flow of two fluids in opposite directions in a heat exchanger.

**critical point** The temperature and pressure for a fluid above which there is no distinction between liquid and gaseous state.

**crossflow** The flow of two fluids perpendicular to each other in a heat exchanger.

**cryogenics** Refrigeration at extremely low temperatures.

**crystallization** The solidification of a solution, in the form of crystals, under certain conditions.

**cut-in point** The temperature or pressure at which a controller closes a circuit.

**cut-out point** The temperature or pressure at which a controller opens a circuit.

**cycle** A series of repeated processes that the refrigerant undergoes.

**damper** A device for regulating the flow of a fluid.

**defrosting** The process of removing accumulated ice or frost from an evaporator surface.

**dehumidification** The condensation of water vapor from air.

**dehydrator** See "drier."

**density** The mass or weight per unit volume of a substance.

**dessicant** A substance that removes moisture (from the refrigeration system).

**dielectric strength** The maximum voltage that an insulator or oil can withstand without conducting electricity.

**differential** The difference between the cut-in and cut-out points of a control.

**direct expansion coil** A tubular coil evaporator for cooling air through which the refrigerant flows without recirculation.

**disconnect switch** A switch for disconnecting a motor from the source of electric power.

**displacement, compressor** The volume swept through by a compressor.

**displacement, theoretical** The volume of gas that a compressor must move to produce a given amount of refrigeration, at suction inlet conditions.

**distributor** A device for dividing the flow of refrigerant into parallel circuits to an evaporator.

**draft** A flow of air resulting from a pressure difference.

**drier** A device for removing moisture from the refrigerating system.

**drift** Unevaporated water carried off by air passing through a cooling tower or evaporative condenser.

**dry ice** Solid carbon dioxide.

**efficiency, volumetric** The ratio of the volume of gas moved by a compressor to the compressor displacement, expressed in percent.

**eliminator** A device to remove entrained liquid particles from a gas stream.

**energy efficiency ratio (EER)** The ratio of the rate of heat removed in Btu/hr to the rate of energy input in kW of a refrigeration system.

**enthalpy** A property of a substance that indicates the stored energy due to temperature and pressure; also called heat content.

**entropy** The ratio of the heat added to a substance to the temperature at which it is added; its change reflects efficiency of energy use.

**equalizer, external** A tube connected from the underside of a thermostatic expansion valve diaphragm to the suction line from the evaporator.

**equalizer, internal** A port connecting the underside of a thermostatic expansion valve diaphragm to the exit side of the valve.

**evaporation** The change of state from a liquid to a gas; also called boiling when it occurs rapidly.

**evaporative cooling** The cooling of water and/or surrounding air by evaporating a portion of the water.

**evaporator** A heat exchanger in which a refrigerant evaporates by absorbing heat from a medium to be cooled.

**evaporator, dry expansion** A tube-type evaporator where liquid refrigerant is fed in one end and gas flows out the other, directly to the suction line.

**evaporator, flooded** An evaporator containing liquid refrigerant at all times.

**expansion valve, constant pressure** A refrigerant flow control device that maintains constant evaporator pressure; also called an automatic expansion valve.

**expansion valve, thermostatic** A refrigerant flow control device responding to superheat leaving the evaporator.

**Fahrenheit** A temperature scale in which the freezing point of water is 32°F and the boiling point is 212°F, at 14.7 psia pressure.

**fill** The material in a cooling tower that breaks up the water to increase surface area.

**filter, refrigerant** A device for removing particles from the refrigerant.

**flash gas** The portion of the refrigerant that suddenly evaporates as the pressure is reduced passing through the expansion device.

**float valve** A valve that controls a liquid level; used as a refrigerant flow control device either as a high-side float or a low-side float, depending on location.

**floodback** A steady flow of liquid refrigerant from the evaporator to the compressor suction.

**flow control device (also called expansion device)** A device that meters the flow of refrigerant to the evaporator.

**foaming** Formation of an oil–refrigerant foam mixture, especially in the compressor crankcase.

**force** A push or pull exerted by one object on another.

**forced draft** The flow of air caused by a fan forcing air through a device.

**fouling factor** The thermal resistance of water in a heat exchanger, affected by foreign material.

**fuse** A safety device in an electric circuit that melts when the circuit is overloaded.

**fusible plug** A safety device with a low melting point that, in case of a fire, will release excess refrigerant pressure due to temperature.

**gage, compression** An instrument for measuring pressures above atmospheric pressure.

**gage, compound** An instrument for measuring pressures both above and below atmospheric pressure.

**gage, vacuum** An instrument for measuring pressures below atmospheric.

**generator (also called concentrator)** A component in an absorption system used to drive refrigerant out of solution.

**halide torch** A device used for detecting halocarbon refrigerant leaks.

**halocarbons** A group of substances of similar chemical structure often used as refrigerants.

**head** Pressure; often expressed as height of liquid.

**head pressure** Condensing pressure

**heat** A form of energy that is transferred because of a temperature difference.

**heat, latent** The change in enthalpy of a substance when it changes state.

**heat, sensible** The change in enthalpy of a substance when its temperature (and not its state) changes.

**heat of compression** The increase in enthalpy resulting from compression of a gas.

**heat of fusion, latent** The change in enthalpy of a substance when it changes between solid and liquid states.

**heat of rejection** The amount of heat rejected from the condenser.

**heat of respiration** The heat produced by the ripening of fruits and vegetables.

**heat of vaporization (or condensation), latent** The change in enthalpy of a substance when it changes between a saturated liquid and a saturated gaseous state.

**heat pump** A refrigerating system used for cooling and heating.

**heat transfer** The flow of heat from one body to another.

**high side** The part of a refrigeration system at the condensing pressure.

**horsepower** A unit of power.

**hot gas line (discharge line)** The refrigerant line leaving the compressor.

**humidity** The water vapor content in atmospheric air.

**induced draft** The flow of air caused by a fan drawing air through a device.

**infiltration** The inward flow of air to a space from the outside through openings and cracks.

**insulation, thermal** A material used to reduce heat flow.

**intercooling** Removal of heat from compressed refrigerant gas between compression stages.

**interlock** A means to prevent some parts of a refrigeration system from operating when other parts are not operating.

**king valve** A service valve located at the liquid receiver outlet.

**leak detector** A device used to detect refrigerant leaks from a system.

**liquid line** The refrigerant line from the condenser or receiver to the evaporator.

**low side** The part of a refrigeration system at the evaporating pressure.

**make-up** Water added to a cooling tower or evaporative condenser to replace losses.

**manometer** An instrument for measuring pressure that uses a column of liquid.

**mass** The quantity of matter in a body.

**miscibility** The degree to which oil and refrigerant mix.

**muffler** A device installed in the compressor discharge line to reduce noise.

**natural convection** Convection caused by natural temperature differences in a fluid.

**natural draft** The flow of air, as in a cooling tower, caused by natural effects.

**noncondensable gas** Gas such as air combined with refrigerant that is not condensed; it usually must be removed.

**oil separator** A device used to remove oil from gaseous refrigerant.

**ozone** A form of oxygen.

**packing** a material placed around the stems of valves or shafts to prevent leakage.

**pH** A measurement of the degree of acidity or alkalinity in an aqueous solution.

**phase** See "state."

**pour point** The lowest temperature at which a liquid (such as oil) will flow.

**power** The time rate of performing work or energy.

**power factor** The ratio of actual to apparent electric power in a load circuit.

**pressure, absolute** Pressure measured above absolute vacuum.

**pressure, atmospheric** The pressure exerted by the envelope of air surrounding the earth.

**pressure, gage** Pressure measured above atmospheric pressure.

**pressure, vacuum** Pressure measured below atmospheric pressure.

**pressure drop** The loss of pressure through a pipe, duct, or device.

**pumpdown** The reduction of pressure in a system.

**purge** To remove impurities, usually noncondensable gases, from a refrigeration system.

**quality** The proportion of weight of a vapor in a mixture of liquid and vapor, to the total weight.

**radiation, thermal** The transfer of heat by electromagnetic waves.

**receiver** A vessel for storing liquid refrigerant.

**rectifier, electrical** A device for converting ac to dc current.

**rectifier, refrigerant** A device for separating the absorbent from the refrigerant in an absorption system.

**refrigerant** A fluid used to produce a cooling effect.

**refrigerant, primary** A fluid in refrigeration equipment used to produce a cooling effect, usually by evaporation.

**refrigerant, secondary** A fluid cooled by a primary refrigerant, then used to cool a final medium or space.

**refrigeration** The removal of heat from (cooling of) a substance to bring it to or maintain it at a relatively low temperature.

**refrigeration effect** The amount of heat absorbed by the refrigerant in an evaporator, in Btu/lb.

**refrigeration load** The rate of heat gain to, or the required rate of heat removal from, the refrigerated medium or space.

**regulator, evaporator pressure** An automatic valve that maintains the evaporator pressure above a preset minimum value.

**regulator, suction pressure (also called crankcase pressure regulator)** An automatic valve that maintains the suction pressure below a preset maximum value.

**relay, electrical** A device that controls an electric circuit in response to a condition in another circuit.

**resistance, thermal** A property of a substance that measures its opposition to heat transfer; the reciprocal of thermal conductance.

**reverse cycle** Operation of a vapor compression refrigeration system to reverse refrigerant flow from the condenser to evaporator; operation of a heat pump in the heating mode.

**reversing valve** A device used to reverse the direction of refrigerant flow.

**saturated air** A mixture of air and water vapor that contains the maximum amount of water vapor possible.

**saturated pressure** The pressure at the boiling (saturated) temperature.

**saturated state** The condition of a substance at which it may boil or condense.

**saturated temperature** The boiling–condensing temperature.

**seal, shaft** A device used to prevent leakage between the shaft and bearing of a compressor or pump.

**service valve** a manual valve used to isolate equipment for service.

**short cycling** Too frequent starting and stopping of a compressor.

**SI** The International System of Units.

**sight glass** A glass window or tube for observing presence of liquid refrigerant or oil level.

**sludge** An undesirable product resulting from decomposition of oil.

**slugging** A condition where chunks of liquid enter a compressor.

**soldering** Joining of two metals by adhesion to a metal melting below about 800°F.

**solenoid valve** An electromagnetically operated valve.

**specific gravity** The ratio of the weight (or mass) of a liquid to that of water.

**specific heat** The quantity of heat required to change a unit mass of a substance one degree (e.g., Btu/lb-°F).

**specific volume** The volume per unit mass of a substance.

**strainer** A device used to remove solid particles from a liquid.

**stroke** The length of travel of a piston.

**subcooling** Cooling of a liquid below its condensing (saturation) temperature.

**suction line** The pipe which carries refrigerant from the evaporator to the compressor.

**suction trap** See "accumulator."

**superheat** The temperature increase above the boiling point (saturation temperature) of a gas.

**surge drum** See "accumulator."

**surging** An unstable operating condition in centrifugal compressors, in which refrigerant gas surges back and forth.

**temperature** The measure of thermal activity of matter; the measure of molecular activity.

**temperature, dry bulb** The temperature of air measured by a thermometer.

**temperature, wet bulb** The temperature of air indicated by a thermometer with the sensing bulb covered by a wet wick.

**thermistor** A semiconductor whose electrical resistance varies with temperature.

**ton of refrigeration** A unit measuring rates of heat energy, used in refrigeration, equal to 12,000 Btu/hr.

**unloader** A device for controlling compressor capacity.

**valve (types)** See specific type names

**vapor** A gas, especially near its condensation temperature.

**vapor compression system** The method of refrigeration in which a refrigerant vapor is compressed, condensed, and evaporated.

**viscosity** A property of fluids that causes a resistance to flow.

**wax** An ingredient in oil which may separate as a solid on cooling of the oil.

**wiredrawing** A restriction in the area of a passage through which a fluid is moving.

**work** The movement of a force through distance.

**work of compression** See "heat of compression."

# Appendix 1

## ABBREVIATIONS AND SYMBOLS

| | | | |
|---|---|---|---|
| $A$ | area | Hg | mercury |
| ac | alternating current | hp | horsepower |
| atm | atmosphere | H.R. | heat of rejection |
| bhp | brake horsepower | hr | hour |
| Btu | British thermal unit | Hz | frequency |
| $c$ | specific heat | $I$ | current |
| $C$ | thermal conductance | in. | inch |
| °C | degrees Celsius | in. Hg | inches of mercury |
| cal | calorie | in. $Hg_a$ | inches of mercury absolute |
| CFM | cubic feet per minute | in. w. | inches of water. |
| COP | coefficient of performance | J | joule |
| CR | compression ratio | $k$ | thermal conductivity |
| $d$ | density | k | thousand (prefix) |
| $D$ | piston diameter (bore) | °K | degrees Kelvin |
| dc | direct current | kcal | kilocalorie |
| DP | double pole | kg | kilogram |
| DX | direct expansion | km | kilometer |
| $E$ | efficiency | kPa | kilopascals |
| $E$ | voltage | kW | kilowatt |
| $E_V$ | volumetric efficiency | $L$ | length; piston stroke; thickness |
| EER | energy efficiency ratio | lb | pound |
| E.L. | equivalent length | m | meter |
| EMF | electromotive force | $m$ | mass; mass flow rate |
| °F | degrees Fahrenheit | m | one thousandth (prefix) |
| $F$ | force | M | million (prefix) |
| FPM | feet \per minute | METD | mean effective temperature difference |
| ft | feet | min | minute |
| ft-lb | foot pounds | mm | millimeter |
| ft w. | feet of water | mmHg | millimeters of mercury |
| g | gram | $N$ | newton |
| gal | gallon | $N$ | number of cylinders |
| GPM | gallons per minute | NC | normally closed |
| $h$ | specific enthalpy | NO | normally open |
| $h_f$ | specific enthalpy of saturated liquid | O.D. | outside diameter |
| $h_{fg}$ | latent heat of vaporization | $p$ | pressure |
| $h_g$ | specific enthalpy of saturated vapor | $p_{abs}$ | pressure, absolute |
| $h_{if}$ | latent heat of fusion | $p_{atm}$ | pressure, atmosphere |
| $H$ | enthalpy | $p_g$ | pressure, gage |
| $H$ | head pressure | $p_{vac}$ | pressure, vacuum |
| $H$ | height | $p$ | power |
| H.C. | heat of compression | Pa | Pascal |

| | | | |
|---|---|---|---|
| *PF* | power factor | *T* | temperature, absolute |
| psf | pounds per square foot | TC | temperature change |
| psi | pounds per square inch | TD | temperature difference |
| psia | pounds per square inch absolute | TEV | thermostatic expansion valve |
| psig | pounds per square inch gage | *t* | temperature |
| psiv | pounds per square inch vacuum | *U* | overall heat transfer coefficient |
| *Q* | heat; heat transfer rate | *v* | specific volume |
| r | ratio of outside to inside tube surface area | *V* | compressor displacement |
| °R | degrees Rankine | *V* | volt |
| *R* | electrical resistance | *V* | volume |
| *R* | gas constant | *v* | specific volume |
| *R* | thermal resistance | $V_t$ | theoretical compressor displacement |
| R.E. | refrigeration effect | W | watt |
| RH | relative humidity | *W* | width |
| rpm | revolutions per minute | *W* | work |
| SDT | saturated discharge temperature | WB | wet bulb temperature |
| sec | second | *w* | weight |
| *s.g.* | specific gravity | x | quality |
| SP | single pole | yd | yard |
| SST | saturated suction temperature | | |

# Appendix 2

# UNIT EQUIVALENTS (CONVERSION FACTORS)

*To change from one set of units to another, multiply known quantity and unit by the ratio of unit equivalents that results in the desired units.*

**LENGTH**
  *U.S.:* 12 in. = 1 ft = 0.333 yd
  *metric:* 1 m = 100 cm = 1000 mm = $10^{-3}$
    km = $10^{6}$  microns
  *U.S.–metric:* 1 ft = 0.30 m
  *SI* unit is the m

**AREA**
  *U.S.:* 144 in.$^2$ = 1 ft$^2$
  *U.S.–metric:* 1 ft$^2$ = 0.093 m$^2$
  *SI* unit is the m$^2$

**VOLUME**
  *U.S.:* 1728 in.$^3$ = 1 ft$^3$ = 7.48 gal.
  *U.S.–metric:* 1 ft$^3$ = 0.0283 m$^3$
  *SI* unit is the m$^3$

**MASS**
  *U.S.:* 1 lb = 16 oz
  *metric:* 1 kg = 1000 g
  *U.S.–metric:* 2.2 lb = 1 kg
  *SI* unit is the kg

**FORCE**
  *U.S.–metric:* 1 lb = 4.45 N
  *SI* unit is the N

**VELOCITY**
  *U.S.:* 1 ft/sec = 0.68 mi/hr
  *SI* unit is the m/sec

**DENSITY**
  *U.S.–metric:* 1 lb/ft$^3$ = 16.0 kg/m$^3$
  *SI* unit is the kg/m$^3$

**PRESSURE**
  *U.S.:* 1 psi = 2.3 ft w. = 2.04 in. Hg
  *metric:* 1 atm = 101,300 N/m$^3$
      1 mm Hg = 133.3 Pa
  *U.S.–metric:* 14.7 psi = 1 atm
  *SI* unit is the N/m$^2$ (Pa)

**TEMPERATURE**
  *U.S.:* F = R − 460
  *metric:* °C = °K − 273
  *U.S.–metric:* °F = (9/5)° C + 32; °C = 5/9
    (°F − 32)
  *SI* unit is the °K

**ENERGY**
  *U.S.:* 1 Btu = 778 ft-lb
  *metric:* 1 J = 1 W-sec = 0.239 cal
  *U.S.–metric:* 1 Btu = 1055 J = 252 cal
  *SI* unit is the J

**POWER (RATE OF ENERGY)**
  2545 Btu/hr = 1 hp = 0.746 kW
              = 33,000 ft-lb/min
  3410 Btu/hr = 1 kW
  1 ton of refrigeration = 12,000 Btu/hr
              = 4.72 HP = 3.52 kW

  *SI* unit is the W

**SPECIFIC HEAT**
  *U.S.–metric:* 1 Btu/lb-F = 1 cal/gm-°C = 4.2
    kJ/kg-°C

**HEAT TRANSFER COEFFICIENT U**
  *U.S.–metric:* 1 Btu/hr-ft$^2$-°F = 5.68 W/m$^2$-°C

**VOLUME FLOW RATE**
  *U.S.–metric:* 1 CFM = 1.70 m$^3$/hr

**USEFUL EQUIVALENTS FOR WATER ONLY (AT 60°F)**
  *Density:* 8.33 lb = 1 gal
       62.4 lb = 1 ft$^3$
  *Flow rate:* 1 GPM = 500 lb/hr

# Appendix 3

## WATER: PROPERTIES OF LIQUID AND SATURATED VAPOR (U.S. UNITS)

| Temperature, °F | Pressure, psia | Specific Volume, ft³/lb | | Specific Enthalpy, Btu/lb | | | Temperature °F |
|---|---|---|---|---|---|---|---|
| | | Liquid, $v_f$ | Vapor, $v_g$ | Liquid, $h_f$ | Latent, $h_{fg}$ | Vapor, $h_g$ | |
| 32 | 0.089 | 0.016 | 3305 | 0.02 | 1075.5 | 1075.5 | 32 |
| 35 | 0.099 | 0.016 | 2948 | 3.00 | 1073.8 | 1076.8 | 35 |
| 40 | 0.122 | 0.016 | 2446 | 8.03 | 1071.0 | 1079.0 | 40 |
| 45 | 0.147 | 0.016 | 2037.8 | 13.04 | 1068.1 | 1081.2 | 45 |
| 50 | 0.178 | 0.016 | 1704.8 | 18.05 | 1065.3 | 1083.4 | 50 |
| 60 | 0.256 | 0.016 | 1207.6 | 28.06 | 1059.7 | 1087.7 | 60 |
| 70 | 0.363 | 0.016 | 868.4 | 38.05 | 1054.0 | 1092.1 | 70 |
| 80 | 0.507 | 0.016 | 633.3 | 48.04 | 1048.4 | 1096.4 | 80 |
| 90 | 0.698 | 0.016 | 468.1 | 58.02 | 1042.7 | 1100.8 | 90 |
| 100 | 0.949 | 0.016 | 350.4 | 68.00 | 1037.1 | 1105.1 | 100 |
| 110 | 1.27 | 0.016 | 265.4 | 77.98 | 1031.4 | 1109.3 | 110 |
| 120 | 1.69 | 0.016 | 203.26 | 87.97 | 1025.6 | 1113.6 | 120 |
| 130 | 2.22 | 0.016 | 157.33 | 97.96 | 1019.8 | 1117.8 | 130 |
| 140 | 2.89 | 0.016 | 123.00 | 107.9 | 1014.0 | 1122.0 | 140 |
| 150 | 3.72 | 0.016 | 97.07 | 117.9 | 1008.2 | 1126.1 | 150 |
| 160 | 4.74 | 0.016 | 77.29 | 127.9 | 1002.2 | 1130.2 | 160 |
| 170 | 5.99 | 0.016 | 62.06 | 137.9 | 996.2 | 1134.2 | 170 |
| 180 | 7.51 | 0.016 | 50.22 | 148.0 | 990.2 | 1138.2 | 180 |
| 190 | 9.34 | 0.017 | 40.96 | 158.0 | 984.1 | 1142.1 | 190 |
| 200 | 11.52 | 0.017 | 33.64 | 168.0 | 977.9 | 1146.0 | 200 |
| 210 | 14.12 | 0.017 | 27.82 | 178.1 | 971.6 | 1149.7 | 210 |
| 212 | 14.7 | 0.017 | 26.80 | 180.1 | 970.3 | 1150.5 | 212 |
| 220 | 17.18 | 0.017 | 23.15 | 188.2 | 965.2 | 1153.4 | 220 |
| 230 | 20.8 | 0.017 | 19.38 | 198.3 | 958.7 | 1157.1 | 230 |
| 240 | 24.9 | 0.017 | 16.32 | 208.4 | 952.1 | 1160.6 | 240 |
| 250 | 29.8 | 0.017 | 13.81 | 218.5 | 945.4 | 1164.0 | 250 |
| 260 | 35.4 | 0.017 | 11.76 | 228.7 | 938.6 | 1167.4 | 260 |
| 270 | 41.8 | 0.017 | 10.06 | 238.9 | 931.7 | 1170.6 | 270 |
| 280 | 49.2 | 0.017 | 8.64 | 249.1 | 924.6 | 1173.8 | 280 |
| 290 | 57.5 | 0.017 | 7.46 | 259.4 | 917.4 | 1176.8 | 290 |
| 300 | 67.0 | 0.017 | 6.46 | 269.7 | 910.0 | 1179.7 | 300 |
| 310 | 77.6 | 0.017 | 5.62 | 280.0 | 902.5 | 1182.5 | 310 |
| 320 | 89.6 | 0.018 | 4.91 | 290.4 | 894.8 | 1185.2 | 320 |
| 340 | 118.0 | 0.018 | 3.78 | 311.3 | 878.8 | 1190.1 | 340 |
| 360 | 153.0 | 0.018 | 2.95 | 332.3 | 862.1 | 1194.4 | 360 |
| 380 | 195.7 | 0.018 | 2.33 | 353.6 | 844.5 | 1198.0 | 380 |
| 400 | 247.2 | 0.019 | 1.863 | 375.1 | 825.9 | 1201.0 | 400 |
| 420 | 308.7 | 0.019 | 1.499 | 396.9 | 806.2 | 1203.1 | 420 |
| 440 | 381.5 | 0.019 | 1.216 | 419.0 | 785.4 | 1204.4 | 440 |
| 460 | 466.9 | 0.019 | 0.994 | 441.5 | 763.2 | 1204.8 | 460 |
| 480 | 566.2 | 0.020 | 0.817 | 464.5 | 739.6 | 1204.1 | 480 |

# Appendix 4

REFRIGERANT 11
(TRICHLOROMONOFLUOROMETHANE)
PROPERTIES OF LIQUID AND
SATURATED VAPOR[a] (U.S. UNITS)

Left portion (Temp −85 °F to 32 °F):

| Temp °F | Pressure psia | Pressure psig | Volume cu ft/lb Vapor $v_g$ | Density lb/cu ft Liquid $1/v_f$ | Enthalpy Btu/lb Liquid $h_f$ | Enthalpy Btu/lb Vapor $h_g$ | Entropy Btu/(lb)(°R) Liquid $s_f$ | Entropy Btu/(lb)(°R) Vapor $s_g$ |
|---|---|---|---|---|---|---|---|---|
| −85 | 0.12658 | 29.66348* | 230.96 | 104.57 | −9.089 | 81.976 | −0.022905 | 0.22015 |
| −80 | 0.15791 | 29.59969* | 187.57 | 104.21 | −8.077 | 82.544 | −.020224 | .21846 |
| −75 | 0.19568 | 29.52280* | 153.32 | 103.85 | −7.067 | 83.116 | −.017580 | .21686 |
| −70 | 0.24091 | 29.43070* | 126.12 | 103.49 | −6.056 | 83.690 | −.014971 | .21534 |
| −65 | 0.29477 | 29.32104* | 104.36 | 103.12 | −5.047 | 84.267 | −.012396 | .21390 |
| −60 | 0.35855 | 29.19119* | 86.857 | 102.76 | −4.037 | 84.847 | −.009855 | .21254 |
| −55 | 0.43365 | 29.03820* | 72.684 | 102.39 | −3.028 | 85.430 | −.007346 | .21125 |
| −50 | 0.52163 | 28.85916* | 61.144 | 102.02 | −2.019 | 86.015 | −.004868 | .21002 |
| −45 | 0.62419 | 28.65034* | 51.695 | 101.65 | −1.010 | 86.603 | −.002419 | .20886 |
| −40 | 0.74317 | 28.40809* | 43.917 | 101.28 | 0.000 | 87.193 | 0.000000 | .20776 |
| −38 | 0.79581 | 28.30092* | 41.198 | 101.14 | 0.404 | 87.429 | 0.000960 | .20734 |
| −36 | 0.85153 | 28.18748* | 38.676 | 100.99 | 0.808 | 87.666 | .001915 | .20693 |
| −34 | 0.91047 | 28.06748* | 36.333 | 100.84 | 1.212 | 87.903 | .002867 | .20652 |
| −32 | 0.97277 | 27.94063* | 34.157 | 100.69 | 1.616 | 88.140 | .003814 | .20613 |
| −30 | 1.0386 | 27.8066* | 32.133 | 100.54 | 2.020 | 88.378 | .004756 | .20574 |
| −28 | 1.1081 | 27.6652* | 30.250 | 100.39 | 2.425 | 88.616 | .005695 | .20536 |
| −26 | 1.1814 | 27.5159* | 28.496 | 100.24 | 2.829 | 88.854 | .006629 | .20499 |
| −24 | 1.2586 | 27.3386* | 26.861 | 100.09 | 3.233 | 89.093 | .007559 | .20463 |
| −22 | 1.3401 | 27.1928* | 25.337 | 99.938 | 3.638 | 89.331 | .008485 | .20428 |
| −20 | 1.4258 | 27.0183* | 23.914 | 99.788 | 4.043 | 89.570 | .009408 | .20393 |
| −18 | 1.5160 | 26.8346* | 22.586 | 99.637 | 4.448 | 89.810 | .010326 | .20360 |
| −16 | 1.6109 | 26.6414* | 21.344 | 99.486 | 4.852 | 90.049 | .011240 | .20327 |
| −14 | 1.7106 | 26.4383* | 20.183 | 99.334 | 5.258 | 90.289 | .012151 | .20294 |
| −12 | 1.8154 | 26.2250* | 19.096 | 99.183 | 5.663 | 90.528 | .013058 | .20263 |
| −10 | 1.9254 | 26.0011* | 18.079 | 99.031 | 6.068 | 90.768 | .013961 | .20232 |
| −8 | 2.0408 | 25.7661* | 17.125 | 98.879 | 6.474 | 91.008 | .014860 | .20202 |
| −6 | 2.1618 | 25.5197* | 16.231 | 98.726 | 6.879 | 91.249 | .015756 | .20173 |
| −4 | 2.2887 | 25.2614* | 15.393 | 98.574 | 7.285 | 91.489 | .016648 | .20144 |
| −2 | 2.4216 | 24.9908* | 14.605 | 98.421 | 7.691 | 91.730 | .017536 | .20116 |
| 0 | 2.5607 | 24.7076* | 13.866 | 98.268 | 8.098 | 91.970 | .018421 | .20088 |
| 2 | 2.7063 | 24.4112* | 13.171 | 98.115 | 8.504 | 92.211 | .019303 | .20062 |
| 4 | 2.8586 | 24.1011* | 12.517 | 97.961 | 8.910 | 92.452 | .020181 | .20036 |
| 5† | 2.9373 | 23.9408* | 12.205 | 97.884 | 9.114 | 92.572 | .020619 | .20023 |
| 6 | 3.0178 | 23.7770* | 11.902 | 97.807 | 9.317 | 92.693 | .021056 | .20010 |
| 8 | 3.1841 | 23.4383* | 11.323 | 97.653 | 9.724 | 92.934 | .021927 | .19985 |
| 10 | 3.3578 | 23.0847* | 10.778 | 97.498 | 10.131 | 93.175 | .022795 | .19961 |
| 12 | 3.5391 | 22.7155* | 10.263 | 97.344 | 10.539 | 93.416 | .023660 | .19937 |
| 14 | 3.7283 | 22.3303* | 9.7785 | 97.189 | 10.946 | 93.658 | .024521 | .19914 |
| 16 | 3.9256 | 21.9286* | 9.3210 | 97.033 | 11.354 | 93.899 | .025379 | .19891 |
| 18 | 4.1313 | 21.5099* | 8.8890 | 96.878 | 11.762 | 94.140 | .026234 | .19869 |
| 20 | 4.3456 | 21.0736* | 8.4810 | 96.722 | 12.170 | 94.382 | .027086 | .19848 |
| 22 | 4.5687 | 20.6192* | 8.0954 | 96.566 | 12.578 | 94.623 | .027935 | .19827 |
| 24 | 4.8010 | 20.1462* | 7.7308 | 96.409 | 12.987 | 94.864 | .028781 | .19806 |
| 26 | 5.0428 | 19.6541* | 7.3859 | 96.253 | 13.396 | 95.106 | .029623 | .19787 |
| 28 | 5.2942 | 19.1422* | 7.0595 | 96.096 | 13.805 | 95.347 | .030463 | .19767 |
| 30 | 5.5556 | 18.6100* | 6.7503 | 95.938 | 14.214 | 95.588 | .031299 | .19748 |
| 32 | 5.8273 | 18.0569* | 6.4574 | 95.781 | 14.624 | 95.830 | .032133 | .19730 |

Right portion (Temp 80 °F to 152 °F):

| Temp °F | Pressure psig | Pressure psia | Volume cu ft/lb Vapor $V_g$ | Density lb/cu ft Liquid $1/v_f$ | Enthalpy Btu/lb Liquid $h_f$ | Enthalpy Btu/lb Vapor $h_g$ | Entropy Btu/(lb)(°R) Liquid $s_f$ | Entropy Btu/(lb)(°R) Vapor $s_g$ |
|---|---|---|---|---|---|---|---|---|
| 80 | 1.537 | 16.233 | 2.4893 | 91.895 | 24.527 | 101.583 | 0.051309 | 0.19409 |
| 81 | 1.850 | 16.546 | 2.4453 | 91.812 | 24.735 | 101.701 | .051693 | .19405 |
| 82 | 2.169 | 16.865 | 2.4021 | 91.728 | 24.943 | 101.820 | .052076 | .19400 |
| 83 | 2.492 | 17.188 | 2.3600 | 91.645 | 25.151 | 101.938 | .052459 | .19396 |
| 84 | 2.820 | 17.516 | 2.3187 | 91.561 | 25.359 | 102.057 | .052841 | .19391 |
| 85 | 3.152 | 17.848 | 2.2783 | 91.477 | 25.567 | 102.175 | .053222 | .19387 |
| 86† | 3.490 | 18.186 | 2.2388 | 91.394 | 25.776 | 102.293 | .053603 | .19383 |
| 87 | 3.833 | 18.529 | 2.2001 | 91.310 | 25.984 | 102.411 | .053983 | .19379 |
| 88 | 4.180 | 18.876 | 2.1622 | 91.226 | 26.192 | 102.529 | .054363 | .19375 |
| 89 | 4.533 | 19.229 | 2.1251 | 91.142 | 26.401 | 102.647 | .054742 | .19371 |
| 90 | 4.891 | 19.587 | 2.0888 | 91.057 | 26.601 | 102.765 | .055121 | .19367 |
| 91 | 5.254 | 19.950 | 2.0532 | 90.973 | 26.818 | 102.883 | .055499 | .19363 |
| 92 | 5.622 | 20.318 | 2.0184 | 90.889 | 27.027 | 103.001 | .055876 | .19359 |
| 93 | 5.995 | 20.691 | 1.9844 | 90.804 | 27.236 | 103.119 | .056253 | .19355 |
| 94 | 6.374 | 21.070 | 1.9510 | 90.719 | 27.445 | 103.236 | .056629 | .19352 |
| 95 | 6.758 | 21.454 | 1.9183 | 90.635 | 27.654 | 103.354 | .057005 | .19348 |
| 96 | 7.147 | 21.843 | 1.8863 | 90.550 | 27.863 | 103.471 | .057380 | .19345 |
| 97 | 7.542 | 22.238 | 1.8549 | 90.465 | 28.072 | 103.588 | .057755 | .19341 |
| 98 | 7.942 | 22.638 | 1.8241 | 90.379 | 28.281 | 103.706 | .058129 | .19338 |
| 99 | 8.348 | 23.044 | 1.7940 | 90.294 | 28.491 | 103.823 | .058502 | .19334 |
| 100 | 8.760 | 23.456 | 1.7645 | 90.209 | 28.700 | 103.940 | .058875 | .19331 |
| 102 | 9.600 | 24.296 | 1.7073 | 90.038 | 29.119 | 104.174 | .059620 | .19325 |
| 104 | 10.463 | 25.159 | 1.6523 | 89.866 | 29.538 | 104.407 | .060362 | .19319 |
| 106 | 11.349 | 26.045 | 1.5995 | 89.694 | 29.958 | 104.640 | .061102 | .19313 |
| 108 | 12.260 | 26.956 | 1.5487 | 89.522 | 30.378 | 104.873 | .061840 | .19307 |
| 110 | 13.194 | 27.890 | 1.4999 | 89.349 | 30.798 | 105.105 | .062575 | .19301 |
| 112 | 14.154 | 28.850 | 1.4530 | 89.175 | 31.219 | 105.337 | .063309 | .19296 |
| 114 | 15.138 | 29.834 | 1.4079 | 89.001 | 31.640 | 105.569 | .064041 | .19291 |
| 116 | 16.148 | 30.844 | 1.3645 | 88.826 | 32.061 | 105.800 | .064770 | .19286 |
| 118 | 17.184 | 31.880 | 1.3227 | 88.651 | 32.483 | 106.030 | .065498 | .19281 |
| 120 | 18.247 | 32.943 | 1.2824 | 88.476 | 32.905 | 106.260 | .066223 | .19277 |
| 122 | 19.336 | 34.032 | 1.2437 | 88.300 | 33.328 | 106.490 | .066947 | .19273 |
| 124 | 20.453 | 35.149 | 1.2064 | 88.123 | 33.751 | 106.719 | .067669 | .19269 |
| 126 | 21.598 | 36.294 | 1.1704 | 87.946 | 34.174 | 106.948 | .068388 | .19265 |
| 128 | 22.771 | 37.467 | 1.1358 | 87.768 | 34.597 | 107.176 | .069106 | .19261 |
| 130 | 23.972 | 38.668 | 1.1024 | 87.589 | 35.021 | 107.404 | .069822 | .19257 |
| 132 | 25.203 | 39.899 | 1.0702 | 87.410 | 35.446 | 107.631 | .070536 | .19254 |
| 134 | 26.463 | 41.159 | 1.0391 | 87.231 | 35.870 | 107.858 | .071248 | .19251 |
| 136 | 27.754 | 42.450 | 1.0091 | 87.051 | 36.296 | 108.084 | .071959 | .19248 |
| 138 | 29.075 | 43.771 | 0.98023 | 86.870 | 36.721 | 108.310 | .072667 | .19245 |
| 140 | 30.427 | 45.123 | 0.95232 | 86.689 | 37.147 | 108.535 | .073374 | .19242 |
| 142 | 31.810 | 46.506 | .92538 | 86.507 | 37.574 | 108.760 | .074079 | .19239 |
| 144 | 33.225 | 47.921 | .89937 | 86.324 | 38.001 | 108.984 | .074783 | .19237 |
| 146 | 34.673 | 49.369 | .87424 | 86.141 | 38.428 | 109.207 | .075484 | .19235 |
| 148 | 36.154 | 50.850 | .84996 | 85.957 | 38.856 | 109.430 | .076184 | .19232 |
| 150 | 37.668 | 52.364 | .82650 | 85.772 | 39.284 | 109.653 | .076883 | .19230 |
| 152 | 39.216 | 53.912 | .80383 | 85.587 | 39.713 | 109.874 | .077579 | .19228 |

(continued)

| Temp F | Pressure psia | Pressure psig | Volume cu ft/lb Vapor $v_g$ | Density lb/cu ft Liquid $1/v_f$ | Enthalpy Btu/lb Liquid $h_f$ | Enthalpy Vapor $h_g$ | Entropy Btu/(lb)(°R) Liquid $s_f$ | Entropy Vapor $s_g$ |
|---|---|---|---|---|---|---|---|---|
| 34 | 6.1094 | 17.4823* | 6.1798 | 95.623 | 15.033 | 96.071 | .032963 | .19712 |
| 36 | 6.4025 | 16.8857* | 5.9166 | 95.464 | 15.443 | 96.312 | .033791 | .19694 |
| 38 | 6.7067 | 16.2664* | 5.6668 | 95.306 | 15.853 | 96.553 | .034616 | .19677 |
| 40 | 7.0223 | 15.6238* | 5.4298 | 95.147 | 16.264 | 96.794 | .035437 | .19660 |
| 41 | 7.1844 | 15.2936* | 5.3158 | 95.067 | 16.469 | 96.915 | .035847 | .19652 |
| 42 | 7.3496 | 14.9574* | 5.2047 | 94.988 | 16.675 | 97.035 | .036256 | .19644 |
| 43 | 7.5178 | 14.6150* | 5.0964 | 94.908 | 16.880 | 97.156 | .036665 | .19636 |
| 44 | 7.6890 | 14.2664* | 4.9908 | 94.828 | 17.086 | 97.276 | .037073 | .19628 |
| 45 | 7.8633 | 13.9115* | 4.8879 | 94.748 | 17.291 | 97.396 | .037480 | .19621 |
| 46 | 8.0407 | 13.5502* | 4.7876 | 94.668 | 17.497 | 97.517 | .037886 | .19613 |
| 47 | 8.2213 | 13.1825* | 4.6897 | 94.588 | 17.702 | 97.637 | .038292 | .19606 |
| 48 | 8.4051 | 12.8083* | 4.5943 | 94.508 | 17.908 | 97.757 | .038697 | .19598 |
| 49 | 8.5922 | 12.4274* | 4.5012 | 94.428 | 18.114 | 97.877 | .039101 | .19591 |
| 50 | 8.7825 | 12.0399* | 4.4105 | 94.347 | 18.320 | 97.998 | .039505 | .19584 |
| 51 | 8.9762 | 11.6456* | 4.3219 | 94.267 | 18.526 | 98.118 | .039907 | .19577 |
| 52 | 9.1733 | 11.2444* | 4.2355 | 94.186 | 18.732 | 98.238 | .040310 | .19570 |
| 53 | 9.3737 | 10.8362* | 4.1512 | 94.106 | 18.938 | 98.358 | .040711 | .19563 |
| 54 | 9.5776 | 10.4211* | 4.0690 | 94.025 | 19.144 | 98.478 | .041112 | .19556 |
| 55 | 9.7850 | 9.9988* | 3.9887 | 93.944 | 19.350 | 98.598 | .041512 | .19549 |
| 56 | 9.9960 | 9.5693* | 3.9103 | 93.864 | 19.556 | 98.718 | .041912 | .19542 |
| 57 | 10.210 | 9.133* | 3.8338 | 93.783 | 19.763 | 98.838 | .042311 | .19536 |
| 58 | 10.429 | 8.688* | 3.7592 | 93.702 | 19.969 | 98.958 | .042709 | .19529 |
| 59 | 10.650 | 8.237* | 3.6863 | 93.620 | 20.176 | 99.078 | .043107 | .19523 |
| 60 | 10.876 | 7.778* | 3.6151 | 93.539 | 20.382 | 99.198 | .043504 | .19517 |
| 61 | 11.105 | 7.311* | 3.5456 | 93.458 | 20.589 | 99.317 | .043900 | .19511 |
| 62 | 11.338 | 6.836* | 3.4777 | 93.377 | 20.795 | 99.437 | .044295 | .19505 |
| 63 | 11.575 | 6.354* | 3.4114 | 93.295 | 21.002 | 99.557 | .044690 | .19499 |
| 64 | 11.816 | 5.864* | 3.3467 | 93.213 | 21.209 | 99.676 | .045085 | .19493 |
| 65 | 12.061 | 5.366* | 3.2834 | 93.132 | 21.416 | 99.796 | .045478 | .19487 |
| 66 | 12.309 | 4.859* | 3.2216 | 93.050 | 21.623 | 99.916 | .045872 | .19481 |
| 67 | 12.562 | 4.345* | 3.1612 | 92.968 | 21.830 | 100.035 | .046264 | .19475 |
| 68 | 12.819 | 3.822* | 3.1022 | 92.886 | 22.037 | 100.154 | .046656 | .19470 |
| 69 | 13.080 | 3.291* | 3.0445 | 92.804 | 22.244 | 100.274 | .047047 | .19464 |
| 70 | 13.345 | 2.752* | 2.9882 | 92.722 | 22.451 | 100.393 | .047437 | .19459 |
| 71 | 13.614 | 2.204* | 2.9331 | 92.640 | 22.658 | 100.512 | .047827 | .19454 |
| 72 | 13.887 | 1.647* | 2.8792 | 92.557 | 22.866 | 100.631 | .048217 | .19448 |
| 73 | 14.165 | 1.081* | 2.8266 | 92.475 | 23.073 | 100.751 | .048605 | .19443 |
| 74 | 14.447 | 0.507* | 2.7751 | 92.392 | 23.280 | 100.870 | .048993 | .19438 |
| 75 | 14.733 | 0.037 | 2.7248 | 92.310 | 23.488 | 100.989 | .049381 | .19433 |
| 76 | 15.024 | 0.328 | 2.6756 | 92.227 | 23.696 | 101.108 | .049768 | .19428 |
| 77 | 15.319 | 0.623 | 2.6275 | 92.144 | 23.903 | 101.226 | .050154 | .19423 |
| 78 | 15.619 | 0.923 | 2.5804 | 92.061 | 24.111 | 101.345 | .050540 | .19419 |
| 79 | 15.924 | 1.228 | 2.5344 | 91.978 | 24.319 | 101.464 | .050925 | .19414 |

| Temp F | Pressure psia | Pressure psig | Volume cu ft/lb Vapor $v_g$ | Density lb/cu ft Liquid $1/v_f$ | Enthalpy Btu/lb Liquid $h_f$ | Enthalpy Vapor $h_g$ | Entropy Btu/(lb)(°R) Liquid $s_f$ | Entropy Vapor $s_g$ |
|---|---|---|---|---|---|---|---|---|
| 154 | 55.494 | 40.798 | .78191 | 85.401 | 40.142 | 110.096 | .078275 | .19227 |
| 156 | 57.111 | 42.415 | .76071 | 85.214 | 40.572 | 110.316 | .078968 | .19225 |
| 158 | 58.763 | 44.067 | .74021 | 85.027 | 41.003 | 110.536 | .079660 | .19223 |
| 160 | 60.451 | 45.755 | .72037 | 84.839 | 41.433 | 110.755 | .080351 | .19222 |
| 162 | 62.176 | 47.480 | .70118 | 84.650 | 41.865 | 110.974 | .081040 | .19221 |
| 164 | 63.937 | 49.241 | .68261 | 84.461 | 42.297 | 111.192 | .081727 | .19219 |
| 166 | 65.736 | 51.040 | .66462 | 84.270 | 42.729 | 111.409 | .082413 | .19218 |
| 168 | 67.572 | 52.876 | .64721 | 84.079 | 43.162 | 111.625 | .083098 | .19217 |
| 170 | 69.447 | 54.751 | .63035 | 83.887 | 43.596 | 111.841 | .083781 | .19216 |
| 172 | 71.361 | 56.665 | .61401 | 83.695 | 44.030 | 112.056 | .084463 | .19216 |
| 174 | 73.314 | 58.618 | .59819 | 83.501 | 44.465 | 112.271 | .085144 | .19215 |
| 176 | 75.307 | 60.611 | .58285 | 83.307 | 44.901 | 112.484 | .085823 | .19214 |
| 178 | 77.340 | 62.644 | .56799 | 83.112 | 45.337 | 112.697 | .086501 | .19214 |
| 180 | 79.414 | 64.718 | .55357 | 82.916 | 45.774 | 112.909 | .087178 | .19213 |
| 182 | 81.529 | 66.833 | .53960 | 82.720 | 46.211 | 113.121 | .087853 | .19213 |
| 184 | 83.687 | 68.991 | .52605 | 82.522 | 46.650 | 113.331 | .088528 | .19212 |
| 186 | 85.887 | 71.191 | .51290 | 82.323 | 47.089 | 113.541 | .089201 | .19212 |
| 188 | 88.130 | 73.434 | .50014 | 82.124 | 47.528 | 113.750 | .089873 | .19212 |
| 190 | 90.416 | 75.720 | .48776 | 81.924 | 47.969 | 113.958 | .090544 | .19212 |
| 192 | 92.747 | 78.051 | .47575 | 81.722 | 48.410 | 114.165 | .091214 | .19212 |
| 194 | 95.122 | 80.426 | .46409 | 81.520 | 48.852 | 114.371 | .091883 | .19212 |
| 196 | 97.542 | 82.846 | .45276 | 81.317 | 49.295 | 114.577 | .092551 | .19212 |
| 198 | 100.01 | 85.31 | .44176 | 81.113 | 49.739 | 114.781 | .093218 | .19212 |
| 200 | 102.52 | 87.82 | .43108 | 80.908 | 50.183 | 114.985 | .093884 | .19212 |
| 210 | 115.79 | 101.10 | .38203 | 79.866 | 52.419 | 115.988 | .097203 | .19213 |
| 220 | 130.31 | 115.61 | .33938 | 78.796 | 54.680 | 116.966 | .10050 | .19215 |
| 230 | 146.14 | 131.44 | .30216 | 77.694 | 56.969 | 117.915 | .10379 | .19216 |
| 240 | 163.35 | 148.65 | .26952 | 76.558 | 59.290 | 118.832 | .10707 | .19217 |
| 250 | 182.03 | 167.33 | .24078 | 75.382 | 61.648 | 119.714 | .11035 | .19218 |
| 260 | 202.24 | 187.55 | .21538 | 74.163 | 64.047 | 120.555 | .11364 | .19216 |
| 270 | 224.09 | 209.39 | .19284 | 72.893 | 66.494 | 121.350 | .11694 | .19212 |
| 280 | 247.63 | 232.94 | .17274 | 71.565 | 68.997 | 122.093 | .12027 | .19205 |
| 290 | 272.98 | 258.28 | .15476 | 70.170 | 71.563 | 122.776 | .12363 | .19194 |
| 300 | 300.21 | 285.51 | .13860 | 68.696 | 74.205 | 123.387 | .12703 | .19177 |
| 310 | 329.42 | 314.73 | .12399 | 67.128 | 76.933 | 123.914 | .13049 | .19153 |
| 320 | 360.71 | 346.02 | .11072 | 65.443 | 79.767 | 124.337 | .13404 | .19120 |
| 330 | 394.19 | 379.49 | .098589 | 63.612 | 82.729 | 124.633 | .13769 | .19076 |
| 340 | 429.96 | 415.26 | .087394 | 61.591 | 85.851 | 124.763 | .14149 | .19015 |
| 350 | 468.14 | 453.44 | .076940 | 59.310 | 89.183 | 124.669 | .14548 | .18931 |
| 360 | 508.84 | 494.15 | .066999 | 56.643 | 92.807 | 124.249 | .14977 | .18813 |
| 370 | 552.21 | 537.52 | .057172 | 53.333 | 96.892 | 123.291 | .15455 | .18636 |
| 380 | 598.40 | 583.70 | .046570 | 48.614 | 101.912 | 121.160 | .16036 | .18328 |
| 388.40 | 639.50 | 624.80 | .028927 | 34.570 | 112.080 | 112.080 | .17219 | .17219 |

[a]From published data (1965) of E. I. du Pont de Nemours & Co., Inc. Used by permission.
*Inches of mercury below one standard atmosphere
**Based on 0 for the saturated liquid at −40 F
†Standard cycle temperatures
Reprinted with permission from the 1977 Fundamentals ASHRAE Handbook & Product Directory

# Appendix 5

## REFRIGERANT 12 (DICHLORODIFLUOROMETHANE) PROPERTIES OF LIQUID AND SATURATED VAPOR[a] (U.S. UNITS)

Upper table (Temperatures 55–104 °F):

| Entropy** Btu/(lb)(°R) Vapor $s_g$ | Entropy** Btu/(lb)(°R) Liquid $s_f$ | Enthalpy** Btu/lb Vapor $h_g$ | Enthalpy** Btu/lb Liquid $h_f$ | Density lb/cu ft Liquid $1/v_f$ | Volume cu ft/lb Vapor $V_g$ | Pressure psia | Pressure psig | Temp F |
|---|---|---|---|---|---|---|---|---|
| 0.16504 | 0.044015 | 82.924 | 20.634 | 84.544 | 0.60453 | 66.743 | 52.047 | 55 |
| .16499 | .044449 | 83.021 | 20.859 | 84.425 | .59495 | 67.853 | 53.157 | 56 |
| .16494 | .044883 | 83.119 | 21.086 | 84.305 | .58554 | 68.977 | 54.281 | 57 |
| .16489 | .045316 | 83.215 | 21.312 | 84.185 | .57632 | 70.115 | 55.419 | 58 |
| .16484 | .045748 | 83.312 | 21.539 | 84.065 | .56727 | 71.267 | 56.571 | 59 |
| 0.16479 | 0.046180 | 83.409 | 21.766 | 83.944 | 0.55839 | 72.433 | 57.737 | 60 |
| .16474 | .046612 | 83.505 | 21.993 | 83.823 | .54967 | 73.613 | 58.917 | 61 |
| .16470 | .047044 | 83.601 | 22.221 | 83.701 | .54112 | 74.807 | 60.111 | 62 |
| .16465 | .047475 | 83.696 | 22.448 | 83.580 | .53273 | 76.016 | 61.320 | 63 |
| .16460 | .047905 | 83.792 | 22.676 | 83.457 | .52450 | 77.239 | 62.543 | 64 |
| 0.16456 | 0.048336 | 83.887 | 22.905 | 83.335 | 0.51642 | 78.477 | 63.781 | 65 |
| .16451 | .048765 | 83.982 | 23.133 | 83.212 | .50848 | 79.729 | 65.033 | 66 |
| .16447 | .049195 | 84.077 | 23.362 | 83.089 | .50070 | 80.996 | 66.300 | 67 |
| .16442 | .049624 | 84.171 | 23.591 | 82.965 | .49305 | 82.279 | 67.583 | 68 |
| .16438 | .050053 | 84.266 | 23.821 | 82.841 | .48555 | 83.576 | 68.880 | 69 |
| 0.16434 | 0.050482 | 84.359 | 24.050 | 82.717 | 0.47818 | 84.888 | 70.192 | 70 |
| .16429 | .050910 | 84.453 | 24.281 | 82.592 | .47094 | 86.216 | 71.520 | 71 |
| .16425 | .051338 | 84.546 | 24.511 | 82.467 | .46383 | 87.559 | 72.863 | 72 |
| .16421 | .051766 | 84.639 | 24.741 | 82.341 | .45686 | 88.918 | 74.222 | 73 |
| .16417 | .052193 | 84.732 | 24.973 | 82.215 | .45000 | 90.292 | 75.596 | 74 |
| 0.16412 | 0.052620 | 84.825 | 25.204 | 82.089 | 0.44327 | 91.682 | 76.986 | 75 |
| .16408 | .053047 | 84.916 | 25.435 | 81.962 | .43666 | 93.087 | 78.391 | 76 |
| .16404 | .053473 | 85.008 | 25.667 | 81.835 | .43016 | 94.509 | 79.813 | 77 |
| .16400 | .053900 | 85.100 | 25.899 | 81.707 | .42378 | 95.946 | 81.250 | 78 |
| .16396 | .054326 | 85.191 | 26.132 | 81.579 | .41751 | 97.400 | 82.704 | 79 |
| 0.16392 | 0.054751 | 85.282 | 26.365 | 81.450 | 0.41135 | 98.870 | 84.174 | 80 |
| .16388 | .055177 | 85.373 | 26.598 | 81.322 | .40530 | 100.36 | 85.66 | 81 |
| .16384 | .055602 | 85.463 | 26.832 | 81.192 | .39935 | 101.86 | 87.16 | 82 |
| .16380 | .056027 | 85.553 | 27.065 | 81.063 | .39351 | 103.38 | 88.68 | 83 |
| .16376 | .056452 | 85.643 | 27.300 | 80.932 | .38776 | 104.92 | 90.22 | 84 |
| 0.16372 | 0.056877 | 85.732 | 27.534 | 80.802 | 0.38212 | 106.47 | 91.77 | 85 |
| .16368 | .057301 | 85.821 | 27.769 | 80.671 | .37657 | 108.04 | 93.34 | †86 |
| .16364 | .057725 | 85.910 | 28.005 | 80.539 | .37111 | 109.63 | 94.93 | 87 |
| .16360 | .058149 | 85.998 | 28.241 | 80.407 | .36575 | 111.23 | 96.53 | 88 |
| .16357 | .058573 | 86.086 | 28.477 | 80.275 | .36047 | 112.85 | 98.15 | 89 |
| 0.16353 | 0.058997 | 86.174 | 28.713 | 80.142 | 0.35529 | 114.49 | 99.79 | 90 |
| .16345 | .059844 | 86.348 | 29.187 | 79.874 | .34518 | 117.82 | 103.12 | 92 |
| .16338 | .060690 | 86.521 | 29.663 | 79.605 | .33540 | 121.22 | 106.52 | 94 |
| .16330 | .061536 | 86.691 | 30.140 | 79.334 | .32594 | 124.70 | 110.00 | 96 |
| .16323 | .062381 | 86.861 | 30.619 | 79.061 | .31679 | 128.24 | 113.54 | 98 |
| 0.16315 | 0.063227 | 87.029 | 31.100 | 78.785 | 0.30794 | 131.86 | 117.16 | 100 |
| .16308 | .064072 | 87.196 | 31.583 | 78.508 | .29937 | 135.56 | 120.86 | 102 |
| .16301 | .064916 | 87.360 | 32.067 | 78.228 | .29106 | 139.33 | 124.63 | 104 |

Lower table (Temperatures −152 to 4 °F):

| Temp F | Pressure psia | Pressure psig | Volume cu ft/lb Vapor $V_g$ | Density lb/cu ft Liquid $1/v_f$ | Enthalpy** Btu/lb Liquid $h_f$ | Enthalpy** Btu/lb Vapor $h_g$ | Entropy** Btu/(lb)(°R) Liquid $s_f$ | Entropy** Btu/(lb)(°R) Vapor $s_g$ |
|---|---|---|---|---|---|---|---|---|
| −152 | 0.13799 | 29.64024* | 197.58 | 104.52 | −23.106 | 60.628 | −0.063944 | 0.20818 |
| −150 | 0.15359 | 29.60849* | 178.65 | 104.36 | −22.697 | 60.837 | −.062619 | .20711 |
| −145 | 0.19933 | 29.51537* | 139.83 | 103.95 | −21.674 | 61.365 | −.059344 | .20452 |
| −140 | 0.25623 | 29.39951* | 110.46 | 103.54 | −20.652 | 61.896 | −.056123 | .20208 |
| −135 | 0.32641 | 29.25663* | 88.023 | 103.13 | −19.631 | 62.430 | −.052952 | .19978 |
| −130 | 0.41224 | 29.08187* | 70.730 | 102.71 | −18.609 | 62.968 | −0.049830 | 0.19760 |
| −125 | 0.51641 | 28.86978* | 57.283 | 102.29 | −17.587 | 63.509 | −.046754 | .19554 |
| −120 | 0.64190 | 28.61429* | 46.741 | 101.87 | −16.565 | 64.052 | −.043723 | .19359 |
| −115 | 0.79200 | 28.30869* | 38.410 | 101.45 | −15.541 | 64.598 | −.040734 | .19176 |
| −110 | 0.97034 | 27.94558* | 31.777 | 101.02 | −14.518 | 65.145 | −.037786 | .19002 |
| −105 | 1.1809 | 27.5169* | 26.458 | 100.59 | −13.492 | 65.696 | −0.034877 | 0.18838 |
| −100 | 1.4280 | 27.0138* | 22.164 | 100.15 | −12.466 | 66.248 | −.032005 | .18683 |
| −95 | 1.7163 | 26.4268* | 18.674 | 99.715 | −11.438 | 66.801 | −.029169 | .18536 |
| −90 | 2.0509 | 25.7456* | 15.821 | 99.274 | −10.409 | 67.355 | −.026367 | .18398 |
| −85 | 2.4371 | 24.9593* | 13.474 | 98.830 | −9.3782 | 67.911 | −.023599 | .18267 |
| −80 | 2.8807 | 24.0560* | 11.533 | 98.382 | −8.3451 | 68.467 | −0.020862 | 0.18143 |
| −75 | 3.3879 | 23.0234* | 9.9184 | 97.930 | −7.3101 | 69.023 | −.018156 | .18027 |
| −70 | 3.9651 | 21.8482* | 8.5687 | 97.475 | −6.2730 | 69.580 | −.015481 | .17910 |
| −65 | 4.6139 | 20.5164* | 7.4347 | 97.016 | −5.2336 | 70.137 | −.012834 | .17812 |
| −60 | 5.3575 | 19.0133* | 6.4774 | 96.553 | −4.1919 | 70.693 | −.010214 | .17714 |
| −55 | 6.1874 | 17.3237* | 5.6656 | 96.086 | −3.1477 | 71.249 | −0.007622 | 0.17621 |
| −50 | 7.1168 | 15.4313* | 4.9742 | 95.616 | −2.1011 | 71.805 | −.005056 | .17533 |
| −45 | 8.1540 | 13.3196* | 4.3828 | 95.141 | −1.0519 | 72.359 | −.002516 | .17451 |
| −40 | 9.3076 | 10.9709* | 3.8750 | 94.661 | 0.0000 | 72.913 | 0.000000 | .17373 |
| −35 | 10.586 | 8.367* | 3.4373 | 94.178 | 1.0546 | 73.464 | .002492 | .17299 |
| −30 | 11.999 | 5.490* | 3.0585 | 93.690 | 2.1120 | 74.015 | 0.004961 | 0.17229 |
| −28 | 12.604 | 4.259* | 2.9214 | 93.493 | 2.5358 | 74.234 | .005942 | .17203 |
| −26 | 13.233 | 2.979* | 2.7917 | 93.296 | 2.9601 | 74.454 | .006919 | .17177 |
| −24 | 13.886 | 1.649* | 2.6691 | 93.098 | 3.3848 | 74.673 | .007894 | .17151 |
| −22 | 14.564 | 0.270* | 2.5529 | 92.899 | 3.8100 | 74.891 | .008864 | .17126 |
| −20 | 15.267 | 0.571 | 2.4429 | 92.699 | 4.2357 | 75.110 | 0.009831 | 0.17102 |
| −18 | 15.996 | 1.300 | 2.3387 | 92.499 | 4.6618 | 75.328 | .010795 | .17078 |
| −16 | 16.753 | 2.057 | 2.2399 | 92.298 | 5.0885 | 75.545 | .011755 | .17055 |
| −14 | 17.536 | 2.840 | 2.1461 | 92.096 | 5.5157 | 75.762 | .012712 | .17032 |
| −12 | 18.348 | 3.652 | 2.0572 | 91.893 | 5.9434 | 75.979 | .013666 | .17010 |
| −10 | 19.189 | 4.493 | 1.9727 | 91.689 | 6.3716 | 76.196 | 0.014617 | 0.16989 |
| −8 | 20.059 | 5.363 | 1.8924 | 91.485 | 6.8003 | 76.411 | .015564 | .16967 |
| −6 | 20.960 | 6.264 | 1.8161 | 91.280 | 7.2296 | 76.627 | .016508 | .16947 |
| −4 | 21.891 | 7.195 | 1.7436 | 91.074 | 7.6594 | 76.842 | .017449 | .16927 |
| −2 | 22.854 | 8.158 | 1.6745 | 90.867 | 8.0898 | 77.057 | .018388 | .16907 |
| 0 | 23.849 | 9.153 | 1.6089 | 90.659 | 8.5207 | 77.271 | 0.019323 | 0.16888 |
| 2 | 24.878 | 10.182 | 1.5463 | 90.450 | 8.9522 | 77.485 | .020255 | .16869 |
| 4 | 25.939 | 11.243 | 1.4867 | 90.240 | 9.3843 | 77.698 | .021184 | .16851 |

### Left section (lower temperatures)

| Temp F | Pressure psia | Pressure psig | Volume cu ft Vapor $v_g$ | Density lb/cu ft Liquid $1/v_f$ | Enthalpy Liquid $h_f$ | Enthalpy Vapor $h_g$ | Entropy Liquid $s_f$ | Entropy Vapor $s_g$ |
|---|---|---|---|---|---|---|---|---|
| †5 | 26.483 | 11.787 | 1.4580 | 90.135 | 9.6005 | 77.805 | .021647 | .16842 |
| 6 | 27.036 | 12.340 | 1.4299 | 90.030 | 9.8169 | 77.911 | .022110 | .16833 |
| 8 | 28.167 | 13.471 | 1.3758 | 89.818 | 10.250 | 78.123 | .023033 | .16815 |
| 10 | 29.335 | 14.639 | 1.3241 | 89.606 | 10.684 | 78.335 | .023954 | .16798 |
| 12 | 30.539 | 15.843 | 1.2748 | 89.392 | 11.118 | 78.546 | .024871 | .16782 |
| 14 | 31.780 | 17.084 | 1.2278 | 89.178 | 11.554 | 78.757 | .025786 | .16765 |
| 16 | 33.060 | 18.364 | 1.1828 | 88.962 | 11.989 | 78.966 | .026699 | .16750 |
| 18 | 34.378 | 19.682 | 1.1399 | 88.746 | 12.426 | 79.176 | .027608 | .16734 |
| 20 | 35.736 | 21.040 | 1.0988 | 88.529 | 12.863 | 79.385 | .028515 | .16719 |
| 22 | 37.135 | 22.439 | 1.0596 | 88.310 | 13.300 | 79.593 | .029420 | .16704 |
| 24 | 38.574 | 23.878 | 1.0220 | 88.091 | 13.739 | 79.800 | .030322 | .16690 |
| 26 | 40.056 | 25.360 | .98612 | 87.870 | 14.178 | 80.007 | .031221 | .16676 |
| 28 | 41.580 | 26.884 | .95173 | 87.649 | 14.618 | 80.214 | .032118 | .16662 |
| 30 | 43.148 | 28.452 | .91880 | 87.426 | 15.058 | 80.419 | .033013 | .16648 |
| 31 | 43.948 | 29.252 | .90286 | 87.314 | 15.279 | 80.522 | .033460 | .16642 |
| 32 | 44.760 | 30.064 | .88725 | 87.202 | 15.500 | 80.624 | .033905 | .16635 |
| 33 | 45.583 | 30.887 | .87197 | 87.090 | 15.720 | 80.726 | .034351 | .16629 |
| 34 | 46.417 | 31.721 | .85702 | 86.977 | 15.942 | 80.828 | .034796 | .16622 |
| 35 | 47.263 | 32.567 | .84237 | 86.865 | 16.163 | 80.930 | .035240 | .16616 |
| 36 | 48.120 | 33.424 | .82803 | 86.751 | 16.384 | 81.031 | .035683 | .16610 |
| 37 | 48.989 | 34.293 | .81399 | 86.638 | 16.606 | 81.133 | .036126 | .16604 |
| 38 | 49.870 | 35.174 | .80023 | 86.524 | 16.828 | 81.234 | .036569 | .16598 |
| 39 | 50.763 | 36.067 | .78676 | 86.410 | 17.050 | 81.335 | .037011 | .16592 |
| 40 | 51.667 | 36.971 | .77357 | 86.296 | 17.273 | 81.436 | .037453 | .16586 |
| 41 | 52.548 | 37.888 | .76064 | 86.181 | 17.495 | 81.537 | .037893 | .16580 |
| 42 | 53.513 | 38.817 | .74798 | 86.066 | 17.718 | 81.637 | .038334 | .16574 |
| 43 | 54.454 | 39.758 | .73557 | 85.951 | 17.941 | 81.737 | .038774 | .16568 |
| 44 | 55.407 | 40.711 | .72341 | 85.836 | 18.164 | 81.837 | .039213 | .16562 |
| 45 | 56.373 | 41.677 | .71149 | 85.720 | 18.387 | 81.937 | .039652 | .16557 |
| 46 | 57.352 | 42.656 | .69982 | 85.604 | 18.611 | 82.037 | .040091 | .16551 |
| 47 | 58.343 | 43.647 | .68837 | 85.487 | 18.835 | 82.136 | .040529 | .16546 |
| 48 | 59.347 | 44.651 | .67715 | 85.371 | 19.059 | 82.236 | .040966 | .16540 |
| 49 | 60.364 | 45.668 | .66616 | 85.254 | 19.283 | 82.334 | .041403 | .16535 |
| 50 | 61.394 | 46.698 | .65537 | 85.136 | 19.507 | 82.433 | .041839 | .16530 |
| 51 | 62.437 | 47.741 | .64480 | 85.018 | 19.732 | 82.532 | .042276 | .16524 |
| 52 | 63.494 | 48.798 | .63444 | 84.900 | 19.957 | 82.630 | .042711 | .16519 |
| 53 | 64.563 | 49.867 | .62428 | 84.782 | 20.182 | 82.728 | .043146 | .16514 |
| 54 | 65.646 | 50.950 | .61431 | 84.663 | 20.408 | 82.826 | .043581 | .16509 |

### Right section (higher temperatures)

| Temp F | Pressure psia | Pressure psig | Volume cu ft/lb Vapor $v_g$ | Density lb/cu ft Liquid $1/v_f$ | Enthalpy Liquid $h_f$ | Enthalpy Vapor $h_g$ | Entropy Liquid $s_f$ | Entropy Vapor $s_g$ |
|---|---|---|---|---|---|---|---|---|
| 106 | 143.18 | 128.48 | .28303 | 77.946 | 32.553 | 87.523 | .065761 | .16293 |
| 108 | 147.11 | 132.41 | .27524 | 77.662 | 33.041 | 87.684 | .066606 | .16286 |
| 110 | 151.11 | 136.41 | .26769 | 77.376 | 33.531 | 87.844 | .067451 | .16279 |
| 112 | 155.19 | 140.49 | .26037 | 77.087 | 34.023 | 88.001 | .068296 | .16271 |
| 114 | 159.36 | 144.66 | .25328 | 76.795 | 34.517 | 88.156 | .069141 | .16264 |
| 116 | 163.61 | 148.91 | .24641 | 76.501 | 35.014 | 88.310 | .069987 | .16256 |
| 118 | 167.94 | 153.24 | .23974 | 76.205 | 35.512 | 88.461 | .070833 | .16249 |
| 120 | 172.35 | 157.65 | .23326 | 75.906 | 36.013 | 88.610 | .071680 | .16241 |
| 122 | 176.85 | 162.15 | .22698 | 75.604 | 36.516 | 88.757 | .072528 | .16234 |
| 124 | 181.43 | 166.73 | .22089 | 75.299 | 37.021 | 88.902 | .073376 | .16226 |
| 126 | 186.10 | 171.40 | .21497 | 74.991 | 37.529 | 89.044 | .074225 | .16218 |
| 128 | 190.86 | 176.16 | .20922 | 74.680 | 38.040 | 89.184 | .075075 | .16210 |
| 130 | 195.71 | 181.01 | .20364 | 74.367 | 38.553 | 89.321 | .075927 | .16202 |
| 132 | 200.64 | 185.94 | .19821 | 74.050 | 39.069 | 89.456 | .076779 | .16194 |
| 134 | 205.67 | 190.97 | .19294 | 73.729 | 39.588 | 89.588 | .077633 | .16185 |
| 136 | 210.79 | 196.09 | .18782 | 73.406 | 40.110 | 89.718 | .078489 | .16177 |
| 138 | 216.01 | 201.31 | .18283 | 73.079 | 40.634 | 89.844 | .079346 | .16168 |
| 140 | 221.32 | 206.62 | .17799 | 72.748 | 41.162 | 89.967 | .080205 | .16159 |
| 145 | 235.00 | 220.30 | .16644 | 71.904 | 42.495 | 90.261 | .082361 | .16135 |
| 150 | 249.31 | 234.61 | .15564 | 71.035 | 43.850 | 90.534 | .084631 | .16110 |
| 155 | 264.24 | 249.54 | .14552 | 70.137 | 45.229 | 90.783 | .086719 | .16083 |
| 160 | 279.82 | 265.12 | .13604 | 69.209 | 46.633 | 91.006 | .088927 | .16053 |
| 165 | 296.07 | 281.37 | .12712 | 68.245 | 48.065 | 91.199 | .091159 | .16021 |
| 170 | 313.00 | 298.30 | .11873 | 67.244 | 49.529 | 91.359 | .093418 | .15985 |
| 175 | 330.64 | 315.94 | .11080 | 66.198 | 51.026 | 91.481 | .095709 | .15945 |
| 180 | 349.00 | 334.30 | .10330 | 65.102 | 52.562 | 91.561 | .098039 | .15900 |
| 185 | 368.11 | 353.41 | .096190 | 63.949 | 54.141 | 91.590 | .10041 | .15850 |
| 190 | 387.98 | 373.28 | .089418 | 62.728 | 55.769 | 91.561 | .10284 | .15793 |
| 195 | 408.63 | 393.93 | .082946 | 61.426 | 57.453 | 91.462 | .10532 | .15727 |
| 200 | 430.09 | 415.39 | .076728 | 60.026 | 59.203 | 91.278 | .10789 | .15651 |
| 205 | 452.38 | 437.68 | .070714 | 58.502 | 61.032 | 90.987 | .11055 | .15561 |
| 210 | 475.52 | 460.82 | .064843 | 56.816 | 62.959 | 90.558 | .11332 | .15453 |
| 215 | 499.53 | 484.83 | .059030 | 54.908 | 65.014 | 89.939 | .11626 | .15320 |
| 220 | 524.43 | 509.73 | .053140 | 52.670 | 67.246 | 89.036 | .11943 | .15149 |
| 225 | 550.26 | 535.56 | .046900 | 49.868 | 69.763 | 87.651 | .12298 | .14911 |
| 230 | 577.03 | 562.33 | .039435 | 45.758 | 72.893 | 85.122 | .12739 | .14512 |
| 233.6 (Critical) | 596.9 | 582.2 | .02870 | 34.84 | 78.86 | 78.86 | .1359 | .1359 |

ªFrom published data (1955 and 1956) of E.I. du Pont de Nemours & Co., Inc. Used by permission.
*Inches of mercury below one standard atmosphere.
**Based on 0 for the saturated liquid at −40 F.
†Standard cycle temperatures.
Reprinted with permission from the 1977 Fundamentals ASHRAE Handbook & Product Directory

# Appendix 6

REFRIGERANT 22
(CHLORODIFLUOROMETHANE)
PROPERTIES OF LIQUID AND
SATURATED VAPOR[a] (U.S. UNITS)

| Entropy** Btu/(lb)(°R) | | Enthalpy** Btu/lb | | Density lb/cu ft | Volume cu ft/lb | Pressure | | Temp F |
|---|---|---|---|---|---|---|---|---|
| Liquid $s_f$ | Vapor $s_g$ | Liquid $h_f$ | Vapor $h_g$ | Liquid $1/v_f$ | Vapor $v_g$ | psia | psig | |
| 0.04855 | 0.21912 | 22.558 | 108.472 | 78.770 | 0.61448 | 89.177 | 74.481 | 44 |
| 0.04967 | 0.21876 | 23.129 | 108.634 | 78.526 | 0.59422 | 92.280 | 77.584 | 46 |
| 0.05079 | 0.21839 | 23.701 | 108.795 | 78.280 | 0.57476 | 95.463 | 80.767 | 48 |
| 0.05190 | 0.21803 | 24.275 | 108.953 | 78.033 | 0.55606 | 98.727 | 84.031 | 50 |
| 0.05301 | 0.21768 | 24.851 | 109.109 | 77.784 | 0.53808 | 102.07 | 87.38 | 52 |
| 0.05412 | 0.21732 | 25.429 | 109.263 | 77.534 | 0.52078 | 105.50 | 90.81 | 54 |
| 0.05523 | 0.21697 | 26.008 | 109.415 | 77.282 | 0.50414 | 109.02 | 94.32 | 56 |
| 0.05634 | 0.21662 | 26.589 | 109.564 | 77.028 | 0.48813 | 112.62 | 97.93 | 58 |
| 0.05745 | 0.21627 | 27.172 | 109.712 | 76.773 | 0.47272 | 116.31 | 101.62 | 60 |
| 0.05855 | 0.21592 | 27.757 | 109.857 | 76.515 | 0.45788 | 120.09 | 105.39 | 62 |
| 0.05966 | 0.21558 | 28.344 | 110.000 | 76.257 | 0.44358 | 123.96 | 109.26 | 64 |
| 0.06076 | 0.21524 | 28.932 | 110.140 | 75.996 | 0.42981 | 127.92 | 113.22 | 66 |
| 0.06186 | 0.21490 | 29.523 | 110.278 | 75.733 | 0.41653 | 131.97 | 117.28 | 68 |
| 0.06296 | 0.21456 | 30.116 | 110.414 | 75.469 | 0.40373 | 136.12 | 121.43 | 70 |
| 0.06406 | 0.21422 | 30.710 | 110.547 | 75.202 | 0.39139 | 140.37 | 125.67 | 72 |
| 0.06516 | 0.21388 | 31.307 | 110.677 | 74.934 | 0.37949 | 144.71 | 130.01 | 74 |
| 0.06626 | 0.21355 | 31.906 | 110.805 | 74.664 | 0.36800 | 149.15 | 134.45 | 76 |
| 0.06736 | 0.21321 | 32.506 | 110.930 | 74.391 | 0.35691 | 153.69 | 138.99 | 78 |
| 0.06846 | 0.21288 | 33.109 | 111.052 | 74.116 | 0.34621 | 158.33 | 143.63 | 80 |
| 0.06956 | 0.21255 | 33.714 | 111.171 | 73.839 | 0.33587 | 163.07 | 148.37 | 82 |
| 0.07065 | 0.21222 | 34.322 | 111.288 | 73.560 | 0.32588 | 167.92 | 153.22 | 84 |
| 0.07175 | 0.21188 | 34.931 | 111.401 | 73.278 | 0.31623 | 172.87 | 158.17 | 86† |
| 0.07285 | 0.21155 | 35.543 | 111.512 | 72.994 | 0.30690 | 177.93 | 163.23 | 88 |
| 0.07394 | 0.21122 | 36.158 | 111.619 | 72.708 | 0.29789 | 183.09 | 168.40 | 90 |
| 0.07504 | 0.21089 | 36.774 | 111.723 | 72.419 | 0.28917 | 188.37 | 173.67 | 92 |
| 0.07613 | 0.21056 | 37.394 | 111.824 | 72.127 | 0.28073 | 193.76 | 179.06 | 94 |
| 0.07723 | 0.21023 | 38.016 | 111.921 | 71.833 | 0.27257 | 199.26 | 184.56 | 96 |
| 0.07832 | 0.20989 | 38.640 | 112.015 | 71.536 | 0.26467 | 204.87 | 190.18 | 98 |
| 0.07942 | 0.20956 | 39.267 | 112.105 | 71.236 | 0.25702 | 210.60 | 195.91 | 100 |
| 0.08052 | 0.20923 | 39.897 | 112.192 | 70.933 | 0.24962 | 216.45 | 201.76 | 102 |
| 0.08161 | 0.20889 | 40.530 | 112.274 | 70.626 | 0.24244 | 222.42 | 207.72 | 104 |
| 0.08271 | 0.20855 | 41.166 | 112.353 | 70.317 | 0.23549 | 228.50 | 213.81 | 106 |
| 0.08381 | 0.20821 | 41.804 | 112.427 | 70.005 | 0.22875 | 234.71 | 220.02 | 108 |
| 0.08491 | 0.20787 | 42.446 | 112.498 | 69.689 | 0.22222 | 241.04 | 226.35 | 110 |
| 0.08601 | 0.20753 | 43.091 | 112.564 | 69.369 | 0.21589 | 247.50 | 232.80 | 112 |
| 0.08711 | 0.20718 | 43.739 | 112.626 | 69.046 | 0.20974 | 254.08 | 239.38 | 114 |
| 0.08821 | 0.20684 | 44.391 | 112.682 | 68.719 | 0.20378 | 260.79 | 246.10 | 116 |
| 0.08932 | 0.20649 | 45.046 | 112.735 | 68.388 | 0.19800 | 267.63 | 252.94 | 118 |
| 0.09042 | 0.20613 | 45.705 | 112.782 | 68.054 | 0.19238 | 274.60 | 259.91 | 120 |
| 0.09153 | 0.20578 | 46.368 | 112.824 | 67.714 | 0.18692 | 281.71 | 267.01 | 122 |
| 0.09264 | 0.20542 | 47.034 | 112.860 | 67.371 | 0.18163 | 288.95 | 274.25 | 124 |
| 0.09375 | 0.20505 | 47.705 | 112.891 | 67.023 | 0.17648 | 296.33 | 281.63 | 126 |
| 0.09487 | 0.20468 | 48.380 | 112.917 | 66.670 | 0.17147 | 303.84 | 289.14 | 128 |
| 0.09598 | 0.20431 | 49.059 | 112.936 | 66.312 | 0.16661 | 311.50 | 296.80 | 130 |

| Temp F | Pressure | | Volume cu ft/lb | Density lb/cu ft | Enthalpy** Btu/lb | | Entropy** Btu/(lb)(°R) | | Temp F |
|---|---|---|---|---|---|---|---|---|---|
| | psia | psig | Vapor $v_g$ | Liquid $1/v_f$ | Liquid $h_f$ | Vapor $h_g$ | Liquid $s_f$ | Vapor $s_g$ | |
| -150 | 0.27163 | 29.36816* | 141.23 | 98.236 | -25.974 | 87.521 | -0.07147 | 0.29501 | -150 |
| -145 | 0.34999 | 29.20861* | 111.34 | 97.800 | -24.851 | 88.100 | -0.06787 | 0.29106 | -145 |
| -140 | 0.44692 | 29.01126* | 88.532 | 97.363 | -23.725 | 88.681 | -0.06432 | 0.28729 | -140 |
| -135 | 0.56584 | 28.76914* | 70.981 | 96.922 | -22.596 | 89.263 | -0.06082 | 0.28369 | -135 |
| -130 | 0.71060 | 28.47441* | 57.356 | 96.480 | -21.463 | 89.848 | -0.05736 | 0.28027 | -130 |
| -125 | 0.88551 | 28.11829* | 46.692 | 96.035 | -20.326 | 90.433 | -0.05394 | 0.27700 | -125 |
| -120 | 1.0954 | 27.6910* | 38.280 | 95.587 | -19.185 | 91.020 | -0.05055 | 0.27388 | -120 |
| -115 | 1.3455 | 27.1818* | 31.594 | 95.137 | -18.038 | 91.608 | -0.04720 | 0.27090 | -115 |
| -110 | 1.6417 | 26.5788* | 26.242 | 94.684 | -16.886 | 92.196 | -0.04389 | 0.26805 | -110 |
| -105 | 1.9903 | 25.8669* | 21.930 | 94.228 | -15.728 | 92.783 | -0.04060 | 0.26533 | -105 |
| -100 | 2.3983 | 25.0383* | 18.433 | 93.770 | -14.564 | 93.371 | -0.03734 | 0.26274 | -100 |
| -98 | 2.5798 | 24.6688* | 17.222 | 93.585 | -14.097 | 93.606 | -0.03605 | 0.26173 | -98 |
| -96 | 2.7724 | 24.2765* | 16.104 | 93.401 | -13.628 | 93.840 | -0.03476 | 0.26074 | -96 |
| -94 | 2.9768 | 23.8604* | 15.072 | 93.215 | -13.158 | 94.075 | -0.03347 | 0.25977 | -94 |
| -92 | 3.1934 | 23.4193* | 14.118 | 93.030 | -12.688 | 94.309 | -0.03219 | 0.25881 | -92 |
| -90 | 3.4229 | 22.9522* | 13.235 | 92.843 | -12.216 | 94.544 | -0.03091 | 0.25787 | -90 |
| -88 | 3.6657 | 22.4579* | 12.417 | 92.657 | -11.743 | 94.777 | -0.02963 | 0.25695 | -88 |
| -86 | 3.9224 | 21.9352* | 11.659 | 92.469 | -11.268 | 95.011 | -0.02836 | 0.25604 | -86 |
| -84 | 4.1936 | 21.3829* | 10.955 | 92.282 | -10.793 | 95.244 | -0.02709 | 0.25515 | -84 |
| -82 | 4.4800 | 20.7998* | 10.302 | 92.093 | -10.316 | 95.478 | -0.02583 | 0.25428 | -82 |
| -80 | 4.7822 | 20.1846* | 9.6949 | 91.905 | -9.838 | 95.710 | -0.02457 | 0.25342 | -80 |
| -78 | 5.1007 | 19.5361* | 9.1301 | 91.715 | -9.359 | 95.943 | -0.02331 | 0.25257 | -78 |
| -76 | 5.4363 | 18.8528* | 8.6043 | 91.525 | -8.878 | 96.175 | -0.02206 | 0.25174 | -76 |
| -74 | 5.7896 | 18.1334* | 8.1145 | 91.335 | -8.397 | 96.406 | -0.02081 | 0.25092 | -74 |
| -72 | 6.1614 | 17.3766* | 7.6579 | 91.144 | -7.914 | 96.637 | -0.01956 | 0.25012 | -72 |
| -70 | 6.5522 | 16.5809* | 7.2318 | 90.952 | -7.429 | 96.868 | -0.01832 | 0.24932 | -70 |
| -68 | 6.9628 | 15.7449* | 6.8339 | 90.760 | -6.944 | 97.098 | -0.01708 | 0.24855 | -68 |
| -66 | 7.3939 | 14.8671* | 6.4621 | 90.568 | -6.457 | 97.328 | -0.01584 | 0.24778 | -66 |
| -64 | 7.8463 | 13.9460* | 6.1144 | 90.374 | -5.968 | 97.557 | -0.01460 | 0.24703 | -64 |
| -62 | 8.3208 | 12.9800* | 5.7891 | 90.180 | -5.479 | 97.786 | -0.01337 | 0.24629 | -62 |
| -60 | 8.8180 | 11.9677* | 5.4844 | 89.986 | -4.987 | 98.014 | -0.01214 | 0.24556 | -60 |
| -58 | 9.3388 | 10.9074* | 5.1989 | 89.791 | -4.495 | 98.241 | -0.01092 | 0.24484 | -58 |
| -56 | 9.8839 | 9.7975* | 4.9312 | 89.595 | -4.001 | 98.468 | -0.00969 | 0.24414 | -56 |
| -54 | 10.454 | 8.636* | 4.6799 | 89.399 | -3.506 | 98.694 | -0.00847 | 0.24345 | -54 |
| -52 | 11.051 | 7.422* | 4.4440 | 89.202 | -3.009 | 98.920 | -0.00725 | 0.24276 | -52 |
| -50 | 11.674 | 6.154* | 4.2224 | 89.004 | -2.511 | 99.144 | -0.00604 | 0.24209 | -50 |
| -48 | 12.324 | 4.829* | 4.0140 | 88.806 | -2.012 | 99.369 | -0.00483 | 0.24143 | -48 |
| -46 | 13.004 | 3.445* | 3.8179 | 88.607 | -1.511 | 99.592 | -0.00361 | 0.24078 | -46 |
| -44 | 13.712 | 2.002* | 3.6334 | 88.407 | -1.009 | 99.814 | -0.00241 | 0.24014 | -44 |
| -42 | 14.451 | 0.498* | 3.4596 | 88.207 | -0.505 | 100.036 | -0.00120 | 0.23951 | -42 |
| -40 | 15.222 | 0.526 | 3.2957 | 88.006 | 0.000 | 100.257 | 0.00000 | 0.23888 | -40 |
| -38 | 16.024 | 1.328 | 3.1412 | 87.805 | 0.506 | 100.477 | 0.00120 | 0.23827 | -38 |
| -36 | 16.859 | 2.163 | 2.9954 | 87.602 | 1.014 | 100.696 | 0.00240 | 0.23767 | -36 |
| -34 | 17.728 | 3.032 | 2.8578 | 87.399 | 1.524 | 100.914 | 0.00359 | 0.23707 | -34 |
| -32 | 18.633 | 3.937 | 2.7278 | 87.195 | 2.035 | 101.132 | 0.00479 | 0.23649 | -32 |

(continued)

| Temp F | Pressure psia | Pressure psig | Volume cu ft/lb Vapor $v_g$ | Density lb/cu ft Liquid $1/v_f$ | Enthalpy** Btu/lb Liquid $h_f$ | Enthalpy** Btu/lb Vapor $h_g$ | Entropy** Btu/(lb)(°R) Liquid $s_f$ | Entropy** Btu/(lb)(°R) Vapor $s_g$ |
|---|---|---|---|---|---|---|---|---|
| −30 | 19.573 | 4.877 | 2.6049 | 86.991 | 2.547 | 101.348 | 0.00598 | 0.23591 |
| −28 | 20.549 | 5.853 | 2.4887 | 86.785 | 3.061 | 101.564 | 0.00716 | 0.23534 |
| −26 | 21.564 | 6.868 | 2.3787 | 86.579 | 3.576 | 101.778 | 0.00835 | 0.23478 |
| −24 | 22.617 | 7.921 | 2.2746 | 86.372 | 4.093 | 101.992 | 0.00953 | 0.23423 |
| −22 | 23.711 | 9.015 | 2.1760 | 86.165 | 4.611 | 102.204 | 0.01072 | 0.23369 |
| −20 | 24.845 | 10.149 | 2.0826 | 85.956 | 5.131 | 102.415 | 0.01189 | 0.23315 |
| −18 | 26.202 | 11.324 | 1.9940 | 85.747 | 5.652 | 102.626 | 0.01307 | 0.23262 |
| −16 | 27.239 | 12.543 | 1.9099 | 85.537 | 6.175 | 102.835 | 0.01425 | 0.23210 |
| −14 | 28.501 | 13.805 | 1.8302 | 85.326 | 6.699 | 103.043 | 0.01542 | 0.23159 |
| −12 | 29.809 | 15.113 | 1.7544 | 85.114 | 7.224 | 103.250 | 0.01659 | 0.23108 |
| −10 | 31.162 | 16.466 | 1.6825 | 84.901 | 7.751 | 103.455 | 0.01776 | 0.23058 |
| −8 | 32.563 | 17.867 | 1.6141 | 84.688 | 8.280 | 103.660 | 0.01892 | 0.23008 |
| −6 | 34.011 | 19.315 | 1.5491 | 84.473 | 8.810 | 103.863 | 0.02009 | 0.22960 |
| −4 | 35.509 | 20.813 | 1.4872 | 84.258 | 9.341 | 104.065 | 0.02125 | 0.22912 |
| −2 | 37.057 | 22.361 | 1.4283 | 84.042 | 9.874 | 104.266 | 0.02241 | 0.22864 |
| 0 | 38.657 | 23.961 | 1.3723 | 83.825 | 10.409 | 104.465 | 0.02357 | 0.22817 |
| 2 | 40.309 | 25.613 | 1.3189 | 83.606 | 10.945 | 104.663 | 0.02472 | 0.22771 |
| 4 | 42.014 | 27.318 | 1.2680 | 83.387 | 11.483 | 104.860 | 0.02587 | 0.22725 |
| 5† | 42.888 | 28.192 | 1.2434 | 83.277 | 11.752 | 104.958 | 0.02645 | 0.22703 |
| 6 | 43.775 | 29.079 | 1.2195 | 83.167 | 12.022 | 105.056 | 0.02703 | 0.22680 |
| 8 | 45.591 | 30.895 | 1.1732 | 82.946 | 12.562 | 105.252 | 0.02818 | 0.22636 |
| 10 | 47.464 | 32.768 | 1.1290 | 82.724 | 13.104 | 105.442 | 0.02932 | 0.22592 |
| 12 | 49.396 | 34.700 | 1.0869 | 82.501 | 13.648 | 105.633 | 0.03047 | 0.22548 |
| 14 | 51.387 | 36.691 | 1.0466 | 82.276 | 14.193 | 105.823 | 0.03161 | 0.22505 |
| 16 | 53.438 | 38.742 | 1.0082 | 82.051 | 14.739 | 106.011 | 0.03275 | 0.22463 |
| 18 | 55.551 | 40.855 | 0.97144 | 81.825 | 15.288 | 106.198 | 0.03389 | 0.22421 |
| 20 | 57.727 | 43.031 | 0.93631 | 81.597 | 15.837 | 106.383 | 0.03503 | 0.22379 |
| 22 | 59.967 | 45.271 | 0.90270 | 81.368 | 16.389 | 106.566 | 0.03617 | 0.22338 |
| 24 | 62.272 | 47.576 | 0.87055 | 81.138 | 16.942 | 106.748 | 0.03730 | 0.22297 |
| 26 | 64.644 | 49.948 | 0.83978 | 80.907 | 17.496 | 106.928 | 0.03844 | 0.22257 |
| 28 | 67.083 | 52.387 | 0.81031 | 80.675 | 18.052 | 107.107 | 0.03958 | 0.22217 |
| 30 | 69.591 | 54.895 | 0.78208 | 80.441 | 18.609 | 107.284 | 0.04070 | 0.22178 |
| 32 | 72.169 | 57.473 | 0.75503 | 80.207 | 19.169 | 107.459 | 0.04182 | 0.22139 |
| 34 | 74.818 | 60.122 | 0.72911 | 79.971 | 19.729 | 107.632 | 0.04295 | 0.22100 |
| 36 | 77.540 | 62.844 | 0.70425 | 79.733 | 20.292 | 107.804 | 0.04407 | 0.22062 |
| 38 | 80.336 | 65.640 | 0.68041 | 79.495 | 20.856 | 107.974 | 0.04520 | 0.22024 |
| 40 | 83.206 | 68.510 | 0.65753 | 79.255 | 21.422 | 108.142 | 0.04632 | 0.21986 |
| 42 | 86.153 | 71.457 | 0.63557 | 79.013 | 21.989 | 108.308 | 0.04744 | 0.21949 |

| Temp F | Pressure psia | Pressure psig | Volume cu ft/lb Vapor $v_g$ | Density lb/cu ft Liquid $1/v_f$ | Enthalpy** Btu/lb Liquid $h_f$ | Enthalpy** Btu/lb Vapor $h_g$ | Entropy** Btu/(lb)(°R) Liquid $s_f$ | Entropy** Btu/(lb)(°R) Vapor $s_g$ |
|---|---|---|---|---|---|---|---|---|
| 132 | 319.29 | 304.60 | 0.16187 | 65.949 | 49.743 | 112.949 | 0.09711 | 0.20393 |
| 134 | 327.23 | 312.54 | 0.15727 | 65.581 | 50.432 | 112.955 | 0.09823 | 0.20354 |
| 136 | 335.32 | 320.63 | 0.15279 | 65.207 | 51.125 | 112.954 | 0.09936 | 0.20315 |
| 138 | 343.56 | 328.86 | 0.14843 | 64.826 | 51.824 | 112.947 | 0.10049 | 0.20275 |
| 140 | 351.94 | 337.25 | 0.14418 | 64.440 | 52.528 | 112.931 | 0.10163 | 0.20235 |
| 142 | 360.48 | 345.79 | 0.14004 | 64.047 | 53.238 | 112.908 | 0.10277 | 0.20194 |
| 144 | 369.17 | 354.48 | 0.13600 | 63.647 | 53.955 | 112.877 | 0.10391 | 0.20152 |
| 146 | 378.02 | 363.32 | 0.13207 | 63.240 | 54.677 | 112.836 | 0.10507 | 0.20109 |
| 148 | 387.03 | 372.33 | 0.12823 | 62.825 | 55.406 | 112.787 | 0.10622 | 0.20065 |
| 150 | 396.19 | 381.50 | 0.12448 | 62.402 | 56.143 | 112.728 | 0.10739 | 0.20020 |
| 152 | 405.52 | 390.83 | 0.12083 | 61.970 | 56.887 | 112.658 | 0.10856 | 0.19974 |
| 154 | 415.02 | 400.32 | 0.11726 | 61.529 | 57.638 | 112.577 | 0.10974 | 0.19926 |
| 156 | 424.68 | 409.99 | 0.11376 | 61.079 | 58.399 | 112.485 | 0.11093 | 0.19878 |
| 158 | 434.52 | 419.82 | 0.11035 | 60.617 | 59.168 | 112.381 | 0.11213 | 0.19828 |
| 160 | 444.53 | 429.83 | 0.10701 | 60.145 | 59.948 | 112.263 | 0.11334 | 0.19776 |
| 162 | 454.71 | 440.01 | 0.10374 | 59.660 | 60.737 | 112.131 | 0.11456 | 0.19723 |
| 164 | 465.07 | 450.37 | 0.10054 | 59.163 | 61.538 | 111.984 | 0.11580 | 0.19668 |
| 166 | 475.61 | 460.92 | 0.097393 | 58.651 | 62.351 | 111.820 | 0.11705 | 0.19611 |
| 168 | 486.34 | 471.65 | 0.094309 | 58.125 | 63.178 | 111.639 | 0.11831 | 0.19552 |
| 170 | 497.26 | 482.56 | 0.091279 | 57.581 | 64.019 | 111.438 | 0.11959 | 0.19490 |
| 172 | 508.37 | 493.67 | 0.088299 | 57.019 | 64.875 | 111.216 | 0.12089 | 0.19425 |
| 174 | 519.67 | 504.97 | 0.085365 | 56.438 | 65.750 | 110.970 | 0.12222 | 0.19358 |
| 176 | 531.17 | 516.47 | 0.082473 | 55.834 | 66.643 | 110.699 | 0.12356 | 0.19287 |
| 178 | 542.87 | 528.18 | 0.079616 | 55.205 | 67.558 | 110.400 | 0.12494 | 0.19212 |
| 180 | 554.78 | 540.09 | 0.076790 | 54.549 | 68.498 | 110.068 | 0.12635 | 0.19133 |
| 182 | 566.90 | 552.21 | 0.073987 | 53.861 | 69.465 | 109.700 | 0.12779 | 0.19050 |
| 184 | 579.24 | 564.54 | 0.071201 | 53.136 | 70.464 | 109.290 | 0.12928 | 0.18960 |
| 186 | 591.80 | 577.10 | 0.068421 | 52.370 | 71.500 | 108.832 | 0.13082 | 0.18864 |
| 188 | 604.58 | 589.88 | 0.065638 | 51.553 | 72.579 | 108.317 | 0.13242 | 0.18760 |
| 190 | 617.59 | 602.89 | 0.062837 | 50.677 | 73.711 | 107.734 | 0.13409 | 0.18646 |
| 192 | 630.84 | 616.14 | 0.059999 | 49.728 | 74.907 | 107.067 | 0.13585 | 0.18520 |
| 194 | 644.33 | 629.64 | 0.057096 | 48.685 | 76.184 | 106.295 | 0.13773 | 0.18380 |
| 196 | 658.08 | 643.38 | 0.054089 | 47.518 | 77.568 | 105.381 | 0.13977 | 0.18218 |
| 198 | 672.08 | 657.39 | 0.050912 | 46.178 | 79.102 | 104.270 | 0.14202 | 0.18029 |
| 200 | 686.36 | 671.66 | 0.047438 | 44.571 | 80.862 | 102.853 | 0.14460 | 0.17794 |
| 202 | 700.91 | 686.21 | 0.043375 | 42.476 | 83.030 | 100.870 | 0.14779 | 0.17475 |
| 204 | 715.75 | 701.05 | 0.037545 | 38.991 | 86.309 | 97.260 | 0.15264 | 0.16914 |
| 204.81 | 721.91 | 707.21 | 0.030525 | 32.760 | 91.329 | 91.329 | 0.16016 | 0.16016 |

aFrom published data (1964) of E.I. du Pont de Nemours & Co., Inc. Used by permission.
*Inches of mercury below one standard atmosphere.
**Based on 0 for the saturated liquid at −40 F.
†Standard cycle temperatures.
Reprinted with permission from the 1977 Fundamentals ASHRAE Handbook & Product Directory

# Appendix 7

REFRIGERANT 502 (AZEOTROPE OF R-22 AND R-115) PROPERTIES OF LIQUID AND SATURATED VAPOR[a] (U.S. UNITS)

| Temp F | Pressure psia | Pressure psig | Volume Vapor vg cu ft/lb | Density Liquid 1/vf lb/cu ft | Enthalpy Liquid hf Btu/lb | Enthalpy Vapor hg Btu/lb | Entropy Liquid sf Btu/(lb)(°R) | Entropy Vapor sg Btu/(lb)(°R) |
|---|---|---|---|---|---|---|---|---|
| −150 | 0.4267 | 29.05* | 69.573 | 102.87 | −21.37 | 59.91 | −0.0585 | 0.2040 |
| −145 | 0.540 | 28.82* | 55.967 | 102.38 | −20.54 | 60.49 | −0.0558 | 0.2017 |
| −140 | 0.677 | 28.54* | 45.200 | 101.89 | −19.71 | 61.08 | −0.0532 | 0.1996 |
| −135 | 0.843 | 28.20* | 36.834 | 101.39 | −18.86 | 61.68 | −0.0506 | 0.1975 |
| −130 | 1.043 | 27.80* | 30.222 | 100.89 | −18.00 | 62.27 | −0.0479 | 0.1956 |
| −125 | 1.281 | 27.31* | 24.958 | 100.39 | −17.13 | 62.87 | −0.0453 | 0.1937 |
| −120 | 1.562 | 26.74* | 20.739 | 99.896 | −16.24 | 63.47 | −0.0427 | 0.1920 |
| −115 | 1.894 | 26.06* | 17.336 | 99.391 | −15.34 | 64.07 | −0.0400 | 0.1904 |
| −110 | 2.283 | 25.27* | 14.572 | 98.882 | −14.42 | 64.67 | −0.0374 | 0.1888 |
| −105 | 2.736 | 24.35* | 12.315 | 98.371 | −13.49 | 65.28 | −0.0348 | 0.1873 |
| −100 | 3.261 | 23.28* | 10.461 | 97.857 | −12.55 | 65.89 | −0.0321 | 0.1860 |
| −98 | 3.493 | 22.81* | 9.8145 | 97.650 | −12.17 | 66.13 | −0.0311 | 0.1854 |
| −96 | 3.739 | 22.31* | 9.2142 | 97.443 | −11.78 | 66.37 | −0.0300 | 0.1849 |
| −94 | 3.998 | 21.78* | 8.6572 | 97.24 | −11.39 | 66.61 | −0.0289 | 0.1844 |
| −92 | 4.272 | 21.22* | 8.1399 | 97.03 | −11.01 | 66.86 | −0.0279 | 0.1839 |
| −90 | 4.5612 | 20.63* | 7.6591 | 96.82 | −10.61 | 67.10 | −0.0268 | 0.1834 |
| −88 | 4.867 | 20.01* | 7.2118 | 96.61 | −10.22 | 67.34 | −0.0258 | 0.1829 |
| −86 | 5.188 | 19.36* | 6.7954 | 96.40 | −9.82 | 67.59 | −0.0247 | 0.1825 |
| −84 | 5.527 | 18.67* | 6.4074 | 96.19 | −9.42 | 67.83 | −0.0236 | 0.1820 |
| −82 | 5.883 | 17.94* | 6.0457 | 95.98 | −9.02 | 68.07 | −0.0226 | 0.1816 |
| −80 | 6.258 | 17.18* | 5.7081 | 95.77 | −8.62 | 68.31 | −0.0215 | 0.1811 |
| −78 | 6.652 | 16.38* | 5.3930 | 95.55 | −8.21 | 68.56 | −0.0204 | 0.1807 |
| −76 | 7.066 | 15.53* | 5.0985 | 95.34 | −7.80 | 68.80 | −0.0194 | 0.1803 |
| −74 | 7.501 | 14.65* | 4.8231 | 95.13 | −7.39 | 69.04 | −0.0183 | 0.1799 |
| −72 | 7.956 | 13.72* | 4.5654 | 94.91 | −6.98 | 69.28 | −0.0172 | 0.1795 |
| −70 | 8.434 | 12.75* | 4.3241 | 94.70 | −6.56 | 69.53 | −0.0162 | 0.1791 |
| −68 | 8.935 | 11.73* | 4.0980 | 94.48 | −6.14 | 69.77 | −0.0151 | 0.1787 |
| −66 | 9.459 | 10.66* | 3.8859 | 94.27 | −5.72 | 70.01 | −0.0140 | 0.1783 |
| −64 | 10.01 | 9.54* | 3.6870 | 94.05 | −5.29 | 70.25 | −0.0129 | 0.1780 |
| −62 | 10.58 | 8.38* | 3.5002 | 93.83 | −4.87 | 70.49 | −0.0119 | 0.1776 |
| −60 | 11.18 | 7.15* | 3.3248 | 93.62 | −4.44 | 70.73 | −0.0108 | 0.1773 |
| −58 | 11.81 | 5.88* | 3.1589 | 93.40 | −4.01 | 70.97 | −0.0097 | 0.1769 |
| −56 | 12.46 | 4.54* | 3.0047 | 93.18 | −3.57 | 71.21 | −0.0086 | 0.1766 |
| −54 | 13.15 | 3.15* | 2.8586 | 92.96 | −3.13 | 71.45 | −0.0076 | 0.1763 |
| −52 | 13.86 | 1.70* | 2.7211 | 92.74 | −2.69 | 71.69 | −0.0065 | 0.1760 |
| −50 | 14.60 | 0.19* | 2.5915 | 92.51 | −2.25 | 71.93 | −0.0054 | 0.1757 |
| −48 | 15.38 | 0.68 | 2.4693 | 92.29 | −1.81 | 72.17 | −0.0043 | 0.1754 |
| −46 | 16.18 | 1.49 | 2.3540 | 92.07 | −1.36 | 72.40 | −0.0033 | 0.1751 |
| −44 | 17.02 | 2.33 | 2.2452 | 91.84 | −0.91 | 72.64 | −0.0022 | 0.1748 |
| −42 | 17.89 | 3.20 | 2.1424 | 91.62 | −0.46 | 72.88 | −0.0011 | 0.1745 |
| −40 | 18.80 | 4.11 | 2.0453 | 91.39 | 0.00 | 73.11 | 0.0000 | 0.1742 |
| −38 | 19.75 | 5.05 | 1.9535 | 91.17 | 0.46 | 73.35 | 0.0011 | 0.1740 |
| −36 | 20.73 | 6.03 | 1.8666 | 90.94 | 0.92 | 73.59 | 0.0022 | 0.1737 |
| −34 | 21.74 | 7.05 | 1.7844 | 90.71 | 1.38 | 73.82 | 0.0033 | 0.1734 |
| −32 | 22.80 | 8.10 | 1.7065 | 90.48 | 1.85 | 74.05 | 0.0043 | 0.1732 |

| Temp F | Pressure psia | Pressure psig | Volume Vapor vg cu ft/lb | Density Liquid 1/vf lb/cu ft | Enthalpy Liquid hf Btu/lb | Enthalpy Vapor hg Btu/lb | Entropy Liquid sf Btu/lb (°R) | Entropy Vapor sg (°R) |
|---|---|---|---|---|---|---|---|---|
| 25 | 73.50 | 58.81 | 0.5575 | 83.50 | 16.14 | 80.35 | 0.0354 | 0.1679 |
| 26 | 74.82 | 60.13 | 0.5478 | 83.37 | 16.41 | 80.46 | 0.0360 | 0.1679 |
| 27 | 76.16 | 61.47 | 0.5384 | 83.23 | 16.67 | 80.56 | 0.0365 | 0.1678 |
| 28 | 77.52 | 62.82 | 0.5291 | 83.10 | 16.94 | 80.66 | 0.0371 | 0.1677 |
| 29 | 78.89 | 64.20 | 0.5201 | 82.97 | 17.21 | 80.76 | 0.0376 | 0.1677 |
| 30 | 80.29 | 65.59 | 0.5112 | 82.83 | 17.48 | 80.86 | 0.0382 | 0.1676 |
| 31 | 81.70 | 67.00 | 0.5025 | 82.70 | 17.75 | 80.96 | 0.0387 | 0.1675 |
| 32 | 83.13 | 68.43 | 0.4940 | 82.56 | 18.02 | 81.06 | 0.0392 | 0.1675 |
| 33 | 84.57 | 69.88 | 0.4857 | 82.43 | 18.29 | 81.16 | 0.0398 | 0.1674 |
| 34 | 86.04 | 71.34 | 0.4775 | 82.29 | 18.56 | 81.26 | 0.0403 | 0.1673 |
| 35 | 87.52 | 72.83 | 0.4695 | 82.16 | 18.84 | 81.36 | 0.0409 | 0.1673 |
| 36 | 89.03 | 74.33 | 0.4616 | 82.02 | 19.11 | 81.46 | 0.0414 | 0.1672 |
| 37 | 90.55 | 75.85 | 0.4539 | 81.88 | 19.38 | 81.56 | 0.0420 | 0.1672 |
| 38 | 92.09 | 77.39 | 0.4464 | 81.75 | 19.65 | 81.66 | 0.0425 | 0.1671 |
| 39 | 93.65 | 78.95 | 0.4390 | 81.61 | 19.93 | 81.75 | 0.0431 | 0.1670 |
| 40 | 95.23 | 80.53 | 0.4318 | 81.47 | 20.02 | 81.85 | 0.0436 | 0.1670 |
| 41 | 96.83 | 82.13 | 0.4246 | 81.33 | 20.48 | 81.95 | 0.0441 | 0.1669 |
| 42 | 98.45 | 83.75 | 0.4177 | 81.19 | 20.75 | 82.04 | 0.0447 | 0.1668 |
| 43 | 100.08 | 85.38 | 0.4108 | 81.05 | 21.03 | 82.14 | 0.0452 | 0.1668 |
| 44 | 101.74 | 87.04 | 0.4041 | 80.91 | 21.31 | 82.24 | 0.0458 | 0.1667 |
| 45 | 103.42 | 88.72 | 0.3976 | 80.77 | 21.58 | 82.33 | 0.0463 | 0.1667 |
| 46 | 105.12 | 90.42 | 0.3911 | 80.62 | 21.86 | 82.43 | 0.0469 | 0.1666 |
| 47 | 106.84 | 92.14 | 0.3848 | 80.49 | 22.14 | 82.52 | 0.0474 | 0.1666 |
| 48 | 108.58 | 93.88 | 0.3786 | 80.35 | 22.42 | 82.61 | 0.0479 | 0.1665 |
| 49 | 110.34 | 95.64 | 0.3725 | 80.20 | 22.70 | 82.71 | 0.0485 | 0.1664 |
| 50 | 112.12 | 97.42 | 0.3666 | 80.06 | 22.98 | 82.80 | 0.0490 | 0.1664 |
| 51 | 113.92 | 99.22 | 0.3607 | 79.91 | 23.26 | 82.89 | 0.0496 | 0.1663 |
| 52 | 115.74 | 101.05 | 0.3550 | 79.77 | 23.54 | 82.98 | 0.0501 | 0.1663 |
| 53 | 117.59 | 102.89 | 0.3493 | 79.62 | 23.82 | 83.08 | 0.0506 | 0.1662 |
| 54 | 119.45 | 104.75 | 0.3438 | 79.48 | 24.10 | 83.17 | 0.0512 | 0.1662 |
| 55 | 121.34 | 106.64 | 0.3383 | 79.33 | 24.38 | 83.26 | 0.0517 | 0.1661 |
| 56 | 123.25 | 108.55 | 0.3330 | 79.19 | 24.66 | 83.35 | 0.0523 | 0.1661 |
| 57 | 125.18 | 110.48 | 0.3278 | 79.04 | 24.95 | 83.44 | 0.0528 | 0.1660 |
| 58 | 127.13 | 112.43 | 0.3226 | 78.89 | 25.23 | 83.53 | 0.0533 | 0.1659 |
| 59 | 129.10 | 114.41 | 0.3176 | 78.74 | 25.51 | 83.62 | 0.0539 | 0.1659 |
| 60 | 131.10 | 116.40 | 0.3126 | 78.59 | 25.80 | 83.70 | 0.0544 | 0.1658 |
| 62 | 135.16 | 120.46 | 0.3030 | 78.29 | 26.37 | 83.88 | 0.0555 | 0.1657 |
| 64 | 139.31 | 124.61 | 0.2937 | 77.99 | 26.94 | 84.05 | 0.0566 | 0.1656 |
| 66 | 143.55 | 128.86 | 0.2847 | 77.68 | 27.52 | 84.22 | 0.0576 | 0.1655 |
| 68 | 147.89 | 133.19 | 0.2761 | 77.37 | 28.09 | 84.39 | 0.0587 | 0.1654 |
| 70 | 152.32 | 137.62 | 0.2677 | 77.06 | 28.67 | 84.55 | 0.0598 | 0.1653 |
| 72 | 156.84 | 142.15 | 0.2596 | 76.75 | 29.25 | 84.72 | 0.0609 | 0.1652 |
| 74 | 161.46 | 146.77 | 0.2518 | 76.43 | 29.83 | 84.88 | 0.0619 | 0.1651 |
| 76 | 166.18 | 151.49 | 0.2443 | 76.11 | 30.41 | 85.04 | 0.0630 | 0.1650 |
| 78 | 171.00 | 156.30 | 0.2370 | 75.78 | 31.00 | 85.19 | 0.0647 | 0.1649 |

| Temp F | Pressure psia | Pressure psig | Volume cu ft/lb Vapor $v_g$ | Density lb/cu ft Liquid $1/v_f$ | Enthalpy Btu/lb Liquid $h_f$ | Enthalpy Btu/lb Vapor $h_g$ | Entropy Btu/(lb)(°R) Liquid $s_f$ | Entropy Btu/(lb)(°R) Vapor $s_g$ |
|---|---|---|---|---|---|---|---|---|
| −30 | 23.90 | 9.20 | 1.6328 | 90.25 | 2.32 | 74.29 | 0.0054 | 0.1729 |
| −28 | 25.03 | 10.34 | 1.5628 | 90.02 | 2.79 | 74.52 | 0.0065 | 0.1727 |
| −26 | 26.21 | 11.52 | 1.4965 | 89.79 | 3.26 | 74.75 | 0.0076 | 0.1725 |
| −24 | 27.43 | 12.74 | 1.4336 | 89.56 | 3.73 | 74.98 | 0.0087 | 0.1722 |
| −22 | 28.70 | 14.00 | 1.3739 | 89.32 | 4.21 | 75.21 | 0.0098 | 0.1720 |
| −20 | 30.01 | 15.31 | 1.3171 | 89.09 | 4.69 | 75.44 | 0.0109 | 0.1718 |
| −18 | 31.36 | 16.66 | 1.2632 | 88.85 | 5.18 | 75.67 | 0.0120 | 0.1716 |
| −16 | 32.76 | 18.07 | 1.2120 | 88.62 | 5.66 | 75.90 | 0.0131 | 0.1714 |
| −14 | 34.21 | 19.52 | 1.1632 | 88.38 | 6.15 | 76.13 | 0.0141 | 0.1712 |
| −12 | 35.71 | 21.01 | 1.1168 | 88.14 | 6.64 | 76.35 | 0.0152 | 0.1710 |
| −10 | 37.26 | 22.56 | 1.0727 | 87.90 | 7.13 | 76.58 | 0.0163 | 0.1708 |
| −8 | 38.85 | 24.16 | 1.0307 | 87.66 | 7.63 | 76.80 | 0.0174 | 0.1706 |
| −6 | 40.50 | 25.81 | 0.9907 | 87.42 | 8.13 | 77.03 | 0.0185 | 0.1704 |
| −4 | 42.21 | 27.51 | 0.9525 | 87.17 | 8.63 | 77.25 | 0.0196 | 0.1702 |
| −2 | 43.96 | 29.27 | 0.9161 | 86.93 | 9.13 | 77.47 | 0.0207 | 0.1700 |
| 0 | 45.78 | 31.08 | 0.8814 | 86.68 | 9.63 | 77.69 | 0.0218 | 0.1698 |
| 1 | 46.70 | 32.01 | 0.8646 | 86.55 | 9.89 | 77.80 | 0.0223 | 0.1698 |
| 2 | 47.64 | 32.95 | 0.8482 | 86.43 | 10.14 | 77.91 | 0.0229 | 0.1697 |
| 3 | 48.60 | 33.90 | 0.8322 | 86.31 | 10.40 | 78.02 | 0.0234 | 0.1696 |
| 4 | 49.57 | 34.87 | 0.8166 | 86.19 | 10.65 | 78.13 | 0.0240 | 0.1695 |
| 5 | 50.55 | 35.86 | 0.8013 | 86.06 | 10.91 | 78.24 | 0.0245 | 0.1694 |
| 6 | 51.55 | 36.86 | 0.7864 | 85.94 | 11.16 | 78.35 | 0.0251 | 0.1693 |
| 7 | 52.57 | 37.87 | 0.7718 | 85.81 | 11.42 | 78.45 | 0.0256 | 0.1693 |
| 8 | 53.59 | 38.90 | 0.7574 | 85.69 | 11.68 | 78.56 | 0.0262 | 0.1692 |
| 9 | 54.64 | 39.94 | 0.7435 | 85.56 | 11.93 | 78.67 | 0.0267 | 0.1691 |
| 10 | 55.70 | 41.00 | 0.7299 | 85.43 | 12.19 | 78.78 | 0.0272 | 0.1690 |
| 11 | 56.77 | 42.08 | 0.7165 | 85.31 | 12.45 | 78.89 | 0.0278 | 0.1689 |
| 12 | 57.86 | 43.17 | 0.7035 | 85.18 | 12.71 | 78.99 | 0.0283 | 0.1689 |
| 13 | 58.97 | 44.27 | 0.6907 | 85.05 | 12.97 | 79.10 | 0.0289 | 0.1688 |
| 14 | 60.09 | 45.39 | 0.673 | 84.93 | 13.23 | 79.20 | 0.0294 | 0.1687 |
| 15 | 61.23 | 46.53 | 0.6660 | 84.80 | 13.49 | 79.31 | 0.0300 | 0.1686 |
| 16 | 62.38 | 47.68 | 0.6541 | 84.67 | 13.76 | 79.42 | 0.0305 | 0.1686 |
| 17 | 63.55 | 48.85 | 0.6424 | 84.54 | 14.02 | 79.52 | 0.0311 | 0.1685 |
| 18 | 64.73 | 50.04 | 0.6310 | 84.41 | 14.28 | 79.63 | 0.0316 | 0.1684 |
| 19 | 65.94 | 51.24 | 0.6198 | 84.28 | 14.55 | 79.73 | 0.0322 | 0.1683 |
| 20 | 67.16 | 52.46 | 0.6088 | 84.15 | 14.81 | 79.84 | 0.0327 | 0.1683 |
| 21 | 68.39 | 53.70 | 0.5981 | 84.02 | 15.07 | 79.94 | 0.0333 | 0.1682 |
| 22 | 69.64 | 54.95 | 0.5876 | 83.89 | 15.34 | 80.04 | 0.0338 | 0.1681 |
| 23 | 70.91 | 56.22 | 0.5774 | 83.76 | 15.60 | 80.15 | 0.0343 | 0.1681 |
| 24 | 72.20 | 57.50 | 0.5673 | 83.63 | 15.87 | 80.25 | 0.0349 | 0.1680 |

| Temp F | Pressure psia | Pressure psig | Volume cu ft/lb Vapor $v_g$ | Density lb/cu ft Liquid $1/v_f$ | Enthalpy Btu/lb Liquid $h_f$ | Enthalpy Btu/lb Vapor $h_g$ | Entropy Btu/(lb)(°R) Liquid $s_f$ | Entropy Btu/(lb)(°R) Vapor $s_g$ |
|---|---|---|---|---|---|---|---|---|
| 80 | 175.92 | 161.22 | 0.2300 | 75.46 | 31.59 | 85.35 | 0.0651 | 0.1647 |
| 82 | 180.94 | 166.24 | 0.2231 | 75.13 | 32.18 | 85.50 | 0.0662 | 0.1646 |
| 84 | 186.06 | 171.36 | 0.2165 | 74.79 | 32.77 | 85.64 | 0.0673 | 0.1645 |
| 86 | 191.28 | 176.59 | 0.2102 | 74.45 | 33.36 | 85.79 | 0.0683 | 0.1644 |
| 88 | 196.62 | 181.92 | 0.2040 | 74.11 | 33.95 | 85.93 | 0.0694 | 0.1643 |
| 90 | 202.05 | 187.36 | 0.1980 | 73.76 | 34.55 | 86.07 | 0.0705 | 0.1642 |
| 92 | 207.60 | 192.90 | 0.1922 | 73.41 | 35.15 | 86.20 | 0.0715 | 0.1641 |
| 94 | 213.25 | 198.56 | 0.1866 | 73.06 | 35.75 | 86.34 | 0.0726 | 0.1639 |
| 96 | 219.02 | 204.32 | 0.1812 | 72.70 | 36.35 | 86.47 | 0.0736 | 0.1638 |
| 98 | 224.90 | 210.20 | 0.1759 | 72.34 | 36.96 | 86.59 | 0.0747 | 0.1637 |
| 100 | 230.89 | 216.19 | 0.1708 | 71.97 | 37.56 | 86.71 | 0.0758 | 0.1636 |
| 102 | 237.00 | 222.30 | 0.1658 | 71.59 | 38.17 | 86.83 | 0.0768 | 0.1634 |
| 104 | 243.22 | 228.52 | 0.1610 | 71.21 | 38.78 | 86.94 | 0.0779 | 0.1633 |
| 106 | 249.56 | 234.87 | 0.1563 | 70.83 | 39.40 | 87.05 | 0.0789 | 0.1632 |
| 108 | 256.02 | 241.33 | 0.1518 | 70.44 | 40.01 | 87.16 | 0.0800 | 0.1630 |
| 110 | 262.61 | 247.91 | 0.1474 | 70.04 | 40.63 | 87.26 | 0.0810 | 0.1629 |
| 112 | 269.31 | 254.62 | 0.1431 | 69.64 | 41.25 | 87.35 | 0.0821 | 0.1627 |
| 114 | 276.15 | 261.45 | 0.1389 | 69.23 | 41.88 | 87.44 | 0.0832 | 0.1626 |
| 116 | 283.10 | 268.41 | 0.1349 | 68.81 | 42.50 | 87.53 | 0.0842 | 0.1624 |
| 118 | 290.19 | 275.50 | 0.1310 | 68.39 | 43.13 | 87.61 | 0.0853 | 0.1623 |
| 120 | 297.41 | 282.71 | 0.1271 | 67.96 | 43.77 | 87.68 | 0.0863 | 0.1621 |
| 122 | 304.76 | 290.06 | 0.1234 | 67.52 | 44.40 | 87.75 | 0.0874 | 0.1619 |
| 124 | 312.25 | 297.55 | 0.1197 | 67.07 | 45.04 | 87.81 | 0.0885 | 0.1617 |
| 126 | 319.87 | 305.17 | 0.1162 | 66.61 | 45.68 | 87.86 | 0.0895 | 0.1615 |
| 128 | 327.63 | 312.94 | 0.1127 | 66.14 | 46.33 | 87.91 | 0.0906 | 0.1613 |
| 130 | 335.54 | 320.84 | 0.1093 | 65.66 | 46.98 | 87.95 | 0.0917 | 0.1611 |
| 132 | 343.59 | 328.89 | 0.1061 | 65.17 | 47.64 | 87.98 | 0.0927 | 0.1609 |
| 134 | 351.79 | 337.09 | 0.1028 | 64.67 | 48.30 | 88.00 | 0.0938 | 0.1607 |
| 136 | 360.13 | 345.44 | 0.09968 | 64.15 | 48.97 | 88.01 | 0.0949 | 0.1604 |
| 138 | 368.63 | 353.94 | 0.09660 | 63.63 | 49.64 | 88.01 | 0.0960 | 0.1602 |
| 140 | 377.29 | 362.60 | 0.09359 | 63.08 | 50.32 | 88.00 | 0.0971 | 0.1599 |
| 145 | 399.64 | 384.95 | 0.08630 | 61.65 | 52.05 | 87.93 | 0.0998 | 0.1592 |
| 150 | 423.06 | 408.35 | 0.07934 | 60.09 | 53.85 | 87.76 | 0.1027 | 0.1583 |
| 155 | 447.61 | 432.91 | 0.07261 | 58.37 | 55.73 | 87.47 | 0.1056 | 0.1573 |
| 160 | 473.38 | 458.69 | 0.06604 | 56.43 | 57.73 | 87.01 | 0.1087 | 0.1560 |
| 165 | 500.50 | 485.80 | 0.05948 | 54.17 | 59.93 | 86.32 | 0.1121 | 0.1544 |
| 170 | 529.11 | 514.41 | 0.05271 | 51.39 | 62.45 | 85.25 | 0.1160 | 0.1522 |
| 175 | 559.41 | 544.72 | 0.04512 | 47.55 | 65.69 | 83.37 | 0.1209 | 0.1488 |
| 179.889 | 591.00 | 576.30 | 0.02857 | 35.00 | 74.69 | 74.65 | 0.1348 | 0.1348 |

a From published data of E.I. du Pont de Nemours & Co. (1969). Used by permission.

*Inches of mercury below standard atmosphere.

**Based on 0 for the saturated liquid at −40 F.

Reprinted with permission from the 1977 Fundamentals ASHRAE Handbook & Product Directory

# Appendix 8

REFRIGERANT 717 (AMMONIA)
PROPERTIES OF LIQUID AND
SATURATED VAPOR[a] (U.S. UNITS)

| Temp F | Pressure | | Volume cu ft/lb | Density lb/cu ft | Enthalpy** Btu/lb | | Entropy** Btu/(lb)(°R) | |
|---|---|---|---|---|---|---|---|---|
| | psia | psig | Vapor $v_g$ | Liquid $1/v_f$ | Liquid $h_f$ | Vapor $h_g$ | Liquid $s_f$ | Vapor $s_g$ |
| −105 | 0.996 | 27.9* | 223.2 | 45.71 | −68.5 | 570.3 | −0.1774 | 1.6243 |
| −104 | 1.041 | 27.8* | 214.2 | 45.67 | −67.5 | 570.7 | −.1744 | 1.6205 |
| −103 | 1.087 | 27.7* | 205.7 | 45.63 | −66.4 | 571.2 | −.1714 | 1.6167 |
| −102 | 1.135 | 27.6* | 197.6 | 45.59 | −65.4 | 571.6 | −.1685 | 1.6129 |
| −101 | 1.184 | 27.5* | 189.8 | 45.55 | −64.3 | 572.1 | −.1655 | 1.6092 |
| −100 | 1.24 | 27.4* | 182.4 | 45.52 | −63.3 | 572.5 | −0.1626 | 1.6055 |
| −99 | 1.29 | 27.3* | 175.3 | 45.47 | −62.2 | 572.9 | −.1597 | 1.6018 |
| −98 | 1.34 | 27.2* | 168.5 | 45.43 | −61.2 | 573.4 | −.1568 | 1.5982 |
| −97 | 1.40 | 27.1* | 162.1 | 45.40 | −60.1 | 573.8 | −.1539 | 1.5945 |
| −96 | 1.46 | 26.9* | 155.9 | 45.36 | −59.1 | 574.3 | −.1510 | 1.5910 |
| −95 | 1.52 | 26.8* | 150.0 | 45.32 | −58.0 | 574.7 | −.1483 | 1.5874 |
| −94 | 1.59 | 26.7* | 144.3 | 45.28 | −57.0 | 575.1 | −0.1452 | 1.5838 |
| −93 | 1.65 | 26.7* | 138.9 | 45.24 | −55.9 | 575.6 | −.1423 | 1.5803 |
| −92 | 1.72 | 26.4* | 133.8 | 45.20 | −54.9 | 576.0 | −.1395 | 1.5768 |
| −91 | 1.79 | 26.3* | 128.9 | 45.16 | −53.8 | 576.5 | −.1366 | 1.5734 |
| −90 | 1.86 | 26.1* | 124.1 | 45.12 | −52.8 | 576.9 | −0.1338 | 1.5699 |
| −89 | 1.94 | 26.0* | 119.6 | 45.08 | −51.7 | 577.3 | −.1309 | 1.5665 |
| −88 | 2.02 | 25.8* | 115.3 | 45.04 | −50.7 | 577.8 | −.1281 | 1.5631 |
| −87 | 2.10 | 25.6* | 111.1 | 45.00 | −49.6 | 578.2 | −.1253 | 1.5597 |
| −86 | 2.18 | 25.5* | 107.1 | 44.96 | −48.6 | 578.6 | −.1225 | 1.5564 |
| −85 | 2.27 | 25.3* | 103.3 | 44.92 | −47.5 | 579.1 | −0.1197 | 1.5531 |
| −84 | 2.35 | 25.1* | 99.68 | 44.88 | −46.5 | 579.5 | −.1169 | 1.5498 |
| −83 | 2.45 | 24.9* | 96.17 | 44.84 | −45.4 | 579.9 | −.1141 | 1.5465 |
| −82 | 2.54 | 24.7* | 92.81 | 44.80 | −44.4 | 580.4 | −.1113 | 1.5432 |
| −81 | 2.64 | 24.5* | 89.59 | 44.76 | −43.3 | 580.8 | −.1085 | 1.5400 |
| −80 | 2.74 | 24.3* | 86.50 | 44.73 | −42.2 | 581.2 | −0.1057 | 1.5368 |
| −79 | 2.84 | 24.1* | 83.54 | 44.68 | −41.2 | 581.6 | −.1030 | 1.5336 |
| −78 | 2.95 | 23.9* | 80.69 | 44.64 | −40.1 | 582.1 | −.1002 | 1.5304 |
| −77 | 3.06 | 23.7* | 77.96 | 44.60 | −39.1 | 582.5 | −.0975 | 1.5273 |
| −76 | 3.18 | 23.5* | 75.33 | 44.56 | −38.0 | 582.9 | −.0947 | 1.5242 |
| −75 | 3.29 | 23.2* | 72.81 | 44.52 | −37.0 | 583.3 | −0.0920 | 1.5211 |
| −74 | 3.42 | 23.0* | 70.39 | 44.48 | −35.9 | 583.8 | −.0892 | 1.5180 |
| −73 | 3.54 | 22.7* | 68.06 | 44.44 | −34.9 | 584.2 | −.0865 | 1.5149 |
| −72 | 3.67 | 22.4* | 65.82 | 44.40 | −33.8 | 584.6 | −.0838 | 1.5119 |
| −71 | 3.80 | 22.2* | 63.67 | 44.36 | −32.8 | 585.0 | −.0811 | 1.5089 |
| −70 | 3.94 | 21.9* | 61.60 | 44.32 | −31.7 | 585.5 | −0.0784 | 1.5059 |
| −69 | 4.08 | 21.6* | 59.61 | 44.28 | −30.7 | 585.9 | −.0757 | 1.5029 |
| −68 | 4.23 | 21.3* | 57.69 | 44.24 | −29.6 | 586.3 | −.0730 | 1.4999 |
| −67 | 4.38 | 21.0* | 55.85 | 44.19 | −28.6 | 586.7 | −.0703 | 1.4970 |
| −66 | 4.53 | 20.7* | 54.08 | 44.15 | −27.5 | 587.1 | −.0676 | 1.4940 |
| −65 | 4.69 | 20.4* | 52.37 | 44.11 | −26.5 | 587.5 | −0.0650 | 1.4911 |
| −64 | 4.85 | 20.0* | 50.73 | 44.07 | −25.4 | 588.0 | −.0623 | 1.4883 |
| −63 | 5.02 | 19.7* | 49.14 | 44.03 | −24.4 | 588.4 | −.0596 | 1.4854 |
| −62 | 5.19 | 19.4* | 47.62 | 43.99 | −23.3 | 588.8 | −.0570 | 1.4826 |

| Temp F | Pressure | | Volume cu ft/lb | Density lb/cu ft | Enthalpy** Btu/lb | | Entropy** Btu/(lb)(°R) | |
|---|---|---|---|---|---|---|---|---|
| | psia | psig | Vapor $v_g$ | Liquid $1/v_f$ | Liquid $h_f$ | Vapor $h_g$ | Liquid $s_f$ | Vapor $s_g$ |
| 12 | 40.31 | 25.6 | 6.996 | 40.80 | 56.0 | 615.5 | .1254 | 1.3118 |
| 13 | 41.24 | 26.5 | 6.847 | 40.75 | 57.1 | 615.8 | .1277 | 1.3099 |
| 14 | 42.18 | 27.5 | 6.703 | 40.71 | 58.2 | 616.1 | .1300 | 1.3081 |
| 15 | 43.14 | 28.4 | 6.562 | 40.66 | 59.2 | 616.3 | 0.1323 | 1.3062 |
| 16 | 44.12 | 29.4 | 6.425 | 40.61 | 60.3 | 616.6 | .1346 | 1.3043 |
| 17 | 45.12 | 30.4 | 6.291 | 40.57 | 61.4 | 616.9 | .1369 | 1.3025 |
| 18 | 46.13 | 31.4 | 6.161 | 40.52 | 62.5 | 617.2 | .1392 | 1.3006 |
| 19 | 47.16 | 32.5 | 6.034 | 40.48 | 63.6 | 617.5 | .1415 | 1.2988 |
| 20 | 48.21 | 33.5 | 5.910 | 40.43 | 64.7 | 617.8 | 0.1437 | 1.2969 |
| 21 | 49.28 | 34.6 | 5.789 | 40.38 | 65.8 | 618.0 | .1460 | 1.2951 |
| 22 | 50.36 | 35.7 | 5.671 | 40.34 | 66.9 | 618.3 | .1483 | 1.2933 |
| 23 | 51.47 | 36.8 | 5.556 | 40.29 | 68.0 | 618.6 | .1505 | 1.2915 |
| 24 | 52.59 | 37.9 | 5.443 | 40.25 | 69.1 | 618.9 | .1528 | 1.2897 |
| 25 | 53.73 | 39.0 | 5.334 | 40.20 | 70.2 | 619.1 | .1551 | 1.2879 |
| 26 | 54.90 | 40.2 | 5.227 | 40.15 | 71.3 | 619.4 | .1573 | 1.2861 |
| 27 | 56.08 | 41.4 | 5.123 | 40.10 | 72.4 | 619.7 | .1596 | 1.2843 |
| 28 | 57.28 | 42.6 | 5.021 | 40.06 | 73.5 | 619.9 | .1618 | 1.2825 |
| 29 | 58.50 | 43.8 | 4.922 | 40.01 | 74.6 | 620.2 | .1641 | 1.2808 |
| 30 | 59.74 | 45.0 | 4.825 | 39.96 | 75.7 | 620.5 | 0.1663 | 1.2790 |
| 31 | 61.00 | 46.3 | 4.730 | 39.91 | 76.8 | 620.7 | .1686 | 1.2773 |
| 32 | 62.29 | 47.6 | 4.637 | 39.86 | 77.9 | 621.0 | .1708 | 1.2755 |
| 33 | 63.59 | 48.9 | 4.547 | 39.82 | 79.0 | 621.2 | .1730 | 1.2738 |
| 34 | 64.91 | 50.2 | 4.459 | 39.77 | 80.1 | 621.5 | .1753 | 1.2721 |
| 35 | 66.26 | 51.6 | 4.373 | 39.72 | 81.2 | 621.7 | .1775 | 1.2704 |
| 36 | 67.63 | 52.9 | 4.280 | 39.67 | 82.3 | 622.0 | .1797 | 1.2686 |
| 37 | 69.02 | 54.3 | 4.207 | 39.63 | 83.4 | 622.2 | .1819 | 1.2669 |
| 38 | 70.43 | 55.7 | 4.126 | 39.58 | 84.6 | 622.5 | .1841 | 1.2652 |
| 39 | 71.87 | 57.2 | 4.048 | 39.54 | 85.7 | 622.7 | .1863 | 1.2635 |
| 40 | 73.32 | 58.6 | 3.971 | 39.49 | 86.8 | 623.0 | 0.1885 | 1.2618 |
| 41 | 74.80 | 60.1 | 3.897 | 39.44 | 87.9 | 623.2 | .1908 | 1.2602 |
| 42 | 76.31 | 61.6 | 3.823 | 39.39 | 89.0 | 623.4 | .1930 | 1.2585 |
| 43 | 77.83 | 63.1 | 3.752 | 39.34 | 90.1 | 623.7 | .1952 | 1.2568 |
| 44 | 79.38 | 64.7 | 3.682 | 39.29 | 91.2 | 623.9 | .1974 | 1.2552 |
| 45 | 80.96 | 66.3 | 3.614 | 39.24 | 92.3 | 624.1 | 0.1996 | 1.2535 |
| 46 | 82.55 | 67.9 | 3.547 | 39.19 | 93.5 | 624.4 | .2018 | 1.2519 |
| 47 | 84.18 | 69.5 | 3.481 | 39.14 | 94.6 | 624.6 | .2040 | 1.2502 |
| 48 | 85.82 | 71.1 | 3.418 | 39.10 | 95.7 | 624.8 | .2062 | 1.2486 |
| 49 | 87.49 | 72.8 | 3.355 | 39.05 | 96.8 | 625.0 | .2083 | 1.2469 |
| 50 | 89.19 | 74.5 | 3.294 | 39.00 | 97.9 | 625.2 | 0.2105 | 1.2453 |
| 51 | 90.91 | 76.2 | 3.234 | 38.95 | 99.1 | 625.5 | .2127 | 1.2437 |
| 52 | 92.66 | 78.0 | 3.176 | 38.90 | 100.2 | 625.7 | .2149 | 1.2421 |
| 53 | 94.43 | 79.7 | 3.119 | 38.85 | 101.3 | 625.9 | .2171 | 1.2405 |
| 54 | 96.23 | 81.5 | 3.063 | 38.80 | 102.4 | 626.1 | .2192 | 1.2389 |
| 55 | 98.06 | 83.4 | 3.008 | 38.75 | 103.5 | 626.3 | .2214 | 1.2373 |

(continued)

| Entropy** Btu/(lb)(°R) | | Enthalpy** Btu/lb | | Density lb/cu ft | Volume cu ft/lb | Pressure | | Temp F |
|---|---|---|---|---|---|---|---|---|
| Liquid sf | Vapor sg | Liquid hf | Vapor hg | Liquid 1/vf | Vapor vg | psig | psia | |
| .2236 | 1.2357 | 104.7 | 626.5 | 38.70 | 2.954 | 85.2 | 99.91 | 56 |
| .2257 | 1.2341 | 105.8 | 626.7 | 38.65 | 2.902 | 87.1 | 101.8 | 57 |
| .2279 | 1.2325 | 106.9 | 626.9 | 38.60 | 2.851 | 89.0 | 103.7 | 58 |
| .2301 | 1.2310 | 108.1 | 627.1 | 38.55 | 2.800 | 90.9 | 105.6 | 59 |
| .2322 | 1.2294 | 109.2 | 627.3 | 38.50 | 2.751 | 92.9 | 107.6 | 60 |
| .2344 | 1.2278 | 110.3 | 627.5 | 38.45 | 2.703 | 94.9 | 109.6 | 61 |
| .2365 | 1.2262 | 111.5 | 627.7 | 38.40 | 2.656 | 96.9 | 111.6 | 62 |
| .2387 | 1.2247 | 112.6 | 627.9 | 38.35 | 2.610 | 98.9 | 113.6 | 63 |
| .2408 | 1.2231 | 113.7 | 628.0 | 38.30 | 2.565 | 101.0 | 115.7 | 64 |
| 0.2430 | 1.2216 | 114.8 | 628.2 | 38.25 | 2.520 | 103.1 | 117.8 | 65 |
| .2451 | 1.2201 | 116.0 | 628.4 | 38.20 | 2.477 | 105.3 | 120.0 | 66 |
| .2473 | 1.2186 | 117.1 | 628.6 | 38.15 | 2.435 | 107.4 | 122.1 | 67 |
| .2494 | 1.2170 | 118.3 | 628.8 | 38.10 | 2.393 | 109.6 | 124.3 | 68 |
| .2515 | 1.2155 | 119.4 | 628.9 | 38.05 | 2.352 | 111.8 | 126.5 | 69 |
| 0.2537 | 1.2140 | 120.5 | 629.1 | 38.00 | 2.312 | 114.1 | 128.8 | 70 |
| .2558 | 1.2125 | 121.7 | 629.3 | 37.95 | 2.273 | 116.4 | 131.1 | 71 |
| .2579 | 1.2110 | 122.8 | 629.4 | 37.90 | 2.235 | 118.7 | 133.4 | 72 |
| .2601 | 1.2095 | 124.0 | 629.6 | 37.84 | 2.197 | 121.0 | 135.7 | 73 |
| .2622 | 1.2080 | 125.1 | 629.8 | 37.79 | 2.161 | 123.4 | 138.1 | 74 |
| 0.2643 | 1.2065 | 126.2 | 629.9 | 37.74 | 2.125 | 125.8 | 140.5 | 75 |
| .2664 | 1.2050 | 127.4 | 630.1 | 37.69 | 2.089 | 128.3 | 143.0 | 76 |
| .2685 | 1.2035 | 128.5 | 630.2 | 37.64 | 2.055 | 130.7 | 145.4 | 77 |
| .2706 | 1.2020 | 129.7 | 630.4 | 37.58 | 2.021 | 133.2 | 147.9 | 78 |
| .2728 | 1.2006 | 130.8 | 630.5 | 37.53 | 1.988 | 135.8 | 150.5 | 79 |
| 0.2749 | 1.1991 | 132.0 | 630.7 | 37.48 | 1.955 | 138.3 | 153.0 | 80 |
| .2769 | 1.1976 | 133.1 | 630.8 | 37.43 | 1.923 | 140.9 | 155.6 | 81 |
| .2791 | 1.1962 | 134.3 | 631.0 | 37.37 | 1.892 | 143.6 | 158.3 | 82 |
| .2812 | 1.1947 | 135.4 | 631.1 | 37.32 | 1.861 | 146.3 | 161.0 | 83 |
| .2833 | 1.1933 | 136.6 | 631.3 | 37.26 | 1.831 | 149.0 | 163.7 | 84 |
| .2854 | 1.1918 | 137.8 | 631.4 | 37.21 | 1.801 | 151.7 | 166.4 | 85 |
| .2875 | 1.1904 | 138.9 | 631.5 | 37.16 | 1.772 | 154.5 | 169.2 | 86† |
| .2895 | 1.1889 | 140.1 | 631.7 | 37.11 | 1.744 | 157.3 | 172.0 | 87 |
| .2917 | 1.1875 | 141.2 | 631.8 | 37.05 | 1.716 | 160.1 | 174.8 | 88 |
| .2937 | 1.1860 | 142.4 | 631.9 | 37.00 | 1.688 | 163.0 | 177.7 | 89 |
| 0.2958 | 1.1846 | 143.5 | 632.0 | 36.95 | 1.661 | 165.9 | 180.6 | 90 |
| .2979 | 1.1832 | 144.7 | 632.1 | 36.89 | 1.635 | 168.9 | 183.6 | 91 |
| .3000 | 1.1818 | 145.8 | 632.2 | 36.84 | 1.609 | 171.9 | 186.6 | 92 |
| .3021 | 1.1804 | 147.0 | 632.3 | 36.78 | 1.584 | 174.9 | 189.6 | 93 |
| .3041 | 1.1789 | 148.2 | 632.5 | 36.73 | 1.559 | 178.0 | 192.7 | 94 |
| 0.3062 | 1.1775 | 149.4 | 632.6 | 36.67 | 1.534 | 181.1 | 195.8 | 95 |
| .3083 | 1.1761 | 150.5 | 632.6 | 36.62 | 1.510 | 184.2 | 198.9 | 96 |
| .3104 | 1.1747 | 151.7 | 632.8 | 36.56 | 1.487 | 187.4 | 202.1 | 97 |
| .3125 | 1.1733 | 152.9 | 632.9 | 36.51 | 1.464 | 190.6 | 205.3 | 98 |
| .3145 | 1.1719 | 154.0 | 632.9 | 36.45 | 1.441 | 193.9 | 208.6 | 99 |

| Temp F | Pressure | | Volume cu ft/lb | Density lb/cu ft | Enthalpy** Btu/lb | | Entropy** Btu/(lb)(°R) | |
|---|---|---|---|---|---|---|---|---|
| | psia | psig | Vapor vg | Liquid 1/vf | Liquid hf | Vapor hg | Liquid sf | Vapor sg |
| −61 | 5.37 | 19.0* | 46.15 | 43.95 | −22.2 | 589.2 | −.0543 | 1.4797 |
| −60 | 5.55 | 18.6* | 44.73 | 43.91 | −21.2 | 589.6 | −0.0517 | 1.4769 |
| −59 | 5.74 | 18.2* | 43.37 | 43.87 | −20.1 | 590.0 | −.0490 | 1.4741 |
| −58 | 5.93 | 17.8* | 42.05 | 43.83 | −19.1 | 590.4 | −.0464 | 1.4713 |
| −57 | 6.13 | 17.4* | 40.79 | 43.78 | −18.0 | 590.8 | −.0438 | 1.4686 |
| −56 | 6.33 | 17.0* | 39.56 | 43.74 | −17.0 | 591.2 | −.0412 | 1.4658 |
| −55 | 6.54 | 16.6* | 38.38 | 43.70 | −15.9 | 591.6 | −.0386 | 1.4631 |
| −54 | 6.75 | 16.2* | 37.24 | 43.66 | −14.8 | 592.1 | −0.0360 | 1.4604 |
| −53 | 6.97 | 15.7* | 36.15 | 43.62 | −13.8 | 592.4 | −.0334 | 1.4577 |
| −52 | 7.20 | 15.3* | 35.09 | 43.58 | −12.7 | 592.9 | −.0307 | 1.4551 |
| −51 | 7.43 | 14.8* | 34.06 | 43.54 | −11.7 | 593.2 | −.0281 | 1.4524 |
| −50 | 7.67 | 14.3* | 33.08 | 43.49 | −10.6 | 593.7 | −0.0256 | 1.4497 |
| −49 | 7.91 | 13.8* | 32.12 | 43.45 | −9.6 | 594.0 | −.0230 | 1.4471 |
| −48 | 8.16 | 13.3* | 31.20 | 43.41 | −8.5 | 594.4 | −.0204 | 1.4445 |
| −47 | 8.42 | 12.8* | 30.31 | 43.37 | −7.4 | 594.9 | −.0179 | 1.4419 |
| −46 | 8.68 | 12.2* | 29.45 | 43.33 | −6.4 | 595.2 | −.0153 | 1.4393 |
| −45 | 8.95 | 11.7* | 28.62 | 43.28 | −5.3 | 595.6 | −0.0127 | 1.4368 |
| −44 | 9.23 | 11.1* | 27.82 | 43.24 | −4.3 | 596.0 | −.0102 | 1.4342 |
| −43 | 9.51 | 10.6* | 27.04 | 43.20 | −3.2 | 596.4 | −.0076 | 1.4317 |
| −42 | 9.81 | 10.0* | 26.29 | 43.16 | −2.1 | 596.8 | −.0051 | 1.4292 |
| −41 | 10.10 | 9.3* | 25.56 | 43.12 | −1.1 | 597.2 | −.0025 | 1.4267 |
| −40 | 10.41 | 8.7* | 24.86 | 43.08 | 0.0 | 597.6 | 0.0000 | 1.4242 |
| −39 | 10.72 | 8.1* | 24.18 | 43.04 | 1.1 | 598.0 | .0025 | 1.4217 |
| −38 | 11.04 | 7.4* | 23.53 | 42.99 | 2.1 | 598.3 | .0051 | 1.4193 |
| −37 | 11.37 | 6.8* | 22.89 | 42.95 | 3.2 | 598.7 | .0076 | 1.4169 |
| −36 | 11.71 | 6.1* | 22.27 | 42.90 | 4.3 | 599.1 | .0101 | 1.4144 |
| −35 | 12.05 | 5.4* | 21.68 | 42.86 | 5.3 | 599.5 | .0126 | 1.4120 |
| −34 | 12.41 | 4.7* | 21.10 | 42.82 | 6.4 | 599.9 | .0151 | 1.4096 |
| −33 | 12.77 | 3.9* | 20.54 | 42.78 | 7.4 | 600.2 | .0176 | 1.4072 |
| −32 | 13.14 | 3.2* | 20.00 | 42.73 | 8.5 | 600.6 | .0201 | 1.4048 |
| −31 | 13.52 | 2.4* | 19.48 | 42.69 | 9.6 | 601.0 | .0226 | 1.4025 |
| −30 | 13.90 | 1.6* | 18.97 | 42.65 | 10.7 | 601.4 | 0.0250 | 1.4001 |
| −29 | 14.30 | 0.8* | 18.48 | 42.61 | 11.7 | 601.7 | .0275 | 1.3978 |
| −28 | 14.71 | 0.0 | 18.00 | 42.57 | 12.8 | 602.1 | .0300 | 1.3955 |
| −27 | 15.12 | 0.4 | 17.54 | 42.54 | 13.9 | 602.5 | .0325 | 1.3932 |
| −26 | 15.55 | 0.8 | 17.09 | 42.48 | 14.9 | 602.8 | .0350 | 1.3909 |
| −25 | 15.98 | 1.3 | 16.66 | 42.44 | 16.0 | 603.2 | .0374 | 1.3886 |
| −24 | 16.42 | 1.7 | 16.24 | 42.40 | 17.1 | 603.6 | .0399 | 1.3863 |
| −23 | 16.88 | 2.2 | 15.83 | 42.35 | 18.1 | 603.9 | .0423 | 1.3840 |
| −22 | 17.34 | 2.6 | 15.43 | 42.31 | 19.2 | 604.3 | .0448 | 1.3818 |
| −21 | 17.81 | 3.1 | 15.05 | 42.26 | 20.3 | 604.6 | .0472 | 1.3796 |
| −20 | 18.30 | 3.6 | 14.68 | 42.22 | 21.4 | 605.0 | 0.0497 | 1.3774 |
| −19 | 18.79 | 4.1 | 14.32 | 42.18 | 22.4 | 605.3 | .0521 | 1.3752 |
| −18 | 19.30 | 4.6 | 13.97 | 42.13 | 23.5 | 605.7 | .0545 | 1.3729 |

| Temp F | Pressure psia | psig | Volume cu ft/lb Vapor $v_g$ | Density lb/cu ft Liquid $1/v_f$ | Enthalpy Btu/lb Liquid $h_f$ | Vapor $h_g$ | Entropy Btu/(lb)(°R) Liquid $s_f$ | Vapor $s_g$ |
|---|---|---|---|---|---|---|---|---|
| −17 | 19.81 | 5.1 | 13.62 | 42.09 | 24.6 | 606.1 | .0570 | 1.3708 |
| −16 | 20.34 | 5.6 | 13.29 | 42.04 | 25.6 | 606.4 | .0594 | 1.3686 |
| −15 | 20.88 | 6.2 | 12.97 | 42.00 | 26.7 | 606.7 | 0.0618 | 1.3664 |
| −14 | 21.43 | 6.7 | 12.66 | 41.96 | 27.8 | 607.1 | .0642 | 1.3643 |
| −13 | 21.99 | 7.3 | 12.36 | 41.91 | 28.9 | 607.5 | .0666 | 1.3621 |
| −12 | 22.56 | 7.9 | 12.06 | 41.87 | 30.0 | 607.8 | .0690 | 1.3600 |
| −11 | 23.15 | 8.5 | 11.78 | 41.82 | 31.0 | 608.1 | .0714 | 1.3579 |
| −10 | 23.74 | 9.0 | 11.50 | 41.78 | 32.1 | 608.5 | 0.0738 | 1.3558 |
| −9 | 24.35 | 9.7 | 11.23 | 41.74 | 33.2 | 608.8 | .0762 | 1.3537 |
| −8 | 24.97 | 10.3 | 10.97 | 41.69 | 34.3 | 609.2 | .0786 | 1.3516 |
| −7 | 25.61 | 10.9 | 10.71 | 41.65 | 35.4 | 609.5 | .0809 | 1.3495 |
| −6 | 26.26 | 11.6 | 10.47 | 41.60 | 36.4 | 609.8 | .0833 | 1.3474 |
| −5 | 26.92 | 12.2 | 10.23 | 41.56 | 37.5 | 610.1 | 0.0857 | 1.3454 |
| −4 | 27.59 | 12.9 | 9.991 | 41.52 | 38.6 | 610.5 | .0880 | 1.3433 |
| −3 | 28.28 | 13.6 | 9.763 | 41.47 | 39.7 | 610.8 | .0904 | 1.3413 |
| −2 | 28.98 | 14.3 | 9.541 | 41.43 | 40.7 | 611.1 | .0928 | 1.3393 |
| −1 | 29.69 | 15.0 | 9.326 | 41.38 | 41.8 | 611.4 | .0951 | 1.3372 |
| 0 | 30.42 | 15.7 | 9.116 | 41.34 | 42.9 | 611.8 | 0.0975 | 1.3352 |
| 1 | 31.16 | 16.5 | 8.912 | 41.29 | 44.0 | 612.1 | .0998 | 1.3332 |
| 2 | 31.92 | 17.2 | 8.714 | 41.25 | 45.1 | 612.4 | .1022 | 1.3312 |
| 3 | 32.69 | 18.0 | 8.521 | 41.20 | 46.2 | 612.7 | .1045 | 1.3292 |
| 4 | 33.47 | 18.8 | 8.333 | 41.16 | 47.2 | 613.0 | .1069 | 1.3273 |
| 5† | 34.27 | 19.6 | 8.150 | 41.11 | 48.3 | 613.3 | .1092 | 1.3253 |
| 6 | 35.09 | 20.4 | 7.971 | 41.07 | 49.4 | 613.6 | .1115 | 1.3234 |
| 7 | 35.92 | 21.2 | 7.798 | 41.01 | 50.5 | 613.9 | .1138 | 1.3214 |
| 8 | 36.77 | 22.1 | 7.629 | 40.98 | 51.6 | 614.3 | .1162 | 1.3195 |
| 9 | 37.63 | 22.9 | 7.464 | 40.93 | 52.7 | 614.6 | .1185 | 1.3176 |
| 10 | 38.51 | 23.8 | 7.304 | 40.89 | 53.8 | 614.9 | 0.1208 | 1.3157 |
| 11 | 39.40 | 24.7 | 7.148 | 40.84 | 54.9 | 615.2 | .1231 | 1.3137 |

| Temp F | Pressure psia | psig | Volume cu ft/lb Vapor $v_g$ | Density lb/cu ft Liquid $1/v_f$ | Enthalpy Btu/lb Liquid $h_f$ | Vapor $h_g$ | Entropy Btu/(lb)(°R) Liquid $s_f$ | Vapor $s_g$ |
|---|---|---|---|---|---|---|---|---|
| 100 | 211.9 | 197.2 | 1.419 | 36.40 | 155.2 | 633.0 | 0.3166 | 1.1705 |
| 101 | 215.2 | 200.5 | 1.397 | 36.34 | 156.4 | 633.1 | .3187 | 1.1691 |
| 102 | 218.6 | 203.9 | 1.375 | 36.29 | 157.6 | 633.2 | .3207 | 1.1677 |
| 103 | 222.0 | 207.3 | 1.354 | 36.23 | 158.7 | 633.3 | .3228 | 1.1663 |
| 104 | 225.4 | 210.7 | 1.334 | 36.18 | 159.9 | 633.4 | .3248 | 1.1649 |
| 105 | 228.9 | 214.2 | 1.313 | 36.12 | 161.1 | 633.5 | 0.3269 | 1.1635 |
| 106 | 232.5 | 217.8 | 1.293 | 36.06 | 162.3 | 633.5 | .3289 | 1.1621 |
| 107 | 236.0 | 221.3 | 1.274 | 36.01 | 163.5 | 633.6 | .3310 | 1.1607 |
| 108 | 239.7 | 225.0 | 1.254 | 35.95 | 164.6 | 633.6 | .3330 | 1.1593 |
| 109 | 243.3 | 228.6 | 1.235 | 35.90 | 165.8 | 633.7 | .3351 | 1.1580 |
| 110 | 247.0 | 232.3 | 1.217 | 35.84 | 167.0 | 633.7 | 0.3372 | 1.1566 |
| 111 | 250.8 | 236.1 | 1.198 | 35.78 | 168.2 | 633.8 | .3392 | 1.1552 |
| 112 | 254.5 | 239.8 | 1.180 | 35.72 | 169.4 | 633.8 | .3413 | 1.1538 |
| 113 | 258.4 | 243.7 | 1.163 | 35.67 | 170.6 | 633.9 | .3433 | 1.1524 |
| 114 | 262.2 | 247.5 | 1.145 | 35.61 | 171.8 | 633.9 | .3453 | 1.1510 |
| 115 | 266.2 | 251.5 | 1.128 | 35.55 | 173.0 | 633.9 | 0.3474 | 1.1497 |
| 116 | 270.1 | 255.4 | 1.112 | 35.49 | 174.2 | 634.0 | .3495 | 1.1483 |
| 117 | 274.1 | 259.4 | 1.095 | 35.43 | 175.4 | 634.0 | .3515 | 1.1469 |
| 118 | 278.2 | 263.5 | 1.079 | 35.38 | 176.6 | 634.0 | .3535 | 1.1455 |
| 119 | 282.3 | 267.6 | 1.063 | 35.32 | 177.8 | 634.0 | .3556 | 1.1441 |
| 120 | 286.4 | 271.7 | 1.047 | 35.26 | 179.0 | 634.0 | 0.3576 | 1.1427 |
| 121 | 290.8 | 275.9 | 1.032 | 35.20 | 180.2 | 634.0 | .3597 | 1.1414 |
| 122 | 294.8 | 280.1 | 1.017 | 35.14 | 181.4 | 634.0 | .3618 | 1.1400 |
| 123 | 299.1 | 284.4 | 1.002 | 35.08 | 182.6 | 634.0 | .3638 | 1.1386 |
| 124 | 303.4 | 288.7 | 0.987 | 35.02 | 183.9 | 634.0 | .3659 | 1.1372 |
| 125 | 307.8 | 293.1 | 0.973 | 34.96 | 185.1 | 634.0 | .3679 | 1.1358 |

aFrom National Bureau of Standards *Circular No. 142* (1945) and *Circular No. 472* (1948).
*Inches of mercury below one standard atmosphere.
**Based on 0 for the saturated liquid at −40 F.
†Standard cycle temperatures.
Reprinted with permission from the 1977 Fundamentals ASHRAE Handbook & Product Directory

# Appendix 9

REFRIGERANT 12
(DICHLORODIFLUOROMETHANE)
PROPERTIES OF LIQUID AND
SATURATED VAPOR (S.I. UNITS)

| Temp K | Pressure MPa | Volume Vapor m³/kg | Density Liquid kg/m³ | Enthalpy Liquid kJ/kg | Enthalpy Vapor kJ/kg | Entropy Liquid kJ/kg·K | Entropy Vapor kJ/kg·K |
|---|---|---|---|---|---|---|---|
| 270 | 0.27811 | 0.06154 | 1405.7 | 415.53 | 569.52 | 4.1735 | 4.7438 |
| 272 | 0.29735 | 0.05775 | 1399.3 | 417.40 | 570.41 | 4.1804 | 4.7429 |
| 274 | 0.31757 | 0.05425 | 1392.9 | 419.27 | 571.29 | 4.1872 | 4.7420 |
| 276 | 0.33881 | 0.05101 | 1386.5 | 421.16 | 572.17 | 4.1940 | 4.7411 |
| 278 | 0.36110 | 0.04800 | 1380.0 | 423.05 | 573.05 | 4.2007 | 4.7403 |
| 280 | 0.38448 | 0.04520 | 1373.4 | 424.95 | 573.91 | 4.2075 | 4.7395 |
| 282 | 0.40896 | 0.04260 | 1366.8 | 426.86 | 574.78 | 4.2142 | 4.7388 |
| 284 | 0.43459 | 0.04018 | 1360.1 | 428.77 | 575.63 | 4.2209 | 4.7380 |
| 286 | 0.46140 | 0.03793 | 1353.4 | 430.70 | 576.48 | 4.2276 | 4.7373 |
| 288 | 0.48943 | 0.03583 | 1346.6 | 432.63 | 577.33 | 4.2343 | 4.7267 |
| 290 | 0.51870 | 0.03386 | 1339.7 | 434.58 | 578.16 | 4.2409 | 4.7360 |
| 292 | 0.54924 | 0.03203 | 1332.7 | 436.53 | 578.99 | 4.2475 | 4.7354 |
| 294 | 0.58111 | 0.03031 | 1325.7 | 438.49 | 579.81 | 4.2542 | 4.7348 |
| 296 | 0.61431 | 0.02870 | 1318.6 | 440.46 | 580.62 | 4.2608 | 4.7343 |
| 298 | 0.64890 | 0.02719 | 1311.4 | 442.44 | 581.42 | 4.2673 | 4.7337 |
| 300 | 0.68491 | 0.02578 | 1304.2 | 444.44 | 582.21 | 4.2739 | 4.7332 |
| 302 | 0.72236 | 0.02445 | 1296.8 | 446.43 | 582.99 | 4.2804 | 4.7326 |
| 304 | 0.76131 | 0.02320 | 1289.3 | 448.44 | 583.76 | 4.2870 | 4.7321 |
| 306 | 0.80177 | 0.02203 | 1281.8 | 450.46 | 584.53 | 4.2935 | 4.7316 |
| 308 | 0.84380 | 0.02092 | 1274.1 | 452.49 | 585.27 | 4.3000 | 4.7311 |
| 310 | 0.88742 | 0.01988 | 1266.4 | 454.53 | 586.01 | 4.3065 | 4.7306 |
| 315 | 1.0037 | 0.01753 | 1246.5 | 459.68 | 587.79 | 4.3227 | 4.7294 |
| 320 | 1.1308 | 0.01549 | 1225.8 | 464.91 | 589.49 | 4.3388 | 4.7281 |
| 325 | 1.2693 | 0.01371 | 1204.1 | 470.21 | 591.07 | 4.3549 | 4.7268 |
| 330 | 1.4198 | 0.01214 | 1181.5 | 475.61 | 592.54 | 4.3710 | 4.7253 |
| 335 | 1.5832 | 0.01077 | 1157.6 | 481.10 | 593.86 | 4.3871 | 4.7237 |
| 340 | 1.7600 | 0.009549 | 1132.3 | 486.71 | 595.02 | 4.4033 | 4.7218 |
| 345 | 1.9510 | 0.008465 | 1105.4 | 492.45 | 595.98 | 4.4195 | 4.7196 |
| 350 | 2.1572 | 0.007493 | 1076.5 | 498.36 | 596.71 | 4.4360 | 4.7170 |
| 355 | 2.3794 | 0.006616 | 1045.3 | 504.47 | 597.14 | 4.4527 | 4.7138 |
| 360 | 2.6188 | 0.005819 | 1011.1 | 510.84 | 597.20 | 4.4699 | 4.7098 |
| 365 | 2.8765 | 0.005085 | 972.99 | 517.57 | 596.77 | 4.4878 | 4.7047 |
| 370 | 3.1541 | 0.004398 | 929.67 | 524.81 | 595.62 | 4.5066 | 4.6980 |
| 375 | 3.4532 | 0.003735 | 878.34 | 532.83 | 593.34 | 4.5273 | 4.6887 |
| 380 | 3.7764 | 0.003048 | 811.63 | 542.34 | 588.78 | 4.5515 | 4.6737 |
| *384.95 | 4.125 | 0.001792 | 588.0 | 566.9 | 566.9 | 4.614 | 4.614 |

| Temp K | Pressure MPa | Volume Vapor m³/kg | Density Liquid kg/m³ | Enthalpy Liquid kJ/kg | Enthalpy Vapor kJ/kg | Entropy Liquid kJ/kg·K | Entropy Vapor kJ/kg·K |
|---|---|---|---|---|---|---|---|
| 170 | 0.000867 | 13.460 | 1686.1 | 328.51 | 523.56 | 3.7732 | 4.9205 |
| 175 | 0.001395 | 8.6113 | 1673.2 | 332.73 | 525.75 | 3.7977 | 4.9006 |
| 180 | 0.002175 | 5.6757 | 1660.1 | 336.96 | 527.97 | 3.8215 | 4.8826 |
| 185 | 0.003298 | 3.8433 | 1647.0 | 341.18 | 530.21 | 3.8446 | 4.8664 |
| 190 | 0.004875 | 2.6673 | 1633.8 | 345.40 | 532.48 | 3.8671 | 4.8517 |
| 195 | 0.007039 | 1.8930 | 1620.5 | 349.63 | 534.77 | 3.8891 | 4.8385 |
| 200 | 0.009948 | 1.3713 | 1607.2 | 353.87 | 537.07 | 3.9105 | 4.8265 |
| 205 | 0.013787 | 1.0121 | 1593.7 | 358.11 | 539.39 | 3.9315 | 4.8157 |
| 210 | 0.018765 | 0.75991 | 1580.1 | 362.37 | 541.72 | 3.9520 | 4.8060 |
| 215 | 0.025118 | 0.57957 | 1566.4 | 366.64 | 544.05 | 3.9721 | 4.7972 |
| 220 | 0.033110 | 0.44844 | 1552.6 | 370.94 | 546.40 | 3.9918 | 4.7893 |
| 222 | 0.036829 | 0.40624 | 1547.1 | 372.66 | 547.33 | 3.9996 | 4.7864 |
| 224 | 0.040876 | 0.36876 | 1541.5 | 374.39 | 548.27 | 4.0073 | 4.7836 |
| 226 | 0.045271 | 0.33540 | 1535.9 | 376.12 | 549.21 | 4.0150 | 4.7809 |
| 228 | 0.050035 | 0.30565 | 1530.3 | 377.85 | 550.15 | 4.0226 | 4.7783 |
| 230 | 0.055189 | 0.27905 | 1524.7 | 379.59 | 551.09 | 4.0302 | 4.7758 |
| 232 | 0.060756 | 0.25522 | 1519.0 | 381.34 | 552.02 | 4.0377 | 4.7734 |
| 234 | 0.066758 | 0.23383 | 1513.3 | 383.08 | 552.96 | 4.0452 | 4.7712 |
| 236 | 0.073218 | 0.21459 | 1507.6 | 384.84 | 553.90 | 4.0526 | 4.7690 |
| 238 | 0.080160 | 0.19726 | 1501.9 | 386.59 | 554.83 | 4.0600 | 4.7669 |
| 240 | 0.087609 | 0.18161 | 1496.1 | 388.36 | 555.77 | 4.0674 | 4.7649 |
| 242 | 0.095589 | 0.16745 | 1490.3 | 390.13 | 556.70 | 4.0747 | 4.7630 |
| 243.36 | 0.101325 | 0.15861 | 1486.3 | 391.33 | 557.33 | 4.0797 | 4.7618 |
| 244 | 0.10413 | 0.15463 | 1484.5 | 391.90 | 557.63 | 4.0820 | 4.7612 |
| 246 | 0.11324 | 0.14299 | 1478.6 | 393.68 | 558.56 | 4.0892 | 4.7595 |
| 248 | 0.12297 | 0.13241 | 1472.7 | 395.46 | 559.49 | 4.0964 | 4.7578 |
| 250 | 0.13334 | 0.12278 | 1466.8 | 397.25 | 560.42 | 4.1036 | 4.7562 |
| 252 | 0.14436 | 0.11399 | 1460.9 | 399.05 | 561.34 | 4.1107 | 4.7547 |
| 254 | 0.15608 | 0.10597 | 1454.9 | 400.86 | 562.26 | 4.1178 | 4.7533 |
| 256 | 0.16852 | 0.09863 | 1448.9 | 402.67 | 563.18 | 4.1249 | 4.7519 |
| 258 | 0.18170 | 0.09191 | 1442.8 | 404.48 | 564.10 | 4.1319 | 4.7506 |
| 260 | 0.19566 | 0.08574 | 1436.7 | 406.31 | 565.01 | 4.1389 | 4.7493 |
| 262 | 0.21042 | 0.08007 | 1430.6 | 408.14 | 565.92 | 4.1459 | 4.7481 |
| 264 | 0.22602 | 0.07486 | 1424.4 | 409.97 | 566.82 | 4.1528 | 4.7470 |
| 266 | 0.24248 | 0.07005 | 1418.2 | 411.82 | 567.73 | 4.1598 | 4.7459 |
| 268 | 0.25983 | 0.06563 | 1412.0 | 413.67 | 568.62 | 4.1667 | 4.7448 |

*Critical point
Reprinted with permission from the 1981 Fundamentals ASHRAE Handbook & Product Directory

# Appendix 10

## REFRIGERANT 22 (CHLORODIFLUOROMETHANE) PROPERTIES OF LIQUID AND SATURATED VAPOR (S.I. UNITS)

| Temp K | Pressure MPa | Volume Vapor m³/kg | Density Liquid kg/m³ | Enthalpy Liquid kJ/kg | Enthalpy Vapor kJ/kg | Entropy Liquid kJ/kg·K | Entropy Vapor kJ/kg·K |
|---|---|---|---|---|---|---|---|
| 175 | 0.002328 | 7.2120 | 1563.6 | 307.02 | 578.66 | 3.6787 | 5.2309 |
| 180 | 0.003638 | 4.7409 | 1550.9 | 313.16 | 581.06 | 3.7133 | 5.2017 |
| 185 | 0.005522 | 3.2061 | 1538.0 | 319.19 | 583.50 | 3.7464 | 5.1751 |
| 190 | 0.008162 | 2.2244 | 1525.0 | 325.13 | 585.93 | 3.7780 | 5.1507 |
| 195 | 0.011774 | 1.5795 | 1511.9 | 330.97 | 588.36 | 3.8083 | 5.1283 |
| 200 | 0.016613 | 1.1454 | 1498.7 | 336.73 | 590.79 | 3.8375 | 5.1078 |
| 205 | 0.022975 | 0.84657 | 1485.3 | 342.42 | 593.21 | 3.8656 | 5.0889 |
| 210 | 0.031194 | 0.63666 | 1471.7 | 348.06 | 595.61 | 3.8927 | 5.0716 |
| 215 | 0.041643 | 0.48641 | 1458.0 | 353.64 | 598.00 | 3.9190 | 5.0555 |
| 220 | 0.054738 | 0.37701 | 1444.0 | 359.19 | 600.37 | 3.9444 | 5.0407 |
| 222 | 0.060817 | 0.34176 | 1438.4 | 361.40 | 601.31 | 3.9544 | 5.0351 |
| 224 | 0.067422 | 0.31043 | 1432.8 | 363.60 | 602.24 | 3.9643 | 5.0296 |
| 226 | 0.074586 | 0.28253 | 1427.1 | 365.81 | 603.17 | 3.9740 | 5.0243 |
| 228 | 0.082341 | 0.25762 | 1421.4 | 368.01 | 604.10 | 3.9837 | 5.0192 |
| 230 | 0.090720 | 0.23533 | 1415.6 | 370.20 | 605.02 | 3.9933 | 5.0142 |
| 232 | 0.099758 | 0.21535 | 1409.9 | 372.40 | 605.93 | 4.0028 | 5.0094 |
| 232.33 | 0.101325 | 0.21223 | 1408.9 | 372.77 | 606.09 | 4.0044 | 5.0086 |
| 234 | 0.10949 | 0.19740 | 1404.0 | 374.60 | 606.84 | 4.0122 | 5.0047 |
| 236 | 0.11995 | 0.18124 | 1398.2 | 376.79 | 607.75 | 4.0215 | 5.0001 |
| 238 | 0.13119 | 0.16667 | 1392.3 | 378.99 | 608.64 | 4.0307 | 4.9956 |
| 240 | 0.14322 | 0.15350 | 1386.4 | 381.19 | 609.53 | 4.0399 | 4.9913 |
| 242 | 0.15611 | 0.14159 | 1380.4 | 383.39 | 610.41 | 4.0490 | 4.9871 |
| 244 | 0.16988 | 0.13078 | 1374.4 | 385.60 | 611.29 | 4.0580 | 4.9830 |
| 246 | 0.18457 | 0.12096 | 1368.3 | 387.80 | 612.16 | 4.0670 | 4.9790 |
| 248 | 0.20023 | 0.11203 | 1362.3 | 390.01 | 613.01 | 4.0759 | 4.9751 |
| 250 | 0.21690 | 0.10389 | 1356.1 | 392.23 | 613.87 | 4.0847 | 4.9713 |
| 252 | 0.23462 | 0.09647 | 1349.9 | 394.45 | 614.71 | 4.0935 | 4.9676 |
| 254 | 0.25344 | 0.08967 | 1343.7 | 396.68 | 615.54 | 4.1023 | 4.9639 |
| 256 | 0.27340 | 0.08346 | 1337.4 | 398.91 | 616.36 | 4.1110 | 4.9604 |
| 258 | 0.29454 | 0.07776 | 1331.1 | 401.15 | 617.18 | 4.1196 | 4.9569 |
| 260 | 0.31690 | 0.07253 | 1324.7 | 403.39 | 617.98 | 4.1282 | 4.9536 |
| 262 | 0.34055 | 0.06772 | 1318.3 | 405.65 | 618.78 | 4.1368 | 4.9503 |
| 264 | 0.36551 | 0.06329 | 1311.8 | 407.91 | 619.56 | 4.1453 | 4.9470 |
| 266 | 0.39185 | 0.05921 | 1305.3 | 410.19 | 620.33 | 4.1538 | 4.9439 |
| 268 | 0.41960 | 0.05544 | 1298.7 | 412.47 | 621.09 | 4.1623 | 4.9407 |
| 270 | 0.44882 | 0.05196 | 1292.1 | 414.76 | 621.84 | 4.1708 | 4.9377 |
| 272 | 0.47955 | 0.04874 | 1285.4 | 417.07 | 622.58 | 4.1792 | 4.9347 |
| 274 | 0.51184 | 0.04576 | 1278.6 | 419.39 | 623.30 | 4.1876 | 4.9318 |
| 276 | 0.54574 | 0.04300 | 1271.7 | 421.71 | 624.01 | 4.1959 | 4.9289 |
| 278 | 0.58131 | 0.04043 | 1264.8 | 424.05 | 624.70 | 4.2043 | 4.9260 |
| 280 | 0.61860 | 0.03804 | 1257.9 | 426.41 | 625.38 | 4.2126 | 4.9232 |
| 282 | 0.65764 | 0.03582 | 1250.8 | 428.78 | 626.05 | 4.2209 | 4.9205 |
| 284 | 0.69851 | 0.03376 | 1243.7 | 431.16 | 626.70 | 4.2292 | 4.9178 |
| 286 | 0.74124 | 0.03183 | 1236.5 | 433.55 | 627.33 | 4.2375 | 4.9151 |
| 288 | 0.78589 | 0.03003 | 1229.2 | 435.97 | 627.95 | 4.2458 | 4.9124 |
| 290 | 0.83252 | 0.02835 | 1221.8 | 438.39 | 628.55 | 4.2541 | 4.9098 |
| 292 | 0.88118 | 0.02678 | 1214.3 | 440.84 | 629.13 | 4.2623 | 4.9072 |
| 294 | 0.93192 | 0.02531 | 1206.6 | 443.30 | 629.69 | 4.2706 | 4.9046 |
| 296 | 0.98479 | 0.02393 | 1199.1 | 445.77 | 630.24 | 4.2788 | 4.9020 |
| 298 | 1.0399 | 0.02264 | 1191.3 | 448.27 | 630.76 | 4.2871 | 4.8994 |
| 300 | 1.0972 | 0.02143 | 1183.5 | 450.78 | 631.26 | 4.2953 | 4.8969 |
| 302 | 1.1568 | 0.02029 | 1175.5 | 453.31 | 631.73 | 4.3035 | 4.8943 |
| 304 | 1.2188 | 0.01921 | 1167.3 | 455.86 | 632.19 | 4.3118 | 4.8918 |
| 306 | 1.2832 | 0.01821 | 1159.1 | 458.43 | 632.61 | 4.3200 | 4.8893 |
| 308 | 1.3500 | 0.01726 | 1150.8 | 461.03 | 633.01 | 4.3283 | 4.8867 |
| 310 | 1.4194 | 0.01637 | 1142.3 | 463.64 | 633.39 | 4.3366 | 4.8841 |
| 312 | 1.4914 | 0.01552 | 1144.7 | 466.28 | 633.73 | 4.3448 | 4.8816 |
| 314 | 1.5661 | 0.01473 | 1124.9 | 468.93 | 634.05 | 4.3531 | 4.8790 |
| 316 | 1.6434 | 0.01397 | 1115.9 | 471.62 | 634.33 | 4.3614 | 4.8763 |
| 318 | 1.7236 | 0.01326 | 1106.8 | 474.33 | 634.58 | 4.3697 | 4.8737 |
| 320 | 1.8066 | 0.01259 | 1097.4 | 477.06 | 634.79 | 4.3781 | 4.8710 |
| 325 | 2.0270 | 0.01105 | 1073.2 | 484.02 | 635.15 | 4.3990 | 4.8640 |
| 330 | 2.2666 | 0.009697 | 1047.5 | 491.18 | 635.22 | 4.4202 | 4.8567 |
| 335 | 2.5266 | 0.008501 | 1019.9 | 498.57 | 634.94 | 4.4417 | 4.8487 |
| 340 | 2.8083 | 0.007435 | 990.13 | 506.25 | 634.24 | 4.4636 | 4.8400 |
| 345 | 3.1130 | 0.006475 | 957.36 | 514.30 | 633.00 | 4.4862 | 4.8302 |
| 350 | 3.4424 | 0.005602 | 920.52 | 522.85 | 631.03 | 4.5098 | 4.8189 |
| 355 | 3.7982 | 0.004792 | 877.59 | 532.12 | 628.01 | 4.5349 | 4.8051 |
| 360 | 4.1829 | 0.004014 | 824.22 | 542.60 | 623.27 | 4.5630 | 4.7871 |
| 365 | 4.5995 | 0.003205 | 746.91 | 555.74 | 614.88 | 4.5978 | 4.7598 |
| *369.30 | 4.9880 | 0.00195 | 513. | 586.5 | 586.5 | 4.680 | 4.680 |

*Critical point

Reprinted with permission from the 1981 Fundamentals ASHRAE Handbook & Product Directory

# Appendix **11**

REFRIGERANT 717 (AMMONIA)
PROPERTIES OF LIQUID AND
SATURATED VAPOR (S.I. UNITS)

| Temp K | Pressure MPa | Volume Vapor m³/kg | Density Liquid kg/m³ | Enthalpy Liquid kJ/kg | Enthalpy Vapor kJ/kg | Entropy Liquid kJ/kg·K | Entropy Vapor kJ/kg·K |
|---|---|---|---|---|---|---|---|
| **195.48 | 0.006075 | 15.648 | 733.86 | -1110.11 | 380.09 | 4.2032 | 11.8265 |
| 200 | 0.008646 | 11.237 | 728.85 | -1088.77 | 388.51 | 4.3111 | 11.6976 |
| 205 | 0.012512 | 7.9469 | 723.25 | -1066.17 | 397.68 | 4.4228 | 11.5635 |
| 210 | 0.017746 | 5.7290 | 717.54 | -1044.12 | 406.68 | 4.5290 | 11.4375 |
| 215 | 0.024706 | 4.2037 | 711.72 | -1022.33 | 415.50 | 4.6315 | 11.3190 |
| 220 | 0.033811 | 3.1351 | 705.80 | -1000.59 | 424.12 | 4.7314 | 11.2072 |
| 222 | 0.038159 | 2.8000 | 703.41 | -991.89 | 427.50 | 4.7707 | 11.1643 |
| 224 | 0.042959 | 2.5065 | 701.00 | -983.18 | 430.85 | 4.8097 | 11.1223 |
| 226 | 0.048248 | 2.2488 | 698.58 | -974.45 | 434.16 | 4.8485 | 11.0812 |
| 228 | 0.054061 | 2.0220 | 696.16 | -965.71 | 437.43 | 4.8870 | 11.0410 |
| 230 | 0.060439 | 1.8219 | 693.72 | -956.95 | 440.66 | 4.9252 | 11.0017 |
| 232 | 0.067420 | 1.6450 | 691.27 | -948.17 | 443.85 | 4.9631 | 10.9632 |
| 234 | 0.075048 | 1.4882 | 688.82 | -939.38 | 447.00 | 5.0009 | 10.9256 |
| 236 | 0.083366 | 1.3490 | 686.36 | -930.56 | 450.11 | 5.0383 | 10.8887 |
| 238 | 0.092420 | 1.2251 | 683.89 | -921.72 | 453.18 | 5.0756 | 10.8525 |
| 239.82 | 0.101325 | 1.1241 | 681.64 | -913.67 | 455.92 | 5.1092 | 10.8203 |
| 240 | 0.10226 | 1.1145 | 681.41 | -912.86 | 456.20 | 5.1126 | 10.8171 |
| 242 | 0.11293 | 1.0157 | 678.92 | -903.98 | 459.17 | 5.1494 | 10.7823 |
| 244 | 0.12448 | 0.92726 | 676.43 | -895.07 | 462.10 | 5.1859 | 10.7483 |
| 246 | 0.13696 | 0.84790 | 673.92 | -886.15 | 464.99 | 5.2223 | 10.7149 |
| 248 | 0.15044 | 0.77657 | 671.40 | -877.20 | 467.82 | 5.2584 | 10.6821 |
| 250 | 0.16496 | 0.71234 | 668.88 | -868.23 | 470.61 | 5.2944 | 10.6499 |
| 252 | 0.18058 | 0.65441 | 666.34 | -859.24 | 473.35 | 5.3301 | 10.6184 |
| 254 | 0.19736 | 0.60206 | 663.79 | -850.23 | 476.04 | 5.3656 | 10.5874 |
| 256 | 0.21536 | 0.55468 | 661.23 | -841.20 | 478.68 | 5.4009 | 10.5569 |
| 258 | 0.23465 | 0.51174 | 658.65 | -832.14 | 481.27 | 5.4361 | 10.5270 |
| 260 | 0.25529 | 0.47274 | 656.06 | -823.06 | 483.80 | 5.4710 | 10.4976 |
| 262 | 0.27733 | 0.43728 | 653.46 | -813.95 | 486.28 | 5.5058 | 10.4687 |
| 264 | 0.30086 | 0.40498 | 650.84 | -804.82 | 488.71 | 5.5403 | 10.4403 |
| 266 | 0.32593 | 0.37553 | 648.20 | -795.67 | 491.07 | 5.5747 | 10.4124 |
| 268 | 0.35262 | 0.34863 | 645.55 | -786.50 | 493.39 | 5.6089 | 10.3849 |
| 270 | 0.38100 | 0.32402 | 642.88 | -777.29 | 495.64 | 5.6430 | 10.3578 |
| 272 | 0.41113 | 0.30148 | 640.19 | -768.07 | 497.84 | 5.6768 | 10.3312 |
| 274 | 0.44310 | 0.28081 | 637.48 | -758.81 | 499.97 | 5.7106 | 10.3049 |
| 276 | 0.47698 | 0.26183 | 634.75 | -749.54 | 502.04 | 5.7441 | 10.2791 |
| 278 | 0.51284 | 0.24438 | 632.00 | -740.23 | 504.05 | 5.7775 | 10.2536 |
| 280 | 0.55077 | 0.22831 | 629.22 | -730.90 | 505.99 | 5.8107 | 10.2284 |
| 282 | 0.59083 | 0.21350 | 626.43 | -721.54 | 507.87 | 5.8438 | 10.2036 |
| 284 | 0.63312 | 0.19984 | 623.61 | -712.15 | 509.68 | 5.8768 | 10.1792 |
| 286 | 0.67771 | 0.18721 | 620.77 | -702.73 | 511.42 | 5.9095 | 10.1550 |
| 288 | 0.72469 | 0.17553 | 617.91 | -693.28 | 513.08 | 5.9422 | 10.1311 |
| 290 | 0.77413 | 0.16472 | 615.02 | -683.81 | 514.68 | 5.9747 | 10.1076 |
| 292 | 0.82613 | 0.15470 | 612.11 | -674.30 | 516.19 | 6.0071 | 10.0843 |
| 294 | 0.88077 | 0.14540 | 609.17 | -664.76 | 517.64 | 6.0393 | 10.0612 |
| 296 | 0.93813 | 0.13676 | 606.20 | -655.19 | 519.00 | 6.0715 | 10.0384 |
| 298 | 0.99830 | 0.12873 | 603.21 | -645.59 | 520.28 | 6.1035 | 10.0158 |
| 300 | 1.0614 | 0.12126 | 600.19 | -635.95 | 521.47 | 6.1354 | 9.9935 |
| 305 | 1.2324 | 0.10472 | 592.50 | -611.70 | 524.08 | 6.2145 | 9.9384 |
| 310 | 1.4235 | 0.09079 | 584.63 | -587.23 | 526.10 | 6.2931 | 9.8845 |
| 315 | 1.6362 | 0.07898 | 576.55 | -562.51 | 527.51 | 6.3710 | 9.8314 |
| 320 | 1.8721 | 0.06893 | 568.24 | -537.53 | 528.24 | 6.4484 | 9.7789 |
| 325 | 2.1327 | 0.06033 | 559.70 | -512.25 | 528.25 | 6.5253 | 9.7268 |
| 330 | 2.4196 | 0.05293 | 550.89 | -486.65 | 527.48 | 6.6019 | 9.6750 |
| 335 | 2.7344 | 0.04653 | 541.79 | -460.68 | 525.86 | 6.6783 | 9.6232 |
| 340 | 3.0789 | 0.04099 | 532.36 | -434.30 | 523.31 | 6.7546 | 9.5711 |
| 345 | 3.4549 | 0.03615 | 522.56 | -407.44 | 519.75 | 6.8309 | 9.5184 |
| 350 | 3.8641 | 0.03191 | 512.34 | -380.02 | 515.07 | 6.9075 | 9.4650 |
| 355 | 4.3085 | 0.02819 | 501.62 | -351.97 | 509.13 | 6.9846 | 9.4103 |
| 360 | 4.7902 | 0.02489 | 490.33 | -323.15 | 501.79 | 7.0625 | 9.3541 |
| 365 | 5.3112 | 0.02197 | 478.35 | -293.42 | 492.81 | 7.1416 | 9.2957 |
| 370 | 5.8740 | 0.01936 | 465.54 | -262.58 | 481.93 | 7.2222 | 9.2345 |
| 375 | 6.4811 | 0.01701 | 451.69 | -230.38 | 468.76 | 7.3051 | 9.1696 |
| 380 | 7.1352 | 0.01489 | 436.52 | -196.46 | 452.74 | 7.3911 | 9.0996 |
| 385 | 7.8395 | 0.01294 | 419.59 | -160.25 | 433.01 | 7.4814 | 9.0224 |
| 390 | 8.5977 | 0.01113 | 400.21 | -120.88 | 408.14 | 7.5783 | 8.9348 |
| 395 | 9.4144 | 0.009410 | 377.04 | -76.642 | 375.49 | 7.6856 | 8.8303 |
| 400 | 10.2956 | 0.007689 | 346.94 | -23.456 | 328.97 | 7.8133 | 8.6943 |
| *405.4 | 11.304 | 0.00426 | 235. | 142.7 | 142.7 | 8.216 | 8.216 |

**Triple point

**Critical point

Reprinted with permission from the 1981 Fundamentals ASHRAE Handbook & Product Directory

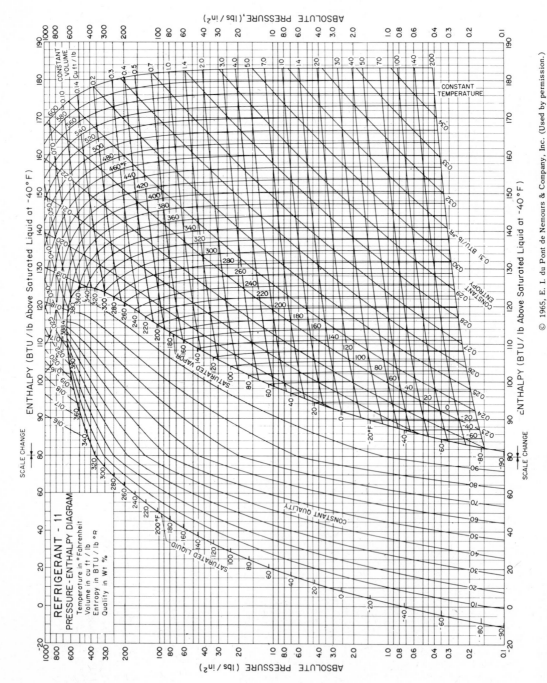

**FIGURE A.1** Pressure–enthalpy diagram for Refrigerant 11 (U.S. units). (Reprinted with permission from the 1981 Fundamentals ASHRAE Handbook & Product Directory)

© 1965, E. I. du Pont de Nemours & Company, Inc. (Used by permission.)

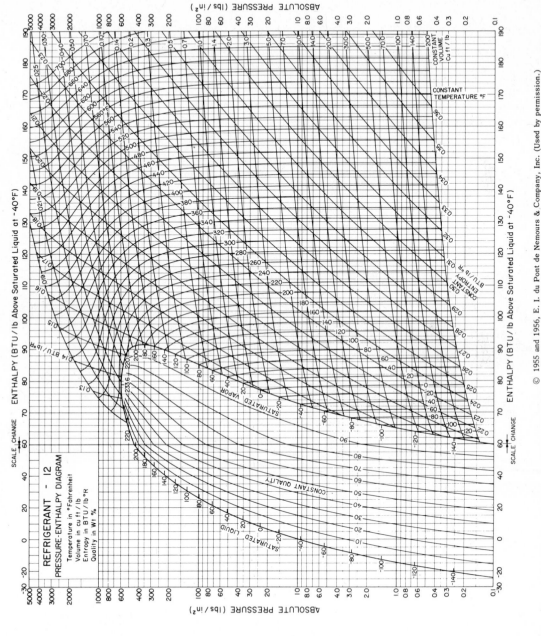

**FIGURE A.2** Pressure–enthalpy diagram for Refrigerant 12 (U.S. units). (Reprinted with permission from the 1981 Fundamentals ASHRAE Handbook & Product Directory)

401

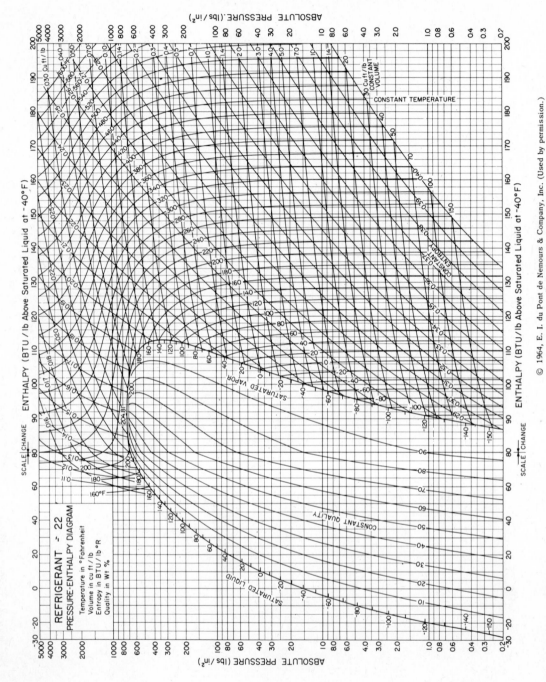

**FIGURE A.3** Pressure–enthalpy diagram for Refrigerant 22 (U.S. units). (Reprinted with permission from the 1981 Fundamentals ASHRAE Handbook & Product Directory)

© 1964, E. I. du Pont de Nemours & Company, Inc. (Used by permission.)

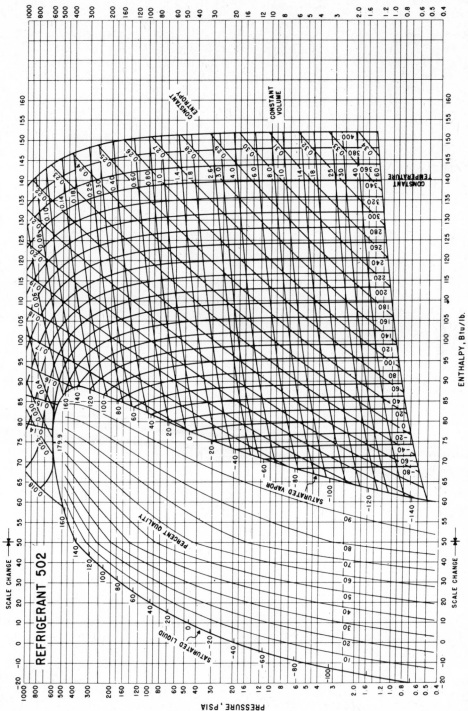

**FIGURE A.4** Pressure–enthalpy diagram for Refrigerant 502 (U.S. units). (Reprinted with permission from the 1981 Fundamentals ASHRAE Handbook & Product Directory)

403

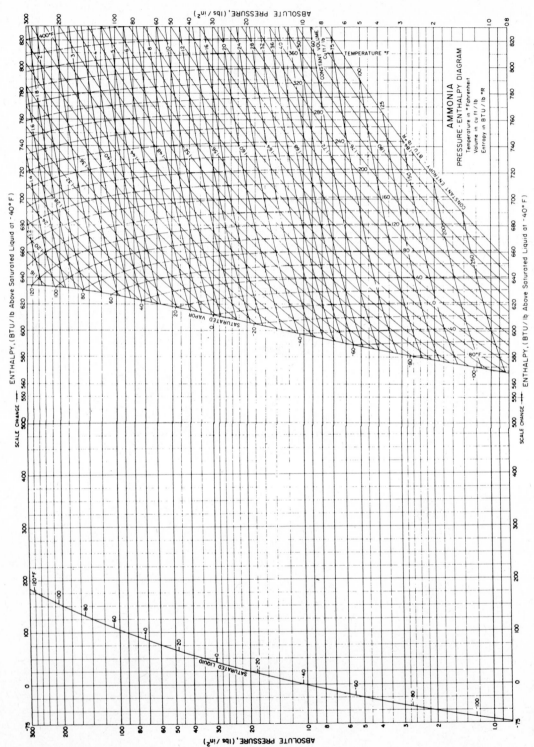

**FIGURE A.5** Pressure–enthalpy diagram for Ammonia (U.S. units). (Reprinted with permission from the 1981 Fundamentals ASHRAE Handbook & Product Directory)

404

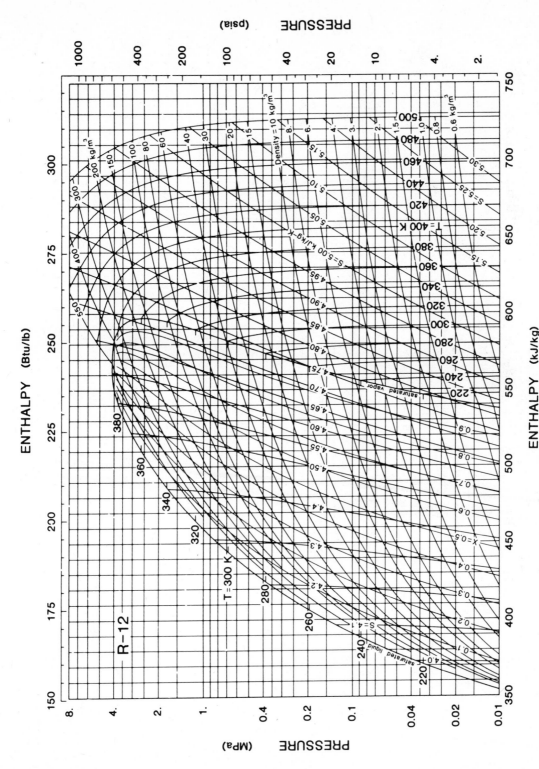

**FIGURE A.6** Pressure–enthalpy diagram for Refrigerant 12 (SI units). (Reprinted with permission from the 1981 Fundamentals ASHRAE Handbook & Directory)

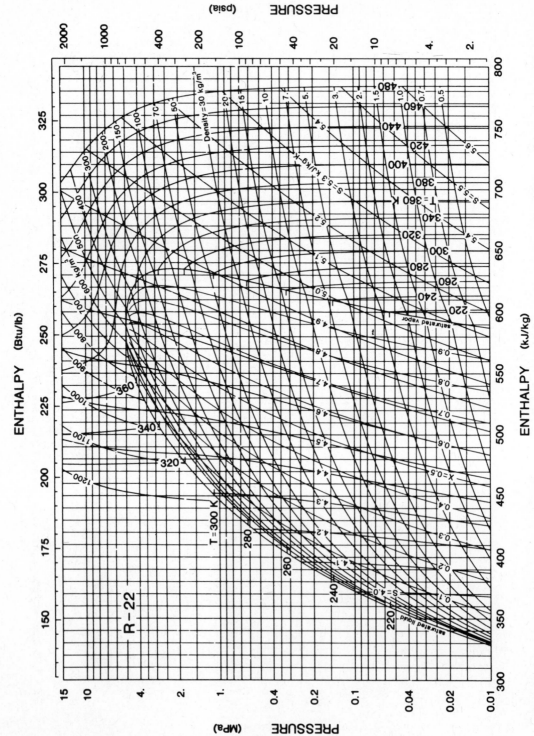

**FIGURE A.7** Pressure–enthalpy diagram for Refrigerant 22 (SI units). (Reprinted with permission from the 1981 Fundamentals ASHRAE Handbook & Directory)

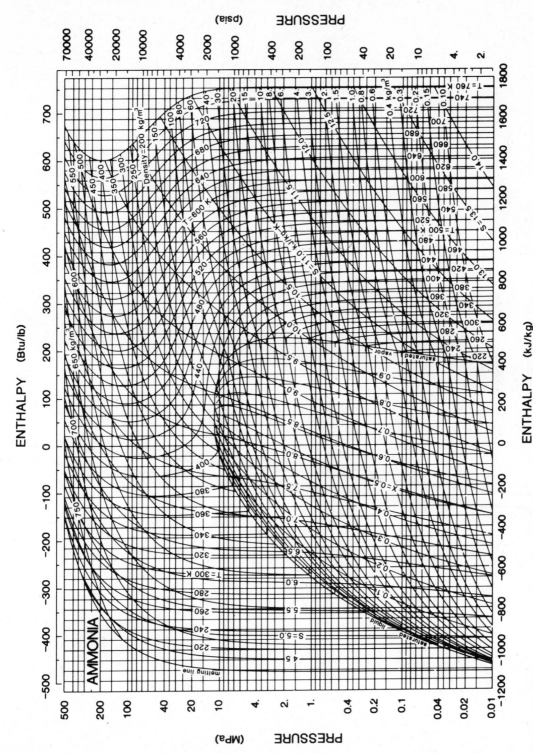

**FIGURE A.8** Pressure–enthalpy diagram for Ammonia (SI units). (Reprinted with permission from the 1981 Fundamentals ASHRAE Handbook & Directory)

407

# Index